An
**INTRODUCTION**
to
**ELEMENTARY PARTICLES**

# PURE AND APPLIED PHYSICS

## A SERIES OF MONOGRAPHS AND TEXTBOOKS

*CONSULTING EDITOR*

### H. S. W. MASSEY

*University College, London, England*

Volume 1. F. H. FIELD and J. L. FRANKLIN, Electron Impact Phenomena and the Properties of Gaseous Ions. 1957

Volume 2. H. KOPFERMANN, Nuclear Moments. English Version Prepared from the Second German Edition by E. E. SCHNEIDER. 1958

Volume 3. WALTER E. THIRRING, Principles of Quantum Electrodynamics. Translated from the German by J. BERNSTEIN. With Corrections and Additions by WALTER E. THIRRING. 1958

Volume 4. U. FANO and G. RACAH, Irreducible Tensorial Sets. 1959

Volume 5. E. P. WIGNER, Group Theory and Its Application to the Quantum Mechanics of Atomic Spectra. Expanded and Improved Edition. Translated from the German by J. J. GRIFFIN. 1959

Volume 6. J. IRVING and N. MULLINEUX, Mathematics in Physics and Engineering. 1959

Volume 7. KARL F. HERZFELD and THEODORE A. LITOVITZ, Absorption and Dispersion of Ultrasonic Waves. 1959

Volume 8. LEON BRILLOUIN, Wave Propagation and Group Velocity. 1960

Volume 9. FAY AJZENBERG-SELOVE (ed.), Nuclear Spectroscopy. Parts A and B. 1960

Volume 10. D. R. BATES (ed.), Quantum Theory. In three volumes. 1961

Volume 11. D. J. THOULESS, The Quantum Mechanics of Many-Body Systems. 1961

Volume 12. W. S. C. WILLIAMS, An Introduction to Elementary Particles. 1961

ACADEMIC PRESS • *New York and London*

# An

# INTRODUCTION

## to

# ELEMENTARY PARTICLES

**W. S. C. WILLIAMS**

Clarendon Laboratory, University of Oxford
Oxford, England

1961

ACADEMIC PRESS    New York and London

ACADEMIC PRESS INC.
111 FIFTH AVENUE
NEW YORK 3, N. Y.

*United Kingdom Edition*
Published by
ACADEMIC PRESS INC. (LONDON) LTD.
17 OLD QUEEN STREET, LONDON S.W. 1

*Library of Congress Catalog Card Number 61-12283*

PRINTED IN THE UNITED STATES OF AMERICA

# PREFACE

This book has been written for research workers in the field of experimental elementary particle physics and is intended to present an introduction to the theoretical methods and ideas which are used to describe the behaviour of elementary particles.

In the last fifteen years there has been a great increase in the use of symmetry properties, and of their associated conservation laws, in the field of elementary particles. These subjects are very important for they give considerable insight into the behaviour of elementary particles without requiring an extensive background of quantum mechanics for their understanding. At the time this book was started there was an obvious need for a book which covered these aspects of elementary particle physics in a manner which would appeal to experimental research workers.

The structure of the book follows my own preference as to the order in which a reader could become familiar with the subjects. In all cases the treatment is as elementary as is consistent with clarity and no claim is made to be rigorous. I felt that I had to draw a line beyond which the book would not go. It was chosen so as to avoid the calculation of transition matrix elements, although use is made of the transition rate formula as a means of comparing cross sections or lifetimes. The inclusion of the calculation of simple matrix elements would merely have covered the material of Fermi's excellent little book, "Elementary Particles". To have gone as far as the covariant calculation of matrix elements would have increased the size of the book to an unreasonable extent. However, field theory plays an important part in the theory of elementary particles and therefore a descriptive chapter on this subject is included. This allows us to use Feynman diagrams and to talk about propagators and vertices without involving the reader in involved matrix element calculations. Dispersion theory is covered briefly but the book is too early to do more than mention the Mandelstam representation and its developments.

I wish to acknowledge the encouragement given to me by Professor J. C. Gunn at the critical stage in the writing of this book. I am indebted to Professor P. I. Dee for the opportunity to write the book and for the encouraging atmosphere in his department, where much of the writing was done. I am also indebted to Professor J. C. Gunn, Professor E. H. Bellamy, Drs. B. H. Bransden, K. Burton, G. M. Lewis, R. G. Moorhouse, D. T. Stewart for reading parts of the manuscript. The first half of the book was the material for a series of graduate lectures and I am grateful for helpful comments and criticisms received from the students. My thanks are due to Miss Ailie Currie for her excellent typing work and to my wife for invaluable help in checking the final typescript.

W. S. C. WILLIAMS

*Department of Natural Philosophy*
*The University, Glasgow, Scotland.*
*February, 1961*

## Acknowledgments

The author is indebted to the authors cited and to the editors of the following journals for permission to reproduce figures:

*The Physical Review* for figures 7.3, 7.4, 7.5, 7.8, 7.9, 13.5, and B.4.
*The Annual Review of Nuclear Science* for figure 7.1.
*Nature* for figure 12.1.

# CONTENTS

# CHAPTER I

# INTRODUCTION

## 1.1 Preamble

The primary objective of this book is to serve as an introduction to the interpretation of some of the phenomena associated with elementary particles. We do not need to confuse the situation by debating the meaning of elementary in this respect: for us the term covers particles which are not, within present experience, bound states of other particles. Thus, the proton is an elementary particle, whereas the deuteron is not. To reduce the complication we only consider processes in which the number of particles in the initial state plus the number in the final state is four or less; this prevents the inclusion of complicated many-body processes and enhances the essential features. An example of this restriction is found in our treatment of the photoproduction of mesons. The description of the production from hydrogen contains the most important features for this book; production from complex nuclei is blurred by the presence of many nucleons and is not considered, except to mention production from deuterium. There is an excuse in this case, since the deuteron is the nearest we can approach to a free neutron target. We shall be discussing $\beta$ decay which does involve complex nuclei; however, this case can fall within our requirement of four or less particles in the initial plus final state if we do not have to concern ourselves with the effects of nuclear structure.

Our treatment of processes is done in the most general way and for the greater part without reference to any specific models other than symmetry. By model we mean any theory or postulate as to the nature of the particles or of the forces involved. Such models come from quantum field theory or by suggesting a simple analytic form for the potential existing between particles. It is possible to obtain a considerable amount of information about the particles not by appealing to such methods, but by the use of various symmetry laws. The description of the application of these laws is the main subject of this book. The material of Chapter IX is perhaps an exception to this restriction for it concerns field theory and the interaction of fields. However, the inclusion of this chapter subsequently allows us to discuss weak interactions (for which symmetries are important) in a more complete manner than would otherwise be possible.

Our plan is to develop the background necessary for the application of these symmetry laws; this will be done in the most elementary way possible and may be illustrated by direct example of actual physical processes. No rigour is claimed for any part of this book and the reader is warned that a more complete approach may be more subtle than is implied in this book; thus the theory of angular momentum can only reach its full development in group theory.

This first chapter is devoted to presenting some of the matter which is the basis of later chapters. We start by a brief statement of the postulates of quantum mechanics followed by a discussion of their implications and of the role of observables; the next section describes the principle of superposition of states. We then discuss the Lorentz transformations and introduce the concepts of invariance and conservation; the chapter finishes with a section on the distinction between laboratory and centre-of-mass coordinates.

## 1.2 The Postulates of Quantum Mechanics

In general, we use the Schrödinger method; we shall start by considering the Schrödinger equation and its interpretation. We assume the existence of a function $\psi(\mathbf{x}, t)$ which is a function of position $\mathbf{x}$, and of time $t$. This function is often called a wave function since the earliest types studied were analytically the same as classical waves; however, a more correct term is "state function" since it describes the state of a particle. We shall use the term, wave function, or, if necessary to stress a point, state function. Similar functions which describe the state of an assembly of particles will have more independent variables of position.

$\psi(\mathbf{x}, t)$ for a single particle is assumed to satisfy the Schrödinger equation

$$-\frac{\hbar^2}{2m}\nabla^2\psi(\mathbf{x}, t) + V(\mathbf{x})\,\psi(\mathbf{x}, t) = +i\hbar\frac{\partial}{\partial t}\psi(\mathbf{x}, t), \qquad (1.1)$$

where $m$ is the mass of the particle, $\hbar$ is Planck's constant divided by $2\pi$, and $V(\mathbf{x})$ is the potential energy of the particle at $\mathbf{x}$.

If the energy $E$ of the particle is a constant, we have

$$i\hbar \frac{\partial}{\partial t} \psi(\mathbf{x}, t) = E\psi(\mathbf{x}, t). \tag{1.2}$$

A solution of Eq. (1.1) is

$$\psi(\mathbf{x}, t) = \psi(\mathbf{x}) \exp\left(-iEt/\hbar\right),$$

where $\psi(\mathbf{x})$ satisfies

$$H\psi = E\psi. \tag{1.3}$$

$H$ represents $(-\hbar^2/2m)\nabla^2 + V(\mathbf{x})$ and is called the Hamiltonian operator.

The important properties of a physical system are the quantities which can be measured or observed; such quantities are called observables and any theory which is to predict the behaviour of the system must give the values of these observables. If the system is described by a state function, then there must be means of predicting the observables from this function and the procedure for doing this is given by a set of postulates. These postulates are the rules for interpreting the state function $\psi(\mathbf{x}, t)$. They are:

(1) To every observable there corresponds an operator.

(2) The result of one measurement of an observable is one of the eigenvalues of the equation

$$P\phi = p\phi,$$

where $P$ is the operator and $p$ is an eigenvalue.

(3) The average value of a large number of measurements of an observable is given by the "expectation value"

$$\langle P \rangle = \int \psi^* P\psi d\mathbf{x}, \tag{1.4}$$

providing that $\int \psi^* \psi d\mathbf{x} = 1$ and that there exist suitable boundary conditions. (The integration is performed over all the space within the boundary. The asterisk indicates the complex conjugate.)

In future we shall abbreviate the integration $\int \psi^* P\psi d\mathbf{x}$ to $(\psi | P | \psi)$. In general, the "matrix element" $(\phi | P | \psi) = \int \phi^* P\psi d\mathbf{x}$. The integral is not always over space ($\int d\mathbf{x}$): it may be necessary to imply integration over other continuous or discontinuous variables.

The formal properties of operators are important and we state some of these.

(a) They are linear: that is, if $\psi = \sum_n c_n \psi_n$, we have that

$$P\psi = \sum_n c_n P\psi_n.$$

(b) They obey the laws of association and distribution: that is, if $P$, $Q$, and $R$ are operators, we have that

$$P(QR) = (PQ)R \quad \text{and} \quad P(Q+R) = PQ + PR.$$

(c) They are Hermitian: that is,

$$\int \phi^* P\psi\, d\mathbf{x} = \int \psi P^* \phi^*\, d\mathbf{x}.$$

(d) As a result of (c) their eigenvalues are real:

$$P\psi_n = p_n \psi_n \quad \text{and} \quad P^* \psi_n^* = p_n \psi_n^*.$$

(e) In postulate 2 the eigenvalues may take on continuous or discrete values depending on the physical situation. Our notation represents the discrete set of eigenfunctions of the operator $P$ by

$$\psi_1, \psi_2, \ldots, \psi_n, \ldots$$

which have the eigenvalues $p_1, p_2, \ldots, p_n, \ldots$, respectively. Then the eigenfunctions form an orthogonal set

$$\int \psi_n^* \psi_m\, d\mathbf{x} = (\psi_n | \psi_m) = 0, \quad m \neq n.$$

The eigenfunctions are orthonormal if

$$(\psi_n | \psi_m) = \delta_{nm}.$$

(f) If the state function is an eigenfunction of the operator $P$, then a measurement of the corresponding observable can only yield a value equal to the eigenvalue.

(g) Operators do not necessarily obey a commutative law; that is, two operators $P$ and $Q$ need not have $PQ\psi = QP\psi$. If $PQ\psi = QP\psi$, the operators are said to commute and this statement is written $[P,Q] = 0$. The state function is implied thus: $[P,Q]\psi = (PQ - QP)\psi$ for all $\psi$.

(h) If $[P,Q] = 0$, then $[P, f(Q)] = 0$, where $f(Q)$ is a function of $Q$ which can be expanded as a power series in $Q$.

(i) If $[P,Q] = 0$ and $P\psi_n = p_n \psi_n$, then $(\psi_m | Q | \psi_n) = 0$ if $m \neq n$.

(j) If $[P,Q] = 0$, then it is possible to find a set of functions which are simultaneously eigenfunctions of $P$ and $Q$. If $[P,Q] \neq 0$, this cannot be done except for a state $\psi$ which has $[P,Q]\psi = 0$.

(k) If $[P,Q] = 0$ and $[P,R] = 0$ but $[Q,R] \neq 0$, then it is not possible to find functions which are simultaneously eigenfunctions of $P$, $Q$, and $R$. It is only possible to find eigenfunctions for $P$ and $Q$ *or* for $P$ and $R$. To correspond to this we can only make simultaneous measurements of the observables corresponding to the pair of operators $P$ and $Q$ *or* to the pair $P$ and $R$: it is not possible to measure all three together. The method of measurement determines the pair observed. The exception occurs for functions which have a zero eigenvalue for $Q$ (or $R$): these can also be eigenfunctions of $R$ (or $Q$). It follows that we can make simultaneous measurements of all three observables on a state represented by such eigenfunctions. Similar properties are obvious for the case of more than three operators.

(l) If $\psi_1, \psi_2, \ldots, \psi_n, \ldots$ are an orthonormal set but are not eigenfunctions of $P$ and $Q$, then

$$(\psi_m | PQ | \psi_n) = \sum_r (\psi_m | P | \psi_r)(\psi_r | Q | \psi_n).$$

The postulates 1, 2, and 3 form the basis of the interpretation of quantum mechanics and the properties of the required operators are the rules by which the interpretation is conducted. In the Schrödinger method the state function is the important part of the mechanics; however, it is also possible to develop certain aspects not by referring to the actual form of the state function, but by developing the formal properties of operators. We shall use this technique in the chapter on angular momentum.

We must end this section by briefly clarifying the methods of manipulating operators and the notation we shall employ. Firstly, we define the adjoint or Hermitian conjugate ($P^\dagger$) of an operator $P$ by the equation

$$(P^\dagger \psi | \phi) = (\psi | P\phi).$$

An operator which is Hermitian has $P^\dagger = P$. It is now easy to prove result (d). Suppose

$$P\psi_n = p_n \psi_n.$$

Then we have

$$(\psi_n | P\psi_n) = p_n(\psi_n | \psi_n).$$

But from the definition of an Hermitian conjugate and of an Hermitian operator we have

$$(\psi_n | P\psi_n) = (P^\dagger \psi_n | \psi_n) = (P\psi_n | \psi_n).$$

Now the matrix elements have the property that

$$(\phi | \psi)^* = (\psi | \phi).$$

Hence we have

$$(\psi_n | P\psi_n) = (\psi_n | P\psi_n)^*.$$

Since we require $(\psi_n | \psi_n)$ to be real, it follows that the eigenvalues of $P$ are real. Finally, we note that a unitary operator $U$ has the property $U^\dagger = U^{-1}$ where $UU^{-1} = 1$.

## 1.3 The Principle of the Superposition of States

A further important principle in quantum mechanics is that of the superposition of states; we shall discuss the principle briefly in order to indicate where its use is essential to describe a physical process and to make the reader aware that it is in almost continual use. For a more complete discussion the reader is referred to the first chapter of Dirac's "Quantum Mechanics" (1947).

Suppose a physical system is in a state which is one of a finite or infinite orthonormal set, *viz.* (e) in Section 1.2. This set of functions $\psi$, however, may not be a unique way of describing the possible states of the system: suppose there exist a second set of functions $\phi$, which also form an orthonormal set and are not in one to one correspondence with the set $\psi$. We shall have that the $\phi$ are eigenvalues of an operator $Q$ with corresponding observable $Q'$, whilst $\psi$ are eigenfunctions of $P$ with observable $P'$. Then a measurement of $Q'$ will always yield an eigenvalue of the equation

$$Q\phi = q\phi.$$

Now $\psi$ is not an eigenfunction $Q$; however, the principle of superposition effectively means that $\psi$ can be expanded as a linear sum of the eigenfunctions $\phi$. The orthonormality of the functions permits this analytically but the principle has deeper significance than reinforcing that possibility. Thus

$$\psi_n = \sum_m a_{nm} \phi_m. \tag{1.5}$$

Then if we make repeated measurement of $Q'$ the average value observed $\langle Q \rangle_n$ for the state $\psi_n$ is given by applying postulate 3, Section 1.2,

$$\langle Q \rangle_n = \int \psi_n^* Q \psi_n \, dx.$$

Substitute Eq. (1.5), then

$$\langle Q \rangle_n = \int \left( \sum_m a_{nm}^* \phi_m^* \right) Q \left( \sum_l a_{nl} \phi_l \right) dx.$$

Using the orthonormality of the set $\phi$ we have

$$\langle Q \rangle_n = \sum_m a_{nm}^* a_{nm} q_m. \tag{1.6}$$

Equation (1.6) also effectively states that if the system is in state $\psi_n$, then the probability of finding it in state $\phi_m$, by measurement of $Q'$, is $(a_{nm}^* a_{nm})$. Thus the observer who makes repeated measurements of $Q'$ on the state $\psi_n$ sees the states $\phi_1, \phi_2, \phi_3, ..., \phi_m, ...$ with respective weights $(a_{n1}^* a_{n1}), (a_{n2}^* a_{n2}), (a_{n3}^*, a_{n3}), ..., (a_{nm}^* a_{nm}), ...$. The sum of these intensities must be unity.

The state $\psi_n$ therefore appears to be a linear superposition of the states $\phi_1, \phi_2, \phi_3, ..., \phi_m, ...$. The inverse is also true: a state $\phi_l$ will appear to be a linear superposition of the states $\psi_1, \psi_2, ..., \psi_n, ...$ if a measurement is made of $P'$. The fact that a particular state can appear to be the sum of other states is a necessary assumption in quantum mechanics; the assumption is defined by the principle of superposition of states.

We can make an extension to this treatment by formally omitting the act of making a measurement of the observables $P'$ or $Q'$. The probability of finding a certain result to the measurement becomes the probability of finding the system in the state which is described by the eigenfunction having the result as eigenvalue. Thus the probability of finding a system described by the state function $\psi_n$ in a state described by $\phi_m$ is $(a_{nm}^* a_{nm})$. Now it is easy to prove that

$$|(\phi_m | \psi_n)|^2 = a_{nm}^* a_{nm},$$

and this leads us to generalize: the probability that a system described by a state function $\psi$ is in a state $\phi$ is

$$|(\phi | \psi)|^2. \tag{1.7}$$

We can mention an excellent example of the meaningfulness of the principle of superposition by introducing the description of polarized light. At the moment we consider only fully polarized light; the complete description of all states of polarization must await Chapter VIII. Classically we know that there are two possible descriptions: one describes a polarized beam by a sum with correct amplitudes and phase of two orthogonal plane polarized beams; the other describes the beam by a sum, with correct amplitudes and phase, of two opposite circularly polarized beams. This kind of summation is exactly like that of Eq. (1.5), and it is possible to construct state functions for all the states of polarization and to find the correct linear sum in either description which describes the state of polarization of photons in the beam. Similarly, operators can be defined which will predict the probability of finding a certain result if a particular measurement of the state of polarization is made on the beam of photons: for example, that a measurement of the state of circular polarization of a plane-polarized photon finds the photon having left- or right-hand circular polarization with equal probability. This description does not add anything to our knowledge of polarized light but does simplify certain problems.

So far in this section the language used has been simple; it is usual to call the set of functions $\psi$ or $\phi$ base vectors and the space in which they exist Hilbert space. A rotation of the axes of this Hilbert space transforms the components of the stationary vector; this is equivalent to transforming from one description to the other, as is implied in Eq. (1.5), that is, from one set of base vectors to another set. In fact, analytically the connection between the components of a vector in rotated and in unrotated space is similar to Eq. (1.5). We shall often use superposition without mentioning it; the vector addition of angular momentum and the partial wave analysis are two examples.

## 1.4 The Lorentz Transformations

All modern quantum mechanics can only proceed meaningfully from its assumptions if these satisfy the requirements of the special theory of relativity (the only exception is the original Schrödinger wave equation; for this reason it can only be used in restricted cases). We will now discuss those postulates of relativity which will affect our subsequent material.

The special theory of relativity postulates that:

(1) The laws of physics formulated by an observer are independent of the state of uniform motion or position of the observer and his apparatus.

(2) The velocity of light *in vacuo* is the same for all such observers.

Let us see how this works by considering two observers who have agreed to make identical observations on identical phenomena. We must distinguish carefully between the adjectives "same" and "identical". We take the words "same phenomenon" to mean a phenomenon which has a common source for both observers; for example, the diffraction of light from a specified star. The same words "same observation" would mean the measurement of a quantity associated with the common phenomenon; for example, the wavelength of a particular hydrogen spectral line in the light from our specified star. Obviously the same quantities will depend on the relative motion of our observers: in our example the Doppler effect alters the wavelength. By "identical phenomena" we mean phenomena which are alike in all respects but do not have a common source; the "identical observations" are the separate measurements of a quantity associated with both these phenomena. Two observers who separately measure the wavelength of a cadmium spectral line from their own local lamp would be measuring identical quantities but not the same quantity. As long as the measurements are not performed in a gravitational field or under conditions of acceleration, two such observers of identical quantities must yield identical results which will be independent of the two observers' state of relative motion. It follows that if our two observers set up separate equations of motion which describe the observed phenomena the two equations will be formally identical.

The system of coordinates which each observer sets up (normally stationary to himself) is called an inertial frame. The coordinate axes of two inertial frames can be connected by one or more of the following: rotation about the origin, displacement of one origin from the other, uniform relative velocity. As observers we are restricted to one inertial frame, but we do know how to transform observables and equations to the values and forms they would have if observed from another inertial frame (here we mean an observable quantity which is the same in the sense defined earlier). This system of transformations is called the Lorentz transformations, after their originator. We have already stated that in formulating a theory for any physical pheno- menon it is essential that the transformation of our equations to the inertial frame of a second observer does not change the consequence of the theory· when this requirement is satisfied the theory is said to be Lorentz covariant. Maxwell's electromagnetic theory, Dirac's equa- tion for the electron, and the Klein–Gordon equation for bosons are all Lorentz covariant. Schrödinger's equation is not.

We shall now consider the Lorentz transformations. We commence by defining two kinds of transformations:

(1) A "passive or coordinate transformation" is one in which the physical system is unchanged and we consider the relation between a quantity as observed from one inertial frame and the same quantity as observed from a second inertial frame; geometrically, this corre- sponds to a displacement and rotation of a four-dimensional coordinate system.

(2) In contrast, an active transformation is one in which a Lorentz transformation is applied to the physical system while the observer's inertial frame is unchanged; geometrically, this corresponds to a rota- tion and displacement of the physical system within a fixed four- dimensional coordinate system.

In mathematical formalism these two types of transformation are indistinguishable; however, for clarity in discussion we shall consider only coordinate transformations. We are therefore interested in the relation between the results of measurements made by two separate observers on the same quantity.

We must classify the Lorentz transformations. There is a general division into two types, defined as follows:

(a) Proper Lorentz transformations are those which can be reached by an integration of a large number of infinitesimal transformations: two inertial frames with a uniform relative velocity or two inertial frames related by a simple rotation are examples of frames connected by proper Lorentz transformations.

(b) Improper Lorentz transformations are those which involve a discontinuity such as reflection through a plane or in time: obviously, improper transformations cannot be reached by a sum of infinitesimal transformations.

We will notice a further division into homogeneous and inhomogeneous transformations:

(a) A homogeneous Lorentz transformation of coordinate axes corresponds to a rotation of the axes in four-dimensional space.

(b) An inhomogeneous Lorentz transformation of coordinate axes corresponds to a rotation of the axes and displacement of the origin in four-dimensional space.

We can clarify these definitions by considering two inertial frames having coordinate axes connected by a proper Lorentz transformation. We write quantities in the first frame unprimed and quantities in the second frame primed; in addition, the coordinates of a point $x, y, z, ict$ ($i = \sqrt{-1}$, $c$ = velocity of light) are written $x_\lambda$ ($\lambda = 1, 2, 3, 4$). Such a point will have different coordinates in the second system; if these coordinates are $x'_\kappa$, then

$$x'_\kappa = \sum_{\lambda=1}^{4} a_{\kappa\lambda} x_\lambda + b_\kappa, \quad (\lambda, \kappa = 1, 2, 3, 4). \tag{1.7a}$$

$a_{\kappa\lambda}$ is a set of 16 appropriate numbers. If we compare this with a simple coordinate transformation in Euclidean space, we see that this equation corresponds to a rotation and a displacement of the axes in four dimensions: it is therefore an inhomogeneous transformation. If $b_\kappa = 0$ ($\kappa = 1, 2, 3, 4$), then the displacement is absent and the transformation is homogeneous. We shall not be concerned with inhomogeneous transformations, except briefly in Section 1.6. The determinant formed from the real quantities $a_{\kappa\lambda}$ has the following properties:

$|a_{\kappa\lambda}| = 1$ for all proper Lorentz transformations;

$\qquad = -1$ for improper transformations, which involve reversal of one or three axes;

$\qquad = +1$ for improper transformations, which involve reversal of two or four axes.

The Lorentz transformations lead to a classification of observable quantities which is widely used in physics; it arises from the connection between the value $Q$ of an observable measured from one inertial frame and the value $Q'$ of the same observable measured from a second frame. In general,

$$Q' = LQ$$

where $L$ is a number, a matrix, or an operator which expresses the connection. The nature of $L$ determines the classification of $Q$.

(a) Scalars: a scalar $S$ is a quantity which transforms:

$$S' = S,$$

that is, $L$ is the identity operator for scalars, or invariants, as they are sometimes called.

(b) Pseudoscalars: a quantity $P$ is said to be pseudoscalar if it transforms according to

$$P' = |a_{\kappa\lambda}| P.$$

The important test of a pseudoscalar is made by reversing the three space axes for which $|a_{\kappa\lambda}| = -1$. For this so-called parity transformation, $P' = -P$.

(c) Vectors: in the theory of relativity, a vector can only be transformed meaningfully if it has four components; a four-vector $V$ is defined by the transformation of its four components

$$V'_\kappa = \sum_{\lambda=1}^{4} a_{\kappa\lambda} V_\lambda \quad (\lambda, \kappa = 1, 2, 3, 4).$$

Equation (1.7a) indicates that the space time coordinates of a point are the components of a four vector.

(d) Pseudo- or axial vectors: four vectors which transform according to the equation

$$A'_\kappa = |a_{\kappa\lambda}| \sum_{\lambda=1}^{4} a_{\kappa\lambda} A_\lambda,$$

are called pseudo- or axial vectors. Under the parity transformation the space components of an axial vector do not change sign whereas those of a vector do change sign.

(e) Tensors: a tensor $T$ of rank $n$ is a quantity of $4^n$ components, each component having $n$ subscripts; the transformation of a tensor requires a summation over each subscript, thus a tensor of rank 3 transforms

$$T'_{\kappa\lambda\mu} = \sum_{\eta=1}^{4} \sum_{\theta=1}^{4} \sum_{\iota=1}^{4} a_{\kappa\eta} a_{\lambda\theta} a_{\mu\iota} T_{\eta\theta\iota}.$$

Scalars and vectors are tensors of zero and unit rank, respectively.

(f) Pseudotensors: tensors for which the transformation includes multiplication by the determinant $|a_{\kappa\lambda}|$ are called pseudotensors. Pseudoscalars and axialvectors are pseudotensors of zero and unit rank, respectively.

(g) Spinors: a spinor is a four-component quantity which transforms in a similar manner to a four-vector, but the coefficients of the transformation are functions of the $a_{\kappa\lambda}$. Spinors are not important except as solutions of the Dirac equation.

There are other quantities, such as tensor densities, which are beyond the scope of this book.

We can now discuss some of the less formal features of these classifications. We can give some examples of scalars by considering the scalar product of two four-vectors; such a product is a scalar in the strict sense. The scalar product of two four-vectors $U$ and $V$ is

$$U \cdot V = \sum_{\lambda=1}^{4} U_\lambda V_\lambda.$$

(1) The space-time coordinates of a point $x, y, z, ict$ are the components of four-vector $x_\lambda$ ($\lambda = 1, 2, 3, 4$). The square of the scalar magnitude of this vector is given by

$$x \cdot x = \sum_{\lambda=1}^{4} x_\lambda x_\lambda = x^2 + y^2 + z^2 - c^2 t^2,$$

and this is a scalar. In actual fact, the true definition of a Lorentz transformation rests upon the required invariance of this interval. The scalar product of two different vectors, $x$ and $x'$, is also invariant.

(2) The momentum and total energy of a particle $(p_x, p_y, p_z, iE/c)$ are the components of a four-vector $p$. Then it follows that

$$p \cdot p = p_x^2 + p_y^2 + p_z^2 - E^2/c^2$$

is a scalar; it is actually $-m^2 c^2$, where $m$ is the rest mass of the particle.

We shall be using the terms pseudoscalar and axial vector mainly in the context of discussions involving the parity transformation; in such cases the time coordinate plays no role and the behaviour of these quantities can be examined using only the three space coordinates. Angular momentum and magnetic field are examples of axial vectors. It follows that the scalar product of a vector and an axial vector is a pseudoscalar and that the scalar product of two axial vectors is a scalar.

We are not interested in tensors except to mention as an example that the six components of an electromagnetic field can be cast into tensor form which correctly describes its transformation properties. Pseudotensors occur in the general theory of relativity; for a complete discussion of tensors in relativity theory we refer the reader to Møller (1952).

In Appendix A of this book we have derived some of the relations between the quantities of nuclear and elementary particle reactions when observed from the two important inertial frames—namely, the laboratory and centre-of-mass systems.

## 1.5 Transformations and Quantum Mechanics

In the last section we examined the Lorentz transformations and their effect on observable quantities; we shall now examine the properties of wave functions and operators under these transformations.

Let us consider a one-component wave function $\psi(x)$ which has the four coordinates $x_\lambda$ ($\lambda = 1, 2, 3, 4$) as independent variables and which describes some feature of a physical system. In particular, it associates a numerical value with the space-time point $P$ which has coordinates $x_\lambda$. If we make a coordinate transformation $L$, such as rotation or displacement, then the coordinates of the point $P$ transform from $x$ to $x'$. There must exist a function which has

$$\psi'(x') = \psi(x). \tag{1.8}$$

This implies that $\psi'$ associates the same numerical value to $P$ as does $\psi$. The existence of $\psi'(x')$ implies the existence of $\psi'(x)$ which is connected to $\psi(x)$ by an operator, thus:

$$\psi'(x) = U\psi(x). \tag{1.9}$$

In the transformed coordinate system, $\psi'(x)$ gives to the point $P'$ having coordinates $x$ in the transformed coordinates the same numerical value as $\psi(x'')$ gives to the point having coordinates $x''$ in the untransformed coordinates where $x$ and $x''$ describe the same space-time point $P'$ (Fig. 1.1).

It is evident that Eq. (1.9) can be defined by the coordinate transformation, as we have done, or by the active transformation which moves the physical system in a direction which is the reverse of the direction of movement of the coordinates in the coordinate transformation. There is thus no formal difference between these two approaches.

Since $\psi(x)$ and $\psi'(x)$ describe features of a physical system, the operator $U$ is unitary (Wightman and Schweber, 1955) and independent

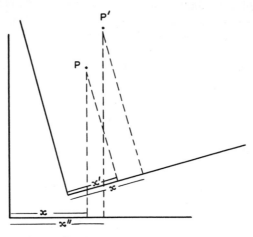

Fig. 1.1. A coordinate transformation in two dimensions.

of $x$. We can show that this must be so if we wish to preserve the normalization condition on the wave functions. We have that

$$(\psi(x)\,|\,\psi(x)) = 1,$$

and we require that

$$(\psi'(x)\,|\,\psi'(x)) = 1.$$

The left-hand side can be expressed

$$(\psi'(x)\,|\,\psi'(x)) = (U\psi(x)\,|\,U\psi(x)) = (\psi(x)\,|\,U^\dagger U\,|\,\psi(x)) = 1.$$

Therefore

$$U^\dagger U = 1,$$

which is the property of a unitary operator; hence the inverse transformation to that of Eq. (1.9) is

$$\psi(x) = U^{-1}\psi'(x)$$

where $U^{-1}$ is the Hermitian conjugate of $U$, thus:

$$U^{-1} = U^\dagger.$$

If the function to be transformed has more than one component, then Eq. (1.8) does not hold, in general. Instead we put

$$\psi'(x') = V\psi(x),$$

where $V$ is a unitary operator which is a function of the twenty quantities $a_{\kappa\lambda}$ and $b_\kappa$ of Eq. (1.7a). If $\psi(x)$ is a one-component wave function, $V$ is a one-component operator. If $V$ is a four-by-four matrix of operators, then $\psi(x)$ is a four-component wave function (a spinor). From the existence of $\psi'(x')$ we can infer the existence of $\psi'(x)$ related to $\psi(x)$ by

$$\psi'(x) = W\psi(x),$$

where again $W$ is a unitary operator.

If $Q$ is the operator associated with an observable, then the expectation value $\langle Q \rangle$ for this observable is given by

$$\langle Q \rangle = (\psi(x)\,|\,Q\,|\,\psi(x)).$$

We assume that an observer will use what is formally the same operator from whatever inertial frame the observation is made. From the transformed coordinate system the observer will find the expectation value $\langle Q \rangle'$:

$$\langle Q \rangle' = (\psi'(x)\,|\,Q\,|\,\psi'(x))$$

$$= (W\psi(x)\,|\,Q\,|\,W\psi(x)) = (\psi(x)\,|\,W^{-1}QW\,|\,\psi(x)). \qquad (1.10)$$

This follows from the properties of unitary operators and the expectation value, Eq. (1.4). The quantities $\langle Q \rangle$ and $\langle Q \rangle'$ will be connected by the appropriate transformation. If, however, $\langle Q \rangle$ is a scalar (invariant) under the transformation induced by $W$, then it follows that

$$\langle Q \rangle = \langle Q \rangle'$$

and

$$W^{-1}QW = Q$$

and hence $Q$ commutes with $W$

$$[Q, W] = 0. \qquad (1.11)$$

This is an important relation between observable operators and the unitary operators which induces transformations in which the observables remain invariant.

In many circumstances it is necessary to know how operators transform under coordinate transformation. Consider an operator $V$ which transforms $\psi \rightarrow \phi$, thus

$$\phi = V\psi.$$

Let us now apply a coordinate transformation for which the corresponding unitary operator is $W$; the functions $\psi$ and $\phi$ transform as follows:

$$\phi' = W\phi, \quad \psi' = W\psi.$$

What is the operator $V'$ which corresponds to $V$ and which transforms $\psi' \to \phi'$? That is

$$\phi' = V'\psi'.$$

The situation can be represented by a square (Fig. 1.2), with corners labelled $\psi$, $\psi'$, $\phi$, and $\phi'$. A change from one corner to another in the direction of the arrows is effected by the operator marked alongside the arrow. Changes against the arrow are made by the reciprocal operator. We can go from $\psi' \to \phi'$ by two routes: the most direct gives

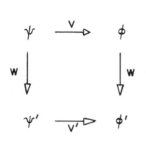

$$\phi' = V'\psi';$$

the indirect route gives

$$\phi' = WVW^{-1}\psi'.$$

FIG. 1.2. A diagram to illustrate the action of a similarity transformation.

Therefore

$$V' = WVW^{-1}. \tag{1.12}$$

This result may appear to be in contradiction to the assumption made in deriving Eq. (1.10). This assumption takes the form of the operator $Q$ connected with an observable to be independent of a coordinate transformation; this means that it is always the same function of the coordinates. Thus the $x$ component of the momentum operator, namely $-i\hbar\partial/\partial x$, always has the same form, but it is evident that it does not have the same effect in all coordinate systems. The relation between operators that do have the same effect is given by Eq. (1.12), and is called a similarity transformation.

## 1.6 Invariance and Transformation Laws

We have observed that the effects of transformations on functions may be described by unitary operators. Such operators may be generated from Hermitian operators by the following expansion:

$$U = 1 + iQ + \frac{(iQ)^2}{2!} + \frac{(iQ)^3}{3!} + \ldots = e^{iQ}.$$

Obviously $U$ is unitary if $Q$ is Hermitian. It follows that for many transformations there will exist an Hermitian operator which generates the corresponding unitary operator. Such Hermitian operators exist for the proper Lorentz transformations and it happens that they are the operators used in the interpretation of wave functions. Thus the generators of time and space displacements in the inhomogeneous Lorentz transformations are the operators of energy and linear momentum. The generators of space rotations are the operators of angular momentum. The improper transformations have no generators. These considerations are complicated in a fully relativistic language: for example, rotations in ordinary three-dimensional space are generated by the operator of angular momentum, whereas a complete description of rotations in four-dimensional space requires the concept of a total angular momentum which contains spin. For a full discussion, readers are referred to Jauch and Rohrlich (1955).

TABLE 1.1

TRANSFORMATIONS AND CONSERVED QUANTITIES

| Transformation | Conserved quantity |
| --- | --- |
| Displacement | Linear momentum |
| Time-wise displacement | Energy |
| Rotations | Total angular momentum |
| Parity transformation | Parity |
| Rotations in isotopic spin space | Isotopic spin |

For many transformations there will exist operators and functions which remain invariant. In particular, we may expect that the behaviour of the system is unchanged and consequently require that the Hamiltonian $H$ of the system be invariant; that is,

$$H' = UHU^{-1} = H;$$

hence

$$[U, H] = 0.$$

For proper Lorentz transformations the result is also true for infinitesimal transformations for which $U = 1 + iQ$ and we have

$$[Q, H] = 0.$$

The eigenvalues of an operator which commutes with the Hamiltonian are constants of the motion by virtue of the equation of motion

$$i\hbar \frac{dQ}{dt} = [Q, H]. \tag{1.13}$$

Hence the eigenvalues of $Q$ are conserved. We can state a general principle: for every transformation which leaves the Hamiltonian invariant, there may be a corresponding operator whose eigenvalues are conserved.

We can make a list of the coordinate transformations which leave the Hamiltonian invariant and alongside the corresponding conserved quantity. This list anticipates much of the material of this book. See Table 1.1.

### 1.7 Parity, the Parity Transformation, and Parity Conservation

Parity is a very important subject. We shall defer until Chapter X a full discussion of its implications and context but, since we need to use its simpler consequences before then, we shall briefly describe what is meant by parity.

Parity is an important property of many functions. Suppose we have a function $f(\mathbf{x})$ of the space coordinates $(x_k, k = 1, 2, 3)$. Then $f(\mathbf{x})$ is said to have even parity if

$$f(-\mathbf{x}) = f(\mathbf{x}),$$

and odd parity if

$$f(-\mathbf{x}) = -f(\mathbf{x}).$$

Many functions do not have a unique parity but are mixtures of functions of opposite parity.

We must now relate this property to the parity transformation which reverses the direction of three spatial axes. Suppose $\psi(\mathbf{x})$ describes some physical system. Then the transformation defines a new function of $\mathbf{x}$, namely $\psi'(\mathbf{x})$, which describes the same physical system in reversed coordinates and a mirror image of this system in the unreversed coordinates. The unitary operator $P$ responsible for this transformation is defined by

$$\psi'(\mathbf{x}) = P\psi(\mathbf{x}).$$

If $\psi(\mathbf{x})$ has even or odd parity, then it is an eigenfunction of $P$ with eigenvalue $+1$ or $-1$ respectively. We shall prove these statements in Chapter X.

The Schrödinger Hamiltonian, Eq. (1.3), is invariant under the transformation $\mathbf{x} \rightarrow -\mathbf{x}$, if the potential $V$ is invariant, and under these circumstances it follows from Eq. (1.11) that $H$ and $P$ commute. This has two consequences: first, that it is possible to find functions which are simultaneously eigenfunctions of $H$ and $P$; second, that the eigenvalues of $P$ are conserved. This latter property is called the conservation of parity, and is a feature of systems which obey the Schrödinger equation. Since the parity transformation defines a mirror image, we find that the system which is a mirror image of such a system behaves in precisely the same way as its mirror twin. This is invariance under the parity transformation. This symmetry is so simple and, in our normal experience, so complete, that this invariance was assumed in all circumstances and, arguing back, the conservation of parity was assumed to be correct in all circumstances. The break-down of this symmetry in certain circumstances is a recent discovery and will form one of the subjects in Chapter X; until then we shall continue to assume parity is conserved.

Parity has important application in elementary particle physics. Let us consider a process in which a particle is produced; for example, radiation by an atomic electron

$$e \to e + \gamma$$

or neutral meson production in a proton–proton collision

$$p + p \to p + p + \pi^0.$$

The total wave functions of the initial and final states are required to have the same parity. When we make an analysis we find that it is sometimes necessary to attribute an odd intrinsic parity to the particle produced, and we then say the particle has odd parity. If it is not necessary to give the particle odd parity, then we say the particle has even parity. Thus in the second reaction parity is only conserved if the pi-meson carries odd parity. Similarly, in almost all atomic radiation processes the photon carries odd parity; however, photons can carry even parity (see Section 4.4). An analysis of the kind which determines parity will be made in Section 7.4, and we refer readers to that place if they wish to study this point immediately.

In modern quantum mechanics, spinless particles which carry odd intrinsic parity are described by field functions which transform like pseudoscalars. Thus odd parity spinless particles such as the pi-meson are often referred to as pseudoscalar, and even parity spinless particles as scalar particles. Even or odd particles with integer spin are referred to as vector or pseudovector, respectively. In fact, such a classification can only be made for bosons (integer spin). Fermi particles (half-odd integer spin) such as electrons or nucleons do not possess intrinsic parity but do have odd parity with respect to their respective anti-particle. This lack of an intrinsic parity does not involve any diffi-culties in making checks on the conservation of parity in nuclear reactions because fermions are conserved and their lack of parity cancels in the parity equation. This can be seen in the two production reactions just mentioned. Some ambiguities arise: for example, if we consider the reaction

$$p + p \rightarrow n + p + \pi^+,$$

it is obvious that the $\pi^+$ could have even parity if the neutron had parity opposite to that of the proton. It is usual to assign the same parity to the charged as to the uncharged mesons, but there is no way of confirming this. This qualification and others to the concept of parity are discussed by Wick *et al.* (1952). We have remarked that invariance under the parity transformation implies that a system and its mirror image behave in the same way; thus it is possible to test various reactions involving spin for equality of cross sections. We shall expand this point when we come to examine the properties of angular momentum under the parity transformation. At present we note that the active parity transformation of a system reverses the sign of all position and linear momentum vectors.

## 1.8 Time Reversal

There is one Lorentz transformation which reverses the sign of the time coordinates ($t \rightarrow -t$, or $x_4 \rightarrow -x_4$) and reverses the direction of the flow of time. Apart from effects such as frictional forces and electrical resistance, the laws of classical physics are invariant under time reversal. This implies that under time reversal they reproduce normal motion in reverse. A similar symmetry appears to apply in quantum mechanics, but again we defer until Chapter X the discussion of time reversal. At the moment we wish to note that the time reversal of a system interchanges the initial and final states, and changes the sign of the linear and angular momentum vectors.

## 1.9 Centre of Mass and Laboratory Coordinates

The postulates of Newtonian mechanics indicate that the centre of mass of an assembly of particles will continue in a state of uniform motion unless disturbed by an external force. Thus the movement of particles within a system uninfluenced by an external force can be separated from the movement of the whole system. This makes it convenient to describe the internal movements of the system by the use of coordinates which have their origin at the centre of mass. This coordinate system is called the centre-of-mass coordinates and may be in a state of uniform motion with respect to the observer. Coordinates which are stationary with respect to the observer are called the laboratory co-ordinates. This separation of motion can be carried out in non-relativistic quantum mechanics; in fact, the Schrödinger equation can be separated into two distinct parts—one which describes the motion of centre of mass, the other which describes the internal motion. We indicate the results for a system of two particles. The reader is referred to other treatises for the more general case (Margenau and Murphy, 1943).

Let a vector $\mathbf{x}$ represent the position of a point in the laboratory coordinates. Primed vectors represent the points in the centre-of-mass coordinates. The subscripts 1 and 2 refer to particles having mass $m_1$ and $m_2$; $\mathbf{x}_0$ is the vector representing the position of the centre of mass in the laboratory coordinates. The Schrödinger equation in the laboratory system is

$$\left\{ -\frac{\hbar^2}{2m_1} \nabla_1^2 - \frac{\hbar^2}{2m_2} \nabla_2^2 + V(\mathbf{x}_1, \mathbf{x}_2) \right\} \psi = E\psi.$$

The operator subscripts indicate the point at which they operate. We assume $\psi$ is separable into $\phi$ and $\xi$, representing respectively the motion of the centre of mass in the laboratory coordinate and the motion of the particles in the centre of mass. We define:

$$\mathbf{x} = \mathbf{x}_1 - \mathbf{x}_2 = \text{distance between } m_1 \text{ and } m_2;$$

$$\mathbf{x}_0 = \frac{m_1 \mathbf{x}_1 + m_2 \mathbf{x}_2}{m_1 + m_2}.$$

Then

$$\left\{ \frac{-\hbar^2}{2(m_1 + m_2)} \nabla_0^2 - \frac{\hbar^2}{2} \left( \frac{1}{m_1} + \frac{1}{m_2} \right) \nabla'^2 + V(\mathbf{x}) \right\} \psi = E\psi,$$

where $V(\mathbf{x})$ is supposed to depend only on the distance between the particles. If $E = E_0 + E'$ where $E_0$ = energy of motion of centre of mass and $E'$ = energy of $m_1$ and $m_2$ within the centre-of-mass coordinates, we have

$$\frac{-\hbar^2}{2(m_1 + m_2)} \nabla_0^2 \phi = E_0 \phi,$$

$$\left\{ \frac{-\hbar^2}{2} \left( \frac{1}{m_1} + \frac{1}{m_2} \right) \nabla'^2 + V(\mathbf{x}) \right\} \xi = E'\xi. \tag{1.14}$$

The second equation describes the motion of $m_1$ and $m_2$ within the centre-of-mass coordinates. Since most interactions between particles occur through a term such as $V(\mathbf{x})$, we can describe such a system in the centre-of-mass coordinates using this equation. The first two terms correspond to the kinetic energies of the two particles; the particles have equal and opposite momentum, as $-\hbar^2 \nabla^2 \xi$ is the same for both particles. If $V(\mathbf{x}) = 0$, then $\exp(i\mathbf{p}\cdot\mathbf{x}/\hbar)$ is a solution and $\mathbf{p}$ is the real momentum of one of the particles, not the relative momentum. Equation (1.14) suggests that the system behaves like a single particle having mass $m$, where

$$\frac{1}{m} = \frac{1}{m_1} + \frac{1}{m_2}.$$

This $m$ is called the reduced mass.

Such a separation cannot be performed for relativistic equations; in fact, there is no necessity or meaning to such separation, since a special relativity tells us that there is no one fundamental set of coordinates or "inertial frame". Therefore the equations of motion will have the same form whatever coordinates system we choose. For convenience it is usual to work in coordinates in which the total momentum is zero. This system is called, rather loosely, the centre of mass. The un-normalized plane wave solution for two particles is then $\exp(i\mathbf{p}\cdot\mathbf{x}/\hbar)$ where $\mathbf{p}$ is the momentum of one of the particles.

The results of calculations made in the centre-of-mass coordinates must be transformed to the laboratory coordinates in which it is usual to make the observations. The nonrelativistic transformations of vectors and scalars can be dealt with quite simply by classical methods; transition rates and cross sections do not change and care has to be taken only with differential cross sections. This point is covered in the Appendix. Relativistic transformations require more care: total cross sections are still invariant but other quantities which are calculated in the centre-of-mass coordinates must be correctly transformed to the laboratory coordinates; see Appendix A.

### 1.10 Conclusion

This chapter has covered a wide range of rather general quantum mechanics, much of which is of considerable conceptual difficulty. This material has been lumped together in one chapter to avoid out-of-context explanations later in the book, and has been given rather cursory treatment to avoid inflation of the scope of this book. Readers who are interested in the formal aspects of quantum mechanics are referred to the works of Dirac (1947) or Wigner (1959).

# CHAPTER II

# ANGULAR MOMENTUM

## 2.1 Introduction

In this chapter we shall discuss the operators and observables of angular momentum; by considering the properties of physical systems under rotations we shall show that some of these operators have eigenvalues which are constants of motion. We shall also consider the vector addition of angular momentum and introduce the spherical harmonics which are eigenfunctions of certain operators. We finish the chapter with a further discussion of rotation.

## 2.2 Orbital Angular Momentum

In Section 1.9 we showed that the motion of a system of particles can be separated into two parts: the first part is the motion of the centre of mass of the system in axes fixed by an external observer; the second part is the motion of the system in the coordinates in which the centre of mass is stationary. In this chapter we are concerned with the angular momentum in this second part. Our starting-point is the classical relation

$$\mathbf{L} = \sum_r \mathbf{x}_r \times \mathbf{p}_r.$$

The quantities are vectors and the sum is taken over all the particles in the system, the $r$th particle having linear momentum $\mathbf{p}_r$ and coordinate $\mathbf{x}_r$ with respect to the centre of mass. The transformation to quantum mechanics is performed by replacing the quantity $\mathbf{p}$ by $-i\hbar\boldsymbol{\nabla}$ and this makes the relation an operator equation; consider the quantities operating on a wave function $\psi$ thus:

$$\mathbf{L}\psi = -i\hbar\mathbf{x} \times \boldsymbol{\nabla}\psi. \tag{2.1}$$

This can be decomposed into Cartesian components and, dropping the $\psi$ for convenience, we have for the three components of **L**

$$\left. \begin{aligned} L_x &= -i\hbar\left(y\frac{\partial}{\partial z} - z\frac{\partial}{\partial y}\right), \\ L_y &= -i\hbar\left(z\frac{\partial}{\partial x} - x\frac{\partial}{\partial z}\right), \\ L_z &= -i\hbar\left(x\frac{\partial}{\partial y} - y\frac{\partial}{\partial x}\right). \end{aligned} \right\} \tag{2.2}$$

The square of the magnitude of the angular momentum is defined thus:

$$L^2 = L_x^2 + L_y^2 + L_z^2. \tag{2.3}$$

As always in quantum mechanics, the commutation relations between the various operators are of interest. By manipulating the operators of (2.2) we find that

$$\left. \begin{aligned} [L_x, L_y] &= +i\hbar L_z, \\ [L_y, L_z] &= +i\hbar L_x, \\ [L_z, L_x] &= +i\hbar L_y, \end{aligned} \right\} \tag{2.4}$$

$$[L_x, L^2] = [L_y, L^2] = [L_z, L^2] = 0. \tag{2.5}$$

These relations are a consequence of the classical definition of angular momentum and of the change to quantum-mechanical formalism. This process cannot be reversed; Eq. (2.1) is not derivable from Eqs. (2.4) and (2.5). In formal quantum theory it is usual to start with relations (2.4) and to develop angular momentum theory from that point, without introducing the more physical picture implied in Eq. (2.1). We shall illustrate this in the case of intrinsic spin for which there is no classical starting-point; the description of spin starts by defining quantities such as those of Eq. (2.4).

The commutation relations between angular momentum operators, Eqs. (2.4) and (2.5), and the rules connecting observables and commuting operators, Section 1.2 (k), show that we can only find eigenfunctions which are simultaneously eigenfunctions of $L^2$ and one of the three operators $L_x, L_y, L_z$. It is usual to choose $L_z$ so that a state of pure orbital angular momentum requires two quantum numbers for its specification. These are $l$ and $l_z$ where the eigenvalues of $L^2$ and $L_z$ are $l(l+1)\hbar^2$ and $l_z\hbar$ respectively (see Section 2.5). The magnitude of the angular momentum is $\hbar\sqrt{l(l+1)}$, but for conciseness we shall often speak of such a state having angular momentum $l$. There is one circumstance in which an eigenfunction can be found for the operator $L^2$ and two of the operators $L_x$, $L_y$, and $L_z$; this happens if the eigenvalue of one of these component operators is zero, in which case this eigenfunction can also be an eigenfunction of one of the other component operators.

## 2.3 Rotations (I)

We wish to show that the angular momentum operators which have been defined by Eqs. (2.4) and (2.5) are the generators of rotations. Consider a scalar function $f(\mathbf{x})$ which gives some numerical value to the space point $\mathbf{x}$, where $\mathbf{x}$ is with respect to a right-handed Cartesian coordinate system $F$. We wish to examine the effect upon $f(\mathbf{x})$ of a rotation of this coordinate system. We make an infinitesimal rotation of the coordinates through an angle $d\phi$ around the $z$ axis. The new coordinates of the same space point in the new coordinate system $F'$ are given by

$$x' = x + y\, d\phi,$$

$$y' = y - x\, d\phi,$$

$$z' = z.$$

There must exist a function $f'(\mathbf{x}')$ which has the same value as has $f(\mathbf{x})$ when $\mathbf{x}$ and $\mathbf{x}'$ describe the same space point from different coordinates. The existence of $f'(\mathbf{x}')$ defines a function $f'(\mathbf{x})$ which has the same value at the point $\mathbf{x}$ referred to $F'$ as $f(\mathbf{x} + \Delta\mathbf{x})$ has at the point $\mathbf{x} + \Delta\mathbf{x}$ referred to $F$, where $\Delta\mathbf{x} = \mathbf{x}' - \mathbf{x}$. We can make a Taylor expansion of $f(\mathbf{x})$ around $\mathbf{x}$ to give

$$f'(\mathbf{x}) = f(\mathbf{x} + \Delta\mathbf{x}) = f(\mathbf{x}) + \left(y\frac{\partial}{\partial x} - x\frac{\partial}{\partial y}\right)f(\mathbf{x})\, d\phi + \dots.$$

For infinitesimal rotations this can be written

$$f'(\mathbf{x}) = \left(1 - \frac{i}{\hbar}L_z\, d\phi\right)f(\mathbf{x}).$$

For finite rotations $d\phi \to \phi$ and we make a summation of the infinitesimal rotations to give

$$f'(\mathbf{x}) = \exp\left(-i\phi L_z/\hbar\right)f(\mathbf{x}).$$

This expression applies to a rotation through an angle $\phi$ about the $z$ axis; it can be generalized for a rotation $\theta$ about a unit vector $\mathbf{n}$ to give

$$f'(\mathbf{x}) = \exp\left[-i\theta(\mathbf{L}\cdot\mathbf{n})/\hbar\right]f(\mathbf{x}).$$

$f(\mathbf{x})$ is a one-component wave function and we say that its transformation properties under rotation are described by the unitary
operator

$$R = \exp[-i\theta(\mathbf{L} \cdot \mathbf{n})/\hbar].$$

We can now put this matter into line with our discussion of Section 1.5.
A one-component wave function transforms under coordinate rota-
tions according to $\psi'(\mathbf{x}) = R\psi(\mathbf{x})$. There are, however, some wave functions which give the values to several quantities at each point in
space; these are multicomponent wave functions. Under coordinate
rotations these wave functions may transform in a way which involves
the components interchanging. The corresponding unitary operator
is not $R$ as generated by $\mathbf{L}$ but a new operator $D$ generated by the
total angular momentum operator $\mathbf{J}$. This description is found to
contain the intrinsic angular momentum or spin of the particles as
well as any angular momentum they may possess due to orbital motion.

If the burden of transformation is placed upon the operators instead
of upon the wave functions, then by the discussion at the end of
Section 1.5 and by Eq. (1.10) we see that an operator $Q$ before rotation
becomes $Q'$ after coordinate rotation, where

$$Q' = D^{-1}QD \tag{2.6}$$

where

$$D = \exp[-i\theta(\mathbf{J} \cdot \mathbf{n})/\hbar].$$

There are many quantities which are invariant under coordinate
rotation; in fact, our discussion in this section has assumed that scalar
(or pseudoscalar) quantities are in this class. For example, the energy
density at a point is a scalar and will not change if the coordinates are
rotated. Suppose such an invariant quantity is an observable associated with an operator $Q$; then

$$Q' = Q = R^{-1}QR.$$

We are restraining our discussion to systems containing only orbital
angular momentum. Without loss we can consider the rotation to be
infinitesimal and about the $z$ axis so that Eq. (2.6) becomes

$$Q = (1 + id\phi L_z/\hbar)Q(1 - id\phi L_z/\hbar),$$

whence

$$[Q, L_z] = 0.$$

This invariance holds also for rotations about the $x$ or the $y$ axis so
we have in addition

$$[Q, L_x] = [Q, L_y] = 0,$$

or more compactly,

$$[Q, \mathbf{L}] = 0.$$

The Hamiltonian is an important operator in this class:

$$H_0 \psi = \left\{ -\frac{\hbar^2}{2m} \nabla^2 + V(\mathbf{x}) \right\} \psi. \tag{2.7}$$

We put the subscript 0 on to $H$ to show that it applies only to systems not containing spin. $\psi$ is a wave function describing a system; it will be an eigenfunction of $H_0$ with eigenvalues equal to the energy of the system. This energy will not change if the coordinates are rotated, provided $V(\mathbf{x})$ is not fixed to the coordinates. It follows that

$$[H, \mathbf{L}] = 0.$$

By rule (h) of Section 1.2 we have also

$$[H, L^2] = 0.$$

Using the equation

$$i\hbar \frac{dQ}{dt} = [Q, H],$$

we see that the eigenvalues of $L^2$ and $L_z$ for a pure state of orbital angular momentum do not change with time; that is, they are conserved.

This discussion merely verifies the matter of Sections 1.5 and 1.6 applied to angular momentum.

## 2.4 Spin and Total Angular Momentum

The intrinsic spin of particles is experienced as an angular momentum. In strict analogy with the orbital angular momentum, we can construct a space with wave functions and operators. Such operators are $\mathbf{S}$, corresponding to $\mathbf{L}$, and $S_x, S_y, S_z$ corresponding to $L_x, L_y, L_z$. Then if $\chi$ is the spin wave function describing the behaviour of a particle in a pure spin state, it is an eigenfunction of the operators $S^2$ and $S_z$ with eigenvalues $s(s+1)\hbar^2$ and $s_z \hbar$ respectively, where $s$ is the spin of the particle and $s_z$ its z component.

The operators $\mathbf{S}$, $S_x$, $S_y$, $S_z$, and $S^2$ are assumed to commute among themselves in a completely analogous way to the orbital angular momentum operators. Since the spin operators operate on wave functions in "spin space", any spin operator commutes with any orbital operator.

Since spin is an angular momentum, it is necessary to construct a total angular momentum operator; that is,

$$\mathbf{J} = \mathbf{L} + \mathbf{S}.$$

Then $\mathbf{J}$ also satisfies the usual angular momentum relations; these can be written

$$[\mathbf{J} \times \mathbf{J}] = i\hbar\mathbf{J}.$$

Our next step is to introduce a new Hamiltonian and investigate its commutation relations. Since our system now contains spin, the Hamiltonian may contain terms dependent on spin. Thus our Schrödinger equation, which reads

$$H_0\psi = E\psi,$$

will now read

$$(H_0 + H_s)\psi\chi = E\psi\chi.$$

$\psi$ is the wave function in space, and $\chi$ is the wave function in spin space. $H_s =$ Hamiltonian for spin, and $H_0 =$ the Hamiltonian defined in Eq. (2.7). Thus

$$H\psi = E\psi$$

where $H = H_0 + H_s$ and $\psi$ is total wave function. $H_s$ is all those parts of the Hamiltonian which must be added to account for the extra energy inherent in the introduction of spin. Thus $H_s$ will contain terms indicating magnetic interaction between the spinning charges of particles or the interaction between the magnetic moment of the spinning charge of a particle and the magnetic field of the charged particle in its orbit. The first gives terms like $\mathbf{S}_1 \cdot \mathbf{S}_2$, the second terms like $\mathbf{L} \cdot \mathbf{S}$. Let us consider a system containing only one particle with spin so that the Hamiltonian does not contain terms $\mathbf{S}_1 \cdot \mathbf{S}_2$. We have that $\mathbf{L}$ does not commute with $\mathbf{L}$ and therefore does not commute with $\mathbf{L} \cdot \mathbf{S}$ or with the new Hamiltonian $H = H_0 + H_s$. Similarly, $\mathbf{S}$ will not commute with $H$. However, $\mathbf{J} = \mathbf{L} + \mathbf{S}$ does commute with $\mathbf{L} \cdot \mathbf{S}$ and therefore with $H$. Operators $L^2, S^2$ commute with $\mathbf{L} \cdot \mathbf{S}$ and with $H$. We can now draw up a list of operators which commute with $H$ and therefore have eigenvalues which are constants of motion

$$S^2, L^2, J^2, \mathbf{J}.$$

Of the three operators in $\mathbf{J}$, only one, $J_z$, is required, since a state can only be an eigenfunction of one of them. Thus our list of commuting operators becomes

$$H, J^2, J_z, L^2, S^2.$$

If the system contains two particles with spin, then the Hamiltonian can contain terms such as $\mathbf{S}_1 \cdot \mathbf{S}_2$ or $(3/r^2)(\mathbf{S}_1 \cdot \mathbf{r})(\mathbf{S}_2 \cdot \mathbf{r}) - \mathbf{S}_1 \cdot \mathbf{S}_2$. The former term commutes with all the operators we have just listed and does not alter the number of the constants of motion. The latter term represents the noncentral tensor force (Section 6.5) and it does not commute with $L^2$ or with $S^2$. These operators must be removed from the list of commuting operators if the tensor force is present, and it follows that in these circumstances $l$ and $s$ are no longer constants of the motion.

Returning to rotation, we see that it is now essential to use **J** to generate rotations rather than **L**, if the system contains spin. This will ensure that the quantities such as $H$ remain invariant.

In future we shall speak of conserved quantities by the eigenvalue parameters; thus if $J^2$ commutes with $H$, then $j(j+1)\hbar^2$ is a constant of motion; for brevity we shall say $j$ is the constant and refer to the total angular momentum as $j$; similarly, we shall use $l$ to specify the eigenvalue of $L^2$, $l_z$ for $L_z$, $j_z$ for $J_z$, etc.

## 2.5 The Eigenvalues of Angular Momentum

We devote this section to developing the formalism of the angular momentum operators. Let us construct a wave function which is simultaneously an eigenfunction of $H, J^2, J_z$; let it be $\phi(E, \alpha, \beta)$. Then

$$H\phi(E, \alpha, \beta) = E\phi(E, \alpha, \beta), \tag{2.8}$$

$$J^2\phi(E, \alpha, \beta) = \alpha\hbar^2\phi(E, \alpha, \beta), \tag{2.9}$$

$$J_z\phi(E, \alpha, \beta) = \beta\hbar\phi(E, \alpha, \beta). \tag{2.10}$$

We introduce two further operators which are defined by

$$J_+ = J_x + iJ_y, \tag{2.11}$$

$$J_- = J_x - iJ_y. \tag{2.12}$$

These operators satisfy the following commutation relations:

$$[J_z, J_+] = +J_+\hbar, \quad [J_z, J_-] = -J_-\hbar, \quad [J_+, J_-] = 2J_z\hbar.$$

We operate on Eq. (2.10) with $J_+$, and substitute the appropriate commutation relation; thus

$$J_+ J_z\phi(E, \alpha, \beta) = \beta\hbar J_+\phi(E, \alpha, \beta)$$

becomes

$$(-J_+\hbar + J_z J_+)\phi(E, \alpha, \beta) = \beta\hbar J_+\phi(E, \alpha, \beta)$$

which can be rearranged to

$$J_z J_+\phi(E, \alpha, \beta) = (\beta + 1)\hbar J_+\phi(E, \alpha, \beta). \tag{2.13}$$

Equation (2.13) indicates that the function $J_+\phi(E, \alpha, \beta)$ is also an eigenfunction of $J_z$ with eigenvalue $(\beta + 1)\hbar$. In a similar way we can show that the function $J_-\phi(E, \alpha, \beta)$ is an eigenfunction of $J_z$ with eigenvalue $(\beta-1)\hbar$:

$$J_z J_- \phi(E, \alpha, \beta) = (\beta-1)\hbar J_- \phi(E, \alpha, \beta). \qquad (2.14)$$

The operators $J_+$ and $J_-$ also commute with $H$ and $J^2$, so that the new functions given by Eqs. (2.13) and (2.14) are still eigenfunctions of $H$ and $J^2$ with the same eigenvalues as the original eigenfunction, as in Eqs. (2.8) and (2.9).

Therefore $J_+$ and $J_-$ have the power to generate, from one eigenfunction of $J_z$, other eigenfunctions of $J_z$ which differ in their eigenvalues by an amount $\pm\hbar$. However, there must be a limit to the repeated application of $J_+$ or of $J_-$. This limit will occur for $J_-$ if, when it is applied to the previously generated eigenfunction $\phi(E, \alpha, \beta_{min})$, we have that

$$J_- \phi(E, \alpha, \beta_{min}) = 0. \qquad (2.15)$$

Operating on Eq. (2.15) with $J_+$, we must have

$$J_+ J_- \phi(E, \alpha, \beta_{min}) = 0. \qquad (2.16)$$

Substitute into (2.16) the operator equality

$$J_+ J_- = J^2 - J_z^2 + J_z\hbar.$$

Evaluating the eigenvalues shows us that

$$\hbar^2(\alpha - \beta_{min}^2 + \beta_{min}) = 0.$$

Thus the last eigenvalue $\beta_{min}$ of $J_z$ which can be generated by $J_-$ is given by

$$\beta_{min}(\beta_{min} - 1) = \alpha. \qquad (2.17)$$

Similarly, the limit to the repeated application of $J_+$ will come when

$$J_+ \phi(E, \alpha, \beta_{max}) = 0. \qquad (2.18)$$

Operating on Eq. (2.18) with $J_-$ and using the operator equality

$$J_- J_+ = J^2 - J_z^2 - J_z\hbar, \qquad (2.19)$$

we find that

$$\beta_{max}(\beta_{max} + 1) = \alpha.$$

Thus

$$\beta_{max} = -\beta_{min}.$$

We see that $\hbar(\beta_{max} - \beta_{min})$ is an integral number of $\hbar$ since $\beta_{max}$ and $\beta_{min}$ are connected by an integral number of operations with $J_+$ or with $J_-$. Therefore we can put

$$\hbar\beta_{max} = \hbar\beta_{min} + n\hbar, \quad n \text{ an integer,}$$

whence

$$\beta_{max} = n/2.$$

Thus we see that the possible values for the eigenvalues of $J_z$ can vary through the series

$$-\frac{n\hbar}{2}, \quad -\frac{n\hbar}{2}+\hbar, \quad ..., \quad \frac{n\hbar}{2}-2\hbar, \quad \frac{n\hbar}{2}-\hbar, \quad \frac{n\hbar}{2}.$$

Substituting in Eq. (2.17), we see that

$$\alpha = \frac{n}{2}\left(\frac{n}{2}+1\right).$$

This is usually expressed as $j(j+1)$, and our eigenequation becomes

$$J^2\phi(E,j,\beta) = j(j+1)\hbar^2\phi(E,j,\beta),$$

whilst the possible eigenvalues of $J_z$ are

$$-j, -j+1, -j+2, ... \quad ..., j-2, j-1, j.$$

The $j$ can have half-integer values.

We know from particular cases in elementary wave mechanics that $L_z$ has eigenvalues which are integer multiples of $\hbar$, whilst the eigenvalues of $S_z$ can be $\pm\hbar/2$. The total angular momentum and its permitted $z$ components consequently may also have values which are half-integer multiples of $\hbar$. The relations among the eigenvalues show that this possibility can be accommodated.

Our eigenfunction $\phi(E,\alpha,\beta)$ is now written $\phi(E,j,j_z)$ where

$$H\phi(E,j,j_z) = E\phi(E,j,j_z), \tag{2.20}$$

$$J^2\phi(E,j,j_z) = j(j+1)\hbar^2\phi(E,j,j_z), \tag{2.21}$$

$$J_z\phi(E,j,j_z) = j_z\hbar\phi(E,j,j_z), \quad -j\leqslant j_z\leqslant j. \tag{2.22}$$

## 2.6 The Matrix Elements of Angular Momentum

In this section attention is devoted to matrix elements of the form

$$(\phi(E,j_2,j_{2z})\,|\,K\,|\,\phi(E,j_1,j_{1z})), \tag{2.23}$$

where $K$ is an operator made up of angular momentum operators; the two states connected in this way are pure states of angular momentum, having the same properties as the eigenfunction defined by Eqs. (2.20)–(2.22). We can abbreviate Eq. (2.23) to

$$(j_2,j_{2z}|\,K\,|j_1,j_{1z}).\tag{2.24}$$

As a trivial example, we put $K = J_z$, $j = j_1 = j_2$, and $j_z = j_{1z} = j_{2z}$; then we must have

$$(j,j_z|\,J_z\,|j,j_z) = j_z\hbar.$$

We wish to consider the operator $J_-J_+$; by Eq. (2.19) this has eigenvalues $\{j(j+1)-j_z(j_z+1)\}\hbar^2$. Thus we have the matrix element

$$(j,j_z|\,J_-J_+\,|j,j_z) = \{j(j+1)-j_z(j_z+1)\}\hbar^2 = (j-j_z)(j+j_z+1)\hbar^2.$$

By the rule (l) of Section 1.2 we can write the left-hand side of this equation as

$$\Sigma(j,j_z|\,J_-\,|j',j_z')(j',j_z'|\,J_+\,|j,j_z).$$

This sum must normally be taken over all possible intermediate states; however, since $H$ and $J^2$ commute with $J_+$ and with $J_-$, all matrix elements are zero, except those connected to intermediate states having the same energy and total angular momentum. Thus the sum is taken over all possible values of $j_z'$; but we know that $J_+$ and $J_-$ only generate states with eigenvalues of $J_z$ differing by óne unit. Therefore, from the orthonormality of states, we see that $J_+|j,j_z)$ can only be matched with the eigenfunction $(j,j_z+1|$, and so on. Again all matrix elements are zero, except those having the two states such that their eigenvalues of $J_z$ differ by one unit. Thus the sum reduces to one term:

$$(j,j_z|\,J_-J_+\,|j,j_z) = (j,j_z|\,J_-\,|j,j_z+1)(j,j_z+1|\,J_+\,|j,j_z).$$

The two terms on the right-hand side are the complex conjugate of one another. Therefore

$$(j-j_z)(j+j_z+1)\hbar^2 = |(j,j_z|\,J_-\,|j,j_z+1)|^2,$$

or

$$(j,j_z|\,J_-\,|j,j_z+1) = e^{i\delta}\hbar\sqrt{(j-j_z)(j+j_z+1)}.\tag{2.25}$$

The $e^{i\delta}$ is a phase term appearing because the matrix elements are complex quantities; there is no observable loss of information in putting $\delta = 0$. Similarly to Eq. (2.25) we have

$$(j,j_z+1|\,J_+\,|j,j_z) = \hbar\sqrt{(j-j_z)(j+j_z+1)}.$$

If we substitute Eqs. (2.11) and (2.12) into these matrix elements, we can solve for the matrix elements of $J_x$ and of $J_y$. The nonzero matrix elements of $J_x$, $J_y$, $J_z$, $J_+$, and $J_-$ are:

$$(j, j_z+1 | J_x | j, j_z) = \tfrac{1}{2}\hbar \sqrt{(j-j_z)(j+j_z+1)}, \tag{2.26}$$

$$(j, j_z | J_x | j, j_z+1) = \tfrac{1}{2}\hbar \sqrt{(j-j_z)(j+j_z+1)}, \tag{2.27}$$

$$(j, j_z+1 | J_y | j, j_z) = -\frac{i}{2}\hbar \sqrt{(j-j_z)(j+j_z+1)}, \tag{2.28}$$

$$(j, j_z | J_y | j, j_z+1) = +\frac{i}{2}\hbar \sqrt{(j-j_z)(j+j_z+1)}, \tag{2.29}$$

$$(j, j_z | J_z | j, j_z) = j_z \hbar, \tag{2.30}$$

$$(j, j_z+1 | J_+ | j, j_z) = \hbar \sqrt{(j-j_z)(j+j_z+1)}, \tag{2.31}$$

$$(j, j_z | J_- | j, j_z+1) = \hbar \sqrt{(j-j_z)(j+j_z+1)}. \tag{2.32}$$

These matrix elements are required in solving various eigenequations for the values of the Clebsch–Gordan coefficients; see the next Section, 2.7.

## 2.7 The Vector Addition of Angular Momentum

In this section we are interested in a physical system containing two angular momenta which are noninteracting. Then the total angular momentum of the system is found by a vector addition. We indicate quantities from the two parts $A$ and $B$ by subscripts $a$ and $b$; the total wave function is then

$$\psi = \phi_a(j_a, j_{az})\, \phi_b(j_b, j_{bz}).$$

This function is already an eigenfunction of $J_z = J_{az} + J_{bz}$ with eigenvalue $j_z = j_{az} + j_{bz}$; however, it is not necessarily an eigenfunction of the operator $J^2 = (\mathbf{J}_a + \mathbf{J}_b)^2$. It is, in fact, a sum of eigenfunctions of $J^2$, the sum being restricted to functions with eigenvalues $j$ which satisfy $-j \leqslant j_z \leqslant +j$ and $|j_a - j_b| \leqslant j \leqslant j_a + j_b$. The first condition arises from ordinary properties of angular momentum, the second from the fact that the sum of two vectors cannot be less than the magnitude of their difference, or greater than the magnitude of their sum. To illustrate this we consider some simple examples of the addition of the two vectors $\mathbf{J}_a$ and $\mathbf{J}_b$. We pick out particular values of the total $z$ component which can be reached in the addition; obviously the possible values must satisfy $-(j_a + j_b) \leqslant j_z \leqslant (j_a + j_b)$. We shall indicate eigenfunctions of $J^2$ and of $J_z$ by $\phi(j, j_z)$.

(a)  If $j_z = j_{az} + j_{bz} = j_a + j_b$, then the total wave function is

$$\psi = \phi_a(j_a, j_a)\, \phi_b(j_b, j_b).$$

The $z$ components of the total and of the separate vectors are at a maximum and the wave function can only be an eigenfunction of $J^2$ with eigenvalue quantum number $(j_a + j_b)$.

(b)  If $j_z = j_a + j_b - 1$, then there are two ways of composing a total wave function with this $J_z$ eigenvalue; they are:

$$\psi = \phi_a(j_a, j_a)\, \phi_b(j_b, j_b - 1), \tag{2.33}$$

$$\psi = \phi_a(j_a, j_a - 1)\, \phi_b(j_b, j_b). \tag{2.34}$$

Neither of these functions is an eigenfunction of $J^2$ since there are two such possible functions with $J_z$ eigenvalues $(j_a + j_b - 1)$. They are:

$$\phi(j_a + j_b, j_a + j_b - 1), \tag{2.35}$$

$$\phi(j_a + j_b - 1, j_a + j_b - 1). \tag{2.36}$$

Either of the functions (2.33) or (2.34) can be expressed as a linear sum of the two functions (2.35) and (2.36), and vice versa. This follows from the principle of superposition, Section 1.3.

(c)  If $j_z = j_a + j_b - 2$, then there are three ways of composing a total wave function with this $J_z$ eigenvalue; we do not give them as they are analogous to Eqs. (2.33) and (2.34). These three functions can each be expressed as a linear sum of the $J^2$ eigenfunctions which have $J_z$ eigenvalues $(j_a + j_b - 2)$ and which are analogous to functions (2.35) and (2.36).

This process continues; any value of $j_z$ selected can have its wave function expressed as a linear sum of eigenfunctions of $J^2$. As we decrease the value of $j_z$, more $J^2$ eigenfunctions are required until $j_z = |j_a - j_b|$, after which no more are needed. When $j_z = -|j_a - j_b|$, the number of eigenfunctions required begins to decrease until only one is required when $j_z = -|j_a + j_b|$.

We can illustrate this vector addition in a naive geometrical picture. Figure 2.1 shows on its left-hand side two vectors $\mathbf{A}$ and $\mathbf{B}$, having $j_a = 2, j_{az} = 1, j_b = 3, j_{bz} = 2$. The vector addition of $\mathbf{A}$ and $\mathbf{B}$ looks like the linear sum of the three vectors on the right of the figure; these vectors have $j = 5, 4,$ and $3$, respectively, and all have $j_z = 3$.

What we have said up to now can be reduced to the simple statement that

$$\phi_a(j_a, j_{az})\, \phi_b(j_b, j_{bz}) = \sum_j C(j, j_z, j_a, j_{az}, j_b, j_{bz})\, \phi(j, j_z = j_{az} + j_{bz}). \tag{2.37}$$

A set of such equations can be solved to give the reverse of an addition; thus, if we know that the total angular momentum $\phi(j,j_z)$ is the vector addition of two angular momenta $j_a$ and $j_b$ with $j_z = j_{az} + j_{bz}$, then it is possible to put

$$\phi(j,j_z) = \sum_{j_{az}} G(j,j_z,j_a,j_{az},j_b,j_{bz})\,\phi_a(j_a,j_{az})\,\phi_b(j_b,j_{bz} = j_z - j_{az}). \qquad (2.38)$$

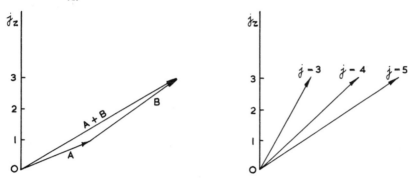

FIG. 2.1. The vector sum $\mathbf{A}+\mathbf{B}$ of the two vectors $\mathbf{A}$ and $\mathbf{B}$ is a linear superposition of the three vectors at the right.

The coefficients of Eqs. (2.37) and (2.38) are the Clebsch–Gordan coefficients; they are tabulated for several low values of $j_a$ and $j_b$ by Condon and Shortley (1951). We shall now show how they are determined. Let us consider the coefficients of Eq. (2.37):

$$C(j,j_z,j_a,j_{az},j_b,j_{bz}).$$

Such a summation is in full accord with the principle of superposition of states. Therefore we must have that

$$\sum_j |C(j,j_z,j_a,j_{az},j_b,j_{bz})|^2 = 1;$$

similarly for the coefficients of Eq. (2.38). In fact, multiplying Eq. (2.37) by the complex conjugate of Eq. (2.38) and integrating shows that

$$C(j,j_z,j_a,j_{az},j_b,j_{bz}) = G^*(j,j_z,j_a,j_{az},j_b,j_{bz}). \qquad (2.39)$$

They can be derived by considering the matrix elements of the operators $J_+$ and $J_-$ acting on a set of equations such as (2.37). As an example of this procedure we shall evaluate some of the coefficients in the addition of the two angular momenta $j_a = 1$ and $j_b = \frac{1}{2}$. The wave function $\phi_a(1,1)\phi_b(\frac{1}{2},\frac{1}{2})$ is already an eigenfunction of $J^2$ and $J_z$; that is, $C(\frac{3}{2},\frac{3}{2},1,1,\frac{1}{2},\frac{1}{2}) = e^{i\gamma}$ and Eq. (2.37) reduces to

$$\phi_a(1,1)\phi_b(\tfrac{1}{2},\tfrac{1}{2}) = e^{i\gamma}\phi(\tfrac{3}{2},\tfrac{3}{2}), \qquad (2.40)$$

where $\gamma$ is a phase factor which is unobservable. We follow the normal convention and put $\gamma = 0$, thus making the coefficient real. This convention is followed throughout so that all the Clebsch–Gordan coefficients are real. We can define the operator $J_- = J_{a-} + J_{b-}$. As in Section 2.5, $J_-$ will generate from $\phi(j, j_z)$ a new eigenfunction of $J_z$; $J_{a-}$ and $J_{b-}$ do the same for the eigenfunctions $\phi_a(j_a, j_{az})$ and $\phi_b(j_b, j_{bz})$ respectively. We operate on Eq. (2.40) with $J_-$:

$$J_- \phi(\tfrac{3}{2}, \tfrac{3}{2}) = \phi_b(\tfrac{1}{2}, \tfrac{1}{2}) J_{a-} \phi_a(1, 1) + \phi_a(1, 1) J_{b-} \phi_b(\tfrac{1}{2}, \tfrac{1}{2}). \qquad (2.41)$$

However, from Eqs. (2.37) and (2.39) we can write

$$\phi(\tfrac{3}{2}, \tfrac{1}{2}) = C(\tfrac{3}{2}, \tfrac{1}{2}, 1, 0, \tfrac{1}{2}, \tfrac{1}{2}) \phi_b(\tfrac{1}{2}, \tfrac{1}{2}) \phi_a(1, 0)$$
$$+ C(\tfrac{3}{2}, \tfrac{1}{2}, 1, 1, \tfrac{1}{2}, -\tfrac{1}{2}) \phi_a(1, 1) \phi_b(\tfrac{1}{2}, -\tfrac{1}{2}). \qquad (2.42)$$

We now multiply Eq. (2.41) by the complex conjugate of Eq. (2.42) and integrate to form a matrix element equation:

$$(\phi(\tfrac{3}{2}, \tfrac{1}{2}) | J_- | \phi(\tfrac{3}{2}, \tfrac{3}{2})) = C(\tfrac{3}{2}, \tfrac{1}{2}, 1, 0, \tfrac{1}{2}, \tfrac{1}{2}) (\phi_a(1, 0) | J_{a-} | \phi_a(1, 1))$$
$$+ C(\tfrac{3}{2}, \tfrac{1}{2}, 1, 1, \tfrac{1}{2}, -\tfrac{1}{2}) (\phi_b(\tfrac{1}{2}, -\tfrac{1}{2}) | J_{b-} | \phi_b(\tfrac{1}{2}, \tfrac{1}{2})).$$

We substitute the known values of the matrix elements from Eqs. (2.30) and (2.31) to find that

$$\sqrt{3} = \sqrt{2}\, C(\tfrac{3}{2}, \tfrac{1}{2}, 1, 0, \tfrac{1}{2}, \tfrac{1}{2}) + C(\tfrac{3}{2}, \tfrac{1}{2}, 1, 1, \tfrac{1}{2}, -\tfrac{1}{2}).$$

Now

$$[C(\tfrac{3}{2}, \tfrac{1}{2}, 1, 0, \tfrac{1}{2}, \tfrac{1}{2})]^2 + [C(\tfrac{3}{2}, \tfrac{1}{2}, 1, 1, \tfrac{1}{2}, -\tfrac{1}{2})]^2 = 1,$$

so that

$$C(\tfrac{3}{2}, \tfrac{1}{2}, 1, 0, \tfrac{1}{2}, \tfrac{1}{2}) = \sqrt{\tfrac{2}{3}},$$

$$C(\tfrac{3}{2}, \tfrac{1}{2}, 1, 1, \tfrac{1}{2}, -\tfrac{1}{2}) = \sqrt{\tfrac{1}{3}}.$$

By starting from the equation

$$\phi(\tfrac{3}{2}, -\tfrac{3}{2}) = \phi_a(1, -1) \phi_b(\tfrac{1}{2}, -\tfrac{1}{2}),$$

and using the operator $J_+$, we can obtain the coefficients

$$C(\tfrac{3}{2}, -\tfrac{1}{2}, 1, 0, \tfrac{1}{2}, -\tfrac{1}{2}) = \sqrt{\tfrac{2}{3}},$$

$$C(\tfrac{3}{2}, -\tfrac{1}{2}, 1, -1, \tfrac{1}{2}, +\tfrac{1}{2}) = \sqrt{\tfrac{1}{3}}.$$

So far we have determined six of the ten coefficients; except for some uncertainty in sign the remainder can be found by inspection and this can be seen by examining the table of coefficients (Table 2.1). As presented, all rows and columns have the property that the sum of the squares of the coefficients is one. The uncertainty in sign lies in the columns for the eigenvalues $\phi(\frac{1}{2}, \frac{1}{2})$ and $\phi(\frac{1}{2}, -\frac{1}{2})$. By considering the $J_+$ or $J_-$ operations which cause transformations from one column to the other, the uncertainty can be reduced to a single ambiguity. We have followed the sign convention used by Condon and Shortley.

TABLE 2.1

CLEBSCH–GORDAN COEFFICIENTS FOR $j_a = 1$ AND $j_b = \frac{1}{2}$

| | $\phi(\frac{3}{2}, \frac{3}{2})$ | $\phi(\frac{3}{2}, \frac{1}{2})$ | $\phi(\frac{3}{2}, -\frac{1}{2})$ | $\phi(\frac{3}{2}, -\frac{3}{2})$ | $\phi(\frac{1}{2}, \frac{1}{2})$ | $\phi(\frac{1}{2}, -\frac{1}{2})$ |
|---|---|---|---|---|---|---|
| $\phi_a(1, 1)\phi_b(\frac{1}{2}, \frac{1}{2})$ | 1 | | | | | |
| $\phi_a(1, 1)\phi_b(\frac{1}{2}, -\frac{1}{2})$ | | $\sqrt{\frac{1}{3}}$ | | | $\sqrt{\frac{2}{3}}$ | |
| $\phi_a(1, 0)\phi_b(\frac{1}{2}, \frac{1}{2})$ | | $\sqrt{\frac{2}{3}}$ | | | $-\sqrt{\frac{1}{3}}$ | |
| $\phi_a(1, 0)\phi_b(\frac{1}{2}, -\frac{1}{2})$ | | | $\sqrt{\frac{2}{3}}$ | | | $\sqrt{\frac{1}{3}}$ |
| $\phi_a(1, -1)\phi_b(\frac{1}{2}, \frac{1}{2})$ | | | $\sqrt{\frac{1}{3}}$ | | | $-\sqrt{\frac{2}{3}}$ |
| $\phi_a(1, -1)\phi_b(\frac{1}{2}, -\frac{1}{2})$ | | | | 1 | | |

Down the left-hand side of this table are the possible products of the separate angular momentum eigenfunctions; along the top of the table are the possible eigenfunctions of $J^2$ and $J_z$. Reading along a row gives the sum of total angular momentum eigenfunctions which equals the eigenfunction product at the begining of the row, as in Eq. (2.37); reading down a column gives an inverse sum as in Eq. (2.38). The only spaces in the table which can contain terms are those for which $j_z = j_{az} + j_{bz}$.

As an example, we suppose it is necessary to express $\phi_a(1, 0)\phi_b(\frac{1}{2}, \frac{1}{2})$ in terms of eigenfunctions of $J^2$ and $J_z$. The table gives

$$\phi_a(1, 0)\phi_b(\tfrac{1}{2}, \tfrac{1}{2}) = \sqrt{\tfrac{2}{3}}\,\phi(\tfrac{3}{2}, \tfrac{1}{2}) - \sqrt{\tfrac{1}{3}}\,\phi(\tfrac{1}{2}, \tfrac{1}{2}).$$

As an example of the opposite process we find that

$$\phi(\tfrac{1}{2}, -\tfrac{1}{2}) = \sqrt{\tfrac{1}{3}}\,\phi_a(1, 0)\phi_b(\tfrac{1}{2}, -\tfrac{1}{2}) - \sqrt{\tfrac{2}{3}}\,\phi_a(1, -1)\phi_b(\tfrac{1}{2}, \tfrac{1}{2}).$$

The importance of these relations between angular momentum functions lies in the fact that it is often necessary to express certain angular momentum functions in terms of eigenfunctions of $J^2$ and $J_z$ as these are the quantities which are conserved in nuclear interactions. However, such a description may not be convenient when it is necessary to present the results of an analysis in an observable form; for instance, $j$ and $j_z$ may be conserved, but it is the orbital angular momentum eigenfunctions which determine the angular distribution of the reaction products. Thus the reaction must be analysed in terms of eigenfunctions of $J^2$ and $J_z$, but the final wave function must be expressed in terms of eigenfunctions of orbital and spin angular momentum; we shall have to use this procedure in later chapters.

## 2.8 Eigenfunctions of Angular Momentum

So far in this chapter the emphasis has been laid upon the operator properties of angular momentum; however, if the operators $L^2$ and $L_z$ are expressed in polar coordinates $\theta$ and $\phi$, then it is possible to find analytic solutions to the eigenequations (do not confuse the use of $\phi$ to represent the azimuthal angle with its previous use to represent a wave function):

$$L^2 \psi(\theta, \phi) = l(l+1)\hbar^2 \psi(\theta, \phi), \tag{2.43}$$

$$L_z \psi(\theta, \phi) = l_z \hbar \psi(\theta, \phi). \tag{2.44}$$

A function which is simultaneously a solution of Eqs. (2.43) and (2.44) is

$$\psi(\theta, \phi) = \sin^m \theta \left(\frac{d}{d \cos \theta}\right)^m \{P_l(\cos \theta)\} \exp(\pm im\phi), \tag{2.45}$$

where $P_l(\cos \theta)$ is the $l$th Legendre polynomial and $l_z = \pm m$. The parameters $l$ and $m$ must be positive integers, having $m \leqslant l$, in order that the solution be meaningful, single-valued, and well-behaved; such conditions are physically essential and thus lead naturally to quantum states. The functions

$$\sin^m \theta \left(\frac{d}{d \cos \theta}\right)^m P_l(\cos \theta)$$

are called the associated Legendre polynomials and are represented by $P_l^m(\cos \theta)$.

These solutions are unnormalized: each solution $P_l^m(\cos \theta) \exp(\pm im\phi)$ must be multiplied by a real numerical factor $C_{lm}$ in order that the condition (e) of Section 1.2 be satisfied. We must have

$$\int \psi^* \psi \, d\mathbf{x} = 1.$$

Now $d\mathbf{x} = -d\phi \, d(\cos \theta)$ for angular functions only; thus

$$-\int_{+1}^{-1} \int_0^{2\pi} |C_{lm} P_l^m(\cos \theta)|^2 \, d(\cos \theta) \, d\phi = 1,$$

whence

$$C_{lm} = \frac{(-1)^m}{\sqrt{2\pi}} \left[\frac{2l+1}{2} \frac{(l-m)!}{(l+m)!}\right]^{\frac{1}{2}}.$$

The $(-1)^m$ is included to make the phases consistent with the choice made in the last section. In future we put

$$C_{l|l_z|} P_l^{|l_z|} (\cos\theta) \exp(il_z\phi) = Y(l, l_z).$$

We shall refer to these functions as spherical harmonics. We tabulate these functions for the first three values of $l$:

$$
\left.
\begin{aligned}
Y(0,0) &= \frac{1}{\sqrt{4\pi}}, \\[2mm]
Y(1,0) &= \sqrt{\frac{3}{4\pi}}\,\cos\theta, \\[2mm]
Y(1,\pm 1) &= \mp\sqrt{\frac{3}{8\pi}}\,\sin\theta\exp(\pm i\phi), \\[2mm]
Y(2,0) &= \sqrt{\frac{5}{16\pi}}\,(3\cos^2\theta - 1), \\[2mm]
Y(2,\pm 1) &= \mp\sqrt{\frac{15}{8\pi}}\,\sin\theta\cos\theta\exp(\pm i\phi), \\[2mm]
Y(2,\pm 2) &= \sqrt{\frac{15}{32\pi}}\,\sin^2\theta\exp(\pm 2i\phi).
\end{aligned}
\right\}
\quad (2.46)
$$

The parity of these angular momentum functions is important. We recall that a test of parity is made by replacing $x$ by $-x$ (Section 1.7). For our spherical functions this corresponds to replacing $\theta$ and $\phi$ by $\pi-\theta$ and $\phi-\pi$. We have that

$$\cos(\pi-\theta) = -\cos\theta,$$

$$\left(\frac{d}{d\cos(\pi-\theta)}\right)^m = (-1)^m\left(\frac{d}{d\cos\theta}\right)^m$$

and

$$\sin(\pi-\theta) = \sin\theta.$$

In addition, we have that

$$e^{im(\phi-\pi)} = (-1)^m e^{im\phi}.$$

Then we find on making the replacement in Eq. (2.45) that the parity of the differential operator and of the exponential cancel and we are left with the parity, the Legendre polynomial, $P_l(\cos\theta)$. This polynomial contains the following powers of $\cos\theta$; $l, l-2, l-4, \ldots$, etc., and therefore has parity $(-1)^l$. Thus the parity of the eigenfunction $Y(l, l_z)$ is $(-1)^l$.

There are no analytic spin functions; however, we can define spin eigenfunctions $\chi(s, s_z)$ by the eigenequations

$$S^2 \chi(s, s_z) = s(s+1) \hbar^2 \chi(s, s_z), \tag{2.47}$$

$$S_z \chi(s, s_z) = s_z \hbar \chi(s, s_z). \tag{2.48}$$

The functions $\chi(s, s_z)$ are orthogonal in the sense

$$(\chi(s_1, s_{1z}) | \chi(s_2, s_{2z})) = \delta_{s_1 s_2} \delta_{s_{1z} s_{2z}}. \tag{2.49}$$

There is no integration over spin space since there are no independent variables such as $\theta$ and $\phi$ in Eq. (2.45).

A particle which is simultaneously in a state of orbital angular momentum $l, l_z$ and of spin angular momentum $s, s_z$ will be described by the wave function

$$Y(l, l_z) \chi(s, s_z).$$

## 2.9 The Pauli Spin Matrices

We can at this point mention a matrix representation of spin operators and eigenvectors which was introduced by Pauli. The three Pauli spin matrices are

$$\sigma_x = \begin{bmatrix} 0 & 1 \\ 1 & 0 \end{bmatrix}, \tag{2.50}$$

$$\sigma_y = \begin{bmatrix} 0 & -i \\ i & 0 \end{bmatrix}, \tag{2.51}$$

$$\sigma_z = \begin{bmatrix} 1 & 0 \\ 0 & -1 \end{bmatrix}. \tag{2.52}$$

If we use the rules of matrix algebra (Margenau and Murphy, 1943) we find that these matrices have the properties

$$\sigma_x \sigma_y + \sigma_y \sigma_x = 2\delta_{xy} I,$$

$$\sigma_x \sigma_y = i\sigma_z,$$

where $x, y, z$ can be cyclically permutated and $I$ is the unit matrix. Hence, if we put

$$S_x = \frac{\hbar}{2}\sigma_x, \quad S_y = \frac{\hbar}{2}\sigma_y, \quad S_z = \frac{\hbar}{2}\sigma_z,$$

we find that the operators $S_x, S_y, S_z$ satisfy Eq. (2.4) in place of $L_x, L_y,$ and $L_z$, and Eq. (2.5) after defining $S^2$ by an equation analogous to (2.3).

This is what we require of angular momentum operators and thus we have a representation of spin angular momentum. It is not a unique representation, as there are, in fact, an infinite number of sets of matrices like those of (2.50) to (2.52) which satisfy our angular momentum commutation relations in the same way; however, a matrix of any other set is a linear combination of the Pauli matrices and the unit matrix. These were chosen so that the $z$ component of angular momentum is quantized. In fact, we find that the column matrices

$$\begin{bmatrix} 1 \\ 0 \end{bmatrix} \quad \text{and} \quad \begin{bmatrix} 0 \\ 1 \end{bmatrix}$$

are eigenfunctions of $S_z$ with eigenvalues $+\frac{1}{2}\hbar$ and $-\frac{1}{2}\hbar$ respectively and are also eigenfunctions of $S^2$, both with eigenvalue $\frac{3}{4}\hbar^2$. We conclude that the representation is one for spin $\frac{1}{2}$.

This representation adds nothing to our knowledge of spin but does give us a convenient means of expressing various relations which we have derived previously and which apply to spin. Similar representations can be constructed for greater spins; we refer readers to Schiff's book (Schiff, 1955) for a fuller discussion.

## 2.10 Rotations (II)

We have seen in Section 2.2 how the angular momentum operators are responsible for generating the unitary operators for rotations; we wish to extend our consideration of these rotations. To do so, we begin by defining the Euler angles which can specify a rotation completely. The orientation of a set of Cartesian coordinates with respect to another set requires three parameters since there are three degrees of freedom; these parameters are the angular rotations made in turning one set of coordinates into the other. Consider a right-handed coordinate system $S_1$, with axes $x_1, y_1, z_1$; rotate the coordinates through an angle $\alpha$ about the $z_1$ axis to generate a new set of coordinates $S_2$ with axes $x_2, y_2, z_2$ $(= z_1)$. (A positive rotation is in the direction which would move a right-handed screw in the positive direction along the axis of rotation.) The second step is to rotate $S_2$ through an angle $\beta$ around $y_2$ to generate a third coordinate system $S_3$ with axes $x_3, y_3 (= y_2), z_3$. Finally, rotate $S_3$ through an angle $\gamma$ around $z_3$ to produce a fourth coordinate system $S_4$ with axes $x_4, y_4, z_4 (= z_3)$. Summarizing the rotation from $S_1 \rightarrow S_4$:

$$S_1 \rightarrow S_2: \text{angle } \alpha \text{ around } z_1,$$

$$S_2 \rightarrow S_3: \text{angle } \beta \text{ around } y_2,$$

$$S_3 \rightarrow S_4: \text{angle } \gamma \text{ around } z_3.$$

$\alpha$, $\beta$, and $\gamma$ are the Euler angles. The $z_4$ axis has conventional polar coordinates in $S_1$, $\theta = \beta$, and $\phi = \alpha$.

Consider a one-component function $\psi(\mathbf{x})$ which describes some physical system in the coordinates $S_1$. The rotation defines a second function $\psi'(\mathbf{x})$ which describes the same system in the transformed coordinate system $S_4$; then

$$\psi'(\mathbf{x}) = D\psi(\mathbf{x})$$

where $D$ is the unitary operator introduced in Section 2.3 and for a rotation defined by the Euler angles is given by

$$D = \exp\left(-\frac{i}{\hbar}J_{z_3}\gamma\right)\exp\left(-\frac{i}{\hbar}J_{y_2}\beta\right)\exp\left(-\frac{i}{\hbar}J_{z_1}\alpha\right). \qquad (2.53)$$

This is an inconvenient form for $D$ as each angular momentum operator is about an axis in different coordinate systems. We can transform these operators using Eq. (1.12). The operator for rotations about $y_1$, that is $\exp\left[(-i/\hbar)J_{y_1}\beta\right]$, is transformed for rotations about $y_2$ by the operator which rotates $S_1 \to S_2$, that is, $\exp\left[(-i/\hbar)J_{z_1}\alpha\right]$; therefore,

$$\exp\left(-\frac{i}{\hbar}J_{y_2}\beta\right) = \exp\left(-\frac{i}{\hbar}J_{z_1}\alpha\right)\exp\left(-\frac{i}{\hbar}J_{y_1}\beta\right)\exp\left(+\frac{i}{\hbar}J_{z_1}\alpha\right).$$

Similarly,

$$\exp\left(-\frac{i}{\hbar}J_{z_3}\gamma\right) = \exp\left(-\frac{i}{\hbar}J_{y_2}\beta\right)\exp\left(-\frac{i}{\hbar}J_{z_2}\gamma\right)\exp\left(+\frac{i}{\hbar}J_{y_2}\beta\right).$$

Substituting in Eq. (2.53), we find

$$D = \exp\left(-\frac{i}{\hbar}J_{z_1}\alpha\right)\exp\left(-\frac{i}{\hbar}J_{y_1}\beta\right)\exp\left(-\frac{i}{\hbar}J_{z_1}\gamma\right). \qquad (2.54)$$

This equation indicates that the rotation from coordinate system $S_1$ to $S_4$ could have been performed equally in the three stages

(1) angle $\gamma$ about $z_1$,

(2) angle $\beta$ about $y_1$,

(3) angle $\alpha$ about $z_1$,

where the directions $z_1$ and $y_1$ mean the original directions occupied by these axes in $S_1$ before rotations.

We are particularly interested in the case which occurs when $\psi(\mathbf{x})$ is an eigenfunction of the angular momentum operators $J^2$ and $J_z$, say

$\psi(j,j_z)$. (We have now dropped the independent variable $x$ and returned to our convention of placing the eigenvalues in the parentheses.) It is evident that $D\psi(j,j_z)$ will also be an eigenfunction of $J^2$ with eigenvalue quantum number $j$ but it will not be an eigenfunction of $J_z$. The eigenfunctions of $J_z$ form an orthonormal set; therefore it is possible to write

$$D\psi(j,j_z) = \sum_{j_z'=-j}^{+j} \mathscr{D}^j_{j_z j_z'}\, \psi(j,j_z').  \tag{2.55}$$

If we multiply each side by $\psi(j,j_z')$ and integrate, we obtain the matrix elements of $D$ and we find that

$$\mathscr{D}^j_{j_z j_z'} = (\psi(j,j_z')\,|\,D\,|\,\psi(j,j_z)\,).  \tag{2.56}$$

Thus the coefficients of the expansion of Eq. (2.55) are the matrix elements of the rotation operator $D$.

We will apply this immediately to the case of a particle having spin $\hbar/2$. Consider such a particle oriented so that every measurement of the spin component $S_{z_1}$ yields the value $\tfrac{1}{2}\hbar$. This pure state can be represented by the Pauli column matrix

$$\begin{bmatrix} 1 \\ 0 \end{bmatrix}$$

and is an eigenfunction of $S_{z_1}$. In a second coordinate system a measurement of $S_{z_2}$ will not always yield the value $\tfrac{1}{2}$ as long as $z_2$ is not parallel to $z_1$. Thus in this second system this pure state is not an eigenfunction $S_{z_2}$ but is a linear sum of the eigenfunctions of $S_z$, namely

$$\begin{bmatrix} 1 \\ 0 \end{bmatrix} \quad \text{and} \quad \begin{bmatrix} 0 \\ 1 \end{bmatrix}.$$

The coefficients in the linear sum are

$$\left( \begin{bmatrix} 1 \\ 0 \end{bmatrix} \middle| D \middle| \begin{bmatrix} 1 \\ 0 \end{bmatrix} \right) \quad \text{and} \quad \left( \begin{bmatrix} 0 \\ 1 \end{bmatrix} \middle| D \middle| \begin{bmatrix} 1 \\ 0 \end{bmatrix} \right)$$

respectively. $D$ is given by Eq. (2.54) with the total angular momentum operator $\mathbf{J}$ replaced by $\mathbf{S}$. We can evaluate these matrix elements using the matrix representation

$$S_{z_1} = \frac{\hbar}{2}\begin{bmatrix} 1 & 0 \\ 0 & -1 \end{bmatrix}, \quad S_{y_1} = \frac{\hbar}{2}\begin{bmatrix} 0 & -i \\ i & 0 \end{bmatrix}.$$

Certain parts of the matrix elements may be evaluated easily; for example,

$$\left(\begin{bmatrix} 1 \\ 0 \end{bmatrix}\right) \exp\left(-\frac{i}{2}\sigma_{z_1}\alpha\right) = \exp\left(+\frac{i\alpha}{2}\right)\left(\begin{bmatrix} 1 \\ 0 \end{bmatrix}\right),$$

$$\left(\begin{bmatrix} 0 \\ 1 \end{bmatrix}\right) \exp\left(-\frac{i}{2}\sigma_{z_1}\alpha\right) = \exp\left(-\frac{i\alpha}{2}\right)\left(\begin{bmatrix} 0 \\ 1 \end{bmatrix}\right),$$

$$\exp\left(-\frac{i}{2}\sigma_{z_1}\gamma\right)\left(\begin{bmatrix} 1 \\ 0 \end{bmatrix}\right) = \left(\begin{bmatrix} 1 \\ 0 \end{bmatrix}\right)\exp\left(-\frac{i\gamma}{2}\right).$$

With these equalities we can reduce the matrix elements to a simpler form involving the matrix $\sigma_{y_1}$ alone which may be evaluated by expanding the exponential and considering the matrix elements of $\sigma_{y_1}$,

$$\left(\begin{bmatrix} 1 \\ 0 \end{bmatrix}\right)\exp\left(-\frac{i}{2}\sigma_{y_1}\beta\right)\left(\begin{bmatrix} 1 \\ 0 \end{bmatrix}\right) = \cos\frac{\beta}{2},$$

$$\left(\begin{bmatrix} 0 \\ 1 \end{bmatrix}\right)\exp\left(-\frac{i}{2}\sigma_{y_1}\beta\right)\left(\begin{bmatrix} 1 \\ 0 \end{bmatrix}\right) = \sin\frac{\beta}{2}.$$

Hence we have that

$$D\begin{bmatrix} 1 \\ 0 \end{bmatrix} = \exp\left(\frac{i\alpha}{2}\right)\exp\left(-\frac{i\gamma}{2}\right)\cos\frac{\beta}{2}\begin{bmatrix} 1 \\ 0 \end{bmatrix}$$
$$+ \exp\left(-\frac{i\alpha}{2}\right)\exp\left(-\frac{i\gamma}{2}\right)\sin\frac{\beta}{2}\begin{bmatrix} 0 \\ 1 \end{bmatrix},$$

$$= \exp\left(-\frac{i\gamma}{2}\right)\begin{bmatrix} \exp\left(\dfrac{i\alpha}{2}\right)\cos\dfrac{\beta}{2} \\[2mm] \exp\left(-\dfrac{i\alpha}{2}\right)\sin\dfrac{\beta}{2} \end{bmatrix}. \tag{2.57}$$

If the $z_1$ axis, i.e., the axis of spin quantization, makes polar angles $\theta, \phi$ with respect to the second coordinate system, we have $\theta = \beta$ and $\phi = \alpha$. Therefore the wave function of a particle of spin $\hbar/2$ whose spin points in a direction $\theta, \phi$ in the second coordinate system is

$$\begin{bmatrix} \exp\left(\dfrac{i\phi}{2}\right)\cos\dfrac{\theta}{2} \\[2mm] \exp\left(-\dfrac{i\phi}{2}\right)\sin\dfrac{\theta}{2} \end{bmatrix}. \tag{2.58}$$

The factor $\exp(-i\gamma/2)$ may be omitted as it acts as an unobservable phase factor; the fact that it cannot be observed in any of its effects reflects the rotational symmetry around the axis of spin quantization $z_1$. The statement that the spin points in the direction $\theta, \phi$ is, of course, imprecise; the statement means that measurements of the spin component along this direction always yield the value $\hbar/2$.

The same procedure may be followed for the orbital angular momentum eigenfunctions. An eigenfunction of $L^2$ and $L_z, \psi(l, l_z)$ in rotated coordinate systems must be expressed as a sum of such eigenfunctions

$$D\psi(l, l_z) = \sum_{l_z'} \mathscr{D}^l_{l_z l_z'} \psi(l, l_z'), \qquad (2.59)$$

where

$$\mathscr{D}^l_{l_z l_z'} = (\psi(l, l_z') \mid D \mid \psi(l, l_z)).$$

These matrix elements may be evaluated readily without putting explicit forms for $\psi(l, l_z)$ and $\psi(l, l_z')$, but by the methods used to find the rotation matrix elements for the spin $\hbar/2$ case. The most awkward elements are of the form

$$\left(\psi(l, l_z') \mid \exp\left(-\frac{i}{\hbar} L_y \beta\right) \mid \psi(l, l_z)\right).$$

$L_y$ has nonzero matrix elements for states differing in $z$ component by $\pm 1$; hence terms such as

$$(\psi(l, l_z') \mid L_y^n \mid \psi(l, l_z))$$

must be expanded further by use of rule (1) (Section 1.2):

$$(\psi(l, l_z') \mid L_y^n \mid \psi(l, l_z)) = \sum_{a,b,c,\ldots r} (\psi(l, l_z') \mid L_y \mid \psi(l, a)) \, (\psi(l, a) \mid L_y \mid \psi(l, b)) \ldots$$
$$\ldots (\psi(l, r) \mid L_y \mid \psi(l, l_z)).$$

The sum is to be evaluated with the following restrictions:

$$a = l_z' \pm 1,$$

$$b = a \pm 1,$$

etc., and

$$l_z = r \pm 1.$$

The evaluation of this sum and the reassembly of the exponential is difficult for all but the lowest values of $l$; as can be expected, the results are trigonometric functions of the Euler angles.

The treatment just mentioned applies also to the case of total angular momentum eigenfunctions. Every value of $j$ has an associated rotation matrix $\mathscr{D}^j$. whose elements $\mathscr{D}^j_{j_z j_{z'}}$ are the coefficients of expansions of the kind used in Eqs. (2.55) and (2.59).

We can briefly examine the physical meaning of the rotation matrix elements. If we use the concepts of the principle of superposition (Section 1.3), we observe that the square of each matrix element is in fact the probability of finding the system in question in a particular state of angular momentum. Thus Eq. (2.58) tells us that a measurement of the $z_2$ component of spin angular momentum will yield a value $+\hbar/2$ with probability $\cos^2 \beta/2$ and a value $-\hbar/2$ with probability $\sin^2 \beta/2$. A similar interpretation applies to the matrix elements of Eq. (2.59).

## 2.11 Conclusion

The rotational properties are of outstanding importance in the advanced theory of angular momentum. In elementary particle and nuclear physics we are often concerned with systems which are in a state of motion specified by several quantum numbers, including $j$ and $j_z$. This state will have several symmetry properties, the most important being those under rotation; these are described by the rotation matrix $\mathscr{D}^j$. If the state emits radiation, then the final state of radiation plus residual must have the same rotational properties and it follows that the probability distribution of the radiation is connected with the rotation matrix and hence to the quantum numbers $j$ and $j_z$. These numbers happen to be the eigenvalues of the angular momentum operators. We see that the angular distribution of nuclear reaction products and the angular correlation of successive nuclear radiations are governed by the angular momentum of the states involved. In this book we will be concerned with a very elementary approach to this problem of angular distributions; this is exemplified in our treatment of the partial wave analysis in the next chapter. However, there are problems of a more advanced nature for which simple techniques are inadequate or too clumsy; for these cases techniques have been developed which start where we are leaving off, i.e., by developing the formalism from a definition of the rotation matrices. This approach is treated in the books of Rose (1957) and of Edmonds (1957) and in the article by Devons and Goldfarb (1957). Earlier treatments are reviewed by Blatt and Biedenharn (1952a) and by Biedenharn and Rose (1953).

# CHAPTER III

# THE PARTIAL WAVE ANALYSIS

## 3.1 Introduction

In this chapter we introduce the partial wave analysis of scattering problems; the analysis is given for the scattering of one particle by another when the two particles are different and without spin. This is extended to the case of one of the particles having spin $\hbar/2$ and applied to the scattering of pi-mesons by hydrogen.

## 3.2 The Partial Wave Analysis

We have seen in the previous chapter that angular momentum is conserved in many situations; if we consider the interaction of two spinless particles, then our conservation principle applies to the orbital momentum $l$, and its $z$ component $l_z$. In quantum-mechanical terms we might expect that initially the particles are in a state of relative motion described by an eigenfunction of $L^2$ and $L_z$. If these operators commute with the Hamiltonian which describes the system and the interaction which causes the scattering, then the final state function of the system will also be an eigenfunction of $L^2$ and $L_z$, with the same eigenvalues. Then the probability distribution of the scattered particles as a function of angle is given by the square of the spherical harmonic which has these eigenvalues. Another scattering might take place in a state of different orbital angular momentum for which a different interaction may apply, and in fact a positive energy scattering situation has an initial state which is not an eigenfunction of $L^2$ but may be represented by a sum of such eigenfunctions; each term in the sum is called a partial wave. The final state is also represented by a sum of the same eigenfunctions each with an amplitude determined by the strength of the interaction. The value of the amplitude is given

47

by a parameter which introduces the effect of the interaction on the partial wave to which the amplitude applies. The sum is the total amplitude of the scattered wave and the differential cross section is the square of the magnitude of the total amplitude.

We shall not give the complete development of the analysis because readers can find rigorous presentations in several places (e.g., Mott and Massey, 1949). However, we summarize the results. We consider a beam of particles which may be scattered by a spherically symmetrical potential which has its centre at the origin of coordinates and which has an infinitely heavy source which therefore does not recoil. Actual cases can be transformed so that the origin of coordinates is at the centre of mass; the two situations are the same and are described by the same wave function. We take the Cartesian coordinates directed so that the $z$ axis is in the direction of motion of the incident particle; the initial state is conveniently described by the plane wave solution of the Schrödinger equation

$$\psi = e^{ikz} \tag{3.1}$$

where $\hbar k$ is the momentum of the incoming particle. After scattering we assume that the unaffected part of the incident wave plus the relatively small scattered wave are represented by

$$\psi = e^{ikz} + e^{ikr}\frac{f(\theta)}{r}; \tag{3.2}$$

$f(\theta)$ is a function to be determined. The variable $\theta$ is the polar angle between the $z$ axis and the scattered wave described by $f(\theta)$.

The incoming wave is already an eigenfunction of $L_z$ with eigenvalue $l_z = 0$; application of the operator

$$L_z = -i\hbar \left( x\frac{\partial}{\partial y} - y\frac{\partial}{\partial x} \right)$$

to (3.1) will confirm this physically evident fact. It is only necessary to decompose the incoming wave into eigenfunctions of $L^2$, thus:

$$e^{ikz} = \sum_{=0}^{\infty} (2l+1)\, i^l\, P_l(\cos\theta)\, F_l(kr); \tag{3.3}$$

$r$ is the distance between the particles, $F_0(kr) = (\sin kr)/kr$, and the other $F_l(kr)$ are connected with the Bessel functions. $P_l(\cos\theta)$ is the $l$th Legendre polynomial and is an eigenfunction of $L^2$ and $L_z$ with $l_z = 0$ (Section 2.8). Then the $f(\theta)$ of the scattered wave is given by

$$f(\theta) = \frac{1}{2ik} \sum_l (2l+1)\, [\exp(2i\delta_l) - 1]\, P_l(\cos\theta). \tag{3.4}$$

In (3.4) $\delta_l$ is the parameter required to describe the effect of the scattering potential in producing a scattered wave from the $l$th partial wave; these parameters are called phase shifts, since the potential actually changes the phase of the scattered wave with respect to the incoming wave by an angle $\delta_l$.

The differential scattering cross section is then given by

$$\frac{d\sigma}{d\Omega} = |f(\theta)|^2 = \frac{1}{k^2}\left|\sum_l (2l+1)\exp(i\delta_l)\sin\delta_l\, P_l(\cos\theta)\right|^2, \qquad (3.5)$$

where $\Omega$ is the solid angle in steradians. The total cross section $\sigma$ is given by

$$\sigma = \int_{-1}^{+1} \frac{d\sigma}{d\Omega}\, 2\pi\, d(\cos\theta) = \frac{4\pi}{k^2}\sum_l (2l+1)\sin^2\delta_l. \qquad (3.6)$$

Equation (3.6) is simpler than (3.5) due to the orthogonality of the Legendre polynomials. The total cross section for the $l$th partial wave has a maximum value of $4\pi(2l+1)/k^2$ when $\delta_l = (2n+1)\pi/2$ ($n$ an integer). In (3.6) the total cross section is shown to be a simple sum of the individual partial wave cross sections, but this is not true of the differential cross section since terms belonging to different $l$ in Eq. (3.5) contribute cross terms in the square of the magnitude; these are the interference terms.

Another useful relation can be extracted from these results; putting $\theta = 0$ in Eq. (3.4), we have

$$f(\theta = 0) = \frac{1}{k}\sum_l (2l+1)\exp(i\delta_l)\sin\delta_l = \frac{1}{k}\sum_l (2l+1)(i\sin^2\delta_l + \cos\delta_l\sin\delta_l).$$

Taking the imaginary part of this amplitude we find that

$$\mathrm{Im}\, f(0) = \frac{1}{k}\sum_l (2l+1)\sin^2\delta_l = \frac{k}{4\pi}\sigma.$$

Therefore

$$\sigma = \frac{4\pi}{k}\mathrm{Im}\, f(0). \qquad (3.7)$$

Thus the total cross section is related to the imaginary part of the forward scattering amplitude.

The phase shifts are the parameters which contain the effect of the actual interaction which causes the scattering, but they are not determined by this analysis. To predict the scattering fully for a given potential, the phase shifts must be found by matching the wave functions inside and outside the potential; this is usually a complex calculation and can only be done analytically for the Coulomb and some other simply shaped potentials. The phase shifts are positive for repulsive and negative for attractive potentials.

The reverse procedure is sometimes valuable; the results of a scattering experiment are subjected to a partial wave analysis which determines the phase shifts, and their behaviour as a function of energy may yield considerable information about the interaction involved. The pi-meson scattering on hydrogen is an outstanding example of the value of this procedure; we shall do this analysis to illustrate the method and to show the results obtained. In this chapter we confine ourselves to the positive pi-meson scattering since this does not involve isotopic spin (Section 3.6); the full analysis is done in Chapter VII.

## 3.3 Amplitudes and Coherence

We wish to redefine some of the quantities in the expression for the differential cross section. Firstly, we replace the Legendre polynomials by spherical harmonics, which have the properties enumerated in Section 2.8. In Eq. (3.3) we substitute

$$Y_l(\cos \theta) = \sqrt{\frac{2l+1}{4\pi}} P_l(\cos \theta)$$

to obtain

$$e^{ikz} = \sqrt{4\pi} \sum_l \sqrt{2l+1} \, i^l Y_l(\cos \theta) \, F_l(kr). \tag{3.8}$$

Equation (3.4) becomes

$$f(\theta) = \frac{1}{k} \sum_l \sqrt{4\pi(2l+1)} \frac{\exp(2i\delta_l) - 1}{2i} Y_l(\cos \theta). \tag{3.9}$$

Equation (3.5) becomes

$$\frac{d\sigma}{d\Omega} = \frac{4\pi}{k^2} \left| \sum_l \sqrt{2l+1} \frac{\exp(2i\delta_l) - 1}{2i} Y_l(\cos \theta) \right|^2. \tag{3.9a}$$

It is convenient to express the results in terms of the spherical harmonics since these are normalized and the coefficients of the series (3.9) can then be thought of as the amplitudes of these partial waves. Later we shall have to make the substitution of $Y_l^m(\cos \theta)$ for $Y_l(\cos \theta)$ which is less confusing with such normalized functions. In future we call the quantities $[\exp(2i\delta_l) - 1]/2i$ the partial wave amplitudes. The quantity $f(\theta)$ is the total scattered wave amplitude.

The differential cross section is proportional to the intensity of particles scattered in the direction implied; thus, this intensity is a square of a sum of partial wave amplitudes. Amplitudes which add in this way are said to be coherent. This coherence is analogous to that occurring in classical physical optics; in that science there are rules for connecting the intensities and amplitudes of light waves, and there are also stringent requirements on the coherence of two sources of waves which are to interfere, where interference implies that the total intensity is found by squaring the sum of amplitudes; waves which interfere are said to be coherent. In quantum mechanics, coherent waves must have the same energy and the same eigenvalues, which are discrete and conserved; the total intensity of such waves is the square of the sum of the amplitudes. Waves not fulfilling these conditions are said to be incoherent and have an intensity which is the sum of amplitudes squared. Situations also occur in which the total wave contains groups of waves which are coherent within each group, but incoherent from group to group; the total intensity of such a wave is the sum of the intensities of all the groups, where each intensity is the square of the sum of all the amplitudes within the group.

If there is any question of the coherence of two incident waves (corresponding to optical sources) which have the same energy, it is usually possible to construct a physically meaningful situation which would make the two waves nondegenerate if they are incoherent. We can give an example of this by considering a wave representing a beam of particles having spin $\hbar/2$; this wave can consist of two parts corresponding to the two possible spin orientations which have equal energy in the absence of electromagnetic fields. The application of a magnetic field will separate the kinetic energies of the two waves and thus the two incident waves and their scattered waves are incoherent; this situation occurs in pi-meson scattering by hydrogen. A coherent incident wave can give rise to two or more incoherent waves; for example, a scattered wave representing elastic scattering is incoherent with a scattered wave representing inelastic scattering.

## 3.4 Scattering with Spin

Actual scattering situations may involve particles with spin, and we now consider a simple example in which the incident particle has spin $\hbar/2$ and the target has no spin. As usual the $z$ axis is taken along the direction of motion of the incident particle, so that the incident wave can be expanded as a sum of eigenvalues of $L^2$ and $L_z$ all having $l_z = 0$. However, the eigenvalue of $J_z$ is $\pm \hbar/2$, depending on the spin orientation. This eigenvalue is a constant of the motion, and the two waves having different values of $j_z$ are incoherent (Section 3.3). For the $l$th partial wave the eigenvalue of $J^2$ is $l + \frac{1}{2}$ or $l - \frac{1}{2}$ by the vector addition of angular momentum, and thus for every value of $l$ there are two phase shifts.

During the collision it is possible for the spin orientation to change but, since $\Delta j_z = 0$, this change can only be made at the expense of a reverse change in $l_z$. Thus this spin flip, $\Delta s_z = \pm 1$, is accompanied by the appearance of a scattered wave having a nonzero $l_z$; i.e., $l_z = \Delta l_z = \mp 1$. This outgoing partial wave is no longer represented by a Legendre polynomial in the equation for the scattered amplitude (3.4), but by an associated Legendre polynomial (see Section 2.8). However, we have noted that it is easier to make this change in Eq. (3.9) where the $Y_l(\cos \theta)$ is replaced by $Y_l^{l_z}(\cos \theta)$; $l_z = -1$ or $+1$, depending on $\Delta l_z$. These functions have different angular dependence and thus the presence of spin affects the distribution of scattered particles. In addition, the spin flip waves are orthogonal to the normally scattered waves and thus these two waves do not interfere and the spin flip contribution appears as an additional intensity of scattered particles.

The case of a spin $\hbar$ particle or of two spin $\hbar/2$ particles are similar; all changes in the $z$ component of the total spin are integer multiples of $\hbar$, and cause an equal and opposite change in the third component of the orbital angular momentum. The maximum value of the integer is $2(|s_1| + |s_2|)$ where $s_1 \hbar$ and $s_2 \hbar$ are the spins involved; what happens in detail depends on the particles and the forces between them. For example, if the particles are the same, then the symmetry requirements on the wave function affect the scattering; and again, if there exist noncentral forces, the analysis is complicated by the fact that the eigenvalue of $L^2$ is no longer a constant of motion and the interaction can cause transitions between initial and final states of different $l$. We shall discuss some of these problems in Chapter VI.

### 3.5 The Effective Partial Waves

We can reduce the complexity of the infinite series (3.5) by general considerations on the partial waves which will be involved in any collision. We consider a collision classically: if the particle momentum in the centre of mass is $\mathbf{p}$ and the impact parameter $b$, then the orbital angular momentum is $pb$, which we can put equal to $\hbar \sqrt{l(l+1)}$. If $b$ is greater than the range $r$, there will be no scattering by the interaction, and since $b \simeq \hbar \sqrt{l(l+1)}/p$ we can express the condition for no scattering as $\hbar \sqrt{l(l+1)}/p > r$. Thus we need only consider the partial waves which have $\sqrt{l(l+1)} \leqslant (pr/\hbar)$. We can apply this to the scattering of pi-mesons by hydrogen; the interaction is expected to have a range of about the Compton wavelength of the pi-meson, $\hbar/m_\pi c$;

consequently, it is only necessary to consider partial waves for which $\sqrt{l(l+1)} \leqslant (p/m_\pi c)$. For pi-mesons, $m_\pi c^2 = 140$ Mev, and if the centre-of-mass kinetic energy is 100 Mev, then $pc = 200$ Mev and we find that scattering only occurs if $\sqrt{l(l+1)} \leqslant 1.4$, that is, if $l \leqslant 1$. Therefore the scattering is well described by an analysis which includes only the first two partial waves, $l = 0$ and $l = 1$, for kinetic energies up to 100 Mev. In fact, such an analysis is adequate up to about 200 Mev in the centre of mass.

The unscreened Coulomb potential has an essentially infinite range and the screened Coulomb potential has a range which is very large compared with nuclear forces; these properties mean that a partial wave analysis of Coulomb scattering must continue up to very high order partial waves (Mott and Massey, 1949). However, Coulomb scattering of high-energy particles is very small compared to nuclear force scattering, except at very small scattering angles, and can normally be neglected unless we are interested in scattering at these small angles (see Section 7.9).

### 3.6 The Scattering of Positive Pi-Mesons by Hydrogen

The pi-meson and proton are elementary particles with spin zero and $\hbar/2$ respectively; at low energies the only possible reaction between a positive pi-meson and a proton is elastic scattering which can be analysed by the partial wave method. The only forces expected between a pi-meson and a proton are the Coulomb potential, a spherically symmetric short-range potential, and a spin-orbit interaction; from the discussion of Section 2.4 we know that the constants of motion are the eigenvalues of $J^2, J_z, L^2, S^2$. The fact that the eigenvalue of $S^2$ is conserved adds nothing, since we know this from physical reasoning, for the scattering is elastic and the total spin of the system remains the same. The initial value of $j_z$ depends on the spin orientation with respect to the $z$ axis; therefore two values are possible, $\pm \frac{1}{2}$, each having statistical weight $\frac{1}{2}$ and incoherent scattering amplitudes. We need only consider one of these values since the scattering can only be the same in the two cases. This statement can be proved if we assume that parity is conserved in the strong meson–nucleon interaction, as it almost certainly is; the argument used can be found in Chapter X. If the scattering were different, then it would be necessary to calculate both cases and average over the two possible initial states.

This leaves the eigenvalues of $J^2$ and $L^2$ and a phase shift must be associated with every pair of values. To reduce the complication, we neglect the Coulomb potential and use the arguments of Section 3.5 to restrict the analysis to the partial waves having $l = 0$ and $l = 1$, spectroscopically the $S$ and $P$ states. For the partial wave $l = 0$ there can only be one value of the eigenvalue of $J^2$, that is the one having $j = \frac{1}{2}$: this is the $S_{\frac{1}{2}}$ state. For the wave having $l = 1$ there are two possibilities, $j = \frac{1}{2}$ and $j = \frac{3}{2}$, which are the $P_{\frac{1}{2}}$ and the $P_{\frac{3}{2}}$ states respectively. With these states we associate the phase shifts $\delta$, $\delta_1$, and $\delta_3$; the lack of a subscript indicates the phase shift for the partial wave having $l = 0$ and the presence of a subscript indicates the shift for the wave $l = 1$, the subscript being twice $j$.

We consider only the initial states having $j_z = s_z = \frac{1}{2}$. Each partial wave is specified by three eigenvalues $l$, $l_z$, and $s_z$, and although we do not need three parameters to specify each incoming partial wave, we include three so as to be consistent with the description of the outgoing waves where three are required; the wave function for this partial wave is then $\psi(l, l_z)\chi(s, s_z)$. Such partial wave states are not necessarily eigenfunctions of $J^2$; however, they can be expressed as a linear sum of such eigenfunctions using the technique described in Section 2.7. We write the eigenfunctions of $J^2$ and $J_z$ as $\phi(l, j, j_z)$; a value for $l$ is included to show to which partial wave the eigenfunction belongs. Using Table 2.1, we can put

Partial wave
state          Eigenstate of $J^2$ and $J_z$

$$\psi(0, 0)\chi(\tfrac{1}{2}, \tfrac{1}{2}) = \phi(0, \tfrac{1}{2}, \tfrac{1}{2}), \tag{3.10}$$

$$\psi(1, 0)\chi(\tfrac{1}{2}, \tfrac{1}{2}) = \sqrt{\tfrac{2}{3}}\,\phi(1, \tfrac{3}{2}, \tfrac{1}{2}) - \sqrt{\tfrac{1}{3}}\,\phi(1, \tfrac{1}{2}, \tfrac{1}{2}). \tag{3.11}$$

The right-hand side of (3.10) is the state $S_{\frac{1}{2}}$; the right-hand side of (3.11) is a sum of the $P_{\frac{1}{2}}$ and the $P_{\frac{3}{2}}$ states. It is necessary to make this decomposition of the partial waves, since the scattering is given by phase shifts which apply to eigenstates of $J^2$. Thus Eq. (3.11) indicates what fraction of the $l = 1$ partial wave scatters via the $\delta_1$ phase shift and how much via the $\delta_3$ phase shift.

We now substitute Eqs. (3.10) and (3.11) into (3.8); this can be done since the $Y_l(\cos\theta)$ are equal to the $\psi(l, 0)$. Equation (3.8) becomes

$$e^{ikz}\chi(\tfrac{1}{2}, \tfrac{1}{2}) = \sqrt{4\pi}\sum_l \sqrt{2l+1}\, i^l \psi(l, 0)\, F_l(kr)\chi(\tfrac{1}{2}, \tfrac{1}{2}). \tag{3.12}$$

Taking the first two partial waves, we have

$$e^{ikz}\chi(\tfrac{1}{2}, \tfrac{1}{2}) \simeq \sqrt{4\pi}\,\{F_0(kr)\,\phi(0, \tfrac{1}{2}, \tfrac{1}{2}) + iF_1(kr)\sqrt{3}[\sqrt{\tfrac{2}{3}}\,\phi(1, \tfrac{3}{2}, \tfrac{1}{2})$$
$$- \sqrt{\tfrac{1}{3}}\,\phi(1, \tfrac{1}{2}, \tfrac{1}{2})]\}. \tag{3.13}$$

This encourages us to treat Eq. (3.9) in a similar way; to reduce the complexity of the equations, we put the partial wave amplitudes

$(e^{2i\delta} - 1)/2i$ equal to $a$, using the same subscript scheme as was used to distinguish the different phase shifts. We find that

$$f(\theta) = \frac{\sqrt{4\pi}}{k}\{a\phi(0, \tfrac{1}{2}, \tfrac{1}{2}) + \sqrt{3}[a_3\sqrt{\tfrac{2}{3}}\,\phi(1, \tfrac{3}{2}, \tfrac{1}{2}) - a_1\sqrt{\tfrac{1}{3}}\,\phi(1, \tfrac{1}{2}, \tfrac{1}{2})]\}. \qquad (3.14)$$

Now the eigenfunctions $\phi(l, j, j_z)$ are not those that give the observable distribution of scattered particles; to find that distribution we must express these functions in terms of the spin and orbital angular momentum eigenfunctions. This is the inverse of the procedure implied in Eqs. (3.10) and (3.11), and from the same table we find that

$$\phi(0, \tfrac{1}{2}, \tfrac{1}{2}) = \psi(0, 0)\chi(\tfrac{1}{2}, \tfrac{1}{2}), \qquad (3.15)$$

$$\phi(1, \tfrac{1}{2}, \tfrac{1}{2}) = \sqrt{\tfrac{2}{3}}\,\psi(1, 1)\chi(\tfrac{1}{2}, -\tfrac{1}{2}) - \sqrt{\tfrac{1}{3}}\,\psi(1, 0)\chi(\tfrac{1}{2}, \tfrac{1}{2}), \qquad (3.16)$$

$$\phi(1, \tfrac{3}{2}, \tfrac{1}{2}) = \sqrt{\tfrac{1}{3}}\,\psi(1, 1)\chi(\tfrac{1}{2}, -\tfrac{1}{2}) + \sqrt{\tfrac{2}{3}}\,\psi(1, 0)\chi(\tfrac{1}{2}, \tfrac{1}{2}). \qquad (3.17)$$

Substituting these equations into (3.14) we obtain an expression for the total scattered wave amplitude

$$f(\theta) = \frac{\sqrt{4\pi}}{k}\left\{a\psi(0, 0)\chi(\tfrac{1}{2}, \tfrac{1}{2}) + \left[\frac{a_1}{\sqrt{3}} + \frac{2}{\sqrt{3}}a_3\right]\psi(1, 0)\chi(\tfrac{1}{2}, \tfrac{1}{2})\right.$$
$$\left. + \left[\sqrt{\tfrac{2}{3}}a_3 - \sqrt{\tfrac{2}{3}}a_1\right]\psi(1, 1)\chi(\tfrac{1}{2}, -\tfrac{1}{2})\right\}. \qquad (3.18)$$

The first term in Eq. (3.18) is the term representing the scattered part of the $l = 0$ partial wave; the second term represents the scattered part of the $l = 1$ wave for which there has been no change in proton spin orientation; however, the third term has $s_z = -\tfrac{1}{2}$ and thus represents a scattered wave which has a different spin orientation from the initial state. This "spin flip" is in accord with the qualitative description given in Section 3.4 and the scattered wave has $l_z = +1$ as required by the conservation of $j_z$.

We now replace the functions by the spherical harmonics as in Section 2.8; the appropriate substitutions are

$$\psi(0, 0) = \frac{1}{\sqrt{4\pi}},$$

$$\psi(1, 0) = \sqrt{\frac{3}{4\pi}}\cos\theta, \quad \psi(1, 1) = -\sqrt{\frac{3}{8\pi}}\sin\theta\, e^{i\phi}.$$

(The usual azimuthal angle $\phi$ must not be confused with the wave functions $\phi$.) The spin flip wave is orthogonal to the normally scattered wave; thus the total cross section is given by

$$\frac{d\sigma}{d\Omega} = |\text{no spin change amplitude}|^2 + |\text{spin flip amplitude}|^2$$

$$= \frac{1}{k^2}\{|a + (a_1 + 2a_3)\cos\theta|^2 + |(a_1 - a_3)\sin\theta|^2\}. \tag{3.19}$$

If we put

$$k^2 \frac{d\sigma}{d\Omega} = A_+ + B_+\cos\theta + C_+\cos^2\theta, \tag{3.20}$$

then

$$A_+ = |a|^2 + |a_1 - a_3|^2 \qquad = \sin^2\delta + \sin^2(\delta_1 - \delta_3),$$

$$B_+ = 2\,\mathrm{Re}\,a^*(a_1 + 2a_3) \quad = 2\sin\delta[\sin\delta_1\cos(\delta_1 - \delta) + 2\sin\delta_3\cos(\delta_3 - \delta)],$$

$$C_+ = |a_1 + 2a_3|^2 - |a_1 - a_3|^2 = 3\sin^2\delta_3 + 6\cos(\delta_3 - \delta_1)\sin\delta_1\sin\delta_3,$$

and the total cross section is given by

$$\sigma = \frac{4\pi}{k^2}(A_+ + C_+/3) = \frac{4\pi}{k^2}(\sin^2\delta + \sin^2\delta_1 + 2\sin^2\delta_3). \tag{3.21}$$

The analysis has reduced the differential cross section to an expansion involving three phase shifts, but these can only be determined by experiment or from theoretical postulates. The former procedure has been used extensively and the value of the phase shifts and their variation with energy indicate the form of the interaction between pi-mesons and protons. We shall defer full discussion of this point until we can include the analysis of the scattering of negative pi-mesons.

However, we can illustrate the possibility of obtaining some information by a simple examination of Eqs. (3.20) and (3.21).

(1) If there is no scattering in the $l = 1$ state, then there is no $\cos^2\theta$ term.

(2) The presence of a $\cos\theta$ term indicates scattering in both the $l = 0$ and the $l = 1$ states. (This is an interference term.)

(3) For small phase shifts, if the sign of the $B_+$ coefficient is negative, the signs of the phase shifts and the scattering potentials of the $S$ state and of at least one of the $P$ states are opposite (i.e., one of $\sin\delta$ and $\sin\delta_1$ or $\sin\delta_3$ is negative).

## 3.7 Angular Distributions in General

The matter of the last section is an example of the methods used to find the angular distribution of particles which are the products of nuclear reactions; the extension of the technique of this analysis from elastic scattering to the more general nuclear reaction is taken as far as the simple $S$ matrix in Chapter V. For a fuller treatment readers are referred to Blatt and Weisskopf (1952). In general, the final state of a reaction must have the same symmetry properties under rotation of the coordinate system as has the initial state. Thus the description of the angular distribution of the reaction products will not contain spherical harmonics of power $(l)$ greater than the maximum angular momentum in the initial state. Hence the greatest complexity of the angular distribution is $\cos^{2l}\theta$ (Yang, 1948). An incident plane wave contains all angular momenta, but only a few of the lowest partial waves come within range of the scattering force and it is this feature which determines the maximum $l$ in the initial state.

We shall now briefly restate the procedure for the general elastic scattering. The initial state may be a sum of states of different $l$, $l_z$, $s$, and $s_z$. Each state can be expressed as a sum of eigenfunctions which have eigenvalues that are constants of motion. To each of these eigenstates there is a scattered wave having an amplitude given by the appropriate phase shift; thus the total scattered amplitude is a sum of the eigenfunctions of the constants of motion. Each of these eigenfunctions must be replaced by the appropriate sum of eigenfunctions of $L^2, L_z, S^2, S_z$ where the orbital functions are in the form of the usual spherical harmonics. The differential scattering cross section is obtained by squaring the amplitude, care being taken to separate the coherent and noncoherent parts.

Similar remarks apply to the decay of free spinning particles. However, if the observed particles are unpolarized, there is no spherical asymmetry in the initial state and there can only be a uniform distribution of decay products; therefore, the following remarks apply only to completely polarized particles or, in a modified form, to partially polarized particles. The initial state is a pure eigenfunction of $J^2$ and $J_z$, since the only angular momentum the particle can have is its own spin. The final state is then also an eigenfunction of the same operators having the same eigenvalues; this state must be decomposed into orbital angular momentum states combined with the appropriate spin functions. The angular distribution in the final state is found, as usual, by squaring the wave function. Particles with spin $\frac{1}{2}$ cannot show anything but a uniform distribution of the decay products unless parity is nonconserved; asymmetries due to such nonconservation occur in $\beta$ decay.

These statements about angular distributions are often condensed into the simple statement already quoted: the initial and final states of a nuclear reaction must always have the same symmetry properties under the simultaneous rotation of space and spin coordinates, that is, under the rotations induced by the operator **J**.

## 3.8 The Angular Momentum Barrier

The theoretical determination of phase shifts requires the matching of wave functions inside and outside the potential. For central forces it is only necessary to do this for the radial part of the wave function, $F(kr)$. The appropriate wave equation, when the orbital angular momentum is $l$, is

$$-\frac{\hbar^2}{2m}\frac{1}{r^2}\frac{d}{dr}\left(r^2\frac{dF}{dr}\right) + \left[V(r)+\frac{l(l+1)}{r^2}\frac{\hbar^2}{2m}\right]F = EF.$$

We notice that the potential energy of the particle when it is at a distance $r$ from the centre of the potential is effectively increased by an amount $\{[l(l+1)]/r^2\}(\hbar^2/2m)$. This quantity acts like a Coulomb barrier and in fact adds to the height of the Coulomb barrier experienced by incoming and outgoing charged particles. Thus states of high angular momentum are less able to cause nuclear reactions and are less accessible to outgoing particles than states of lower angular momentum. The same applies to the decay of free particles: a particle with a large spin which decays into particles of small spin has to put these products into states of high orbital angular momentum and this inhibits the decay. High spins were attributed to the $V$ particles discovered in cosmic radiation, in order to explain their unexpectedly long lifetime; however, the spins required, $7\hbar/2$ to $13\hbar/2$, were too large to satisfy aesthetic feeling on the matter and more satisfactory explanations are now postulated (Section 12.3).

For a full treatment of the angular momentum barrier the reader is again referred to Blatt and Weisskopf (1952).

## 3.9 Conclusion

This chapter will have introduced the reader to the simpler concepts employed in the analysis of the angular distributions in nuclear and particle reactions but it is not an exhaustive treatment. We have yet to consider the electromagnetic interaction and its distributive effects, and elsewhere the theory has been subjected to a logical analysis which is more complete but less immediately applicable. For further reading we refer readers to the bibliography at the end of Section 2.11.

# CHAPTER IV

# SPACE PROPERTIES OF VECTOR FIELDS

## 4.1 Introduction

In the previous two chapters we have examined the properties and uses of angular momentum as applied to particle states; in this chapter we shall do the same for the electromagnetic field. Classically, the behaviour of this field is described by Maxwell's equations and its quantized version naturally introduces the quantum of the electromagnetic field, which we shall call the photon. Photons are easily observable in those parts of the electromagnetic spectrum which have wavelengths shorter than infrared light and they are assumed to exist at the longer wavelengths. We start our analysis by considering the rotational properties of a general vector field and how such fields can be expanded into a sum of eigenfunctions of angular momentum operators; the results of this discussion are applied to the electromagnetic field. We then proceed to show how the angular distribution of electromagnetic radiation is related to its angular momentum properties and close by discussing situations in which this relation can be exploited.

## 4.2 The Rotation of a Vector Field

We consider a vector field **A** under observation from a point **x**. If the field is rotated around the $z$ axis, the field **A** at **x** is replaced by the field **A′** which was previously at a point **x′**. As usual, we need only consider an infinitesimal rotation $\phi$, in which case the components of **A** and **A′** can be related by the equations

$$A'_x = A_x + \frac{\partial A_x}{\partial x} \Delta x + \frac{\partial A_x}{\partial y} \Delta y, \tag{4.1}$$

$$A'_y = A_y + \frac{\partial A_y}{\partial x} \Delta x + \frac{\partial A_y}{\partial y} \Delta y, \tag{4.2}$$

$$A'_z = A_z. \tag{4.3}$$

The quantities $\Delta x$ and $\Delta y$ are components of the vector $\mathbf{x}' - \mathbf{x}$. By considering a rotation $-\phi$ of the coordinates we find that the components of $\mathbf{x}$ and $\mathbf{x}'$ are related by

$$x' = x\cos\phi + y\sin\phi, \tag{4.4}$$

$$y' = y\cos\phi - x\sin\phi, \tag{4.5}$$

$$z' = z. \tag{4.6}$$

Hence if $\phi$ is very small we have that

$$\Delta x = y\phi$$

and

$$\Delta y = -x\phi.$$

Substituting in Eqs. (4.1) and (4.2), we find that

$$A'_x + iA'_y = A_x + iA_y + \phi y \frac{\partial}{\partial x}(A_x + iA_y) - \phi x \frac{\partial}{\partial y}(A_x + iA_y)$$

$$= \left(1 - \frac{i}{\hbar}\phi L_z\right)(A_x + iA_y). \tag{4.7}$$

Equation (4.7) is the relation between the Cartesian components of the field at $\mathbf{x}$ and the components at $\mathbf{x}'$. However, to the observer the field has been rotated so that he sees the field that was at $\mathbf{x}'$ with the vector $\mathbf{A}'$ rotated through an angle $\phi$. Thus he sees the components of $\mathbf{A}'$ redistributed; let this final vector be $\mathbf{a}$. We can find the relation between $\mathbf{a}$ and $\mathbf{A}'$ by examination of a simple geometrical picture in which a rotation of $\mathbf{A}'$ by an angle $\phi$ around $z$ brings it into coincidence with $\mathbf{a}$; then

$$\left.\begin{aligned}
a_x &= A'_x\cos\phi - A'_y\sin\phi, \\
a_y &= A'_y\cos\phi + A'_x\sin\phi, \\
a_z &= A'_z.
\end{aligned}\right\} \tag{4.8}$$

As usual, we suppose that $\phi$ is very small and substitute from Eq. (4.7) to find that

$$\left.\begin{aligned}
a_x &= A_x - \phi\left(x\frac{\partial}{\partial y} - y\frac{\partial}{\partial x}\right)A_x - \phi A_y, \\
a_y &= A_y - \phi\left(x\frac{\partial}{\partial y} - y\frac{\partial}{\partial x}\right)A_y + \phi A_x, \\
a_z &= A_z.
\end{aligned}\right\} \tag{4.9}$$

We now write Eq. (4.9) in operator form using Eq. (2.2):

$$a_x = \left(1 - \frac{i}{\hbar}\phi L_z - \frac{i}{\hbar}S_z\right)A_x,$$

$$a_y = \left(1 - \frac{i}{\hbar}\phi L_z - \frac{i}{\hbar}S_z\right)A_y, \qquad (4.10)$$

$$a_z = A_z.$$

$S_z$ is an operator which has the properties

$$S_z A_x = -i\hbar A_y,$$
$$S_z A_y = +i\hbar A_x, \qquad (4.11)$$
$$S_z A_z = 0.$$

For finite rotations Eq. (4.10) becomes

$$\mathbf{a} = \exp\left[-\frac{i}{\hbar}\phi(L_z + S_z)\right]\mathbf{A}$$

and, in general, for a rotation about the unit vector $\mathbf{n}$,

$$\mathbf{a} = \exp\left[-\frac{i}{\hbar}\phi(\mathbf{L}+\mathbf{S})\cdot\mathbf{n}\right]\mathbf{A}.$$

We must now investigate the properties of the operators $\mathbf{S}$. This can be done by expressing $\mathbf{A}$ as a column matrix

$$\begin{bmatrix} A_x \\ A_y \\ A_z \end{bmatrix}.$$

Then

$$S_x = \hbar\begin{bmatrix} 0 & 0 & 0 \\ 0 & 0 & -i \\ 0 & i & 0 \end{bmatrix}, \quad S_y = \hbar\begin{bmatrix} 0 & 0 & i \\ 0 & 0 & 0 \\ -i & 0 & 0 \end{bmatrix}, \quad S_z = \hbar\begin{bmatrix} 0 & -i & 0 \\ +i & 0 & 0 \\ 0 & 0 & 0 \end{bmatrix}.$$

The matrix $S_z$ satisfies Eq. (4.11) and the remainder satisfy the analogous equations for rotations about their own subscript axes. These matrices are Hermitian and satisfy Eqs. (2.4) and (2.5); the operator $S^2 = S_x^2 + S_y^2 + S_z^2$ is $2\hbar^2 I$ where $I$ is the unit matrix. From our knowledge of angular momentum operators we can conclude that these matrices are a representation of an angular momentum $\hbar$, and that the vector field carries an intrinsic angular momentum $\hbar$ or "spin one".

## 4.3 The Vector Spherical Harmonics

In the previous chapter we introduced the partial wave analysis which is essentially an expansion of incoming and outgoing wave functions in terms of eigenfunctions of angular momentum. These wave functions were scalar in character and we are now presented with the necessity of expanding a vector field in a similar manner.

We define a set of functions—the vector spherical harmonics, which are eigenfunctions of $J^2$, $J_z$, $L^2$, and $S^2$, $\mathbf{Y}(j,j_z,l,s)$. Since we are dealing with a field which has $s = 1$, there are three such eigenfunctions for each value of $j$; these have $l = j-1$, $j$, and $j+1$ respectively. (This is in addition to the $2j+1$ eigenfunctions corresponding to different eigenvalues of $J_z$.) Each harmonic can be expressed as a sum of products of orbital and spin angular momentum eigenfunctions. Thus, by Eq. (2.38), we have

$$\mathbf{Y}(j,j_z,l,s) = \sum_{s_z=-1}^{+1} \sum_{l_z=-l}^{+l} C(j,j_z,l,l_z,s,s_z)\, Y(l,l_z)\chi(s,s_z), \qquad (4.12)$$

where $s = 1$, and the summation is performed under the restriction $j_z = l_z+s_z$. The $C$ coefficients are the Clebsch–Gordan coefficients; since $s = 1$ these are zero unless $l = j-1$, $j$, or $j+1$.

Any arbitrary vector field can be expressed as a sum of vector spherical harmonics thus:

$$\mathbf{A}(\mathbf{x}) = \sum_{j=1}^{\infty} \sum_{j_z=-j}^{+j} \mathbf{A}(j,j_z,\mathbf{x}), \qquad (4.13)$$

where

$$\mathbf{A}(j,j_z,\mathbf{x}) = \sum_{l=j-1}^{j+1} g(j,j_z,l,s = 1,r)\, \mathbf{Y}(j,j_z,l,s). \qquad (4.13a)$$

$g$ is a coefficient of the series and is a function of the radial distance $|\mathbf{x}| = r$. $\mathbf{Y}(j,j_z,l,s)$ contains ordinary spherical harmonics and is therefore a function of the polar coordinate angles. The electromagnetic field will be decomposed in this way under Section 4.5.

The spherical harmonic $Y(l,l_z)$ has parity $(-1)^l$ and consequently the vector harmonic $\mathbf{Y}(j,j_z,l,s)$ also has parity $(-1)^l$. Since $l$ is $j-1$, $j$, or $j+1$, a vector field of total angular momentum $j$ can have either parity. Of the three terms in the expansion of Eq. (4.13a), two have parity $(-1)^{j\pm1}$ and one has parity $(-1)^j$.

We have defined the functions $\mathbf{Y}(j,j_z,l,s)$ where $s = 1$ for a vector field; for any value of $j$ there can only be three values of $l$, namely $j-1$, $j$, and $j+1$. Of these three harmonics, we are particularly interested in that one which has $l = j$; we write $\mathbf{X}(j,j_z) = \mathbf{Y}(j,j_z,j,1)$. We shall find that the angular distribution can be expressed in terms of harmonics like $\mathbf{X}(j,j_z)$ alone, thus we must be able to express these functions in terms of ordinary spherical harmonics.

Now we have

$$\mathbf{Y}(j,j_z,l,s = 1) = \sum_{l_z}\sum_{s_z} C(j,j_z,l,l_z,s = 1,s_z)\, Y(l,l_z)\chi(s,s_z),$$

where $j_z = l_z + s_z$. Hence

$$\mathbf{X}(j,j_z) = \sum_{s_z} C(j,j_z,l,l_z = j_z - s_z,s = 1,s_z)\, Y(l,l_z)\chi(s,s_z).$$

Now $s_z = -1$, $0$, and $+1$, and we find that

$$\mathbf{X}(j,j_z) = \frac{+j_z}{\sqrt{j(j+1)}}\, Y(j,j_z)\chi(1,0) - \sqrt{\frac{(j+j_z)(j-j_z+1)}{2j(j+1)}}$$
$$\times\, Y(j,j_z-1)\chi(1,1) + \sqrt{\frac{(j-j_z)(j+j_z+1)}{2j(j+1)}}\, Y(j,j_z+1)\chi(1,-1).$$

Here we have used the Clebsch–Gordan coefficients for the vector addition of two angular momenta $j$ and $1$. (See Condon and Shortley, 1951, Table $2^3$.) We shall be interested in observable quantities such as $\mathbf{X}^\dagger(j,j_z)\mathbf{X}(j,j_z)$. Due to the orthonormality of the spin functions, we find

$$\mathbf{X}^\dagger(j,j_z)\mathbf{X}(j,j_z) = \frac{j_z^2}{j(j+1)}\,|\,Y(j,j_z)\,|^2 + \frac{(j+j_z)(j-j_z+1)}{2j(j+1)}\,|\,Y(j,j_z-1)\,|^2$$
$$+ \frac{(j-j_z)(j+j_z+1)}{2j(j+1)}\,|\,Y(j,j_z+1)\,|^2.$$

These functions have the property that

$$\int \mathbf{X}^\dagger(j,j_z)\mathbf{X}(j,j_z)\,d\Omega = 1.$$

It is essential to bear in mind that vector spherical harmonics having $j = 0$ cannot exist since the field must carry at the least its intrinsic angular momentum $\hbar$.

## 4.4 The Electromagnetic Field

Maxwell's equations for the electromagnetic field in free space are

$$\left.\begin{aligned}
\operatorname{div} \mathbf{D} &= 0, \\
\operatorname{div} \mathbf{B} &= 0, \\
\operatorname{curl} \mathbf{E} &= -\frac{\partial \mathbf{B}}{\partial t}, \\
\operatorname{curl} \mathbf{H} &= \frac{\partial \mathbf{D}}{\partial t},
\end{aligned}\right\} \tag{4.14}$$

where $\mathbf{D} = \epsilon\mathbf{E}$ and $\mathbf{B} = \mu\mathbf{H}$. The units are consistently electrostatic units or electromagnetic units. In the former system $\epsilon = 1$ and $\mu = (1/c^2)$ where $c$ is the velocity of light; in the latter system, $\mu = 1$ and $\epsilon = (1/c^2)$. The vectors $\mathbf{E}$ and $\mathbf{H}$ satisfy the classical wave equations

$$\left.\begin{aligned}
\nabla^2 \mathbf{E} - \epsilon\mu \frac{\partial^2 \mathbf{E}}{\partial t^2} &= 0, \\
\nabla^2 \mathbf{H} - \epsilon\mu \frac{\partial^2 \mathbf{H}}{\partial t^2} &= 0.
\end{aligned}\right\} \tag{4.15}$$

The solutions of these equations represent waves moving with velocity $c$ and with instantaneous energy flux $\mathbf{P} = (1/4\pi)\,\mathbf{E} \times \mathbf{H}$. $\mathbf{P}$ is the "Poynting vector" and is a vector in the sense of Section 1.4. It therefore has odd parity and we deduce that $\mathbf{E}$ and $\mathbf{H}$ must have opposite parity, although for an arbitrary field the parity of each vector may not be established.

The vector potential $\mathbf{A}$ is defined by the relation

$$\mathbf{B} = \operatorname{curl} \mathbf{A}. \tag{4.16}$$

From Eq. (4.14) it follows that

$$\operatorname{curl}\left(\mathbf{E} + \frac{\partial \mathbf{A}}{dt}\right) = 0. \tag{4.17}$$

The curl grad of a scalar is zero, so we put

$$\mathbf{E} + \frac{\partial \mathbf{A}}{\partial t} = -\operatorname{grad} \phi, \tag{4.18}$$

where $\phi$ is taken to be the ordinary static electric potential. These equations do not fully determine $\mathbf{A}$ and it is usual to add the Lorentz condition to the equations satisfied by $\mathbf{A}$: it is

$$\operatorname{div} \mathbf{A} + \epsilon\mu \frac{\partial\phi}{\partial t} = 0. \tag{4.19}$$

In free space $\mathbf{A}$ and $\phi$ satisfy the homogeneous wave equation

$$\nabla^2 - \epsilon\mu \frac{\partial^2}{\partial t^2} = 0. \tag{4.20}$$

The components of $\mathbf{A}$ and $ic\phi$ together are the components of a four-vector.

The interaction Hamiltonian between the electromagnetic field and any electric currents present is given by

$$H_I = \int \mathbf{j} \cdot \mathbf{A}\, d\mathbf{x}$$

where $\mathbf{j}$ is the current density vector and possesses odd parity. Meanwhile, $\mathbf{A}$ has a parity opposite to that of $\mathbf{B}$ [Eq. (4.16)]. Consequently, $H_I$ is scalar or pseudoscalar according to whether $\mathbf{H}$ has even or odd parity. $H_I$ is the operator responsible for a transition between two states of a system involving the emission or absorption of a photon; excluding the photon, these two states have opposite parity if $H_I$ is pseudoscalar. It follows that parity conservation is maintained by assigning to the interacting photon the parity of its own magnetic vector.

The electric and magnetic fields can be decomposed into vector spherical harmonics. If the field carries total angular momentum specified by the quantum number $j$, then we can write by means of Eq. (4.13):

$$\begin{aligned}
\mathbf{H}(j,j_z,\mathbf{x}) &= f(j,j_z,j-1,r)\,\mathbf{Y}(j,j_z,j-1,1) \\
&\quad + g(j,j_z,j,r)\,\mathbf{Y}(j,j_z,j,1) \\
&\quad + h(j,j_z,j+1,r)\,\mathbf{Y}(j,j_z,j+1,1).
\end{aligned}$$

The field $\mathbf{H}$ is a function of position $\mathbf{x}$, and this is allowed by making the three coefficients $f$, $g$, and $h$ functions of the radial distance $r$. The three components have parities $(-1)^{j-1}$, $(-1)^j$, $(-1)^{j+1}$ respectively, whilst the corresponding components of the associated electric field have opposite parities. As we employ the photon parity assignment introduced in the last paragraph, it follows that a photon can have either odd or even parity for the same $j$. However, for the same $j$, the two parity possibilities, $(-1)^j$ and $(-1)^{j+1}$, are given the names electric and magnetic multipoles of order $j$ respectively.

The first three multipoles having $j = 1$, 2, and 3 are named dipole, quadrupole, and octopole respectively. The parity carried by any of these multipoles can be found in Table 4.1. These photon states are often described by the notation $E_j$ or $M_j$ for the electric or magnetic $j$th multipole.

TABLE 4.1

THE PARITY OF ELECTROMAGNETIC MULTIPOLES

| Photon polarity | Electric multipole parity | Magnetic multipole parity |
|---|---|---|
| Dipole, $j = 1$ | $-1$ | $+1$ |
| Quadrupole, $j = 2$ | $+1$ | $-1$ |
| Octopole, $j = 3$ | $-1$ | $+1$ |
| Multipole $j$ | $(-1)^j$ | $(-1)^{j+1}$ |

It is important to stress again that the photon does not carry the parity assigned to it by this convention. The assigned parity is even (or odd) if the transition in which the photon is absorbed or emitted is between states with the same (or opposite) parity; in this sense, the photon is not included in the assessment of the parity of the initial and final states.

## 4.5 The Multipole Expansion of the Electromagnetic Plane Wave

We wish to consider a plane electromagnetic wave moving in the $z$ direction with wave number $k$. The nature of Maxwell's equations requires that $E_z = H_z = 0$ and $\mathbf{E} \cdot \mathbf{H} = 0$; hence the vectors $\mathbf{E}$, $\mathbf{H}$, and $\mathbf{k}$ are mutually orthogonal. It is therefore convenient to use the set of orthogonal unit electric vectors $\boldsymbol{\epsilon}_x$, $\boldsymbol{\epsilon}_y$, and $\boldsymbol{\epsilon}_z$ which possess the property

$$\boldsymbol{\epsilon}_x \times \boldsymbol{\epsilon}_y = \boldsymbol{\epsilon}_z.$$

A plane polarized wave could have an electric vector described by the equation

$$\mathbf{E}(\mathbf{x}, t) = \boldsymbol{\epsilon}_x \exp i(kz - \omega t).$$

The electric field is a real quantity and it is therefore the real part of this equation.

However, it happens that the most convenient representation is not in terms of the two plane polarized states but in terms of the two circularly polarized states. The electric vector of a circularly polarized state is described by

$$\mathbf{E}(\mathbf{x}, t) = \frac{1}{\sqrt{2}} (\boldsymbol{\epsilon}_x \pm i\boldsymbol{\epsilon}_y) \exp i(kz - \omega t). \tag{4.21}$$

The upper sign refers to right circularly polarized light which implies that $\mathbf{E}$ is rotating in clockwise fashion around the $z$ axis. Conversely, the lower sign refers to left circularly polarized light which has $\mathbf{E}$ rotating in the opposite sense. These rotations are as viewed from the origin in the direction of the $z$ axis and thus our convention is opposite to that of classical optics. If we use the relations

$$\frac{\partial \mathbf{H}}{\partial t} = -\frac{1}{\mu} \operatorname{curl} \mathbf{E},$$

$$\operatorname{curl} \{(\boldsymbol{\epsilon}_x \pm i\boldsymbol{\epsilon}_y) e^{ikz}\} = \pm (\boldsymbol{\epsilon}_x \pm i\boldsymbol{\epsilon}_y) k e^{ikz},$$

$$\omega = kc,$$

we find that the magnetic vector of this plane wave is described by

$$\mathbf{H}(\mathbf{x}, t) = \mp \frac{\epsilon c i}{\sqrt{2}} (\boldsymbol{\epsilon}_x \pm i\boldsymbol{\epsilon}_y) \exp i(kz - \omega t). \tag{4.21a}$$

The factor $i$ indicates $\mathbf{H}$ is instantaneously orthogonal to $\mathbf{E}$. It can be shown (Beth, 1936) that the states of right and left circular polarization are eigenstates of the operator $S_z(= J_z)$ with respective eigenvalues $+\hbar$ and $-\hbar$. This can be confirmed if we express the eigenfunctions and operators in the matrix form introduced in Section 4.2, putting

$$\boldsymbol{\epsilon}_x = \begin{bmatrix} 1 \\ 0 \\ 0 \end{bmatrix} \quad \boldsymbol{\epsilon}_y = \begin{bmatrix} 0 \\ 1 \\ 0 \end{bmatrix} \quad \text{etc.}$$

Thus we can write

$$\mp \frac{1}{\sqrt{2}} (\boldsymbol{\epsilon}_x \pm i\boldsymbol{\epsilon}_y) = \chi(1, \pm 1). \tag{4.22}$$

The extra sign on the left-hand side is essential if our scheme is to remain consistent with our choice of relative phase in Eq. (2.25). This can be seen by operating on $(\boldsymbol{\epsilon}_x - i\boldsymbol{\epsilon}_y)/\sqrt{2}$ with the matrix $(S_x + iS_y)^2$ for which the matrix element $(\chi(1, +1)|(S_x + iS_y)^2|\chi(1, -1))$ should be $+2$ ($\hbar$ omitted).

The spin functions on the right-hand side of Eq. (4.22) are analogous to those defined in Section 2.8. The state having $s_z = 0$ does not exist and this property is due to the nature of the Maxwell field which can only describe a "particle" with two states of polarization. Again this depends on the fact that the field has zero rest mass. A vector field having nonzero rest mass can have three states of polarization.

Returning to the electromagnetic field, we can write Eq. (4.21) in the form

$$\mathbf{E}(\mathbf{x}) = \mp e^{ikz} \chi(1, \pm 1).$$

We have dropped the time variation as this remains unaffected by the analysis to follow.

From Eq. (3.8) we have

$$e^{ikz} = \sqrt{4\pi} \sum_l \sqrt{2l+1}\, i^l Y_l(\cos\theta)\, F_l(kr). \tag{4.23}$$

The plane wave has $l_z = 0$ and we have $s_z = j_z = \pm 1$; hence

$$\mathbf{E}(\mathbf{x}) = \mp \sum_l \sqrt{4\pi(2l+1)}\, i^l F_l(kr)\, Y(l, 0)\chi(1, \pm 1). \tag{4.24}$$

We now apply our knowledge of vector addition to express the combined orbital and spin angular momentum functions in terms of eigenfunctions of $J^2$ and $J_z$. Inverting Eq. (4.12), we can put

$$Y(l, 0)\chi(1, \pm 1) = \sum_{j=l-1}^{j=l+1} C(j, \pm 1, l, 0, 1, \pm 1)\mathbf{Y}(j, \pm 1, l, 1). \tag{4.25}$$

Therefore

$$\mathbf{E}(\mathbf{x}) = \mp \sum_l \sum_{j=l-1}^{j=l+1} \sqrt{4\pi(2l+1)}\, i^l F_l(kr)\, C(j, \pm 1, l, 0, 1, \pm 1)\mathbf{Y}(j, \pm 1, l, 1) \tag{4.26}$$

$$= \mp \sum_{j=1}^{\infty} \sum_{l=j-1}^{j+1} \sqrt{4\pi(2l+1)}\, i^l F_l(kr)\, C(j, \pm 1, l, 0, 1, \pm 1)\mathbf{Y}(j, \pm 1, l, 1). \tag{4.27}$$

We now wish to divide this series into parts due to electric multipoles and into parts due to magnetic multipoles. We do this in such a way that we need only be concerned with those vector harmonics which have $j = l$; therefore we contract $\mathbf{Y}(j, \pm 1, j, 1)$ to $\mathbf{X}(j, \pm 1)$ which has parity $(-1)^j$. Now the electric vector of a magnetic multipole has parity $(-1)^j$; hence it is the vector harmonics having $j = l$ which are the magnetic multipole parts. Thus breaking Eq. (4.27), we have

$$\mathbf{E}(\mathbf{x}) = \mp \sum_{j=1}^{\infty} \{\sqrt{4\pi(2j+1)}\, i^j F_j(kr)\, C(j, \pm 1, l = j, 0, 1, \pm 1)\mathbf{X}(j, \pm 1)$$

$$+ \text{terms having } l = j \pm 1 \text{ due to electric multipole}$$

$$\text{radiation}\}. \tag{4.28}$$

By collecting Eqs. (4.21a), (4.23), and (4.25), we find that

$$\mathbf{H(x)} = \epsilon c i \sum_{j=1}^{\infty} \sum_{l=j-1}^{j+1} \sqrt{4\pi(2l+1)}\, i^l F_l(kr)\, C(j, \pm 1, l, 0, 1, \pm 1)\, \mathbf{Y}(j, \pm 1, l, 1). \tag{4.29}$$

This can also be divided into parts due to electric and magnetic multipoles. The former have parity $(-1)^j$ and can again be expressed in terms of the vector harmonics $\mathbf{X}(j,j_z)$; the remaining terms will be due to magnetic multipoles. Thus

$$\mathbf{H(x)} = \epsilon c i \sum_{j=1}^{\infty} \{\sqrt{4\pi(2j+1)}\, i^j F_j(kr)\, C(j, \pm 1, l = j, 0, 1, \pm 1)\, \mathbf{X}(j, \pm 1)$$

$$+ \text{terms having } l = j \pm 1 \text{ due to magnetic multipole}$$

$$\text{radiation} \}. \tag{4.30}$$

The inexplicitly expressed terms can be evaluated by considering the relations between $\mathbf{E}$ and $\mathbf{H}$. We have

$$\operatorname{curl} \mathbf{H} = \epsilon \frac{\partial \mathbf{E}}{\partial t} = -i\omega\epsilon\mathbf{E},$$

$$\operatorname{curl} \mathbf{E} = -\mu \frac{\partial \mathbf{H}}{\partial t} = +i\omega\mu\mathbf{H}.$$

The terms due to electric multipoles in the expansion of $\mathbf{E(x)}$, Eq. (4.28), are just $-\operatorname{curl}/i\omega\epsilon$ of the terms due to electric multipoles in the expansion of $\mathbf{H(x)}$, Eq. (4.30). Thus (4.28) becomes

$$\mathbf{E(x)} = \mp \sum_{j=1}^{\infty} \sqrt{4\pi(2j+1)}\, i^j\, C(j, \pm 1, j, 0, 1, \pm 1) \left\{ F_j(kr)\, \mathbf{X}(j, \pm 1) \right.$$

$$\left. - \frac{1}{k} \operatorname{curl} [F_j(kr)\, \mathbf{X}(j, \pm 1)] \right\}. \tag{4.31}$$

In a similar way, we can express Eq. (4.30) thus:

$$\mathbf{H(x)} = \epsilon c \sum_{j=1}^{\infty} \sqrt{4\pi(2j+1)}\, i^j\, C(j, \pm 1, j, 0, 1, \pm 1) \left\{ iF_j(kr)\, \mathbf{X}(j, \pm 1) \right.$$

$$\left. \pm \frac{i}{k} \operatorname{curl} [F_j(kr)\, \mathbf{X}(j, \pm 1)] \right\}. \tag{4.32}$$

Finally, we put the Clebsch–Gordan coefficients (Table $2^3$ in Condon and Shortley, 1951)

$$C(j, \pm 1, j, 0, 1, \pm 1) = \mp \sqrt{\tfrac{1}{2}}$$

and arrange the terms in the brace so that the electric multipole terms are placed first:

$$\mathbf{E}(\mathbf{x}) = \sum_{j=1}^{\infty} \sqrt{2\pi(2j+1)} i^j \left\{ \pm \frac{1}{k} \operatorname{curl} [F_j(kr) \mathbf{X}(j, \pm 1)] + F_j(kr) \mathbf{X}(j, \pm 1) \right\},$$

$$\mathbf{H}(\mathbf{x}) = \epsilon c \sum_{j=1}^{\infty} \sqrt{2\pi(2j+1)} i^j$$
$$\times \left\{ \mp i F_j(kr) \mathbf{X}(j, \pm 1) - \frac{i}{k} \operatorname{curl} [F_j(kr) \mathbf{X}(j, \pm 1)] \right\}.$$

This is the multipole expansion of the representation of a circularly polarized electromagnetic plane wave.

## 4.6 The General Multipole Expansion of the Electromagnetic Field

The plane wave expansion into multipoles is a particular example of the more general expansion. We are most often interested in a single source of radiation such as the nucleus in an excited state. Let us consider such a source of radiation which is at the centre of mass of the system. Outgoing waves of multipole order $j$ are not restricted to describing photons moving along the $z$ axis and can thus have any value of $j_z$ between $-j$ and $+j$; thus in describing multipole order it is essential to specify both $j$ and $j_z$.

First, it is necessary to express the real electric and magnetic vectors in terms of complex vector quantities

$$\mathbf{E}(\mathbf{x}, t) = \mathbf{E}(\mathbf{x}) e^{-i\omega t} + \mathbf{E}^*(\mathbf{x}) e^{+i\omega t},$$

$$\mathbf{H}(\mathbf{x}, t) = \mathbf{H}(\mathbf{x}) e^{-i\omega t} + \mathbf{H}^*(\mathbf{x}) e^{+i\omega t}.$$

Let us consider the magnetic multipoles, using the subscript $M$ to distinguish the associated quantities. The complex vector amplitude can be expressed as series, as in Eqs. (4.13) and (4.13a), from which terms of the wrong parity have been dropped. Hence

$$\mathbf{E}_M(j, j_z, \mathbf{x}) = f_M(j, j_z, r) \mathbf{X}(j, j_z).$$

Using the arguments of last section, we have

$$\mathbf{H}_M(j, j_z, \mathbf{x}) = \frac{1}{i\omega\mu} \operatorname{curl} \mathbf{E}_M(j, j_z, \mathbf{x}) = -\frac{i\epsilon c}{k} \operatorname{curl} [f_M(j, j_z, r) \mathbf{X}(j, j_z)].$$

The time-independent vectors $\mathbf{H}_M$ and $\mathbf{E}_M$ are solutions of the operator equation

$$\operatorname{curl} \operatorname{curl} + k^2 = 0,$$

where $k = \omega/c$. Hence $rf_M(j, j_z, r)$ satisfies

$$\left(\frac{\partial^2}{\partial r^2} - \frac{j(j+1)}{r^2} + k^2\right) rf_M(j, j_z, r) = 0.$$

Since the solutions depend only on $j$ and $r$, we write them $U(j, r)/k$. For large $r$, $U(j, r) \simeq e^{i(kr - j\pi/2)}$. Then we have

$$\mathbf{E}_M(j, j_z, r) = \frac{U(j, r)}{kr} \mathbf{X}(j, j_z), \tag{4.33}$$

$$\mathbf{H}_M(j, j_z, r) = -\frac{i\epsilon c}{k} \operatorname{curl} \mathbf{E}_M(j, j_z, r). \tag{4.34}$$

By analogous arguments the magnetic and electric vectors of the electric multipole are given by

$$\mathbf{H}_E(j, j_z, r) = \epsilon c \frac{U(j, r)}{kr} \mathbf{X}(j, j_z), \tag{4.35}$$

$$\mathbf{E}_E(j, j_z, r) = +\frac{i}{\epsilon\omega} \operatorname{curl} \mathbf{H}_E(j, j_z, r). \tag{4.36}$$

Then, in accordance with Eq. (4.13a), any general outgoing electromagnetic field can be expanded in the following manner:

$$\mathbf{E}(\mathbf{x}) = \sum_{j=1}^{\infty} \sum_{j_z=-j}^{+j} \{a_E(j, j_z) \mathbf{E}_E(j, j_z, \mathbf{x}) + a_M(j, j_z) \mathbf{E}_M(j, j_z, \mathbf{x})\}, \tag{4.37}$$

$$\mathbf{H}(\mathbf{x}) = \sum_{j=1}^{\infty} \sum_{j_z=-j}^{+j} \{a_E(j, j_z) \mathbf{H}_E(j, j_z, \mathbf{x}) + a_M(j, j_z) \mathbf{H}_M(j, j_z, \mathbf{x})\}. \tag{4.38}$$

The coefficients $a$ are the amplitudes of the corresponding multipole fields.

We now wish to calculate the intensity of radiation from the multipole expansion. We do this by using the Poynting vector

$$\mathbf{P}(\mathbf{x}, t) = \frac{1}{4\pi} \mathbf{E}(\mathbf{x}, t) \times \mathbf{H}(\mathbf{x}, t)$$

which gives the instantaneous energy flux of radiation if the vectors are time-dependent. The mean energy flux is $(1/2\pi) \operatorname{Re}[\mathbf{E}^*(\mathbf{x}) \times \mathbf{H}(\mathbf{x})]$, the electromagnetic vectors being the complex time-independent amplitudes. At large distances from the source, $\mathbf{E}$, $\mathbf{H}$, and the direction of motion are orthogonal; hence the magnitude of outgoing energy flux at the point $\mathbf{x}$ is $\epsilon c |\mathbf{E}|^2/2\pi$ or $|\mathbf{H}|^2/2\pi\epsilon c$. The actual flux of photons, $N(\mathbf{x})$, will be thus divided by $\hbar\omega$, that is,

$$N(\mathbf{x}) = \frac{\epsilon|\mathbf{E}|^2}{2\pi\hbar k} = \frac{\mu|\mathbf{H}|^2}{2\pi\hbar k}.$$

The angular distribution of a pure multipole radiation can now be found. Let $P_E(j,j_z,\Omega)\,d\Omega$ be the probability that a photon leaves the source into solid angle $d\Omega$ about direction $\Omega$ in one second, carrying electric multipole order $j,j_z$; $P_M(j,j_z,\Omega)\,d\Omega$ is similarly defined for a magnetic multipole. To find $P_E$ we use $N(\mathbf{x}) = (\mu|\mathbf{H}|^2/2\pi\hbar k)$ and substitute for $\mathbf{H}$ from the electric term in the expansion of Eq. (4.38); then we have that

$$P_E(j,j_z,\Omega)\,d\Omega = N(r)\,r^2\,d\Omega,$$

$$= \frac{\epsilon\,d\Omega}{2\pi\hbar k^3} |a_E(j,j_z)|^2 |\mathbf{X}(j,j_z)|^2.$$

We have used the asymptotic properties of $U(j,r)$. To find $P_M$, we use $N(\mathbf{x}) = (\epsilon|\mathbf{E}|^2/2\pi\hbar k)$. Then

$$P_M(j,j_z,\Omega)\,d\Omega = \frac{\epsilon\,d\Omega}{2\pi\hbar k^3} |a_M(j,j_z)|^2 |\mathbf{X}(j,j_z)|^2.$$

The electrical unit $\epsilon$ appears in these equations because the way we have defined $\mathbf{X}(j,j_z)$ gives it the dimensions of electric field, i.e. it contains the unit electric vectors $\boldsymbol{\epsilon}_x, \boldsymbol{\epsilon}_y$. If the source emits radiation of more than one multipole order, then it is possible for interference to occur between the different orders and the distribution becomes more complicated. We cannot consider this situation here except to note that its evaluation requires the use of a multipole expansion of the vector potential rather than of the fields (Devons and Goldfarb 1957; Rose, 1955, and references quoted therein).

We notice that the angular distribution depends only on the multipole order and is independent of the electric or magnetic nature. Hence it is impossible to measure the parity of radiation by means of its angular distribution.

### 4.7 The Angular Distribution of Photons

The conservation of angular momentum appears to apply rigorously to all electromagnetic interactions and this principle can therefore be applied to the analysis of angular distributions of the photons produced in nuclear reactions or of the products of reactions induced by the absorption of photons. This kind of analysis gives information on the spins and parity of the states involved, and on the relative strengths of various multipole interactions; in Section 7.10 we shall give an example of such an analysis by calculating the angular distribution of mesons produced by high-energy photons incident upon nucleons. A similar analysis can be applied to angular correlations which occur between photons emitted from nuclei during de-excitation. This can become a very complex situation and in this section we shall do no more than outline the methods of analysis and give one example. Readers who are interested in pursuing the subject in more detail should consult the review article by Devons and Goldfarb (1957) or the work of Deutsch and Kofoed-Hansen (1959) and their bibliographies.

An immediate consequence of the conservation of angular momentum and parity is that we can state the selection rules which apply to electromagnetic transitions. We consider a transition between an initial state (particle or nucleus) having angular momentum quantum numbers $j_a$, $j_{az}$ and parity $\rho_a$ to a final state containing a residual particle or nucleus having quantum numbers $j_b$, $j_{bz}$ and parity $\rho_b$ and an outgoing photon carrying away angular momentum $j$, $j_z$ and parity $\rho$. The selection rules are:

conservation of parity: $\rho_a = \rho\rho_b$;
conservation of angular momentum:

$$j_{az} = j_{bz} + j_z,$$

$$|j_a - j_b| \leqslant j \leqslant j_a + j_b.$$

Since $j \geqslant 1$, a transition between $j_a = 0$ and $j_b = 0$ is forbidden.

We will now discuss some simple cases to illustrate how the angular distribution of photons is given by the angular momentum changes.

### a. Photon Emission from Polarized Nuclei

For simplicity we suppose $j_b = 0$ so that $j = j_a$ and $j_z = j_{az}$. If the assembly of nuclei is fully polarized, they will all be in the same eigenstate of $J_{az}$, provided we orient our $z$ axis correctly, and the radiation will have the angular distribution given by $|\mathbf{X}(j,j_z)|^2$ independent of the parity change. If the initial assembly is partially polarized, it is effectively an incoherent sum of different eigenstates of $J_{az}$ and the outgoing photon distribution is given by sum of terms like $|\mathbf{X}(j,j_z)|^2$ each with intensity given by the intensity of the corresponding initial state. For an unpolarized source these intensities add to give an isotropic distribution. The case of $j_a = 0$ and $j_b \neq 0$ is identical to the one just discussed; of course the distribution is isotropic unless there is some way of observing only that radiation which leaves the residual nucleus in a particular eigenstate of $J_{bz}$.

## b. *Transition from Polarized Source, $j_a \neq 0$, $j_b \neq 0$*

All multipoles consistent with the selection rules are possible, but, if the wavelength of the emitted radiation is long compared to the dimensions of the emitting system, the transition rate falls off rapidly with increasing $j$ and the radiation is very predominantly of the lowest order allowed. The photon intensity is a sum of multipole intensities, the summation being performed over all unobserved quantum numbers. If the source is partially polarized, then a further sum must be made over values of $j_{az}$ with appropriate intensities.

## c. *Angular Correlation of Successive Photon Emissions*

The difficulty of polarizing the nuclei in a radioactive specimen makes the measurement of angular distributions by this method rather unusual. However, the measurement of angular correlations between successive photons emitted from the same nucleus has the same kind of result and will give the same kind of information. Let us consider the emission of a photon of pure multipole order and nature from a nucleus (state $a$) which is one of an assembly of such nuclei having no polarization. The emission of this first photon is, of course, isotropic, but it will leave the residual nucleus (state $b$) in a certain angular momentum eigenstate. The population of the various eigenstates of $J_{bz}$ for the assembly can be calculated knowing that the population of the states of $J_{az}$ was uniform. In general, the former population is not uniform and the residual state is polarized or aligned with respect to the direction of the first photon (see Section 8.2). If the nuclei in this polarized state each emit a further photon, these photons will, in general, have a nonisotropic distribution with respect to the direction of the first photon. Once the polarization of the residual nucleus is known, the distribution of the second photon can be calculated as in (a) or (b). However, let us give an example.

A nucleus $a$, of total angular momentum $j_a = 0$, decays by photon emission to $b$ of total angular momentum $j_b = 1$ which subsequently decays into nucleus $c$ of total angular momentum $j_c = 0$; both transitions are dipole. Let us consider radiation emitted from an assembly of nuclei type $a$, which is, of course, unpolarized. Let us orient our $z$ axis along the direction of the first photon. This must have $j = 1$ and $j_z = \pm 1$; therefore the residual nucleus $b$ is in either of the states $j_{bz} = \mp 1$ with equal probability. The second photon must leave a nucleus $c$ with $j_{cz} = 0$ so it is a dipole $j = 1$, $j_z = \mp 1$. Therefore the intensity of the second photon is given by the probability distribution

$$I(\theta) \propto \tfrac{1}{2}|\mathbf{X}(1, +1)|^2 + \tfrac{1}{2}|\mathbf{X}(1, -1)|^2.$$

Substituting for the vector spherical harmonics (Section (4.3)), we find that

$$I(\theta) \propto \frac{3}{8\pi}(1 + \cos^2\theta),$$

where $\theta$ is the angle between successive photons.

#### d. *Polarization of the Outgoing Radiation*

If the photons emitted in any of the situations discussed above are detected only if they are in a certain state of polarization, then the observed distributions may be modified. Formally, this corresponds to one less summation in the calculation of photon intensities; in fact, detectors or polarization discriminators are never 100% efficient and it is necessary to sum over intensities and detector efficiencies. This kind of measurement becomes necessary if we wish to discover the parity changes involved in electromagnetic transitions. A simple example of this is the neutral pi-meson decay

$$\pi^0 \to 2\gamma.$$

The parity of the $\pi^0$ meson can only be discovered if a measurement is made of the correlation between the polarization of the outgoing photons. This is discussed in more detail in Section 7.5.

The procedure for deriving formulae which describe polarization plus angular correlations in photon emission becomes very involved and complex. We refer readers to more advanced treatises (Rose, 1955; Coester and Jauch, 1953; Devons and Goldfarb, 1957).

We have involved polarization in our discussions as if this were a very familiar phenomenon; in fact, its rigorous manipulation requires special techniques which will be discussed in Chapter VIII. We also note that we have neglected any effects which may depolarize or precess the intermediate stage in successive photon emissions; these effects can be important in certain circumstances.

### 4.8 Conclusion

This chapter has done no more than introduce the subject of electromagnetic transitions. Our main object has been to give the reader an idea of the main symmetry changes which can take place when a system radiates or absorbs radiation. We have not discussed the calculation of transition rates, for this would involve us in a treatment of nuclear models which we feel is outside the scope of this book; however, we can refer readers to Blatt and Weisskopf (1952).

# CHAPTER V

# TRANSITIONS

## 5.1 Introduction

In Chapters II to IV of this book we have dealt with the properties of angular momentum and with the influence these properties have upon nuclear reactions. In particular, we have noticed that the possibility of analysing the angular distribution of nuclear reaction products arises from the fact that the symmetry properties of the initial state under rotation are the same as those of the final state. Before introducing any further symmetry properties we shall briefly describe more definite ways of examining the transition from the initial to the final state; this procedure will allow us more scope when we come to use symmetry properties such as that which exists for rotations in isotopic spin space. The first part of this chapter describes the formula which gives the transition rate and the quantities involved. The later parts of the chapter are concerned with the qualifications and consequences to this formula and with an extension of the partial wave analysis.

## 5.2 The Transition Rate Formula

In this section we are interested in a system described by the initial wave function $\psi_\alpha$, which is able to make a transition to a state described by the final wave function $\psi_\beta$. $\psi_\alpha$ and $\psi_\beta$ will contain a certain number of particles interacting; if $H$ is the Hamiltonian for the system, we can put $H = H_0 + H_I$ where $H_0 \psi_\alpha = E\psi_\alpha$ is the eigenequation which has the total energy of the free particles without interaction as its eigenvalue. If the interaction is included, there is an extra term and the eigenequation becomes

$$(H_0 + H_I)\psi = E\psi. \tag{5.1}$$

It can be shown that $H_I$ induces transitions between possible states of $\psi$ for which energy and momentum are conserved. If we pick out, in particular, our initial $\psi_\alpha$ and final wave function $\psi_\beta$ which satisfy Eq. (5.1), then the probability that a transition from $\psi_\alpha$ to $\psi_\beta$ will occur in one second is given by

$$\omega = \frac{2\pi}{\hbar} |(\psi_\beta | H_I | \psi_\alpha)|^2 \frac{dN}{dE}. \tag{5.2}$$

$(\psi_\beta | H_I | \psi_\alpha)$ is the matrix element for the transition and, in line with our notation is $\int \psi_\beta^* H_I \psi_\alpha \, dx$, the integral to be taken over the normalization volume. $dN/dE$ is the density of states like $\psi_\beta$ around the energy $E$; we shall describe this factor shortly (see Section 5.3).

This formula is derived from perturbation theory and is only an approximation; a more correct formula takes account of intermediate states. However, the inclusion of further terms often introduces misleading divergence difficulties, and the quoted formula suffices for many applications. When applied to cross-section calculations, the initial and final wave functions are often approximated by plane waves; this is a Born approximation. Later in this chapter we shall be concerned with the more general properties of transitions and we shall indicate a complete matrix element for a transition by the letter $M$; this is the quantity which replaces $(\psi_\beta | H_I | \psi_\alpha)$ in Eq. (5.2) when the theory which is used to calculate the transition rate is exact, rather than the approximate perturbation theory.

The transition probability has dimensions (time)$^{-1}$ and can be related to more directly observable quantities. Suppose the initial state $\psi_\alpha$ describes a radioactive particle and that we have $Q_0$ such particles at time $t = 0$. Then at time $t$ let there be $Q$ particles. The differential equation for $Q$ is

$$dQ = -Q\omega \, dt,$$

whence

$$Q = Q_0 e^{-\omega t},$$

where $\omega$ is the transition rate for the radioactive decay; this is the familiar law of radioactive decay.

If the initial wave function represents two particles, then we wish to relate the transition rate to a cross section. This can best be done by considering the role of the normalizing volume mentioned above. If this volume is a cube of dimensions $L$ and volume $L^3$, all single-particle wave functions will be proportional to $L^{-\frac{3}{2}}$, so that if there are $n$ particles in the final state, we shall have

$$(\psi_\beta | H_I | \psi_\alpha) \propto L^{-3n/2}.$$

The density of states factor contains a factor $L^{3(n-1)}$ (see below and Appendix B), so the transition rate $\omega$ is proportional to $L^{-3}$. We assume that the target particle is restrained inside the normalizing volume and the incident particle is to pass through the volume at velocity $v$; then it will spend a time $L/v$ inside the volume giving a probability that a transition will occur $\omega L/v$. Now the target particle represents one particle per area $L^2$ whilst the cross section ($\sigma$) is the reaction probability when there is one target particle per unit area. Therefore $\sigma = \omega L^3/v$. Now $\omega$ contains $L^{-3}$, so we see that the cross section is independent of the normalizing volume, as would be expected. To calculate the cross section it is only necessary to be consistent and put the same volume in the matrix element and in the density of states factor. Then the cross section $\sigma$ is given by

$$\sigma = \frac{\text{transition rate}}{\text{relative initial velocity between colliding particles}}. \qquad (5.3)$$

This formula has come from a simple approach to the situation; in fact, the result is independent of the shape of the normalizing volume and is quite general. It is also essential that the transition rate applied to a radioactive decay be independent of the normalizing volume. A similar analysis shows this is so.

For elementary application of the transition rate formula in the Born approximation, see Fermi's *Elementary Particles* (1951).

## 5.3 The Density of States Factor

The density of states factor, $dN/dE$, must now be explained; essentially it is the number of states available to a particle per unit energy interval evaluated at the particle energy. We shall clarify this by considering the solution of the Schrödinger equation for a particle in a box having a volume $L^3$ and impenetrable walls. There are an infinite number of such solutions, all having the analytic form of classical stationary waves; each normalized solution is characterized by three positive integer parameters $l, m, n$, and has the form

$$\psi_{lmn} = \left(\frac{8}{L^3}\right)^{\frac{1}{2}} \sin\left(\frac{xl\pi}{L}\right) \sin\left(\frac{ym\pi}{L}\right) \sin\left(\frac{zn\pi}{L}\right).$$

Since this is a stationary state, the right-hand side of the Schrödinger equation is $E\psi$ and $\psi_{lmn}$ becomes an eigenfunction of the Hamiltonian with eigenvalues equal to the energy. Operating on $\psi_{lmn}$ with the Hamiltonian gives

$$E_{lmn} = \frac{\pi^2 \hbar^2}{2ML^2} (l^2 + m^2 + n^2).$$

Each possible state is specified by a set of quantum numbers $l, m, n$. If the particle has a particular energy $E$, the value of $(l^2 + m^2 + n^2)$ is fixed; in fact, we can imagine a three-dimensional system in which a point is described by coordinates $(l, m, n)$ with respect to three Cartesian axes. Then there is a spherical surface which represents $(l^2 + m^2 + n^2) = $ constant. Every possible state of the particle occupies a unit volume in this space so that the total number of states $(N)$ with energy less than or equal to $E$ is the volume of an octant of the sphere, lying between the $l$, $m$, and $n$ axes. If the energy is increased, there exists a differential $dN/dE$ which is the density of states factor

$$\frac{dN}{dE} = \frac{d}{dE}\left[\frac{\pi}{6}(l^2 + m^2 + n^2)^{\frac{3}{2}}\right] = \frac{4\pi L^3}{(2\pi\hbar)^3}(2M^3 E)^{\frac{1}{2}}.$$

Expressed in terms of momentum instead of energy, we see that

$$\frac{dN}{dE} = \left(\frac{L}{2\pi\hbar}\right)^3 4\pi p M.$$

This expression indicates a more fundamental approach. We introduce the concept of phase space, in which a point represents the state of motion of a particle and consequently the three Cartesian coordinates which describe the position of the point are the three momenta $p_x, p_y, p_z$. Due to quantization inside the finite volume $L^3$, the points representing different possible states of the particle in a box are separated by a finite distance; this is equivalent to saying that each possible state occupies a finite volume in phase space and that the volumes due to different states do not overlap. This volume is $(2\pi\hbar/L)^3$. If our particle has energy $E$, then it will be in states which lie in the surface of a sphere in phase space described by

$$p^2 = p_x^2 + p_y^2 + p_z^2 = 2ME.$$

The total number of states $N$ inside this sphere is its volume divided by the volume allocated to each state:

$$N = \frac{4\pi}{3}p^3\left(\frac{L}{2\pi\hbar}\right)^3.$$

Therefore

$$\frac{dN}{dp} = \left(\frac{L}{2\pi\hbar}\right)^3 4\pi p^2.$$

Since $dp/dE = M/p$, we have

$$\frac{dN}{dE} = \left(\frac{L}{2\pi\hbar}\right)^3 4\pi p M,$$

which agrees with the result derived above.

This is the density of states factor for one particle (nonrelativistic) emitted from an infinitely heavy source. The cases for two or more particles are considered in a fully relativistic treatment in Appendix B.

Before closing this section we must consider what happens if any of the particles in the initial or final states have intrinsic spin. In these circumstances the reaction matrix element is only defined for transitions between specified initial and final spin states. Normally, spin is not observed among the reaction products and the initial states are unpolarized; in this case, all the initial spin states are equally probable and each may be able to proceed into one or more of the final spin states. Then the effective matrix element squared which is to be inserted into Eq. (5.2) is the average over all initial spin states of the sum of squared matrix elements between an initial state and all final spin states. This "sum over final states and average over initial states" can be expressed thus

$$|M|^2 = \frac{1}{r}\sum_\alpha \sum_\beta |M_{\alpha\beta}|^2$$

where $\alpha$ specifies the spin of the initial state $\psi_\alpha$, and $\beta$ specifies the spin of the final state $\psi_\beta$. $M_{\alpha\beta}$ is the matrix element between the states $\psi_\alpha$ and $\psi_\beta$. The summations are performed over all initial and final spin states—that is, over all states which differ only in their spin quantum numbers. The number of such initial states is $r$, and of final states is $s$. We can define a mean square matrix element $\overline{|M|^2}$ by the equation

$$\overline{|M|^2} = \frac{1}{rs}\sum_\alpha \sum_\beta |M_{\alpha\beta}|^2 \tag{5.4}$$

so that

$$|M|^2 = s\overline{|M|^2}. \tag{5.5}$$

If we use this mean square matrix element in Eq. (5.2), then it is necessary to include $s$ in the density of states factor and it is as if each cell in phase space is degenerate by the number of final spin states.

We shall be using the transition rate formula to compare cross sections and reaction rates under conditions in which the matrix elements for the compared processes are expected to be identical. Thus in Chapter VII we shall show that there is a simple relation, which has been experimentally verified, between the cross section for the scattering of positive pi-mesons by protons and the cross section for scattering of negative pi-mesons by protons. This relation comes only from the assumption that the interaction Hamiltonian is always the same at the same energy, for the same state of the meson–proton system; here the definition of the state includes relative angular momentum and isotopic spin.

## 5.4 The Scattering Matrix

In this section we wish to introduce the so-called scattering matrix which effectively extends the partial wave analysis. We shall start by rewriting the partial wave expansion of the incident plane wave:

$$e^{ikz} = \sqrt{4\pi} \sum_l \sqrt{2l+1}\, i^l\, F_l(kr)\, Y_l(\cos\theta). \tag{5.6}$$

$F_l(kr)$ is a solution of the radial wave equation and has asymptotic value as $r \to \infty$ given by

$$\lim_{r\to\infty} F_l(kr) = \frac{1}{kr}\sin(kr - l\pi/2) = \frac{1}{kr}\frac{\exp[i(kr - \tfrac{1}{2}l\pi)] - \exp[-i(kr - \tfrac{1}{2}l\pi)]}{2i}.$$

Therefore, as $r \to \infty$,

$$e^{ikz} = \frac{\sqrt{\pi}}{kr}\sum_l \sqrt{2l+1}\, i^{l+1}\{\exp[-i(kr - \tfrac{1}{2}l\pi)] - \exp[i(kr - \tfrac{1}{2}l\pi)]\}\, Y_l(\cos\theta).$$

Thus we have two spherical waves, one travelling toward $r = 0$, the other travelling outward from the same point. The existence of the scattering potential at $r = 0$ will alter the outgoing wave; therefore at large distances

$$e^{ikz} + \frac{f(\theta)}{r}e^{ikr} = \frac{\sqrt{\pi}}{kr}\sum_l \sqrt{2l+1}\, i^{l+1}\{\exp[-i(kr - \tfrac{1}{2}l\pi)]$$
$$- S_l\exp[i(kr - \tfrac{1}{2}l\pi)]\}\, Y_l(\cos\theta), \tag{5.7}$$

where $S_l$ is a quantity which modifies the outgoing wave. Therefore

$$\frac{f(\theta)}{r}e^{ikr} = \frac{\sqrt{\pi}}{kr}\sum_l \sqrt{2l+1}\, i^{l+1}(1 - S_l)\exp[i(kr - \tfrac{1}{2}l\pi)]\, Y_l(\cos\theta),$$
$$= \frac{\sqrt{4\pi}}{kr}\sum_l \sqrt{2l+1}\,\frac{(S_l - 1)}{2i}e^{ikr}\, Y_l(\cos\theta). \tag{5.8}$$

Thus if we compare this with Eq. (3.9) we see that $S_l = \exp 2i\delta_l$ where $\delta_l$ is the phase shift for the $l$th partial wave.

We can now generalize this treatment to cases more complex than elastic scattering; it is possible to widen the use of $S$ to include all other reactions. We consider the interaction of two particles which form an intermediate system; this system can decompose into two bodies which are in one of the accessible final states. These states are designated by subscripts $\alpha, \beta, \gamma, \ldots$, etc. and are called channels. Each channel is described by the type, spins, and relative angular momentum of the two particles involved; it is not necessary to include energy as this is uniquely determined by the energy of the initial state. The intermediate state which disintegrates into these channels can obviously be formed via the same channels with appropriate energy in each channel. Thus all channels lead to or away from the same intermediate state, where the qualification "same" includes the energy of this state.

We now introduce a set of quantities such as $S_{\alpha\beta l}$ which will be related to the probability that a reaction initiated via channel $\alpha$, with relative orbital angular momentum $l$, will decay via channel $\beta$ with the same relative orbital momentum. We notice that at present we are restricting ourselves to situations in which the orbital angular momentum is conserved. This only happens when all particles present, before and after the reaction, have no intrinsic spin; the treatment for the case of particles with spin is too complicated for our present needs. The quantity $S_l$ used above in Eq. (5.7) is of the kind $S_{\alpha\alpha l}$. We now proceed to reformulate the partial wave analysis. However, we must exercise some care in the construction of wave functions. In the elastic scattering the incoming and outgoing waves have the same velocity, reduced mass, and wave number. This is not generally so for transitions from one channel to another and consequently a wave $e^{ikr}/r$ represents an outgoing stream of particles with a flux which depends on $k$; we shall be in trouble with conservation requirements unless this factor is corrected. Therefore all incoming waves are of the form

$$\frac{1}{v^{\frac{1}{2}}} \frac{e^{-ikr}}{r},$$

where $v = \hbar k/m$ is the channel velocity, $k$ is the channel wave number, and $m$ is the reduced mass in the channel. Outgoing waves are of the form

$$\frac{1}{v^{\frac{1}{2}}} \frac{e^{ikr}}{r}.$$

Subscripts will be added to $v$, $k$, and $m$ to indicate the channel. These two waves each represent a flux of one particle per second per steradian.

Suppose that the intermediate state is formed via channel $\alpha$, then the radial part of the asymptotic wave function is given by

$$\psi_l = \frac{\exp(-ik_\alpha r)}{v_\alpha^{\frac{1}{2}} r} - \sum_\beta \frac{S_{\alpha\beta l}\exp(ik_\beta r)}{v_\beta^{\frac{1}{2}} r}, \qquad (5.9)$$

where the relative orbital angular momentum is $l$.

The probability that the incoming flux of one particle per second per steradian induces a reaction into channel $\beta$ in one second per steradian is $|S_{\alpha\beta l}|^2$. To convert to cross sections we need to relate the incoming part of this wave function to the incoming part of the plane wave expansion. We multiply Eq. (5.9) by

$$\frac{\sqrt{\pi v_\alpha}}{k_\alpha} \sum_l \sqrt{2l+1}\, i^{l+1} \exp(il\pi/2)\, Y_l(\cos\theta)$$

and put the left-hand side equal to a new wave function

$$\Psi = \frac{\sqrt{\pi v_\alpha}}{k_\alpha r} \sum_l \sqrt{2l+1}\, i^{l+1} \left\{ \frac{\exp[-i(k_\alpha r - \frac{1}{2}l\pi)]}{v_\alpha^{\frac{1}{2}}} \right.$$
$$\left. - \sum_\beta S_{\alpha\beta l} \frac{\exp(il\pi)\exp[i(k_\beta r - \frac{1}{2}l\pi)]}{v_\beta^{\frac{1}{2}}} \right\} Y_l(\cos\theta). \qquad (5.10)$$

A careful comparison of this wave function with Eq. (5.7) shows that it represents an incident plane wave plus a scattered wave, plus outgoing reaction products. The incident plane wave has flux $v_\alpha$ particles per second per unit area; the outgoing wave in channel $\beta$ where $\beta \neq \alpha$ is

$$\frac{\sqrt{\pi v_\alpha}}{k_\alpha} \sum_l \sqrt{2l+1}\, i^{l+1} S_{\alpha\beta l} \frac{\exp[i(k_\beta r - \frac{1}{2}l\pi)]}{v_\beta^{\frac{1}{2}} r} Y_l(\cos\theta). \qquad (5.10a)$$

From our construction of wave functions we see that this represents an outgoing flux of particles

$$\frac{v_\alpha \pi}{k_\alpha^2} \left| \sum_l \sqrt{2l+1}\, S_{\alpha\beta l} Y_l(\cos\theta) \right|^2 \text{ particles sec}^{-1} \text{ sterad}^{-1}. \qquad (5.11)$$

Therefore the differential cross section is found by dividing by the incident velocity, $v_\alpha$,

$$\frac{d\sigma}{d\Omega}\bigg|_{\alpha\to\beta} = \frac{\pi}{k_\alpha^2} \left| \sum_l \sqrt{2l+1}\, S_{\alpha\beta l} Y_l(\cos\theta) \right|^2.$$

For elastic scattering it is necessary to subtract from $\Psi$ [Eq. (5.10)] the unaffected incident plane wave [Eq. (5.6)]. The result is that

$$\frac{d\sigma}{d\Omega}\bigg|_{\alpha\to\alpha} = \frac{\pi}{k_\alpha^2}\left|\sum_l \sqrt{2l+1}\,(S_{\alpha\alpha l}-1)\,Y_l(\cos\theta)\right|^2.$$

Comparing this equation with Eq. (3.9a), which gives the elastic scattering cross section in terms of partial waves, we find that $S_{\alpha\alpha l} = \exp 2i\delta_l$.

If there are $N$ channels leading to the compound state, then there are $N^2$ quantities like $S_{\alpha\beta l}$ or $2N^2$ real quantities. Taken together, the quantities $S_{\alpha\beta l}$ make up a matrix $S$ which is called the collision or scattering matrix—or simply the $S$-matrix.

We complete this section by a proof of the unitary property of the $S$-matrix. An examination of the $S$-matrix formalism will indicate that, if the intermediate state is formed through channel $\alpha$, where the incoming flux of particles is one per second, then the outgoing flux of particles in channel $\beta$ is $|S_{\alpha\beta}|^2$ particles per second (we have absorbed the specification $l$ into $\alpha$ and $\beta$). Since every intermediate state must disintegrate into one of the available channels, we must have

$$\sum_\beta |S_{\alpha\beta}|^2 = 1.$$

We now consider the same intermediate state being formed by a simultaneous flux of incoming particles in two channels $\alpha$ and $\alpha'$; the two incoming waves must be orthonormal:

$$(\psi_\alpha | \psi_{\alpha'}) = 0 \quad (\alpha \neq \alpha').$$

Each incoming wave gives rise to an outgoing wave in each accessible channel and these two sets of outgoing waves must also be orthonormal. Applying this requirement to the outgoing waves, we find that

$$\sum_\beta S_{\alpha\beta}^* S_{\alpha'\beta} = 0, \quad \alpha \neq \alpha'.$$

If we combine this with the first property that we proved, we find that

$$\sum_\beta S_{\alpha\beta}^* S_{\alpha'\beta} = \delta_{\alpha\alpha'}. \tag{5.12}$$

This is the property associated with the elements of a unitary matrix. To show this, we recall that a unitary matrix has (Section 1.2)

$$SS^\dagger = 1.$$

Writing this multiplication in full, we have

$$\sum_\lambda S_{\kappa\lambda}(S^\dagger)_{\lambda\mu} = \delta_{\kappa\mu}.$$

However, $(S^\dagger)_{\lambda\mu} = S^*_{\mu\lambda}$, and therefore

$$\sum_\lambda S_{\kappa\lambda} S^*_{\mu\lambda} = \delta_{\kappa\mu},$$

which is the same as Eq. (5.12). Therefore $S$ is unitary and there are $\frac{1}{2}N(N+1)$ restrictions upon the $2N^2$ real parameters contained in this $N \times N$ matrix.

## 5.5 Reciprocity

In this section we wish to investigate the relation between a reaction and its reverse. We shall do this through the formalism of the $S$-matrix. However, it is necessary to anticipate the material of Chapter X, which deals with the subject of time reversal. However, at this point we shall only state some results. Suppose we have a system represented by the wave function $\psi(\mathbf{x}, t)$ which is a solution of the Schrödinger equation

$$H\psi = i\hbar \frac{\partial \psi}{\partial t}.$$

Then if $H$, the Hamiltonian, is real, $\psi^*(\mathbf{x}, t)$ is a solution of the same equation and develops in the direction of reversed time in the same way as does $\psi(\mathbf{x}, t)$ in the direction of normal time. This statement requires some qualification if the system has spin or orbital angular momentum. In these cases it is necessary to reverse the direction of all the angular momentum vectors in making the time reversal transformation implied in changing $\psi(\mathbf{x}, t)$ to $\psi^*(\mathbf{x}, t)$.

We now return to the $S$-matrix and consider a system without angular momentum having an intermediate state generated via channel $\alpha$ and decaying via channel $\beta$. We represent incoming waves by $\psi_\alpha$. A wave of the phase and amplitude implied by $\psi_\alpha$ gives rise to an outgoing wave in channel $\beta$, having the phase and amplitude implied by the wave function $\psi_\beta^*$. The following equation defines this wave function:

$$\psi_\beta^* = -S_{\alpha\beta}\psi_\alpha. \tag{5.13}$$

If we multiply $\psi_\beta^*$ by $S^*_{\alpha'\beta}$ and sum over $\beta$, we have

$$-\sum_\beta S^*_{\alpha'\beta}\psi_\beta^* = \sum_\beta S^*_{\alpha'\beta}S_{\alpha\beta}\psi_\alpha = \delta_{\alpha'\alpha}\psi_\alpha,$$

hence

$$\psi_\alpha = -\sum_\beta S^*_{\alpha\beta}\psi_\beta^*$$

If we take the complex conjugate of this equation, we have

$$\psi_\alpha^* = -\sum_\beta S_{\alpha\beta}\psi_\beta. \tag{5.14}$$

This equation can be interpreted from our statements about time reversal. To a normal observer, $\psi_\alpha^*$ develops like an outgoing wave whilst $\psi_\beta$ develops like an incoming wave; thus Eq. (5.14) expresses a reaction initiated by waves in all channels but with phases and amplitudes such that the intermediate state decays into one channel only. This means that, with an incoming wave $\psi_\beta$ given by Eq. (5.13) in each respective channel, all the outgoing waves in each channel interfere destructively, except in channel $\alpha$. We can express this interference mathematically. The incoming wave in channel $\beta$ gives rise to an outgoing wave in channel $\gamma$ ($\gamma \neq \alpha$) of $-S_{\beta\gamma}\psi_\beta$; summed over all channels, the result is zero, thus:

$$\psi_\gamma^* = -\sum_\beta S_{\beta\gamma}\psi_\beta = 0.$$

Now the $\psi_\beta$ which must satisfy this requirement and also satisfy Eq. (5.14) are given by Eq. (5.13), that is

$$\psi_\beta = -S_{\alpha\beta}^*\psi_\alpha^*. \tag{5.15}$$

Therefore

$$\psi_\gamma^* = \sum_{\beta \neq \alpha} S_{\beta\gamma} S_{\alpha\beta}^*\psi_\alpha^* = 0, \tag{5.16}$$

or

$$\sum_{\beta \neq \alpha} S_{\alpha\beta}^* S_{\beta\gamma} = 0.$$

Combining this with Eq. (5.12), we have that

$$\sum_\beta S_{\alpha\beta}^* S_{\beta\gamma} = \delta_{\alpha\gamma}. \tag{5.17}$$

If the quantities $S_{\kappa\lambda}$ are the elements of a matrix $S$, this equation implies

$$S^*S = 1. \tag{5.18}$$

But we have already shown in Eq. (5.12) that

$$SS^\dagger = 1.$$

Transposing Eq. (5.18), we have

$$\tilde{S}S^\dagger = 1,$$

hence

$$\tilde{S} = S,$$

or

$$S_{\alpha\beta} = S_{\beta\alpha}, \tag{5.19}$$

for all subscripts $\alpha$ and $\beta$.

Equation (5.19) states that the reaction from channel $\alpha$ to channel $\beta$ is reversible and thus the reaction and its reverse proceed with the same $S$-matrix element. However, we have restricted ourselves to systems without angular momentum. If this is not the case, then the reversed reaction only proceeds with the same $S$-matrix element if all the angular momentum vectors are reversed in direction, that is, $j_z \to -j_z$, $s_z \to -s_z$, and $l_z \to -l_z$. We can represent any channel $\alpha$ in the reversed state by the subscript $-\alpha$; then

$$S_{\alpha\beta} = S_{-\beta-\alpha}. \qquad (5.20)$$

This is the Law of Reciprocity.

If the system is in an external field such as $\mathbf{H}$, then reciprocity no longer holds, since quantities like $\boldsymbol{\sigma} \cdot \mathbf{H}$ and $\mathbf{L} \cdot \mathbf{H}$, which are likely to occur in the Hamiltonian, change sign under the time reversal transformation and prevent the Hamiltonian from being invariant, a necessary condition in the above proof. (We ensured that the Hamiltonian was invariant by stating that it was a real quantity.)

We must consider carefully what is meant by the reversed reaction in the sense of the reciprocity law that we have just introduced. We consider the reaction

$$a + b \to c + d.$$

The channels involved are labelled $\alpha$ for the initial state of particles $a$ and $b$ and $\beta$ for the final state of particles $c$ and $d$. The spins and momenta of all particles are specified completely by these labels; thus channel $\alpha$ has momenta and spins $(\mathbf{p}_a, \mathbf{p}_b, \mathbf{s}_a, \mathbf{s}_b)$ and channel $\beta$ has $(\mathbf{p}_c, \mathbf{p}_d, \mathbf{s}_c, \mathbf{s}_d)$. Let us call the reaction which proceeds from channel $\alpha$ to channel $\beta$ the "forward reaction" and write it in a form which shows all particle states, $viz.$,

$$\text{forward reaction (I): } (\mathbf{p}_a, \mathbf{p}_b, \mathbf{s}_a, \mathbf{s}_b) \to (\mathbf{p}_c, \mathbf{p}_d, \mathbf{s}_c, \mathbf{s}_d).$$

The channels which have labels $-\alpha$ and $-\beta$ are the channels $\alpha$ and $\beta$ respectively with all linear and angular momenta reversed. The reaction which proceeds from channel $-\beta$ to channel $-\alpha$ is the time-reversed edition of the direct reaction, and we call this the "time-reversed reaction". In our convention we have

$$\text{time-reversed reaction (II): }$$
$$(-\mathbf{p}_c, -\mathbf{p}_d, -\mathbf{s}_c, -\mathbf{s}_d) \to (-\mathbf{p}_a, -\mathbf{p}_b, -\mathbf{s}_c, -\mathbf{s}_d).$$

The Law of Reciprocity connects the transition rates for two reactions related in this time-reversed manner. A consequence of reciprocity is that the complete matrix elements for the two reactions are equal; we shall now prove this for reactions in the absence of spin. We shall use a quantity which is the amplitude of the outgoing wave $A\,e^{ikr}/v^{\frac{1}{2}}r$; by our definitions in Section 5.4 this represents a flux of $|A|^2$ particles per second per steradian. For the direct reaction $\alpha \to \beta$ the outgoing wave amplitude $A_{\alpha\beta}$ in direction $\theta$ is given by Eq. (5.10a), thus:

$$A_{\alpha\beta} = \frac{\sqrt{v_\alpha}\,\pi}{k_\alpha} \sum_l \sqrt{2l+1}\, i^{l+1} S_{\alpha\beta l} \exp\left(-il\pi/2\right) Y_l(\cos\theta). \qquad (5.21)$$

This equation applies in the centre of mass for our reactions. It follows that the angle $\theta$ is the same for the forward- and time-reversed reaction if it is always defined by the directions of the same two particles. Thus the amplitude for the time-reversed reaction is given by

$$A_{-\beta-\alpha} = \frac{\sqrt{v_\beta}\,\pi}{k_\beta} \sum_l \sqrt{2l+1}\, i^{l+1} S_{\alpha\beta l} \exp\left(-il\pi/2\right) Y_l(\cos\theta), \qquad (5.22)$$

where we have put $S_{-\beta-\alpha l} = S_{\alpha\beta l}$. From Eqs. (5.21) and (5.22) we find

$$\frac{k_\alpha}{v_\alpha^{\frac{1}{2}}} A_{\alpha\beta} = \frac{k_\beta}{v_\beta^{\frac{1}{2}}} A_{-\beta-\alpha}. \qquad (5.23)$$

We write the matrix element for the direct reaction $M_{\alpha\beta}$ and for the reversed reaction $M_{-\beta-\alpha}$. These matrix elements are functions of $\theta$. The differential cross section for the direct reaction to occur in direction is therefore

$$\frac{d\sigma}{d\Omega}\Big|_{\alpha\to\beta} = \frac{2\pi}{\hbar} \frac{1}{v_\alpha} |M_{\alpha\beta}|^2 \frac{d^2 N}{d\Omega\,dE},$$

the density of states $d^2 N/d\Omega\,dE = m_\beta k_\beta \hbar/(2\pi\hbar)^3$ where $m_\beta$ and $k_\beta$ are the reduced mass and wave number in the outgoing channel. Now we have

$$\frac{d\sigma}{d\Omega}\Big|_{\alpha\to\beta} = \frac{1}{v_\alpha} |A_{\alpha\beta}|^2,$$

and hence

$$\frac{k_\alpha}{v_\beta^{\frac{1}{2}}} |A_{\alpha\beta}| = (m_\alpha m_\beta k_\alpha k_\beta)^{\frac{1}{2}} \frac{2\pi}{(2\pi\hbar)^3} |M_{\alpha\beta}|.$$

Similarly, considering the time-reversed reaction

$$\frac{k_\beta}{v_\beta^{\frac{1}{2}}} |A_{-\beta,-\alpha}| = (m_\alpha m_\beta k_\alpha k_\beta)^{\frac{1}{2}} \frac{2\pi}{(2\pi\hbar)^3} |M_{-\beta-\alpha}|.$$

From Eq. (5.23) it follows that

$$|M_{\alpha\beta}|^2 = |M_{-\beta-\alpha}|^2. \tag{5.24}$$

This equality of the magnitude of the matrix elements has been proved for the centre of mass for the two reactions. Although the matrix element is not invariant, an equality holds in any inertial frame from which the two reactions are observed.

## 5.6 Principle of Detailed Balance

We will now consider a relation of less generality but of greater use than reciprocity. We proceed by considering the same forward reaction proceeding from channel $\alpha$ to channel $\beta$: let the initial and final states be $\psi_\alpha$ and $\psi_\beta$ respectively. If $H_I$ is the interaction Hamiltonian, the matrix element $T_{\alpha\beta}$ in first-order perturbation theory for the forward reaction is given by

$$T_{\alpha\beta} = (\psi_\beta | H_I | \psi_\alpha).$$

Now $H_I$ is an Hermitian operator so that

$$T_{\beta\alpha} = (\psi_\beta | H_I | \psi_\alpha) = T_{\alpha\beta}. \tag{5.25}$$

This is not a connection between the forward reaction and its time reverse. This equality actual connects transition rates for the two reactions:

$$\text{I}: (\mathbf{p}_a, \mathbf{p}_b, \mathbf{s}_a, \mathbf{s}_b) \rightarrow (\mathbf{p}_c, \mathbf{p}_d, \mathbf{s}_c, \mathbf{s}_d);$$

$$\text{III}: (\mathbf{p}_c, \mathbf{p}_d, \mathbf{s}_c, \mathbf{s}_d) \rightarrow (\mathbf{p}_a, \mathbf{p}_b, \mathbf{s}_a, \mathbf{s}_b).$$

We shall call the last reaction the "complementary reaction" in contrast to the first which is the forward reaction. The equality of their matrix elements implied by Eq. (5.25) is called the "principle of detailed balance". The principle is only correct in so far as first-order perturbation theory is correct.

In Fig. 5.1 we have illustrated the course of events in the forward, time-reversed, and complementary reactions. In this figure each of the particles $a$, $b$, $c$, and $d$ are represented by heavy dots and their direction of motion by arrows. The particle spins are indicated by small labelled arrows placed close to the appropriate dot; these spins have been chosen arbitrarily so as to illustrate the relation between the three reactions, and for convenience the spin vectors are parallel to the particle momentum.

The interaction which is responsible for the reaction will, in general, be invariant under the parity transformation (parity conservation), and this means that the matrix element for a reaction is the same as that for the reaction which is its mirror image. We can therefore construct reaction IV, which is the "parity transform of the time-reversed reaction" and by reciprocity and by invariance under the

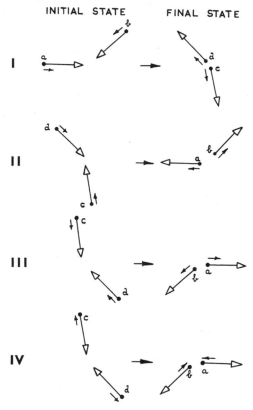

FIG. 5.1. Diagrams illustrating the course of events in the four reactions discussed in the text. The large arrows indicate the momenta and the small arrows the spins of the particles involved. The arrows between initial and final state indicate the reaction direction. I, the forward reaction. II, the time-reversed reaction. III, the complementary reaction. IV, the parity transform of the time-reversed reaction.

parity transformation we have that the matrix elements for reactions I, II, and IV are all identical. Reaction IV is shown in Fig. 5.1 and is obtained by taking a mirror image of reaction II and rotating the image 180° around an axis perpendicular to the mirror: this procedure reverses all linear momenta (vectors) and leaves unchanged all angular and spin momenta (pseudovectors):

Reaction IV: $(\mathbf{p}_c, \mathbf{p}_d, -\mathbf{s}_c, -\mathbf{s}_d) \to (\mathbf{p}_a, \mathbf{p}_b, -\mathbf{s}_a, -\mathbf{s}_b)$.

An examination of reactions III and IV shows that they are the same apart from spin orientations and we conclude that in the absence of spin all four matrix elements are identical. Hence detailed balance is correct under all circumstances in which spin is absent and parity is conserved; this is our first conclusion about detailed balancing.

We are not normally in a position to specify precisely the spins of the particles involved in a nuclear reaction and for unpolarized beams and targets all possible spin orientations will occur with equal probability in the initial state; thus the total reaction probability $\omega$ will be proportional to the sum over all initial and final spin states of the squared matrix elements

$$\omega \propto \sum_{\substack{\text{initial} \\ \text{spins}}} \sum_{\substack{\text{final} \\ \text{spins}}} |M_{\alpha\beta}|^2.$$

We now make such a sum of the reactions III and IV; since we cover all possible spin orientation, we find that for each term of the sum for one reaction there is the identical term in the sum for the other reaction. Hence

$$\Sigma\Sigma |M_{\text{III}}|^2 = \Sigma\Sigma |M_{\text{IV}}|^2.$$

By reciprocity and parity conservation we must have

$$\Sigma\Sigma |M_{\text{I}}|^2 = \Sigma\Sigma |M_{\text{IV}}|^2,$$

hence

$$\Sigma\Sigma |M_{\text{III}}|^2 = \Sigma\Sigma |M_{\text{I}}|^2. \tag{5.26}$$

Equation (5.26) tells us that the principle of detailed balance is correct if we sum over all initial and final spin states. This is our second conclusion about detailed balancing.

The sums over spins in Eq. (5.26) are directly related to the mean of the squares of the matrix elements of Eq. (5.4). Since the spin degeneracies of channels $\alpha$ and $\beta$ are independent of the direction of the reaction, we deduce that this mean is independent of the direction. In these circumstances we can compare the rate of a reaction and its reverse by using Eqs. (5.2) and (5.3) provided that we include the final state spin degeneracy in counting the density of final states. The comparison provides an exact relation between cross sections for reactions in which the initial state particles are unpolarized and in which no attempt is made to distinguish between final states of different polarization.

At this point we must cover some points not previously discussed. Firstly, we examine in the Fig. 5.1 the parity transformation which we employed to change reaction II into reaction IV in order to compare the former with reaction III. In the figure it appears that reaction II is just reaction III rotated through 180° and that it is unnecessary to make any comparison via reaction IV; however, this is not correct and the fault lies in the interpretation of the two-dimensional diagram. If any spin in the forward reaction has a component along a direction perpendicular to the plane of figures, the derived reactions II and III are not related by a simple rotation and it is necessary to make the comparison via reaction IV. This discussion indicates a further conclusion which can be drawn; namely, if all the particle spin vectors lie in the plane of the reaction then detailed balancing is correct. This follows from the fact that under such circumstances reactions II and III are related by a simple rotation. The conclusion is independent of the invariance, or otherwise, of the interaction under the parity transformation. In fact, it is impossible to produce a spin state which has the spin vector confined along a given direction or in a given plane; the correct statement is that detailed balance holds if all the polarization vectors lie in the plane of the reaction (Chapter VIII). This will occur only in the very rare scattering reactions involving weak interactions alone (Chapter XI).

We can now derive the formula which is used in the application of detailed balance. We work entirely in the centre-of-mass coordinates for the two-body reactions

$$a + b \rightleftharpoons c + d.$$

These two reactions are to be compared at the same total centre-of-mass energy and in circumstances for which detailed balance is correct. The reaction cross sections are proportional to:

$$\frac{\text{density of final states} \times \text{spin degeneracy in final state}}{\text{relative velocity in initial state}}$$

The constants of proportionality are the same for both reactions under the detailed balancing conditions.

Let the momentum of the particles in the left-hand state be $\mathbf{p}$ and in the right-hand state $\mathbf{p}'$. The masses of the particles are $m_a$, $m_b$, $m_c$, and $m_d$, respectively. The spins are $s_a, s_b, s_c, s_d$, in units of $\hbar$. We proceed relativistically.

For the forward reaction ($\rightarrow$) the density of states is given by

$$\frac{d}{dE} 4\pi p'^3 = \frac{4\pi p'^2}{\dfrac{p'}{\epsilon_c} + \dfrac{p'}{\epsilon_d}},$$

where $E$ is the total energy in the centre of mass and $\epsilon$ is the total energy of a particle, also in the centre of mass. The relative velocity in the initial state is

$$\left(\frac{p}{\epsilon_a} + \frac{p}{\epsilon_b}\right)$$

and the spin degeneracy in the final state is $(2s_c + 1)(2s_d + 1)$. Therefore

$$\sigma(\rightarrow) \propto \frac{4\pi p'^2 (2s_c + 1)(2s_d + 1)}{\left(\dfrac{p}{\epsilon_a} + \dfrac{p}{\epsilon_b}\right)\left(\dfrac{p'}{\epsilon_c} + \dfrac{p'}{\epsilon_d}\right)}.$$

The complementary or the time-reversed reaction has a cross section given by

$$\sigma(\leftarrow) \propto \frac{4\pi p^2 (2s_a + 1)(2s_b + 1)}{\left(\dfrac{p}{\epsilon_a} + \dfrac{p}{\epsilon_b}\right)\left(\dfrac{p'}{\epsilon_c} + \dfrac{p'}{\epsilon_d}\right)},$$

hence

$$\sigma(\rightarrow) = \left(\frac{p'}{p}\right)^2 \frac{(2s_c + 1)(2s_d + 1)}{(2s_a + 1)(2s_b + 1)} \sigma(\leftarrow). \tag{5.27}$$

The differential cross sections may be related in the same manner provided, of course, the cross sections apply to the same centre-of-mass angle. In Eq. (5.27) a cross section $\sigma$ is replaced by $d\sigma/d\Omega$.

We must exercise care if the particles on one side of the reaction are identical. The requirements of symmetry (Section 6.2) halve the number of states available in the final state of identical particles and the spin degeneracy is reduced from $(2s+1)^2$ to $\frac{1}{2}(2s+1)^2$. If we are comparing the differential cross sections, the detector will record particles from two reaction angles for which the cross sections must be equal, hence the factor of $\frac{1}{2}$ is cancelled and the differential form of Eq. (5.27) is correct. On integrating to obtain the total cross sections we must take care not to count the identical particles twice and the result is that the reduced spin degeneracy appears in Eq. (5.27). Readers interested in an immediate application of detailed balance are referred to Section 7.3.

## 5.7 Conclusion

This chapter has covered some of the more elementary aspects of transitions and reactions, but for a more comprehensive treatment readers are referred to other works; for example, to Blatt and Weisskopf (1952) for a general and particular treatment of the theory of nuclear reactions and transitions, to Blatt and Biedenharn (1952a) for a review of $S$-matrix theory, including spin. Fermi (1951) has given some elementary applications of the transition rate formula which are very enlightening to the uninitiated.

# CHAPTER VI

# SYMMETRY AND ISOTOPIC SPIN

## 6.1 Introduction

In this chapter we shall be concerned with preparations for the construction of wave functions which we shall use when examining various phenomena. We shall first deal with the restrictions imposed by the requirement that wave functions have a certain symmetry property under the transformation which interchanges identical particles. Secondly, we shall introduce the concept of isotopic spin and postulate the invariance of physical processes under rotations in isotopic spin space; this leads to a further conservation law and makes it necessary to construct isotopic spin wave functions. We apply these concepts to the two-nucleon system and briefly indicate how a phase shift analysis of nucleon–nucleon scattering proceeds.

## 6.2 Symmetry and Antisymmetry

We have already discussed the concept of particle spin; such intrinsic angular momentum associated with a free particle was discovered for the electron by Goudsmidt and Uhlenbeck during their investigations on atomic energy levels and on the removal of level degeneracies by an applied magnetic field—the Zeeman effect. This discovery was applied, in conjunction with Bohr theory of atomic structure, to explaining atomic structure and the periodic table. To do this satisfactorily it was necessary to postulate an exclusion principle, due to Pauli, which states that no electron state may be occupied by more than one electron. The description of the state includes a spin quantum number and thus each orbital state can be occupied by two electrons which will have oppositely aligned spin angular momentum vectors. This exclusion principle has its origins in more fundamental field theory. Pauli was able to show that basic physical inconsistencies would occur unless the field operators satisfied various commutation or anticommutation laws. In the case of particles having a spin which was an odd number of units of $\hbar/2$, the rules lead immediately to the exclusion principle; such particles include electrons and nucleons and they are given the generic name "Fermi–Dirac" particles or "fermions", since they must obey the Fermi–Dirac statistics. In the case of particles having a spin which is zero or an even number of units of $\hbar/2$, the necessary commutation rules do not lead to an exclusion principle and the particles obey the Bose–Einstein statistics; they are called "Bose–Einstein" particles or "bosons". Among the bosons are photons and the pi-mesons.

We now wish to see how these properties effect systems consisting of several identical fermions or bosons; however, we cannot work from the commutation rules mentioned at our present level and instead we shall proceed in a simple physically obvious manner (see, however, Section 9.6).

Let a system containing $n$ identical particles having labels $a, b, c, \ldots, r$ be described by a wave function

$$\psi(\mathbf{x}_1, \mathbf{x}_2, \ldots, \mathbf{x}_n).$$

We interpret this function in the following way. The quantity $Q$ is defined thus:

$$Q = \psi^*(\mathbf{x}_1, \mathbf{x}_2, \ldots, \mathbf{x}_n)\,\psi(\mathbf{x}_1, \mathbf{x}_2, \ldots, \mathbf{x}_n)\,d\mathbf{x}_1\,d\mathbf{x}_2 \ldots d\mathbf{x}_n.$$

$Q$ is expected to be the probability of simultaneously finding particle label $a$ in volume element $d\mathbf{x}_1$, particle $b$ in $d\mathbf{x}_2$, and so on. $Q$ should not be different if we interchange any two identical particles; e.g.,

$$|\psi(\mathbf{x}_1, \mathbf{x}_2, \mathbf{x}_3, \ldots, \mathbf{x}_n)|^2 = |\psi(\mathbf{x}_2, \mathbf{x}_1, \mathbf{x}_3, \ldots, \mathbf{x}_n)|^2. \tag{6.1}$$

Thus

$$\psi(\mathbf{x}_1, \mathbf{x}_2, \mathbf{x}_3, \ldots, \mathbf{x}_n) = \pm\, e^{i\delta}\, \psi(\mathbf{x}_2, \mathbf{x}_1, \mathbf{x}_3, \ldots, \mathbf{x}_n). \tag{6.2}$$

The phase factor is not physically observable and is put equal to unity. If the sign is positive, the wave function is said to be symmetric; if it is negative, antisymmetric.

If we now assume that there is no interaction between the particles, we can decompose the wave function into individual particle wave functions

$$\psi(\mathbf{x}_1, \mathbf{x}_2, \ldots, \mathbf{x}_n) = \psi_a(\mathbf{x}_1)\,\psi_b(\mathbf{x}_2) \ldots \psi_r(\mathbf{x}_n). \tag{6.3}$$

This decomposition does not satisfy Eq. (6.1) which it must do if the particles are identical. To satisfy (6.1) we express $\psi$ of the left-hand side of Eq. (6.3) as a linear superposition of separated wave functions $\phi_j$, each $\phi$ differing from all the others by permutation of the particles among the states

$$\psi = \sum_j a_j \phi_j, \quad \text{where} \quad \sum_j |a_j|^2 = 1. \tag{6.4}$$

Each $\phi_j$ represents one of the $n!$ ways of distributing $n$ particles among $n$ states. If we now define an operator $P$ which interchanges any two particles, we have by (6.1)

$$|P\psi|^2 = |\psi|^2. \tag{6.5}$$

This requirement applied to Eq. (6.4) immediately restricts the coefficients $a_j$, and in fact only two expansions are physically possible,

$$\psi_s = \frac{1}{\sqrt{n!}} \sum_j \phi_j,$$

$$\psi_a = \frac{1}{\sqrt{n!}} \sum (-1)^{p_j} \phi_j.$$

Here $p_j$ represents the number of particle interchanges required to generate $\phi_j$ from $\phi_1$; $\psi_s$ and $\psi_a$ are the symmetric and antisymmetric wave functions respectively, and have the property

$$P\psi_s = \psi_s,$$

$$P\psi_a = -\psi_a.$$

The expansion for $\psi_a$ can be put into determinant form:

$$\psi_a = \begin{vmatrix} \psi_a(\mathbf{x}_1) & \psi_a(\mathbf{x}_2) & \cdots & \psi_a(\mathbf{x}_n) \\ \psi_b(\mathbf{x}_1) & \cdots & & \\ \vdots & & & \\ \psi_r(\mathbf{x}_1) & \cdots & & \end{vmatrix}.$$

If any two particle states are the same the determinant vanishes. It follows that, if the total wave function is antisymmetric, it is impossible for two particles to occupy the same state; this is essentially the exclusion principle for identical fermions. An assembly of bosons will have a total wave function which is symmetric but there will be no restrictions on the occupation of states.

The above expansions were made assuming no interaction amongst the identical particles; this is rarely the case, but the symmetry requirements and exclusion effects continue to apply.

## 6.3 Nucleon Wave Functions

In this section we shall describe the construction of wave functions applicable to two identical fermions. For simplicity we can consider two protons, which are fermions with spin $\hbar/2$; they must therefore have an antisymmetric total wave function. We have previously used orbital and spin wave functions in conjunction to describe completely the state of a particle; for example, Eq. (3.9). We can construct a similar wave function $\phi$ to describe the two protons. This total wave function is the product of the orbital wave function $\psi$ and the spin wave function $\chi$

$$\phi = \psi\chi.$$

The $\phi$ must be antisymmetric under the interchange of the two protons; thus if $\psi$ is symmetric, then $\chi$ must be antisymmetric and vice versa. Let us construct the physically possible spin wave functions:

$$\chi(1, 1) = \chi_a(\tfrac{1}{2}, \tfrac{1}{2})\,\chi_b(\tfrac{1}{2}, \tfrac{1}{2}), \tag{6.6}$$

$$\chi(1, 0) = \frac{1}{\sqrt{2}}\{\chi_a(\tfrac{1}{2}, \tfrac{1}{2})\,\chi_b(\tfrac{1}{2}, -\tfrac{1}{2}) + \chi_a(\tfrac{1}{2}, -\tfrac{1}{2})\,\chi_b(\tfrac{1}{2}, \tfrac{1}{2})\}, \tag{6.7}$$

$$\chi(1, -1) = \chi_a(\tfrac{1}{2}, -\tfrac{1}{2})\,\chi_b(\tfrac{1}{2}, -\tfrac{1}{2}), \tag{6.8}$$

$$\chi(0, 0) = \frac{1}{\sqrt{2}}\{\chi_a(\tfrac{1}{2}, \tfrac{1}{2})\,\chi_b(\tfrac{1}{2}, -\tfrac{1}{2}) - \chi_a(\tfrac{1}{2}, -\tfrac{1}{2})\,\chi_b(\tfrac{1}{2}, \tfrac{1}{2})\}. \tag{6.9}$$

The notation on the right is such that the wave-function parenthesis contains the quantum numbers associated with the operators $S^2$ and $S_z$ for the particle whose letter label lies in the subscript. The notation on the left will be clarified shortly. These four functions satisfy Eq. (6.5); functions (6.6) to (6.8) are symmetric and (6.9) is antisymmetric. If we apply our knowledge of angular momentum we discover that the quantum numbers of the eigenvalues of the total spin operator $S^2$ are $1, 1, 1, 0$, respectively; i.e., these are the values of $s$ when the actual eigenvalue is $s(s+1)\hbar^2$, and the eigenvalue quantum numbers of $S_z$ are $1, 0, -1, 0$, respectively. This explains the figures in parentheses on the left of these equations: $\chi(s, s_z)$. The wave functions of (6.6) to (6.8) are the three functions describing the three "triplet" spin states which have $s = 1$; function (6.9) is the wave function describing the "singlet" spin state which has $s = 0$. Returning to the business of symmetry, we observe that, in order to maintain over-all antisymmetry if the protons are in the singlet spin state, they must be in a symmetric orbital state, whereas if they are in a triplet spin state their orbital state must be antisymmetric.

We now examine the symmetry of the orbital states. The orbital wave function can be decomposed into a partial wave series, each wave having a symmetric radial function multiplied by a spherical harmonic and the symmetry of the partial wave being that of the spherical harmonics. Let us consider the angular part of the $l$th partial wave

$$Y(l, m) \propto e^{\pm im\phi} \sin^m \theta \left(\frac{d}{d \cos \theta}\right)^m P_l(\cos \theta).$$

The transformation which interchanges the particles is that which reverses the direction of the vector which joins them. Under this change the polar coordinates of the vector change $\theta \to \pi - \theta$ and $\phi \to \phi - \pi$. Then we have

$$P Y(l, m) \propto e^{\pm im\phi} \sin^m \theta \left(\frac{d}{d \cos \theta}\right)^m P_l[\cos (\pi - \theta)].$$

$P_l(\cos \theta)$ only contains terms $\cos^l \theta$, $\cos^{l-2} \theta$, ..., etc., so that this transformation is such that $P_l[\cos (\pi - \theta)] = (-1)^l P_l(\cos \theta)$ and therefore

$$P Y(l, m) = (-1)^l Y(l, m).$$

Therefore, the $l$th partial wave is symmetric if $l$ is even and is antisymmetric if $l$ is odd.

The final effect on the two-proton system can now be stated. If the two protons are in the singlet spin state, then their orbital wave function can only contain partial waves with $l$ even—that is, in spectroscopic notation, the $^1S$, $^1D$, $^1G$, etc., states; the superscript 1 indicates the total spin degeneracy, which is one in these singlet spin states. On the other hand, if the two protons are in the triplet spin state, only partial waves with $l$ odd are allowed; these states are: $^3P$, $^3F$, ..., etc. Again, the superscript indicates the spin degeneracy, triplet in this case. Thus any two-proton state can only be a linear superposition of the series of states which commences

$$^1S, \ ^3P, \ ^1D, \ ^3F, \ ^1G, \ ^3H, \ \ldots, \text{etc.}$$

The case of two neutrons is exactly the same; the case of a neutron and proton is different in that the particles are different and there are no symmetry requirements; thus, the $np$ system can be a linear superposition of the series of states

$$^1S, \ ^3S, \ ^1P, \ ^3P, \ ^1D, \ ^3D, \ ^1F, \ ^3F, \ ^1G, \ ^3G., \ \ldots, \text{etc.}$$

The vector addition of the total spin angular momentum with orbital angular momentum to find the total angular momentum and the eigenfunctions present can be done by the means described in Chapter III.

Thus the $^3P$ state can have $j = 2, 1, 0$, and this state is therefore a linear superposition of the three corresponding eigenfunctions. The $^1P$ state can have $j = 1$ only.

The case of more than two identical fermions becomes more complicated but is still governed by the total antisymmetry requirement under the exchange of any two particles.

We have not considered the case of two identical bosons. An example occurs in the decay of one of the heavier mesons where it is necessary to construct the wave function for two neutral pi-mesons; they have no spin so the symmetry requirement restricts their state of relative motion to one containing only partial waves with even $l$ (Section 12.8).

## 6.4 Isotopic Spin

We are now in a position to consider a concept which simplifies further the construction of nucleon–nucleon wave functions. An examination of the energy levels of mirror nuclei, e.g., $C^{13}$ and $N^{13}$, indicated similarities which could be explained by assuming that the force between two neutrons is identical to that between two protons if the Coulomb force is neglected; this is the postulate of charge symmetry. An extension of this, the postulate of charge independence, states that the force between any two nucleons depends only on their state of spin and relative orbital angular momentum. Thus the force between two protons in the $^1S$ state is expected to be identical, apart from Coulomb forces, to that between a neutron and proton or to that between two neutrons in the same state. The first equality is found to be true from an analysis of low-energy $p$–$p$ and $n$–$p$ scattering measurements. The consequences of charge independence include all the consequences of charge symmetry and others not given by that postulate.

The postulate of charge symmetry appears to be well supported by experimental evidence, whilst charge independence, although well supported, lacks verification for very energetic particle interactions. We shall now introduce the formalism which describes the significance of this postulate.

A neutron and a proton are supposed to be two manifestations of the same particle—a nucleon. The nondegeneracy which makes them different particles is assumed to disappear if we switch off the Coulomb field. Since the nondegeneracy is a doublet, the ordinary spin properties suggest that the two states of the doublet correspond to the two different orientations of an "isotopic" spin vector of value $\frac{1}{2}$. The space in which this orientation is described is not physically realizable but is called "isotopic spin space". In direct analogy with ordinary spin, we construct three operators $N_1, N_2, N_3$ corresponding to $S_x, S_y, S_z$;

also operators $\mathbf{N}$ and $N^2$ corresponding to $\mathbf{S}$ and $S^2$. A pure spin state is usually specified by the quantum number associated with the operators $S^2$ and $S_z$, and this convention is followed for isotopic spin space so that a pure isotopic spin state is specified by the quantum numbers $n, n_3$ associated with the operators $N^2$ and $N_3$. Thus nucleons have $n_3 = +\frac{1}{2}$, or $n_3 = -\frac{1}{2}$, according as to whether the nucleon is a proton or neutron. The charge is an eigenvalue of the operator $e(N_3 + \frac{1}{2})$. In all this we no longer have the $\hbar$ which occurs in angular momentum eigenequations.

The operators $N^2$, $\mathbf{N}$, $N_1$, $N_2$, and $N_3$ satisfy the same commutation relations as do the corresponding angular momentum operators; thus the analogy between spin and isotopic spin is very close and the isotopic spin operators can be manipulated in the same way as spin operators. For example, two isotopic spin vectors can be added in the same way as two angular momentum vectors. To illustrate this and to continue the matter of the last section, we consider the case of two nucleons. We can write down combinations of the individual isotopic spin wave functions to give the total isotopic spin function. These total wave functions must satisfy Eq. (6.5) and must be eigenfunctions of $T^2$ and $T_3$ which are total isotopic spin operators; by complete analogy with Eqs. (6.6) to (6.9), we have that

$$\tau(1, 1) = \nu_a(\tfrac{1}{2}, \tfrac{1}{2})\, \nu_b(\tfrac{1}{2}, \tfrac{1}{2}), \tag{6.10}$$

$$\tau(1, 0) = \frac{1}{\sqrt{2}} \{\nu_a(\tfrac{1}{2}, \tfrac{1}{2})\, \nu_b(\tfrac{1}{2}, -\tfrac{1}{2}) + \nu_a(\tfrac{1}{2}, -\tfrac{1}{2})\, \nu_b(\tfrac{1}{2}, \tfrac{1}{2})\}, \tag{6.11}$$

$$\tau(1, -1) = \nu_a(\tfrac{1}{2}, -\tfrac{1}{2})\, \nu_b(\tfrac{1}{2}, -\tfrac{1}{2}), \tag{6.12}$$

$$\tau(0, 0) = \frac{1}{\sqrt{2}} \{\nu_a(\tfrac{1}{2}, \tfrac{1}{2})\, \nu_b(\tfrac{1}{2}, -\tfrac{1}{2}) - \nu_a(\tfrac{1}{2}, -\tfrac{1}{2})\, \nu_b(\tfrac{1}{2}, \tfrac{1}{2})\}. \tag{6.13}$$

The notation on the right is such that the quantities in the parenthesis of a function give the quantum number associated with the operators $N^2$ and $N_3$ for the particle labelled by the letter in the subscript. The notation on the left is such that the numbers in the parenthesis are the quantum numbers of the eigenvalues of the total isotopic spin operators $T^2$ and $T_3$. Those with $t = 1$ are symmetric and belong to the triplet isotopic spin state; that with $t = 0$ is antisymmetric and belongs to the singlet isotopic spin state.

We must relate this description of two nucleons to physical situations. Two protons have individual isotopic spin wave functions $\nu_a(\frac{1}{2}, \frac{1}{2})$ and $\nu_b(\frac{1}{2}, \frac{1}{2})$; thus their total isotopic spin function is $\tau(1, 1)$. Similarly, two neutrons have $\tau(1, -1)$. A proton and a neutron do not make a state which is an eigenfunction of $T^2$ and $T_3$. Actually such a pair of nucleons has an isotopic spin state which is a superposition of the two eigenstates $\tau(1, 0)$ and $\tau(0, 0)$. Thus

$$\nu_a(\tfrac{1}{2}, \tfrac{1}{2})\,\nu_b(\tfrac{1}{2}, -\tfrac{1}{2}) = \frac{1}{\sqrt{2}}\{\tau(1, 1) + \tau(0, 0)\}.$$

This arises from solving Eqs. (6.11) and (6.13) and is equivalent to the procedure of vector addition of angular momentum.

If we now construct the total wave function for the two nucleons in terms of space, spin, and isotopic spin functions, we have

$$\Psi = \psi\chi\tau.$$

Since the nucleons are fermions, this complete wave function must be antisymmetric under exchange of the two nucleons. We have already shown how this is done in the case of two protons or two neutrons; for these cases $\psi\chi$ is antisymmetric. When we add the isotopic spin function, the symmetry must not change and we are therefore restricted to symmetric isotopic spin functions. Thus for the proton pair the function is given by Eq. (6.10), and for the neutron pair the function is that of Eq. (6.12). If the system is a neutron and proton with antisymmetric space-spin functions, then the $\tau$ function is again symmetric and it can only be that given by Eq. (6.11). We now notice that the antisymmetric space-spin functions for two nucleons go with isotopic spin functions having total isotopic spin of one. Finally, if the neutron–proton system is in a symmetric space-spin state, then the isotopic spin function must be antisymmetric. This requirement is fulfilled by the function of Eq. (6.13), which has zero total isotopic spin.

So far we have added nothing to our description of the forces between nucleons as these are already completely specified by the spin and orbital momentum states and do not require any further parameters. However, we notice that charge independence implies that, for a given orbital momentum, the force between two nucleons depends on the total isotopic spin, not upon their charge states. In addition we now have a uniformly antisymmetric description of two nucleon states and a formalism which will permit a simple description of some postulated nucleon–nucleon forces and an important extension of charge independence.

We will now show that the postulate of charge independence implies that the interaction Hamiltonian is invariant under rotations in isotopic spin space. Charge independence requires that the interaction between two nucleons depends on their total isotopic spin state but not upon their individual charge states if we neglect Coulomb forces. Hence the interaction Hamiltonian contains terms depending on the total isotopic spin, that is, operators such as $T^2$ or $\mathbf{N}_a \cdot \mathbf{N}_b$. (The operator $\mathbf{N}_a \cdot \mathbf{N}_b$ has eigenvalues $-\frac{1}{4}$ or $+\frac{3}{4}$ for the triplet and singlet isotopic spin two-nucleon states respectively.) These operators commute with the operators which are the generators of rotations in isotopic spin space, namely $\mathbf{T}$, $T_1$, $T_2$, and $T_3$. By complete analogy with the situation in angular momentum (Section 2.4) we can state that eigenvalues of $T^2$ and $T_3$ will be conserved quantities in transitions caused by the Hamiltonian. Thus for the two-nucleon system charge independence requires the conservation of total isotopic spin and of its third component. The conservation of the eigenvalue of $T_3$ is a natural outcome of the conservation of electric charge since we associated electric charge with this third component. (This is no longer true for strange particles; see Chapter XII.)

We shall apply the conservation of isotopic spin to the two-nucleon interaction in order to derive a relation between the scattering cross sections; readers who are interested in studying this application of charge independence immediately are referred to Section 6.5.

We must notice at this point that the arguments used above about a two-nucleon interaction are misleading in that such a direct interaction does not exist except in the weak $\beta$-decay interaction. The observed strong interaction takes place through the intermediary of the meson field and we should therefore base all our discussion on the meson–nucleon interaction. Our knowledge of this interaction is incomplete, but if it is charge-independent, then nucleon–nucleon forces will be likewise, and isotopic spin will be conserved in meson–nucleon and in nucleon–nucleon interactions. If we make such an assumption a priori, then it transpires that we are able to arrive at a consistent interpretation of meson scattering which suggests the correctness of the assumption. This matter will be the subject of Sections 7.6 onward.

Before closing this section we must note that transitions involving the electromagnetic field cannot be expected to conserve isotopic spin since it is the absence of this field which permits charge independence.

## 6.5 Nucleon–Nucleon Scattering

We wish to discuss briefly the phase shift analysis of the nucleon–nucleon scattering. This is a very complex subject for reasons which will become evident and we will only be able to give an outline of the methods used. Let us first decide upon the quantities which we expect to be conserved: they are the eigenvalues (quantum numbers $j, j_z$) of the total angular momentum operators $J^2$ and $J_z$, the eigenvalues $(t, t_3)$ of total isotopic spin operators $T^2$ and $T_3$ (charge independence), and parity. Let us consider firstly the angular momentum in the proton–proton scattering. This system is a pure triplet isotopic spin state and the asymmetry requirements rest upon the angular momentum states; those permitted are (Section 6.3):

| State: | $^1S_0$ | $^3P_{0,1,2}$ | $^1D_2$ | $^3F_{2,3,4}$ | $^1G_4$ | $^3H_{4,5,6}$, | etc. |
|---|---|---|---|---|---|---|---|
| Parity: | $+1$ | $-1$ | $+1$ | $-1$ | $+1$ | $-1$ | |

where the notation has been described above. We notice that if parity is conserved there can be no transitions between singlet and triplet states since these always have opposite parity; thus the total spin is a conserved quantity. Transitions can occur between states of different $l$ but same $j$ and parity; for example, in the series given above,

$$^3P_2 \rightleftharpoons {}^3F_2 \quad \text{and} \quad {}^3F_4 \rightleftharpoons {}^3H_4.$$

Other transitions can be found if the triplet series is extended. It is evidently possible to define phase shifts for all initial states which cannot change their $l$ value. However, the triplet spin states having $l = 2, 4, 6$, etc. can undergo such $l$-mixing transitions and it is necessary to define quantities which give the degree to which $l$-mixing transitions occur as well as redefining the phase shifts for these states. This is done through the formalism of the scattering matrix. Although we did not extend this formation to the case of particles having spin, it is not difficult to indicate how it applies for $p$–$p$ scattering. Consider the two incoming channels having the same parity and $j$ but different orbital angular momenta $l = j - 1$ and $j + 1$ respectively. There are two outgoing elastic scattering channels having the same properties. These channels are connected by a $2 \times 2$ submatrix $S'$ of the entire scattering matrix $S$. The diagonal elements of $S$ cannot conveniently be put equal to $e^{2i\delta_l}$ as if there were no $l$ mixing, for $\delta_l$ would then be a complex quantity, and the parameters of $S'$, such as $\delta_l$, would no longer be independent. In fact, there are only three independent real parameters to $S'$ and the problem is to find them. This process of parametrization leads to the definition of two "eigenphase shifts" $\delta_{j-1}$ and $\delta_{j+1}$, and a "mixing parameter" $\epsilon_j$, so that

$$S' = \begin{bmatrix} \cos^2 \epsilon_j \, e^{2i\delta_{j-1}} + \sin^2 \epsilon_j \, e^{2i\delta_{j+1}} & \frac{1}{2} \sin^2 \epsilon_j [e^{2i\delta_{j-1}} - e^{2i\delta_{j+1}}] \\ \frac{1}{2} \sin^2 \epsilon_j [e^{2i\delta_{j-1}} - e^{2i\delta_{j+1}}] & \sin^2 \epsilon_j \, e^{2i\delta_{j-1}} + \cos^2 \epsilon_j \, e^{2i\delta_{j+1}} \end{bmatrix}.$$

The meaning of these parameters is given by the following properties: consider waves in the incoming channels with amplitudes in the ratio

$A_{j-1}/A_{j+1}$ such that the amplitude ratio $B_{j-1}/B_{j+1}$ in the outgoing channel is the same. These waves are behaving as if there were no $l$-mixing, and the incoming and outgoing waves of the same $l$ are merely shifted in phase. There are two solutions to this situation having ratios

$$\left(\frac{A_{j-1}}{A_{j+1}}\right)_1 = \tan \epsilon_j, \quad \text{and} \quad \left(\frac{A_{j-1}}{A_{j+1}}\right)_2 = -\cot \epsilon_j,$$

which both give

$$B_{j-1} = A_{j-1} \exp 2i\delta_{j-1} \quad \text{and} \quad B_{j+1} = A_{j+1} \exp 2i\delta_{j+1}. \tag{6.14}$$

The simple relations of Eq. (6.14) are just like those that occur for the transition in which $l$ is conserved and thus the real quantities $\delta$ are behaving like phase shifts. As we have indicated, they are called eigenphase shifts.

The pure nuclear effects in proton–proton scattering are modified by the presence of Coulomb scattering which must be correctly incorporated in the analysis if we require the phase shifts to have a purely nuclear origin. Procedures for doing this are given by Clementel and Villi (1955).

Neutron–proton scattering is complicated by the presence of both singlet and triplet spin states for a given value of $l$. This corresponds to the presence of both singlet and triplet isotopic spin states in the $n$–$p$ system in contrast to the $p$–$p$ system which contains only triplet isotopic spin states. We enumerate some of the lower angular momentum states of the neutron–proton system in Table 6.1.

TABLE 6.1

THE ANGULAR MOMENTUM STATES OF THE NEUTRON–PROTON SYSTEM

| Singlet isotopic spin | | Triplet isotopic spin | |
|---|---|---|---|
| Angular momentum | Parity | Angular momentum | Parity |
| $^3S_1$ | $+1$ | $^1S_0$ | $+1$ |
| $^1P_1$ | $-1$ | $^3P_{0,1,2}$ | $-1$ |
| $^3D_{1,2,3}$ | $+1$ | $^1D_2$ | $+1$ |
| $^1F_3$ | $-1$ | $^3F_{2,3,4}$ | $-1$ |
| etc. | | etc. | |

Consider a given value of $j$, e.g., $j = 2$; the following states are involved:

| State: | $^1D_2$ | $^3D_2$ | $^3P_2$ | $^3F_2$ |
|---|---|---|---|---|
| $t$: | $+1$ | $0$ | $+1$ | $+1$ |
| Parity: | $+1$ | $+1$ | $-1$ | $-1$ |

By the conservation of parity and isotopic spin we observe that $l$-mixing can only occur between $^3P_2$ and $^3F_2$ states, so there are phase shifts for the $^1D_2$ and $^3D_2$ states and two eigenphase shifts and a mixing parameter for $^3P_2$ and $^3F_2$. By charge independence, any of these parameters which belong to the triplet isotopic spin state will be identical with those applying to the $p$–$p$ scattering (and to $n$–$n$ scattering).

We cannot concern ourselves with the development of the formulae for cross sections in terms of the phase shifts and mixing parameters. Readers are referred to the following works: for a general approach, see Blatt and Biedenharn (1952a); the same authors have also discussed the $n$–$p$ phase shift analysis (1952b). For $p$–$p$ analysis, see Clementel and Villi (1955). Wright (1955) gives complete formulae for all the quantities required in scattering and polarization experiments (see Chapter VIII).

The derivation of phase shifts from differential and total scattering cross-section data is of considerable difficulty. For example, the nuclear part of the $p$–$p$ scattering is isotropic in the centre of mass in the energy range up to about 400 Mev, but the actual value of the differential cross section is too high for this to be due to $S$-wave scattering alone. The actual mixture of waves present is not easily deduced from scattering data alone and in this respect polarization experiments contribute indispensable information; even so, the phase shifts are often ambiguous and uncertain. An opposite approach is to postulate a potential which is supposed to exist between two nucleons and to calculate the phase shifts and thence the observable quantities. This method has not been startlingly successful; readers are referred to the article by Signell and Marshak (1958) which reviews earlier work in this field and makes a further contribution to this approach. These authors use a potential due to Gartenhaus (1956), which is derived from the Chew meson theory, and add to it a spin-orbit potential. The final potential consists of three parts: a central potential, a tensor potential (noncentral), and the spin-orbit force. The tensor term contains the operator

$$S_{ab} = \frac{3}{r^2}(\boldsymbol{\sigma}_a \cdot \mathbf{r})(\boldsymbol{\sigma}_b \cdot \mathbf{r}) - \boldsymbol{\sigma}_a \cdot \boldsymbol{\sigma}_b$$

which describes a noncentral force. Such a force causes a mixing of $l$ among states of the same $j$ and must be present if the potential is to predict the quadrupole moment of the deuteron which is due to a 4% (approximately) admixture of $^3D_2$ to the major $^3S_2$ state. For a discussion of the properties of the tensor force, see Blatt and Weisskopff (1952). We notice that the tensor force is absent in singlet states.

The central and tensor potentials are independent of the energy, in contrast to the spin-orbit potential which is derived by the operator $\mathbf{L} \cdot \mathbf{S}$. This gives rise to a force which is energy-dependent, since an increase in velocity gives rise to a larger number of effective partial waves which experience a force having a value which increases with $l$. This Signell–Marshak potential gives fair agreement with the observed data but there is room for improvement. For a review of the experimental data, see the article by Hess (1958).

There is an inequality relation between differential cross sections for $pp$ and $np$ scattering at $90°$ (centre of mass) and at the same energy which must hold if charge independence is correct; it states that

$$4 \frac{d\sigma_{np}}{d\Omega}(90°) \geqslant \frac{d\sigma_{pp}}{d\Omega}(90°).$$

This result appears naturally in the phase-shift analysis as described above, but it is very simple to prove using the isotopic spin formalism and we shall do it by using the transition rate formula [Eq. (5.2)]. If the comparison is made at identical energies and angles, factors such as spin and space wave functions, density of states and relative velocity drop out and we need only consider the isotopic spin functions. The interaction Hamiltonian is divided into two parts, $H_3$ and $H_1$, which cause transitions in the triplet and singlet isotopic spin states respectively. The initial and final states for $n$–$p$ scattering at $\theta°$ are $(1/\sqrt{2})\{\tau(1,0) + \tau(0,0)\}$; $n$–$p$ scattering at $\pi$–$\theta$ corresponds to interchanging the final state nucleons and therefore has a final state function of $(1/\sqrt{2})\{\tau(1,0) - \tau(0,0)\}$; $pp$ scattering functions are both $\tau(1,1)$. Therefore

$$\frac{d\sigma_{np}}{d\Omega}(\theta) \propto \tfrac{1}{4} |(\tau(1,0) + \tau(0,0)|H_3 + H_1|\tau(1,0) + \tau(0,0))|^2,$$

$$\frac{d\sigma_{np}}{d\Omega}(\pi - \theta) \propto \tfrac{1}{4} |(\tau(1,0) - \tau(0,0)|H_3 + H_1|\tau(1,0) + \tau(0,0))|^2,$$

$$\frac{d\sigma_{pp}}{d\Omega}(\theta) \propto |(\tau(1,1)|H_3|\tau(1,1))|^2.$$

We contract the matrix elements thus:

$$(\tau(1,t_3)|H_3|\tau(1,t_3)) = H_3,$$

$$(\tau(0,0)|H_1|\tau(0,0)) = H_1.$$

Then

$$\sqrt{\left[\frac{d\sigma_{np}}{d\Omega}(\theta)\right]} \propto \tfrac{1}{2}|H_3 + H_1|,$$

$$\sqrt{\left[\frac{d\sigma_{np}}{d\Omega}(\pi - \theta)\right]} \propto \tfrac{1}{2}|H_3 - H_1|,$$

$$\sqrt{\left[\frac{d\sigma_{pp}}{d\Omega}(\theta)\right]} \propto |H_3|.$$

The matrix elements are complex quantities and so we can represent them as vectors on an Argand diagram. In Fig. 6.1 we have

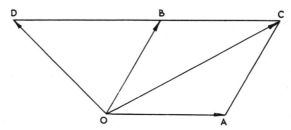

FIG. 6.1. An Argand diagram of the four matrix elements involved in nucleon–nucleon scattering.

$$OA = H_1, \quad OB = H_3, \quad OC = H_3 + H_1, \quad OD = H_3 - H_1.$$

We can apply the triangular inequality to $\triangle ODC$,

$$|H_3 - H_1| + |H_3 + H_1| \geqslant 2H_1$$

or

$$2\sqrt{\left[\frac{d\sigma_{np}}{d\Omega}(\pi - \theta)\right]} + 2\sqrt{\left[\frac{d\sigma_{np}}{d\Omega}(\theta)\right]} \geqslant 2\sqrt{\left[\frac{d\sigma_{pp}}{d\Omega}(\theta)\right]}.$$

At 90° we have $\theta = \pi - \theta$ and hence we expect that

$$4\frac{d\sigma_{np}}{d\Omega}(90°) \geqslant \frac{d\sigma_{pp}}{d\Omega}(90°)$$

which completes the proof.

In Fig. 6.2 we show the values of these quantities as functions of energy; it is seen that the inequality is satisfied. This does not, of course, establish charge independence.

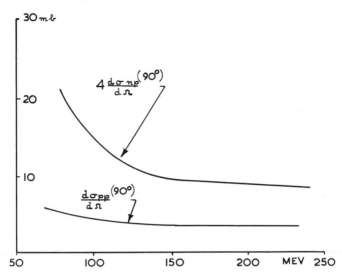

FIG. 6.2. The differential cross section for neutron–proton and proton–proton scattering at 90° in the centre of mass as a function of incident nucleon energy in the laboratory.

## 6.6 Conclusion

In this chapter we have considered the important restriction on the wave function of two or more identical particles, that of symmetry or antisymmetry. This restriction was applied to the two-nucleon system. In the final sections we were concerned with isotopic spin and its conservation and have thus completed the list of conserved quantities which was compiled in Section 1.6. These concepts were then applied in an introduction to the phase-shift analysis of nucleon–nucleon scattering. Using the isotopic spin formalism a certain inequality among nucleon–nucleon cross sections was derived.

# CHAPTER VII

# THE PI-MESON

## 7.1 Introduction

Up to this point in the book we have emphasized the quantum-mechanical theory usually without stopping to apply the results of the discussions to any physically observable system. We now change our procedure and in this chapter will concern ourselves with the analysis of experimental work on pi-mesons (or, as these particles are sometimes called, pions) in order to discover the basic properties of this particle. In our experience this particle occurs via its interaction with nucleons and therefore we are essentially examining the pi-meson–nucleon system.

The nucleons are partially described by the Dirac equation but have anomalous magnetic moments indicating that this theory is inadequate and that nucleons have closely associated meson fields. The meson field and the particle which must exist in the quantized field were predicted by Yukawa (1935) to explain the strong forces which exist between nucleons. From the properties of these forces Yukawa predicted that the meson would have a mass of about $200m_e$. The pi-mesons discovered in 1947 (Lattes *et al.*, 1947) are probably the Yukawa meson, although his theory has not continued its preliminary success by predicting the full properties of the pi-meson and its interactions.

## 7.2 Preliminary Discussion of Pi-Meson Properties

We will now enumerate the more immediately observable properties of the pi-mesons. The discovery of pi-mesons was made in the cosmic radiation; their properties were evaluated in detail at accelerators able to produce mesons artificially.

1. *Electric charge.* Three kinds of pi-meson exist, namely, positive, negative, and uncharged, which we indicate by $\pi^+$, $\pi^-$, and $\pi^0$, respectively. The triplet nature of the charge properties of the meson field

permit an immediate isotopic spin assignment which is discussed in Section 7.6.

2. *Mass.* The charged pi-mesons have a mass of $273.3m_e$, the uncharged pi-meson $264.4m_e$. We shall not discuss the determination of the masses but refer readers to the analysis given by Cohen *et al.* (1957).

3. *Lifetime.* The direct measurement of the mean lifetime of the $\pi^+$ at rest in scintillating material gives $(2.56 \pm 0.05) \times 10^{-8}$ sec (Shapiro, 1956); nuclear capture prevents a similar measurement of the $\pi^-$ lifetime, but it is assumed to be the same in the absence of nuclear capture. The $\pi^0$ lifetime can only be inferred indirectly to be $< 4 \times 10^{-16}$ sec (Shapiro, 1956) and since the uncertainty in its mass is certainly much less than 0.1 Mev, the uncertainty principle indicates that its lifetime is $> 10^{-20}$ sec.

4. *Decay products.* The $\pi^+$ is observed to decay into a $\mu$ meson and a neutrino

$$\pi^+ \rightarrow \mu^+ + \nu.$$

The $\mu$ meson is a spin $\frac{1}{2}$ fermion of mass $206.9m_e$ (Cohen *et al.*, 1957) which we shall discuss later. It appears to play no part in the pi-meson–nucleon interaction. Other decay modes have a branching ratio of $< 1 \times 10^{-4}$; if our present knowledge of elementary particles is correct, we might expect other decays to be observed. Those with three or less final particles are:

$$\pi^+ \rightarrow e^+ + \nu,$$

$$\pi^+ \rightarrow \mu^+ + \nu + \gamma,$$

$$\pi^+ \rightarrow e^+ + \nu + \gamma,$$

$$\pi^+ \rightarrow \pi^0 + e^+ + \nu.$$

Only the first has been observed (Fazzini *et al.*, 1958; Impeduglia *et al.*, 1958). It is impossible to observe the $\pi^-$ decay at rest. It is known to decay into a $\mu^-$ meson in flight with about the same lifetime as the $\pi^+$. The $\pi^0$ is observed to decay

$$\pi^0 \rightarrow \gamma + \gamma,$$

$$\pi^0 \rightarrow \gamma + e^+ + e^-, \qquad \text{branching ratio about } 1/80$$
$$\text{(Dalitz, 1951),}$$

$$\pi^0 \rightarrow e^+ + e^- + e^+ + e^-, \text{ branching ratio about } 1/30{,}000$$
$$\text{(Plano *et al.*, 1959).}$$

Other decays which are energetically possible but have not been observed are

$$\pi^0 \to \mu^+ + e^-,$$

$$\pi^0 \to \mu^- + e^+,$$

$$\pi^0 \to e^+ + e^-, \text{ etc.}$$

Decay into more than two photons has not been observed; the two-photon decay permits us to conclude that the spin of the $\pi^0$ meson is zero or an even integer—see Section 7.5.

5. *Spin.* In fact, the pi-meson appears to have no spin; this is the result of an analysis discussed in Sections 7.3 and 7.5.

6. *Parity.* A study of the absorption of $\pi^-$ mesons in deuterium indicates that this particle carries odd intrinsic parity (Section 7.4). As we expect all the pi-mesons to have the same parity, this is normally assumed.

7. *Interaction properties.* The pi-mesons interact strongly with nucleons and the properties of the interaction are of considerable interest and will be discussed at some length in this chapter.

### 7.3 The Spin of the Positive Pi-Meson

The spin of the positive pi-meson is deduced from a study of a pi-meson production reaction and its inverse:

$$p + p \to \pi^+ + d, \tag{7.1}$$

$$\pi^+ + d \to p + p. \tag{7.2}$$

These reactions are observed for unpolarized beams and without distinguishing different final spin states. We can therefore apply detailed balance arguments in comparing cross sections measured at the same centre-of-mass total energy.

Let $s_\pi$, $s_p$, and $s_d$ be the spins (in units of $\hbar$) of the pi-meson, proton, and deuteron, respectively. Let $\sigma_1$ and $\sigma_2$ be the cross sections for the reactions (7.1) and (7.2), respectively. At the same centre-of-mass energy the cross sections are related by the appropriate form of Eq. (5.27), viz.,

$$\frac{d\sigma_1}{d\Omega} = \left(\frac{p_\pi}{p_p}\right)^2 \frac{(2s_\pi + 1)(2s_d + 1)}{(2s_p + 1)^2} \frac{d\sigma_2}{d\Omega}, \tag{7.3}$$

where $p_\pi$ is the $\pi^+$ (or $d$) momentum and $p_p$ is the proton momentum, in the centre of mass. Now $s_d = 1$ and $s_p = \frac{1}{2}$ so that Eq. (7.3) becomes

$$\frac{d\sigma_1}{d\Omega} = \frac{3}{4}\left(\frac{p_\pi}{p_p}\right)^2 (2s_\pi + 1) \frac{d\sigma_2}{d\Omega}.$$

We find the relation for the total cross sections by integrating, taking care not to count each proton twice, as described in Section 5.7. We find

$$\sigma_1 = \frac{3}{2}\left(\frac{p_\pi}{p_p}\right)^2 (2s_\pi + 1)\,\sigma_2. \tag{7.4}$$

We use this equation to compare the observed cross sections and hence determine the value of $s_\pi$. It is sufficient for our immediate purpose to use the following data:

(1) The total cross section for reaction (7.1) at an incident proton energy of 340 Mev is $0.18 \pm 0.06$ millibarn (Cartwright et al., 1953). This incident energy corresponds to $\pi^+$ mesons produced with an energy of 22.3 Mev in the centre of mass.

(2) The total cross section for reaction (7.2) at an incident pi-meson energy of 29 Mev is $3.1 \pm 0.3$ millibarns (Durbin et al., 1951). The incident pi-meson 29-Mev energy in the laboratory corresponds to 25-Mev pi-mesons in the centre of mass. Since $s_\pi$ is an integer, we do not require great precision for its determination and we can use nonrelativistic approximations. The centre-of-mass energies are sufficiently equal for the reactions to be compared.

Now

$$\frac{p_\pi}{p_p} = \frac{p_\pi/m_\pi c}{p_p/m_p c} \times \frac{m_\pi}{m_p};$$

$p/mc$ is the momentum of a particle in units of its natural momentum $mc$. If $T$ is the kinetic energy of the particle, we have

$$p/mc = \sqrt{(2T/mc^2)},$$

which is an equation easily evaluated if the energies $T$ and $mc^2$ are expressed in Mev. Evaluating the momenta in the centre of mass, we have

$T_\pi = 23$ Mev and $p_\pi/m_\pi c = 0.576,$

$T_p = 85$ Mev (kinetic energy of one proton in the centre-of-mass) and $p_p/m_p c = 0.426,$

hence

$$p_\pi/p_p = 0.201.$$

Substituting our data in Eq. (7.4), we find that

$$(0.18 \pm 0.06) = (3.1 \pm 0.3)\, 0.0606(2s_\pi + 1).$$

The nearest integer for $s_\pi$ is obviously zero.

A more complete justification for this conclusion is found in a paper by Rosenfeld (1954) in which the pi-meson production reactions are analysed. In accumulating data on reaction (7.1), Rosenfeld takes the experimental data on reaction (7.2), assumes $s_\pi = 0$, inverts the data by detailed balance, and adds the result to the experimental data for reaction (7.1). The consistency of the total data from a large number of measurements at different energies justifies his assumption of $s_\pi = 0$.

We conclude that the $\pi^+$ meson has zero spin. The analysis would be invalid if, by chance, the $\pi^+$ did have spin and the meson beams used were polarized; however, it is very unlikely that the pi-meson beams produced by cyclotrons are sufficiently polarized (Clark et al., 1951) to give an accidental spin zero result, and our conclusion is almost certainly correct.

We make the natural assumption that the $\pi^-$ has the same spin as the $\pi^+$, a step which is justified by the consistency of our interpretation of meson phenomena after making this assumption. We also expect the $\pi^0$ to have spin zero, but such a conclusion can be checked by an analysis of the decay properties of the $\pi^0$; this is discussed in Section 7.5.

Some further experimental evidence of spin 0 charged mesons comes from the fact that no asymmetries are observed in the decay of these particles (Crewe et al., 1957).

## 7.4 The Parity of Pi-Mesons

The absorption of slow $\pi^-$ mesons in liquid hydrogen and liquid deuterium are two very important processes. The steps which lead to the nuclear absorption of most of the high-energy pi-mesons incident upon the liquid target are:

(1) Slowing down of mesons by ordinary stopping power mechanism which finally leaves the incident pion with a velocity comparable to the electron orbital velocities; the time taken is about $10^{-10}$ sec. Nuclear interaction in flight can take place but the probability is small compared with stopping if the meson range is small.

(2) Capture into an excited Bohr orbit around a proton (or deuteron)

(3) De-excitation of this mesonic atom by inelastic collisions with neighbouring molecules. Nuclear absorption does not become effective until the atom is in its ground state (Brueckner et al., 1951) and thus de-excitation has only to compete with the normal decay. In liquid hydrogen or deuterium the chance of decay is only $10^{-3}$ and thus the atom almost always reaches ground state. At this point nuclear absorption becomes the predominant process.

These arguments are important as we want to know with some certainty the total angular momentum and parity of the state which exists before the absorption takes place. For a fuller discussion of the situation, see Burhop (1952). In addition, more recent investigations have suggested that another mechanism is operating which increases the probability that absorption takes place from an $s$ state. This is discussed in connection with $K^-$ meson absorption in hydrogen in Section 12.7.

In hydrogen the absorption reactions which occur are as follows (Panofsky *et al.*, 1951):

$$\pi^- + p \rightarrow \pi^0 + n, \tag{7.5}$$

$$\pi^- + p \rightarrow \gamma + n. \tag{7.6}$$

The ratio of the probability that reaction (7.5) takes place to the probability that reaction (7.6) takes place is $1.50 \pm 0.11$ (Cassels *et al.*, 1957). This is the famous Panofsky ratio. In deuterium the energetically possible reactions are:

$$\pi^- + d \rightarrow \pi^0 + 2n, \tag{7.7}$$

$$\pi^- + d \rightarrow \gamma + 2n, \tag{7.8}$$

$$\pi^- + d \rightarrow 2n. \tag{7.9}$$

Reaction (7.7) is unobserved and the probability ratio for reactions (7.9) to (7.8) is $2.36 \pm 0.36$ (Kuehner *et al.*, 1958; Panofsky *et al.*, 1951).

The hydrogen absorption reactions lead immediately to the conclusion that the $\pi^-$ meson is a boson. From that point we proceed directly to the deuterium absorption as it gives us immediately more information. We assume that the proton and neutron have even relative parity and that the $\pi^-$ spin is zero. We know absorption takes place from the $S$ state of orbital motion, so we have that the total angular momentum ($j$) of the initial state is just the deuteron spin, which is one. Therefore $j = 1$ and the initial state is $^3S_1$, in spectroscopic notation. The deuteron has an even parity wave function (it is a superposition of the even states $^3S_1$ and $^3D_1$); the orbital $S$ state is even, so the parity of the initial state is that of the meson. We now examine the final state of reaction (7.9); from Section 6.3 we know that the only permitted states for two neutrons are, in spectroscopic notation,

$$^1S_0, \ ^3P_0, \ ^3P_1, \ ^3P_2, \ ^1D_2, \ ^3F_2, \ ^3F_3, \ ..., \ \text{etc.}$$

The only state with $j = 1$ is $^3P_1$, which has odd parity; hence the fact that reaction (7.9) occurs indicates that the $\pi^-$ meson has odd parity.

An odd parity assignment to the $\pi^0$ is weakly supported by the non-occurrence of reaction (7.7). In this case the energy available to the two neutrons is very small and it is very unlikely that they can be in any state of relative motion other than $^1S_0$ (cf. argument of Section 3.5). From conservation of angular momentum it follows that the meson must be in an orbital angular momentum state $l = 1$, i.e., a $P$ state, relative to the centre of mass of the two neutrons; the angular momentum barrier strongly inhibits the reaction going into this state on account of low $\pi^0$ kinetic energy. However, this final state is forbidden by conservation of parity if the $\pi^0$ and the $\pi^-$ have the same parity. Taken together, we see that we cannot definitely assign odd parity to the $\pi^0$ since the nonoccurrence of (7.7) could be due to the angular momentum barrier. Nevertheless, it is usual to assume that all three types of $\pi$-meson have odd intrinsic parity.

We have noted that we are assuming that the proton and neutron have even relative parity. If the relative parity were odd, then we would assign opposite parities to the charged and uncharged meson. It is impossible to determine the charged meson intrinsic parity independently of the nucleon although it is possible to measure the intrinsic parity of the neutral meson (Section 7.5). We shall therefore continue to assume that all $\pi$-mesons have the same parity.

We now return to the absorption in hydrogen and find that for reaction (7.5) the initial and final states are $^2S_{\frac{1}{2}}$ with odd parity. For reaction (7.6) this implies that the outgoing photon is due to an electric dipole transition in which the nucleon spin has flipped. The surprising thing about these reactions is that (7.5) is only 50% more probable than (7.6) when the former is expected to be six times as frequent as the latter. This expectation comes from the knowledge that the electromagnetic interaction has about $1/137$ the strength of the meson–nucleon interaction and the weight of the density of states factors. The observed ratio suggests that (7.5) is inhibited in some way. In fact, the meson–nucleon interaction is much weaker when the relative orbital angular momentum is zero compared with its value when the relative motion is a $P$ state. Thus we have anticipated a result which is brought out more strongly by the meson-scattering experiments.

### 7.5 The Spin and Parity of the Neutral Pi-Meson

We will now examine the significance of the observed decay of the neutral pi-meson into two photons. This process is governed by various symmetry and conservation laws with results which were first discussed by Yang (1950). We follow his analysis in a modified way. We proceed by setting up a Cartesian coordinate system in the centre of mass, having its $z$ axis along the direction of motion of one of the outgoing photons. We are then interested in the properties of the initial state

(the $\pi^0$ meson) and of the final state (two photons) under three transformations. The first is the parity transformation, the second is rotation around the $z$ axis, and the third is rotation through 180° around
the $x$ axis. The effect of each transformation on the state functions is
represented by an operator and in some cases the functions are eigenfunctions of these operators. We expect that these transformations do
not change the physical consequences and, as a result of our arguments of Section 1.6, that the operators commute with the Hamiltonian
operator for the complete system; it follows that the initial and final
states must have the same eigenvalues. Thus we shall investigate the
eigenvalues for both initial and final states to discover the values of
spin and parity that the $\pi^0$ meson can have if it decays into two
photons. Actually, the selection rules we derive can be applied to any
decay into two photons, for example, to positron annihilation.

We firstly examine the properties of the transformations.

(1) Parity transformation: this transformation $P$ has the effect of
reversing the direction of motion of all particles whilst leaving all
angular momenta unchanged.

(2) Rotation around the $z$ axis: a function is only an eigenfunction
of this rotation operator $R_z$ if it is a pure state having a discrete value
of the $z$ component of angular momentum, $j_z$. For a rotation through
an angle $\alpha$ the eigenvalue is $\exp ij_z \alpha$.

(3) Rotation through 180° around the $x$ axis: for two photons
moving along the $z$ axis this rotation $R_x$ has the effect of reversing the
direction of movement and the intrinsic angular momentum of each
photon. In the case of a single particle state this rotation has the
same effect as it would have on the spherical harmonic having the
same angular momentum eigenvalues.

We remind readers that the rotation operators $R_z$ and $R_x$ are generated by the angular momentum operators $J_z$ and $J_x$, and that, due to
the commutation relations (2.5), pure states can have only one component of the angular momentum quantized, conventionally the
$z$ component; when this is the case no other component is quantized.
Thus a state having a discrete eigenvalue $j_z$ cannot have a discrete
eigenvalue $j_x$ and the state will not be an eigenfunction of the rotation
operator $R_x$. However, when $j_z = 0$ (the eigenvalue of $R_z$ will be 1)
we have that
$$J_x J_y - J_y J_x = -i\hbar J_z = 0,$$
and we can quantize $J_x$ and expect the state to be an eigenfunction
of $R_x$. Thus the eigenvalue of the functions under transformation 3,
$R_x$, are only significant when the eigenvalues under transformation 1,
$R_z$, have value 1.

We will consider the final state of two photons. From our knowledge of the electromagnetic field we know that a photon carries intrinsic angular momentum (spin) $\pm \hbar$ directed along its direction of motion. We call the photon having $+\hbar$ right-hand polarized, whilst that having $-\hbar$ is called left-hand polarized. In our case the two photons are moving in opposite directions along the $z$ axis and we describe the two photons by two arrows, the first applying to the photon moving in the $+z$ direction, the second applying to that moving in the $-z$ direction; the arrow points up ($\uparrow$) if the $z$ component of the photon spin is $+\hbar$ and points down ($\downarrow$) if it is $-\hbar$. Thus $\uparrow\downarrow$ indicates that both photons are right-hand polarized, and so on. There are four such "wave functions" and we are interested in those or their combinations which are eigenfunctions of $P$ and $R_z$; they are

$$\uparrow\uparrow, \quad \downarrow\downarrow, \quad \uparrow\downarrow+\downarrow\uparrow, \quad \text{and} \quad \uparrow\downarrow-\downarrow\uparrow.$$

The properties of our transformation operators are such that:

(1) $P$ exchanges the arrows;

(2) $R_z$ does nothing to the arrows but multiplies the functions by $\exp i j_z \alpha$;

(3) $R_x$ exchanges the arrows and turns each arrow upside down.

We can now construct a table of the eigenvalues (Table 7.1).

TABLE 7.1

EIGENVALUES OF TWO-PHOTON FINAL STATES

| Spin function | Transformation 1 $P$ | 2 $R_z$ | 3 $R_x$ |
|---|---|---|---|
| $\uparrow\uparrow$ | $+1$ | $e^{2i\alpha}$ | $-$ |
| $\downarrow\downarrow$ | $+1$ | $e^{-2i\alpha}$ | $-$ |
| $\uparrow\downarrow+\downarrow\uparrow$ | $+1$ | $+1$ | $+1$ |
| $\uparrow\downarrow-\downarrow\uparrow$ | $-1$ | $+1$ | $+1$ |

We can now do the same for the initial state, which is the neutral pi-meson at rest. If this particle has spin $j$ and $z$ component of spin $j_z$, then its properties under rotation are the same as those of the spherical harmonic having $l = j$ and $l_z = j_z$ [Eq. (2.46)]. Then $R_z$ has eigenvalues $\exp i j_z \alpha$. If $j_z = 0$, then $R_x$ has eigenvalues $(-1)^j$. We can now construct a second table, Table 7.2, which sets out the eigenvalues for initial $\pi^0$ states of different spin and parity. This initial state can have any value of $j_z$ from $-j$ to $+j$ and in general will be a coherent sum of all these states; therefore the column of $R_z$ eigenvalues includes $2j+1$ possibilities.

TABLE 7.2
EIGENVALUES OF POSSIBLE $\pi^0$ STATES

| Spin $j$ | 1 $P$ | 2 $R_z$ | 3 $R_x$ |
|---|---|---|---|
| 0 | $\begin{cases} +1 \\ -1 \end{cases}$ | $\begin{matrix} +1 \\ +1 \end{matrix}$ | $\begin{matrix} +1 \\ +1 \end{matrix}$ |
| 1 | $\begin{cases} +1 \\ -1 \end{cases}$ | $e^{i\alpha}, 1, e^{-i\alpha}$ | $\begin{cases} -1 \\ -1 \end{cases}$ |
| 2, 4, 6, ... | $\begin{cases} +1 \\ -1 \end{cases}$ | $e^{ij\alpha}, ..., 1, ..., e^{-ij\alpha}$ | $\begin{cases} +1 \\ +1 \end{cases}$ |
| 3, 5, 7, ... | $\begin{cases} +1 \\ -1 \end{cases}$ | $e^{ij\alpha}, ..., 1, ..., e^{-ij\alpha}$ | $\begin{cases} -1 \\ -1 \end{cases}$ |

We now compare the rows of the two tables, 7.1 and 7.2, to construct a final table, 7.3, which indicates the two photon states which

TABLE 7.3
TWO-PHOTON STATES FOR DECAY OF VARIOUS TYPES OF $\pi^0$ MESON

| Parity \ Spin $j$ | 0 | 1 | 2, 4, ... | 3, 5, ... |
|---|---|---|---|---|
| Even | ↑↓+↓↑ | Forbidden | ↑↑, ↓↓ and ↑↓+↓↑ | ↑↑ and ↓↓ |
| Odd | ↑↓−↓↑ | Forbidden | ↑↓−↓↑ | Forbidden |

are accessible to a decaying neutral meson having the spin and parity indicated. We will describe this comparison in two cases. Consider the meson having spin 1 and of either intrinsic parity; only the state having $R_z = 1$ can decay into two photons, and since this corresponds to $j_z = 0$, we may also examine the eigenvalues of $R_x$ which is $-1$ for the meson. There is no two-photon state having this eigenvalue and we conclude that a spin 1 state cannot decay into two photons. Our second example is that of a meson having even spin of 2 or greater and even parity. If $j_z = 0$ ($R_z = 1$), then the particle can decay into ↑↓+↓↑; if $j_z = +2$ or $-2$ ($R_z = e^{2i\alpha}, e^{-2i\alpha}$), it decays into ↑↑ or ↓↓, respectively, for which the $R_x$ eigenvalue has no influence.

As it is almost certain that the $\pi^0$ has zero spin, we find that a pseudoscalar $\pi^0$ will decay into the two photons with the wave function

$$↑↓−↓↑.$$

For convenience we can rewrite this wave function in a way which indicates the polarizations of the two photons. Using the relation between polarization, direction of motion, and spin $z$ component we find that this wave function corresponds to

$$\sqrt{\tfrac{1}{2}}\{\psi_+^R \psi_-^R - \psi_-^L \psi_+^L\}. \tag{7.10}$$

In this equation the subscript indicates the direction of motion, the superscript the polarization. Similarly, the scalar meson decays into the state

$$\sqrt{\tfrac{1}{2}}\{\psi_+^R \psi_-^R + \psi_+^L \psi_-^L\}. \tag{7.11}$$

We now wish to examine the effect of making polarization measurements on these two outgoing photons. If we were to make a measurement of the polarization of one of the outgoing photons, then we would find left-hand or right-hand polarization with equal probability, independent of the parity of the decaying meson. This follows from the fact that $\psi^R$ and $\psi^L$ have same amplitudes throughout both the photon wave functions (7.10) and (7.11). The next step would be to measure the circular polarization state of both outgoing photons and we can predict the results of such measurements by finding the probability of obtaining a particular result. Thus the probability of finding both photons left-hand polarized is the square of the matrix element between the state $\psi_+^L \psi_-^L$ and the state under observation; for scalar or pseudoscalar mesons this is

$$|(\, (\psi_+^L \psi_-^L)\,|\sqrt{\tfrac{1}{2}}\,(\psi_+^R \psi_-^R \pm \psi_+^L \psi_-^L)\,)|^2 = \tfrac{1}{2}.$$

The probability is the same for finding both photons right circularly polarized, but the probability for finding the photons oppositely polarized is zero. These results are all independent of the wave functions for the two photons and we conclude that it is impossible to determine the parity of the $\pi^0$ meson by measuring the circular polarization of its decay photons.

However, it is possible to deduce the parity by measuring the state of plane polarization of both photons. We proceed by rewriting the two wave functions (7.10) and (7.11). To do this we recall that a right (or left) circular polarized photon can also be described by a sum of two wave functions with correct relative phase, where one wave function $\psi^x$ represents a photon plane polarized with its electric vector in the $xz$ plane and the other $\psi^y$ represents a photon polarized with its electric vector in the $yz$ plane. Thus, using the phases of Eq. (4.22),

$$\psi^R = -\sqrt{\tfrac{1}{2}}\,(\psi^x + i\psi^y), \tag{7.12}$$

$$\psi^L = \sqrt{\tfrac{1}{2}}\,(\psi^x - i\psi^y). \tag{7.13}$$

We substitute (7.12) and (7.13) into the photon wave functions (7.10) and (7.11) to find that the two photon wave functions are

$\pi^0$ pseudoscalar: $\qquad -i\sqrt{\tfrac{1}{2}}\{\psi_+^y\,\psi_-^x + \psi_+^x\,\psi_-^y\};$

$\pi^0$ scalar: $\qquad \sqrt{\tfrac{1}{2}}\{\psi_+^x\,\psi_-^x + \psi_+^y\,\psi_-^y\}.$

An examination of these wave functions indicates immediately that if the $\pi^0$ meson is pseudoscalar the two photons are always oppositely plane polarized. If the meson is scalar, the two photons have the same plane polarization. This determination of photon polarization has not been done directly as there is no way known at present of measuring the plane polarization of high-energy photons with high efficiency. However, the decay of $\pi^0$ meson into two electron–positron pairs does reflect this polarization correlation in a correlation between the planes of the pairs. If the angle between these planes is $\phi$, the correlation is

$$P_p(\phi) = 1 - a\cos 2\phi,$$

$$P_s(\phi) = 1 + a\cos 2\phi.$$

$a$ is a positive quantity which is a function of the energies and angles of the pairs. The subscript $s$ or $p$ indicates the correlation for even or odd parity meson respectively. The observed correlation (Plano et al., 1959) is unambiguously of the kind expected for an odd parity $\pi^0$. The remaining uncertainties are due to any uncertainties there may be in the use of quantum electrodynamics applied to the internal conversion in $\pi^0$ decay. It is believed that the theory is reliable.

Further discussion of the connection between the photon polarization and $\pi^0$ parity has been given for the case of $\pi^0$ having spin 2 or greater (Kinoshita and Peierls, 1957).

## 7.6 Isotopic Spin and the Meson–Nucleon System

We shall now examine the isotopic spin properties of the meson–nucleon system. We require a large number of symbols which we have

TABLE 7.4

SYMBOLS FOR SPIN AND ISOTOPIC SPIN

|  | Operators | Eigenvalue parameters | Eigenfunctions |
|---|---|---|---|
| Ordinary spin | $S^2\, S_z$ | $s,\, s_z$ | $\chi(s, s_z)$ |
| Meson isotopic spin | $\Pi^2\, \Pi_3$ | $p,\, p_3$ | $\pi(p, p_3)$ |
| Nucleon isotopic spin | $N^2\, N_3$ | $n,\, n_3$ | $\nu(n, n_3)$ |
| Total isotopic spin | $T^2\, T_3$ | $t,\, t_3$ | $\tau(t, t_3)$ |

tabulated for convenience (Table 7.4). Due to the equivalence of the
isotopic spin formalism and the angular momentum formalism, we are
able to include in this table the angular momentum symbols which
have corresponding properties. We note that the component of isotopic spin that we have chosen to be discrete is subscripted 3 corresponding to a third axis in isotopic spin space, just as it is normal to
make the $z$ component of angular moment discrete where $z$ is the third
of the three Cartesian axes. As usual, the correct eigenvalues, $s(s+1)$,
of operators like $S^2$ have been contracted to $s$ for convenience.

TABLE 7.5

ISOTOPIC SPIN FUNCTIONS FOR PI-MESON–NUCLEON SYSTEM

| Particle state | Isotopic spin function | |
|---|---|---|
| $\pi^+ p$ | $\pi(1,1)\,\nu(\tfrac{1}{2},\tfrac{1}{2})$ | $= \tau(\tfrac{3}{2},\tfrac{3}{2})$ |
| $\pi^0 p$ | $\pi(1,0)\,\nu(\tfrac{1}{2},\tfrac{1}{2})$ | $= \sqrt{\tfrac{2}{3}}\,\tau(\tfrac{3}{2},\tfrac{1}{2}) - \sqrt{\tfrac{1}{3}}\,\tau(\tfrac{1}{2},\tfrac{1}{2})$ |
| $\pi^- p$ | $\pi(1,-1)\,\nu(\tfrac{1}{2},\tfrac{1}{2})$ | $= \sqrt{\tfrac{1}{3}}\,\tau(\tfrac{3}{2},-\tfrac{1}{2}) + \sqrt{\tfrac{2}{3}}\,\tau(\tfrac{1}{2},-\tfrac{1}{2})$ |
| $\pi^+ n$ | $\pi(1,1)\,\nu(\tfrac{1}{2},-\tfrac{1}{2})$ | $= \sqrt{\tfrac{1}{3}}\,\tau(\tfrac{3}{2},\tfrac{1}{2}) + \sqrt{\tfrac{2}{3}}\,\tau(\tfrac{1}{2},\tfrac{1}{2})$ |
| $\pi^0 n$ | $\pi(1,0)\,\nu(\tfrac{1}{2},-\tfrac{1}{2})$ | $= \sqrt{\tfrac{2}{3}}\,\tau(\tfrac{3}{2},-\tfrac{1}{2}) - \sqrt{\tfrac{1}{3}}\,\tau(\tfrac{1}{2},-\tfrac{1}{2})$ |
| $\pi^- n$ | $\pi(1,-1)\,\nu(\tfrac{1}{2},-\tfrac{1}{2})$ | $= \tau(\tfrac{3}{2},-\tfrac{3}{2})$ |

We assume that the three types of pi-meson are indistinguishable
when the electromagnetic field is turned off and thus the pi-meson is
a triplet charge state corresponding to isotopic spin 1. We associate
the functions $\pi(1,1)$, $\pi(1,0)$, $\pi(1,-1)$ with the $\pi^+$, $\pi^0$, and $\pi^-$ mesons,
respectively. The pi-meson charge is the eigenvalue of the operator $e\Pi_3$.
There are only two charge states of the nucleon, which is therefore a
doublet charge state and corresponds to isotopic spin $\tfrac{1}{2}$. We associate
the functions $\nu(\tfrac{1}{2},\tfrac{1}{2})$ and $\nu(\tfrac{1}{2},-\tfrac{1}{2})$ with the proton ($p$) and neutron ($n$)
respectively. The nucleon charge is the eigenvalue of the operator
$e(N_3+\tfrac{1}{2})$.

We can now examine the isotopic spin function for the system
consisting of one meson and one nucleon. The functions for such
systems can be written immediately $\pi(p,p_3)\nu(n,n_3)$, but in this form
they are not, in general, eigenfunctions of the total isotopic spin
operators. However, just as in the theory of angular momentum, we
can write such functions as sums of eigenfunction of the total isotopic
spin operators. We follow precisely the procedure for adding two
angular momenta of $\hbar/2$ and $\hbar$; this requires the use of the Clebsch–
Gordan coefficients of Table 2.1, Section 2.7. The results are shown in
Table 7.5 where each physically observable system is given its wave
function in total isotopic spin eigenfunctions. We see that the pi-
meson–nucleon system is in general a mixture of states of total iso-
topic spin $\tfrac{3}{2}$ and $\tfrac{1}{2}$. The equations of Table 7.5 can be solved to give

the total isotopic spin functions in terms of the observable pi-meson–nucleon states. These solutions are given in Table 7.6. In this table

TABLE 7.6

ISOTOPIC SPIN FUNCTIONS FOR PI-MESON–NUCLEON SYSTEM

| Total isotopic spin state | Particle states |
|---|---|
| $\tau(\frac{3}{2}, \frac{3}{2})$ | $\pi^+ p$ |
| $\tau(\frac{3}{2}, \frac{1}{2})$ | $\sqrt{\frac{1}{3}}\, \pi^+ n + \sqrt{\frac{2}{3}}\, \pi^0 p$ |
| $\tau(\frac{3}{2}, -\frac{1}{2})$ | $\sqrt{\frac{2}{3}}\, \pi^0 n + \sqrt{\frac{1}{3}}\, \pi^- p$ |
| $\tau(\frac{3}{2}, -\frac{3}{2})$ | $\pi^- n$ |
| $\tau(\frac{1}{2}, \frac{1}{2})$ | $\sqrt{\frac{2}{3}}\, \pi^+ n - \sqrt{\frac{1}{3}}\, \pi^0 p$ |
| $\tau(\frac{1}{2}, -\frac{1}{2})$ | $\sqrt{\frac{1}{3}}\, \pi^0 n - \sqrt{\frac{2}{3}}\, \pi^- p$ |

we have replaced the products of single-particle isotopic spin functions with simple particle symbols, e.g.,

$$\pi(1, 1)\nu(\tfrac{1}{2}, -\tfrac{1}{2}) \equiv \pi^+ n,$$

$$\pi(1, -1)\nu(\tfrac{1}{2}, \tfrac{1}{2}) \equiv \pi^- p, \text{ etc.}$$

This procedure will be continued now we have made clear how the functions behave.

The application of charge independence to the meson–nucleon system is made by requiring that isotopic spin be a conserved quantity. The conservation of the eigenvalue of $T_3$ is automatically satisfied by charge conservation; thus we only need add the requirement that the eigenvalue of $T^2$ be conserved. This implies that the meson–nucleon interaction depends upon the total isotopic spin of the system and not upon its charge state. We shall apply charge independence in our analysis of meson–nucleon scattering.

## 7.7 Pi-Meson–Nucleon Scattering (1)

The properties of mesons and nucleons only permit us to make direct experimental observations on the following scattering reactions:

$$\pi^+ + p \rightarrow \pi^+ + p \quad \text{(1) elastic scattering,} \tag{7.14}$$

$$\pi^- + p \rightarrow \pi^- + p \quad \text{(2) elastic scattering,} \tag{7.15}$$

$$\pi^- + p \rightarrow \pi^0 + n \quad \text{(3) charge exchange scattering,} \tag{7.16}$$

$$\pi^- + p \rightarrow \gamma + n \quad \text{(4) radiative scattering.} \tag{7.17}$$

We consider only the energy range up to 250 Mev incident pi-meson kinetic energy, thus excluding reactions which produce strange particles or extra mesons, and permitting us to make partial wave analysis in terms of $l = 0$ and $l = 1$ waves only. Radiative scattering is known to have a relatively small cross section and can be ignored; this is convenient as the reaction does not conserve isotopic spin and excluding it allows us to analyse the other reactions assuming charge independence.

The first experimental results obtained by Fermi and his co-workers (Anderson *et al.*, 1953) indicated that at the same angle the differential cross section for the reactions (7.14), (7.15), and (7.16) were approximately in the ratio $9:1:2$. This result applies to measurements made at the same centre-of-mass energy for all reactions and can be immediately interpreted as a manifestation of charge independence. We shall examine the analysis which leads to this result; we commence by assuming that charge independence is correct and that isotopic spin is a conserved quantity. It follows that the interaction Hamiltonian for the system $H_I$ consists of two parts, $H_3 + H_1$. The first part, $H_3$, describes the interaction between meson and nucleon in the total isotopic spin state $t = \frac{3}{2}$ and causes transitions between initial and final states having $t = \frac{3}{2}$; the second part, $H_1$, does the same for the $t = \frac{1}{2}$ states.

The cross section for any reaction ($\sigma$) is proportional to the square of the matrix element between initial and final states:

$$\sigma \propto |(\psi_\beta | H_I | \psi_\alpha)|^2.$$

Applying this to our three reactions and expanding the initial and final states into total isotopic spin eigenfunctions, we have

$$\sigma_1 \propto |(\pi^+ p | H_I | \pi^+ p)|^2 = |(\tau(\tfrac{3}{2}, \tfrac{3}{2}) | H_I | \tau(\tfrac{3}{2}, \tfrac{3}{2}))|^2,$$

$$\sigma_2 \propto |(\pi^- p | H_I | \pi^- p)|^2$$
$$= |(\sqrt{\tfrac{1}{3}}\tau(\tfrac{3}{2}, -\tfrac{1}{2}) + \sqrt{\tfrac{2}{3}}\tau(\tfrac{1}{2}, -\tfrac{1}{2}) | H_I | \sqrt{\tfrac{1}{3}}\tau(\tfrac{3}{2}, -\tfrac{1}{2}) + \sqrt{\tfrac{2}{3}}\tau(\tfrac{1}{2}, -\tfrac{1}{2}))|^2,$$

$$\sigma_3 \propto |(\pi^0 n | H_I | \pi^- p)|^2$$
$$= |(\sqrt{\tfrac{2}{3}}\tau(\tfrac{3}{2}, -\tfrac{1}{2}) - \sqrt{\tfrac{1}{3}}\tau(\tfrac{1}{2}, -\tfrac{1}{2}) | H_I | \sqrt{\tfrac{1}{3}}\tau(\tfrac{3}{2}, -\tfrac{1}{2}) + \sqrt{\tfrac{2}{3}}\tau(\tfrac{1}{2}, -\tfrac{1}{2}))|^2.$$

The subscripts 1, 2, and 3 refer to reactions (7.14), (7.15), and (7.16), respectively. If all other things, such as energy and angle of scattering, are equal, the constants of proportionality are the same and we have

$$\sigma_1 : \sigma_2 : \sigma_3 = |M_3|^2 : |\tfrac{1}{3}M_3 + \tfrac{2}{3}M_1|^2 : |\tfrac{1}{3}\sqrt{2}\,M_3 - \tfrac{1}{3}\sqrt{2}\,M_1|^2,$$

where we have written

$$M_3 = (\tau(\tfrac{3}{2}, t_3) \,|\, H_3 \,|\, \tau(\tfrac{3}{2}, t_3)),$$

$$M_1 = (\tau(\tfrac{1}{2}, t_3) \,|\, H_1 \,|\, \tau(\tfrac{1}{2}, t_3)).$$

If $M_1$ is small compared with $M_3$, we see immediately that

$$\sigma_1 : \sigma_2 : \sigma_3 = 9 : 1 : 2. \tag{7.18}$$

That this result was observed at energies around 150 Mev indicates that charge independence was at least approximately valid and that the meson–nucleon interaction was particularly strong in the state having total isotopic spin $t = \tfrac{3}{2}$. A more complete analysis shows that $M_1$ is not negligible but does not change our conclusions.

## 7.8 Pi-Meson–Nucleon Scattering (II)

We are now in a position to make a complete partial wave analysis of pi-meson scattering which we started in Section 3.6. We are still considering the three reactions (7.14)–(7.16) introduced in the last section.

TABLE 7.7

PHASE SHIFT AND AMPLITUDE NOTATION

| State | | | Phase shift | Amplitude |
|---|---|---|---|---|
| $l$ | $t$ | $j$ | | |
| 0 | $\tfrac{1}{2}$ | $\tfrac{1}{2}$ | $\delta_1$ | $\alpha_1$ |
| 0 | $\tfrac{3}{2}$ | $\tfrac{1}{2}$ | $\delta_3$ | $\alpha_3$ |
| 1 | $\tfrac{1}{2}$ | $\tfrac{1}{2}$ | $\delta_{11}$ | $\alpha_{11}$ |
| 1 | $\tfrac{3}{2}$ | $\tfrac{1}{2}$ | $\delta_{31}$ | $\alpha_{31}$ |
| 1 | $\tfrac{1}{2}$ | $\tfrac{3}{2}$ | $\delta_{13}$ | $\alpha_{13}$ |
| 1 | $\tfrac{3}{2}$ | $\tfrac{3}{2}$ | $\delta_{33}$ | $\alpha_{33}$ |

We start by drawing up a list of conserved quantities. As in $\pi^+$ scattering, the operators $L^2, J^2, J_z, S^2$ have eigenvalues which are conserved, and to include $\pi^-$ scattering we add $T^2$ and $T_3$. The results do not depend on $S^2$, $J_z$, or $T_3$, and we have only to introduce a phase shift for each eigenstate of the operators $L^2$, $J^2$, and $T^2$. If $l = 0$, then $j = \tfrac{1}{2}$ and there are two phase shifts $\delta_3$ and $\delta_1$ for the eigenstates of $T^2$ having $t = \tfrac{3}{2}$ and $\tfrac{1}{2}$ respectively (i.e., phase shifts are $\delta_{2t}$). If $l = 1$ and $j = \tfrac{1}{2}$, the phase shifts are $\delta_{31}$ and $\delta_{11}$ for $t = \tfrac{3}{2}$ and $\tfrac{1}{2}$ respectively (i.e., phase shifts are $\delta_{2t2j}$). If $l = 1$ and $j = \tfrac{3}{2}$, the phase shifts are $\delta_{33}$ and $\delta_{13}$ (again $\delta_{2t2j}$). The arrangement of subscripts indicates immediately the state to which each phase shift applies; they are summarized in Table 7.7. For convenience we write $\alpha(= (e^{2i\delta} - 1)/2i)$ with the same subscripts.

Our analysis of the $\pi^+ p$ scattering in Section 3.6 is still correct as it takes place entirely in the state $t = \frac{3}{2}$; we have only to change the subscripts to indicate this. In Section 3.6 the phase shifts $\delta, \delta_1, \delta_3$ become $\delta_3, \delta_{31}, \delta_{33}$ and $a, a_1, a_3$ become $\alpha_3, \alpha_{31}, \alpha_{33}$.

We now consider the $\pi^- p$ scattering. The incoming wave functions can be expanded into partial waves which are eigenfunctions of $L^2$, $L_z$, $S^2$, $S_z$, $N^2$, $N_3$, $\pi^2$, $\pi_3$; viz.,

$$\psi(l, 0)\chi(\tfrac{1}{2}, \pm\tfrac{1}{2})\nu(\tfrac{1}{2}, \tfrac{1}{2})\pi(1, -1).$$

These terms must be expanded into eigenfunctions of $L^2, J^2, J_z$ expressed as $\phi(l,j,j_z)$ and of $T^2$ and $T_3$ expressed as $\tau(t, t_3)$. As for $\pi^+$ scattering, we take $j_z = s_z = \frac{1}{2}$ (proton spin along the $z$ axis). Then the expansions required are:

$S$ waves: $\psi(0, 0)\chi(\tfrac{1}{2}, \tfrac{1}{2})\nu(\tfrac{1}{2}, \tfrac{1}{2})\pi(1, -1)$

$$= \phi(0, \tfrac{1}{2}, \tfrac{1}{2})\,[\sqrt{\tfrac{1}{3}}\,\tau(\tfrac{3}{2}, -\tfrac{1}{2}) - \sqrt{\tfrac{2}{3}}\,\tau(\tfrac{1}{2}, -\tfrac{1}{2})], \tag{7.19}$$

$P$ waves: $\psi(1, 0)\chi(\tfrac{1}{2}, \tfrac{1}{2})\nu(\tfrac{1}{2}, \tfrac{1}{2})\pi(1, -1)$

$$= [\sqrt{\tfrac{2}{3}}\,\phi(1, \tfrac{3}{2}, \tfrac{1}{2}) - \sqrt{\tfrac{1}{3}}\,\phi(1, \tfrac{1}{2}, \tfrac{1}{2})]\,[\sqrt{\tfrac{1}{3}}\,\tau(\tfrac{3}{2}, -\tfrac{1}{2}) - \sqrt{\tfrac{2}{3}}\,\tau(\tfrac{1}{2}, -\tfrac{1}{2})]. \tag{7.20}$$

Equations (7.19) and (7.20) are strictly analogous to Eqs. (3.10) and (3.11), differing only in the addition of the isotopic spin function. If we substitute Eqs. (7.19) and (7.20) into (3.8) and include the proton spin and the isotopic spin functions, we find, in analogy with Eq. (3.13),

$$e^{ikz}\chi(\tfrac{1}{2}, \tfrac{1}{2})\pi^- p$$
$$= \sqrt{4\pi}\,[F_0(kr)\,\phi(0, \tfrac{1}{2}, \tfrac{1}{2}) + iF_1(kr)\sqrt{3}\,\{\sqrt{\tfrac{2}{3}}\,\phi(1, \tfrac{3}{2}, \tfrac{1}{2}) - \sqrt{\tfrac{1}{3}}\,\phi(1, \tfrac{1}{2}, \tfrac{1}{2})\}$$
$$+ \text{higher partial waves}]\,[\sqrt{\tfrac{1}{3}}\,\tau(\tfrac{3}{2}, -\tfrac{1}{2}) - \sqrt{\tfrac{2}{3}}\,\tau(\tfrac{1}{2}, -\tfrac{1}{2})].$$

We can now pick out each term and associate with it the outgoing amplitude $\alpha$, to find the total outgoing amplitude $f(\theta)$, as in Eq. (3.14):

$$f(\theta) =$$
$$\frac{\sqrt{4\pi}}{k}\{[\alpha_3 \phi(0, \tfrac{1}{2}, \tfrac{1}{2}) + \sqrt{3}\,\{\alpha_{33}\sqrt{\tfrac{2}{3}}\,\phi(1, \tfrac{3}{2}, \tfrac{1}{2}) - \alpha_{31}\sqrt{\tfrac{1}{3}}\,\phi(1, \tfrac{1}{2}, \tfrac{1}{2})\}]\sqrt{\tfrac{1}{3}}\,\tau(\tfrac{3}{2}, -\tfrac{1}{2})$$
$$- [\alpha_1 \phi(0, \tfrac{1}{2}, \tfrac{1}{2}) + \sqrt{3}\,\{\alpha_{13}\sqrt{\tfrac{2}{3}}\,\phi(1, \tfrac{3}{2}, \tfrac{1}{2}) - \alpha_{11}\sqrt{\tfrac{1}{3}}\,\phi(1, \tfrac{1}{2}, \tfrac{1}{2})\}]\sqrt{\tfrac{2}{3}}\,\tau(\tfrac{1}{2}, -\tfrac{1}{2})\}.$$

This outgoing wave must be recomposed into observable eigenfunctions as in the step from Eqs. (3.14) to (3.18). Using Eqs. (3.15) to (3.17) and Table 7 6, we find

$$f(\theta) = \frac{\sqrt{4\pi}}{k} \pi^- p \{\tfrac{1}{3}(\alpha_3 + 2\alpha_1) \psi(0,0) \chi(\tfrac{1}{2}, \tfrac{1}{2}) + \tfrac{1}{3}\sqrt{\tfrac{1}{3}} (2\alpha_{33} + \alpha_{31} + 4\alpha_{13} + 2\alpha_{11})$$

$$\times \psi(1,0) \chi(\tfrac{1}{2}, \tfrac{1}{2}) + \tfrac{1}{3}\sqrt{\tfrac{2}{3}} (\alpha_{33} - \alpha_{31} + 2\alpha_{13} - 2\alpha_{11}) \psi(1,1) \chi(\tfrac{1}{2}, -\tfrac{1}{2})\}$$

$$+ \frac{\sqrt{4\pi}}{k} \pi^0 n \{\tfrac{1}{3}\sqrt{2} (\alpha_3 - \alpha_1) \psi(0,0) \chi(\tfrac{1}{2}, \tfrac{1}{2}) + \tfrac{1}{3}\sqrt{\tfrac{1}{3}} (2\alpha_{33} + \alpha_{31} - 2\alpha_{13} - \alpha_{11})$$

$$\times \psi(1,0) \chi(\tfrac{1}{2}, \tfrac{1}{2}) + \tfrac{2}{3}\sqrt{\tfrac{1}{3}} (\alpha_{33} - \alpha_{31} - \alpha_{13} + \alpha_{11}) \psi(1,1) \chi(\tfrac{1}{2}, -\tfrac{1}{2})\}.$$

We can now extract the two differential cross sections required; a subscript 2 or 3 indicates to which reaction (elastic or charge exchange) the cross section belongs. Substituting the spherical harmonics of Section 2.8 and separating the spin flip amplitudes from the total amplitude, we find that

$$\frac{d\sigma_2}{d\Omega} = \frac{1}{9k^2} \{|(\alpha_3 + 2\alpha_1) + (2\alpha_{33} + \alpha_{31} + 4\alpha_{13} + 2\alpha_{11}) \cos\theta|^2$$

$$+ |(\alpha_{33} - \alpha_{31} + 2\alpha_{13} - 2\alpha_{11}) \sin\theta|^2\}, \tag{7.21}$$

and

$$\frac{d\sigma_3}{d\Omega} = \frac{2}{9k^2} \{|(\alpha_3 - \alpha_1) + (2\alpha_{33} + \alpha_{31} - 2\alpha_{13} + 2\alpha_{11}) \cos\theta|^2$$

$$+ |(\alpha_{33} - \alpha_{31} - \alpha_{13} + \alpha_{11}) \sin\theta|^2\}. \tag{7.22}$$

For comparison we have the $\pi^+ p$ differential scattering cross section

$$\frac{d\sigma_1}{d\Omega} = \frac{1}{k^2} \{|\alpha_3 + (2\alpha_{33} + \alpha_{31}) \cos\theta|^2 + |(\alpha_{33} - \alpha_{31}) \sin\theta|^2\}. \tag{7.23}$$

Throughout

$$\alpha = (e^{2i\delta} - 1)/2i.$$

We notice immediately that if only the $t = \tfrac{3}{2}$ state acts ($\alpha_1 = \alpha_{13} = \alpha_{11} = 0$) then the cross sections 1, 2, and 3 are in the ratio $9 : 1 : 2$, as we have already shown.

The most important and obvious fact about our analysis is that it has permitted us to describe three differential cross sections in terms of six phase shifts, whereas without the simplification of charge independence the number would be nine. Thus if we determine the differential cross sections at three angles for each of the three reactions, it should be possible to overdetermine the phase shifts and supply a check on the principle of charge independence. Unfortunately, the statistical accuracy of the experiments is insufficient to enable this to be done and in practice all the data at one energy are processed to find the phase shifts which best fit the data; this is done by a least squares fit (Anderson *et al.*, 1953). The equations do not hide the complexity of this manœuvre, which has to be performed on a high-speed computing machine. There is a graphical method due to Ashkin (Ashkin and Vosko, 1953). We shall discuss the results of these analyses in the next section.

## 7.9 The Results of the Phase Shift Analysis

We have already noticed that scattering in the meson–nucleon state $t = \frac{3}{2}$, $j = \frac{3}{2}$ is very important and we therefore start our discussion by assuming that all phase shifts are zero except $\delta_{33}$. The $\pi^+$ scattering cross section is described by Eq. (7.23), which reduces to the form

$$k^2 \frac{d\sigma_1}{d\Omega} = \sin^2 \delta_{33}(3 \cos^2 \theta + 1),$$

and the total cross section is given by

$$\sigma_1 = \frac{8\pi}{k^2} \sin^2 \delta_{33}.$$

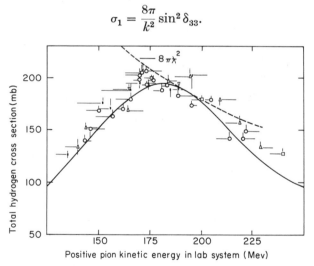

FIG. 7.1. Graph of the total cross section for positive pi-mesons in hydrogen as a function of energy in a range around the resonance maximum. The solid line is the contribution from the $\delta_{33}$ phase shift as given by a Serber–Lee plot of the data. The experimental points are from several sources (Lindenbaum and Yuan, 1958).

Under the conditions assumed, the $\pi^-$ cross sections are given by the ratios of Eq. (7.18). The maximum total cross section ($\pi^+$) which can occur at any energy is $8\pi/k^2$, but this happens only if $\delta_{33} = \frac{1}{2}\pi, \frac{3}{2}\pi, \ldots$, etc.; if the phase shift varies with energy in such a way that it passes through one of these values, there is resonance at that energy. In

Fig. 7.1 we show the data assembled by Lindenbaum and Yuan (1958) for the total cross section for $\pi^+$ mesons in hydrogen around 180 Mev. The data indicate that the cross section is at least $8\pi/k^2$ at about 190 Mev; any excess can be attributed to other states, although their phase shifts must be small since the experimental cross sections are not significantly greater than $8\pi/k^2$. In Fig. 7.2, $\pi^-$ and $\pi^+$ total cross

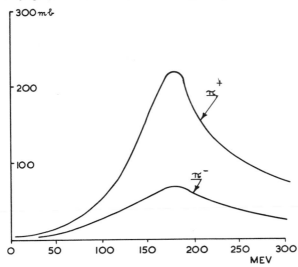

FIG. 7.2. Graph of the total cross section for positive and negative pi-mesons in hydrogen in the energy range 0 to 300 Mev (kinetic energy of incident mesons in laboratory).

sections in hydrogen are plotted together as a function of meson energy. The fact that the $\pi^-$ curve is just $\frac{1}{3}$ of the $\pi^+$ curve verifies the ratios derived in Section 7.7 and indicates the predominance of the 33 phase shift over a wide range of energies. The prominence of the peak at about 200 Mev in the cross-section curves is a feature of the "resonance" which occurs as $\delta_{33}$ passes through 90°. The variation of $\delta_{33}$ with energy is fairly well described by a formula derived by Chew and Low (1956a) in an approximate solution of the scattering problem in the symmetric pseudoscalar meson theory; it is

$$\frac{\eta^3}{\omega}\cot\delta_{33} = \frac{3}{4f^2}\left(1 - \frac{\omega}{\omega_0}\right).$$

Serber and Lee (see Castillejo et al., 1956) obtain a similar formula for the charged and neutral scalar meson theory:

$$\frac{\eta^3}{\omega}\cot\delta_{33} - \frac{1}{\omega} = \frac{3}{4f^2}\left(1 - \frac{\omega}{\omega_0}\right).$$

In both these formulae $\eta$ is the centre-of-mass pi-meson momentum in units of $m_\pi c$ and $\omega$ is the total energy in the centre of mass, less the nucleon rest mass, in units of $m_\pi c^2$; $\omega_0$ is the resonance value of $\omega$ and $f^2$ is a constant which is a measure of the strength of the pi-meson–nucleon interaction (Section 9.10). A plot of $(\eta^3/\omega)\cot\delta_{33}$ as a function of $\omega$ should yield a straight line if the Chew–Low formula is correct.

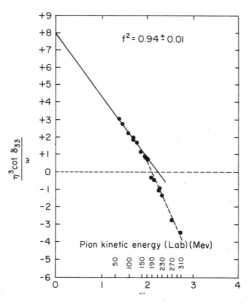

FIG. 7.3. A Chew–Low plot. For the source of the experimental points see the source of this figure (Lindenbaum and Yuan, 1958).

Lindenbaum and Yuan (1958) have plotted the data that they collected and their graph is shown in Fig. 7.3. There is a distinct break in the line joining the experimental points at about 190 Mev which might be due to the onset of effects due to inelastic scattering. A Serber–Lee plot (Lindenbaum, 1957) has the same break. Extrapolated to $\omega = 0$, these plots lead to values for $f^2$ of $0.094 \pm 0.010$ and $0.107 \pm 0.010$, respectively. Recently, more accurate data have become available, and Bernardini (1959) has reported that the Chew–Low plot now gives $f^2 = 0.081 \pm 0.007$. Bernardini reviews this and other determinations of $f^2$ and concludes that the best value is $0.0813 \pm 0.0035$. The resonance condition $\delta_{33} = 90°$ is the energy at which the ordinate on the Chew–Low plot is zero, or at which it is $-1/\omega$ on the Serber–Lee plot. Due to the break in the plotted lines there is some uncertainty in the position of the resonance. Lindenbaum concludes that it is at $190 \pm ^{20}_{10}$ Mev laboratory pi-meson kinetic energy.

The predominance of the $\delta_{33}$ phase shift leads to a $1 + 3\cos^2\theta$ form for the differential scattering cross section. In Fig. 7.4 we show as an

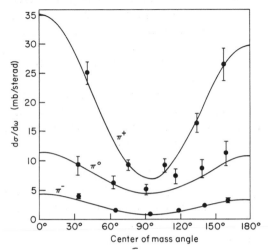

FIG. 7.4. Graph of the three differential scattering cross sections of pi-meson scattering at hydrogen as a function of centre-of-mass scattering angle at an incident laboratory energy of 189 Mev (Anderson et al., 1955a).

example the results of Anderson et al. (1955a); the angular distribution is very close to the form expected from this predominance. However, the data are normally sufficiently accurate to allow the remaining phase shifts to be determined; this procedure was first used by Fermi and his co-workers at Chicago (Anderson et al., 1953) and since that time all pi-meson–proton scattering experiments below 300 Mev have been analysed in this way. The analyses often yield several sets of phase shifts all of which fit the observations; one set will contain a predominant $\delta_{33}$ phase shift, and is the only one which varies with energy in a way which is physically acceptable. It is called the Fermi set. There have been several reviews of the properties of the phase shifts. Bethe and de Hoffmann (1955) gave an extensive discussion of the phase shift analysis and Orear (1955, 1956) showed that all the data were consistent with the following energy variation for the Fermi phase shifts:

$$\delta_1 = (0.167 \pm 0.012)\,\eta, \tag{7.24}$$

$$\delta_3 = -(0.105 \pm 0.010)\,\eta, \tag{7.25}$$

where $\eta$ is the momentum of the pi-meson in the centre of mass in units of $m_\pi c$. Orear takes $\delta_{33}$ to vary according to the Chew–Low formula with $f^2 = 0.087$ and $\omega_0 = 2.17$. This $f^2$ is different from the value given by Lindenbaum and Yuan, a fact probably to be attributed to the more extensive data available to the latter authors. The small phase shifts which Orear puts equal to zero cannot be found reliably from the experimental results and no consistent behaviour has been found except for $\delta_{31}$, which is small and negative up to 300 Mev (Ferrari *et al.*, 1956, and Mukhin *et al.*, 1957). There is a slight flaw in Orear's proposal concerning the behaviour of $\delta_3$: experimental results suggest that its absolute value is increasing more rapidly above 180 Mev than Eq. (7.25) allows. This may be due to not allowing for the presence of some $D$ wave. The Chew–Low theory predicts that there should be some $D$ wave at these energies.

We have already referred to the nonuniqueness of any set of phase shifts. The outstanding ambiguity is one of sign as it is possible to change simultaneously the sign of all phase shifts and leave the cross sections unchanged. This difficulty is resolved by searching for interference between the ordinary Coulomb scattering and the nuclear scattering (Van Hove, 1952). The Coulomb scattering is predominant at very small angles of scattering, is comparable to the nuclear scattering at about 10° for 120-Mev pi-mesons, and is negligible at larger angles. Around 10° any interference between the two is marked and will be constructive or destructive as the $\delta_{33}$ phase shift is negative or positive respectively. Orear (1954) finds destructive interference and thus fixes the sign of all the appreciable phase shifts. Figure 7.5 shows the angular distribution observed by Orear compared with the best fits for positive and negative $\delta_{33}$.

For every Fermi set of phase shifts there exists a second set, discovered by Yang, which has phase shifts (primed) related to the Fermi phase shifts (unprimed) by the equations:

$$\delta_{33} - \delta_{31} = -(\delta'_{33} - \delta'_{31}),  \tag{7.26}$$

$$2\exp(2i\delta_{33}) + \exp(2i\delta_{31}) = 2\exp(2i\delta'_{33}) + \exp(2i\delta'_{31}).  \tag{7.27}$$

However, this Yang set passes through three resonances by the time the Fermi set has reached the $\delta_{33}$ resonance; such behaviour is considered unlikely and is not supported by the results of applying dispersion relations (Section 13.4). Fermi (1953) has shown that a measurement of the polarization of the nucleons recoiling from meson scattering would be a test for the correctness of any proposed set of phase shifts (see Section 8.3). Measurements of this polarization could not be made before the discovery that nucleon scattering at carbon or helium was a good way of analysing for polarization in the required energy range. The results obtained by Kunze *et al.* (1960) are in favour of the Fermi set.

Another set of phase shifts can be generated by the so-called Minami ambiguity (Minami, 1954). This set also fails to withstand the application of dispersion relations (Section 13.4).

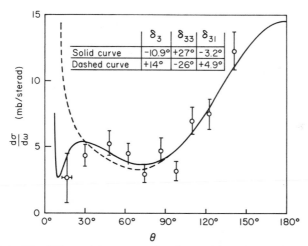

| | $\delta_3$ | $\delta_{33}$ | $\delta_{31}$ |
|---|---|---|---|
| Solid curve | $-10.9°$ | $+27°$ | $-3.2°$ |
| Dashed curve | $+14°$ | $-26°$ | $+4.9°$ |

FIG. 7.5. The differential cross section for positive pi-meson scattering at hydrogen at 122 Mev showing the interference between Coulomb and nuclear scattering (Orear, 1954).

The total and differential cross sections at energies above 300 Mev do not yield to analysis in terms of $S$ and $P$ waves alone. Higher partial waves and the addition of a number of inelastic channels make the problem complicated. For a fuller discussion we refer readers to Lindenbaum's review (1957).

## 7.10 Introduction to Pi-Meson Photoproduction

Pi-mesons can be produced by the absorption of high-energy photons by nucleons:

$$\gamma + p \rightarrow \pi^+ + n, \tag{7.28}$$

$$\gamma + p \rightarrow \pi^0 + p, \tag{7.29}$$

$$\gamma + n \rightarrow \pi^- + p, \tag{7.30}$$

$$\gamma + n \rightarrow \pi^0 + n. \tag{7.31}$$

The last two reactions can only be observed in complex nuclei. The threshold for production from protons is about 150 Mev for $\pi^+$ and 145 Mev for $\pi^0$. The total cross sections for the production reactions from protons are shown in Figs. 7.6 and 7.7; between threshold and

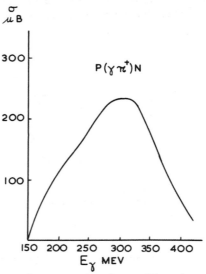

FIG. 7.6. The total cross section for positive pi-meson photoproduction from hydrogen as a function of incident photon energy.

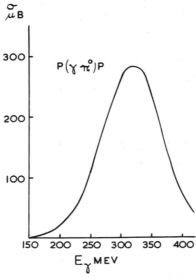

FIG. 7.7. The total cross section for neutral pi-meson photoproduction from hydrogen as a function of incident photon energy.

about 200 Mev the angular distribution of $\pi^+$ mesons is approximately uniform in the centre of mass, but becomes anisotropic between 200 and 300 Mev. In the same energy range the distribution of photo-produced $\pi^0$ mesons is very close to $2 + 3\sin^2\theta$. We can use the observed distributions to confirm some of our findings about the meson–nucleon interaction. We notice that, just above threshold, $\pi^0$ production is small compared to $\pi^+$ production, and becomes comparable near 300-Mev photon energy.

TABLE 7.8

DETAILS OF THE SIMPLEST ELECTROMAGNETIC TRANSITIONS IN THE PHOTOPRODUCTION OF MESONS

| Multi-pole order | Parity | Total angular momentum | Simplest accessible meson–nucleon state | Angular distribution | Momentum depen-dence |
|---|---|---|---|---|---|
| Electric dipole | 1 | − | $\frac{1}{2}$ | $S_{1/2}$ | 1 | $p$ |
| | | | $\frac{3}{2}$ | $D_{3/2}$ | $2 + 3\sin^2\theta$ | $p^5$ |
| Magnetic dipole | 1 | + | $\frac{1}{2}$ | $P_{1/2}$ | 1 | $p^3$ |
| | | | $\frac{3}{2}$ | $P_{3/2}$ | $2 + 3\sin^2\theta$ | $p^3$ |
| Electric quadrupole | 2 | + | $\frac{3}{2}$ | $P_{3/2}$ | $1 + \cos^2\theta$ | $p^3$ |
| | | | $\frac{5}{2}$ | $F_{5/2}$ | $1 + 6\cos^2\theta - 5\cos^4\theta$ | $p^7$ |
| Magnetic quadrupole | 2 | − | $\frac{3}{2}$ | $D_{3/2}$ | $1 + \cos^2\theta$ | $p^5$ |
| | | | $\frac{5}{2}$ | $D_{5/2}$ | $1 + 6\cos^2\theta - 5\cos^4\theta$ | $p^5$ |

It is possible to use parity and angular momentum conservation arguments to determine the electromagnetic transitions responsible for the pi-meson production. We start by displaying the outgoing meson–nucleon state which can be generated by the four simplest multipoles (we assume pseudoscalar mesons). Using the data of Table 4.1, we can calculate the possible total angular momentum states accessible to the initial state consisting of the target proton and the specified photon multipole. Using these values and the parity of the initial state, we can find the simplest possible state of the outgoing meson–nucleon system. This information is given in Table 7.8.

The penultimate column of Table 7.8 shows the angular distribution of the outgoing pi-meson in the centre of mass; we shall now proceed to show how the distributions are calculated. The incoming photon has an angular momentum state determined by its polarity and the two possible orientations of its "spin", along or against the $z$ axis which we take in the direction of incidence of the photon; for convenience, we indicate the value of this spin component by the notation $l_z$, where $l$ is the photon polarity. The proton target has spin $s = \frac{1}{2}$ and two possible values of its $z$ component, $s_z = \pm \frac{1}{2}$; we need only consider one of these, as we shall consider both photon spin orientations (the initial state with the opposite proton spin leads to the same angular distribution given by an amplitude which is incoherent with the first). We have chosen to deal with magnetic dipole absorption leading to a $P_{3/2}$ meson–nucleon state. The incoming photon is represented by one of the angular momentum functions $\gamma(1, \pm 1)$ and proton by the spin function $\chi(\frac{1}{2}, \frac{1}{2})$. By the rules of vector addition we can decompose either initial state into total angular momentum eigenfunctions $\phi(j, j_z)$, thus:

$$\gamma(1, +1)\chi(\tfrac{1}{2}, \tfrac{1}{2}) = \phi(\tfrac{3}{2}, \tfrac{3}{2}),$$

$$\gamma(1, -1)\chi(\tfrac{1}{2}, \tfrac{1}{2}) = \sqrt{\tfrac{1}{3}}\,\phi(\tfrac{3}{2}, -\tfrac{1}{2}) - \sqrt{\tfrac{2}{3}}\,\phi(\tfrac{1}{2}, -\tfrac{1}{2}).$$

We are interested only in the states having $j = \frac{3}{2}$; each of the two occurring can be decomposed into outgoing $P$ waves and proton spin states; thus:

$$\phi(\tfrac{3}{2}, \tfrac{3}{2}) = \psi(1, 1)\chi(\tfrac{1}{2}, \tfrac{1}{2}),$$

$$\phi(\tfrac{3}{2}, -\tfrac{1}{2}) = \sqrt{\tfrac{1}{3}}\,\psi(1, -1)\chi(\tfrac{1}{2}, \tfrac{1}{2}) + \sqrt{\tfrac{2}{3}}\,\psi(1, 0)\chi(\tfrac{1}{2}, -\tfrac{1}{2}).$$

The final state amplitude is a sum of these eigenfunctions weighted by the amplitude with which they occur in the initial state; thus for our case the final state amplitudes are

$$f_{+1}(\theta) = \psi(1, 1)\chi(\tfrac{1}{2}, \tfrac{1}{2}), \text{ for photon spin in } z \text{ direction,}$$

$$f_{-1}(\theta) = \tfrac{1}{3}\psi(1, -1)\chi(\tfrac{1}{2}, \tfrac{1}{2}) + \sqrt{\tfrac{2}{3}}\,\psi(1, 0)\chi(\tfrac{1}{2}, -\tfrac{1}{2}), \text{ for photon spin in } -z$$
direction.

Substituting the spherical harmonics, we find the intensities from these two states to be given by

$$I_{+1} = \frac{3}{8\pi} \sin^2 \theta,$$

and

$$I_{-1} = \frac{1}{24\pi} \sin^2 \theta + \frac{1}{6\pi} \cos^2 \theta.$$

If there is no polarization in the incoming photon beam, these states are incoherent with weights $\frac{1}{2}$, and therefore the final outgoing intensity is

$$I(\theta) = \frac{3}{16\pi}\left(\sin^2\theta + \frac{1}{9}\sin^2\theta + \frac{4}{9}\cos^2\theta\right)$$

or

$$I(\theta) \propto 2 + 3\sin^2\theta.$$

In this way it is possible to calculate the distributions given in the penultimate column of Table 7.8. In the last column we have indicated how the cross section for production is expected to depend on the momentum $p$ of the outgoing meson, namely $p^{2l+1}$, $l$ being the orbital state of the pi-meson. This dependence can be seen by applying the transition rate formula. The density of the meson wave function at very small distances is $p^l$, so the matrix element squared is proportional to $p^{2l}$; the density of states factor multiplies in a further $p$, giving an over-all effect of a cross section proportional to $p^{2l+1}$. For a full discussion we refer readers to an article by Feld (1955); the result is only valid for energies not too far above threshold.

We can now make a preliminary comparison with the experimental data. Just above threshold, $150\ \mathrm{Mev} < E_\gamma < 200\ \mathrm{Mev}$, the meson is produced with low energy and consequently we expect it to be produced in an $S$ state of orbital angular momentum. The $\pi^+$ differential cross section is uniform and the momentum dependence is $p$; all this is consistent with an electric dipole interaction to produce an $S_{1/2}$ final state. At higher energies the onset of the $2 + 3\sin^2\theta$ distribution for the $\pi^0$ mesons and a cross section, which is increasing approximately as $p^3$ (for $E_\gamma < 280\ \mathrm{Mev}$), indicate that the predominant interaction is magnetic dipole absorption to give a $P_{3/2}$ final state. That this is a strongly interacting meson–nucleon state we know already from the results of scattering experiments; it is also a resonant state and this is reflected in the photoproduction cross sections by the maximum, which occurs at about 330-Mev incident photon energy. The meson kinetic energy at which $\sigma k_\pi^2$ is a maximum for scattering is 127 Mev in the centre-of-mass coordinates, whilst $\sigma k_\gamma^2$ is a maximum for photoproduction at a meson kinetic energy of 121 Mev in the centre of mass. The closeness of these energies is striking.

Our arguments and conclusions from the conservation of parity and angular momentum can only be approximate as we have not taken into account the possibility of absorption of several different multipoles leading to a mixture of different final states and consequent changes in distribution due to interference. We now proceed to give a fuller discussion which attempts to connect photoproduction with the results of scattering experiments.

## 7.11 The Complete Partial Wave Analysis of Photoproduction

We wish to analyse the four photoproduction reactions [Eqs. (7.28)–(7.31)] assuming that only $S$ and $P$ wave final states are important. There are four transitions to these states (Table 7.8) and we therefore require 16 matrix elements or 32 real numbers to describe these reactions. These 32 numbers are not independent and can be reduced to 24 by applying an analysis based on the isotopic spin formalism. In addition, the requirement of invariance under time reversal and the insertion of the meson–nucleon scattering phase shifts allow a final reduction to 12 numbers (Table 7.9). This reduction of 32 numbers to 12 is a complex procedure and the algebraic equations tend to become cumbersome; we shall have to make several contractions in nomenclature.

We consider one of the angular momentum states as specified by the transitions given in Table 7.8. Such a transition can apply to the four reactions and there are therefore four transition matrix elements for this angular momentum state. If, instead of by reaction products, the final states are specified by isotopic spin quantum numbers, then there are two matrix elements corresponding to the two final states having $t = \frac{3}{2}$ and $t = \frac{1}{2}$ respectively; unfortunately, these elements depend on $t_3$, which can be $+\frac{1}{2}$ or $-\frac{1}{2}$, and again we have four matrix elements. The electromagnetic interaction does not conserve isotopic spin so that there is no immediately obvious relation between these matrix elements. However, Watson (1952) has shown that they are not independent and can be reduced to three. We are not in a position to follow his analysis carefully, but we can outline the procedure. Watson shows that the electromagnetic interaction can be broken down into two parts, one of which is a scalar $S$ in isotopic spin space, and the other which is a vector $\mathbf{V}$. The scalar part can only cause transitions in which the total isotopic spin does not change, $\Delta t = 0$. The vector can cause transitions in which the changes in total isotopic spin are

$$\Delta t = \pm 1 \qquad \text{if} \quad t_3 = 0,$$

$$\Delta t = 0, \pm 1 \qquad \text{if} \quad t_3 \neq 0.$$

Here $\Delta t$ is the change in total isotopic spin from the initial to the final state. Since the initial state is a nucleon alone, the initial state has total isotopic spin $= n = \frac{1}{2}$ using the nomenclature of Table 7.4. The final state is a meson plus nucleon which has $t = \frac{3}{2}$ or $\frac{1}{2}$. Then

$$t - n = \Delta t = 0 \text{ or } +1.$$

We are interested in matrix elements of the kind

$$(\tau(t, t_3) \,|\, S + \mathbf{V} \,|\, \nu(n, n_3)\,).$$

By conservation of charge $n_3 = t_3 = \pm \frac{1}{2}$. It can be shown (Condon and Shortley, 1951) that the matrix element of $S$ is independent of $t_3$ as is the matrix element of $\mathbf{V}$ when $t = n + 1$. However, the matrix element of $\mathbf{V}$ when $t = n$ is proportional to $t_3$. Thus, using our information on $S$ and $V$, we can define $S_1$, $V_1$, and $V_3$ by

$$S_1 = (\tau(\tfrac{1}{2}, \pm \tfrac{1}{2}) \,|\, S \,|\, \nu(\tfrac{1}{2}, \pm \tfrac{1}{2})\,), \tag{7.32}$$

$$\pm \tfrac{1}{2} V_1 = (\tau(\tfrac{1}{2}, \pm \tfrac{1}{2}) \,|\, \mathbf{V} \,|\, \nu(\tfrac{1}{2}, \pm \tfrac{1}{2})\,), \tag{7.33}$$

$$\sqrt{2}\, V_3 = (\tau(\tfrac{3}{2}, \pm \tfrac{1}{2}) \,|\, \mathbf{V} \,|\, \nu(\tfrac{1}{2}, \pm \tfrac{1}{2})\,). \tag{7.34}$$

The subscripts on the left are $2t$. A $\sqrt{2}$ and $\frac{1}{2}$ are kept in Eqs. (7.32)–(7.34) as $V_1$ and $V_3$ are then more closely related (see Condon and Shortley, 1951). We have already noted that only one matrix element ($V_1$) depends on $t_3$, that is, on whether the target nucleon is a proton or a neutron; this effectively reduces the four matrix elements to three. Of course, these three matrix elements continue to depend on energy and on the angular momentum states. For one energy and angular momentum state we can compute the appropriate matrix element for all four reactions in terms of $S_1$, $V_1$, and $V_3$. This is done as in the following example; consider

$$\gamma + p \rightarrow \pi^+ + n.$$

The final state in the total matrix element is expanded into eigenfunctions of total isotopic spin:

$$\begin{aligned}(\pi^+ n \,|\, S + \mathbf{V} \,|\, \gamma p) &= (\sqrt{\tfrac{1}{3}}\,\tau(\tfrac{3}{2}, \tfrac{1}{2}) + \sqrt{\tfrac{2}{3}}\,\tau(\tfrac{1}{2}, \tfrac{1}{2}) \,|\, S + \mathbf{V} \,|\, \nu(\tfrac{1}{2}, \tfrac{1}{2})\,) \\ &= \sqrt{\tfrac{1}{3}}\,\{\sqrt{2}\, V_3 - \sqrt{\tfrac{1}{2}}(2S_1 + V_1)\}. \end{aligned} \tag{7.35}$$

Similarly,

$$(\pi^0 p \,|\, S + \mathbf{V} \,|\, \gamma p) = \sqrt{\tfrac{1}{3}}\,\{2V_3 - \tfrac{1}{2}(2S_1 + V_1)\}, \tag{7.36}$$

$$(\pi^- p \,|\, S + \mathbf{V} \,|\, \gamma n) = \sqrt{\tfrac{1}{3}}\,\{\sqrt{2}\, V_3 + \sqrt{\tfrac{1}{2}}\,(2S_1 - V_1)\}, \tag{7.37}$$

$$(\pi^0 n \,|\, S + \mathbf{V} \,|\, \gamma n) = \sqrt{\tfrac{1}{3}}\,\{2V_3 - \tfrac{1}{2}(2S_1 - V_1)\}. \tag{7.38}$$

Thus for any photoproduction reaction two matrix elements operate, one causing transitions to the $t = \frac{3}{2}$ state and proportional to $V_3$, the other causing transitions to the $t = \frac{1}{2}$ state and proportional to $2S_1 \pm V_1$, the sign being $+$ when the target is a proton and $-$ when it is a neutron. We shall use these matrix elements in an extended form in the subsequent analysis, but as they only apply to one angular momentum state the notation must be expanded as shown in Table 7.9.

The procedure just described has reduced our 32 real numbers to 24; we can now halve this number by relating the matrix elements to the scattering phase shifts by a procedure which is essentially the application of time reversal invariance. This relation is established by constructing an $S$-matrix which must have general properties which were derived in Chapter V. We first choose and enumerate all the channels of interest. There are six channels corresponding to the six meson–nucleon scattering phase shifts and these are involved as the final states in photoproduction. The initial photon states contribute another three channels corresponding to electric and magnetic dipole, and to electric quadrupole as permitted by parity and angular momentum conservation (Table 7.8). There are, therefore, nine channels contributing to the $S$-matrix. If there are no off-diagonal elements, then transitions between channels are impossible. If we assume charge independence holds as well as the conservation of angular momentum, there can be no off-diagonal elements connecting different meson–nucleon states. If the electromagnetic interaction is switched off, there can be no photon scattering (diagonal elements = 1) and no photoproduction, and all off-diagonal elements are zero. We call this matrix $S_0$; it is

$$S_0 =$$

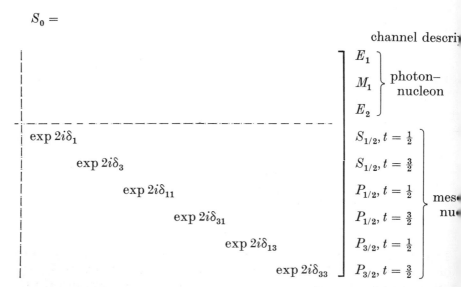

channel descri

$$\left.\begin{array}{l} E_1 \\ M_1 \\ E_2 \end{array}\right\} \begin{array}{l} \text{photon–} \\ \text{nucleon} \end{array}$$

$$\begin{array}{l} \exp 2i\delta_1 \\ \quad \exp 2i\delta_3 \\ \qquad \exp 2i\delta_{11} \\ \qquad\quad \exp 2i\delta_{31} \\ \qquad\qquad \exp 2i\delta_{13} \\ \qquad\qquad\quad \exp 2i\delta_{33} \end{array} \left.\begin{array}{l} S_{1/2}, t = \tfrac{1}{2} \\ S_{1/2}, t = \tfrac{3}{2} \\ P_{1/2}, t = \tfrac{1}{2} \\ P_{1/2}, t = \tfrac{3}{2} \\ P_{3/2}, t = \tfrac{1}{2} \\ P_{3/2}, t = \tfrac{3}{2} \end{array}\right\} \begin{array}{l} \text{mes} \\ \text{nu} \end{array}$$

All other elements are zero; the dotted lines are for the convenience of the discussion that follows.

If the electromagnetic interaction is turned on, the following changes occur.

(a) Charge independence can be violated, allowing transition between different meson–nucleon states; however, these violations are certainly very small and in this analysis can be neglected. Therefore all off-diagonal elements in the bottom right division of $S_0$ remain zero.

(b) Photon scattering will occur, altering the diagonal elements in the top left rectangle of $S_0$. However, photon scattering cross sections are very small and the real elements are only slightly different from 1. In our approximation these elements are unchanged.

(c) Photoproduction occurs and will be described by the only appreciable off-diagonal elements in a complete $S$-matrix; these will be in the top right and bottom left rectangles. The symmetry of the $S$-matrix allows us to confine our attention to the top right rectangle. Some of the elements in this rectangle are zero by virtue of the requirements of parity and angular momentum conservation. Using the information of Table 7.8, we can indicate these elements thus:

$$
\begin{bmatrix}
 & 0\ 0\ 0\ 0 \\
0\ 0 & \\
0\ 0\ 0\ 0 & \\
\hline
 &
\end{bmatrix}
$$

The remaining elements, which are left blank, describe photoproduction; these elements are small compared with the diagonal elements.

In view of these three points (a)–(c), we write the final $S$-matrix $S$ as

$$S = S_0 + i\epsilon$$

where $\epsilon$ is a matrix with no diagonal elements and small off-diagonal elements.

The $S$-matrices $S_0$ and $S$ have the following properties [Eq. (5.12)]:

$$S_0 S_0^\dagger = 1 \quad \text{and} \quad SS^\dagger = 1.$$

Substituting, we have

$$(S_0 + i\epsilon)(S_0^\dagger - i\epsilon^\dagger) = 1,$$

or

$$S_0 S_0^\dagger + i\epsilon S_0^\dagger - iS_0 \epsilon^\dagger + \epsilon\epsilon^\dagger = 1.$$

Now $\epsilon\epsilon^\dagger$ is of second-order smallness, so we find that

$$\epsilon S_0^\dagger = S_0 \epsilon^\dagger.$$

This is an equality between matrices and we examine an element of the left-hand side

$$(\epsilon S_0^\dagger)_{mn} = (\epsilon)_{mn}\,(S_0^\dagger)_{nn} = (\epsilon)_{mn}\,(S^*)_{nn}.$$

These relations follow from the diagonal nature of $S_0$. The on-diagonal elements of $S_0$ are of the form $\exp 2i\delta$ where $\delta$ is a scattering phase shift; hence

$$(\epsilon S_0^\dagger)_{mn} = (\epsilon)_{mn}\exp(-2i\delta_n).$$

Similarly,

$$(S_0\,\epsilon^\dagger)_{mn} = (S_0)_{mm}\,(\epsilon^\dagger)_{mn} = \exp(2i\delta_m)\,(\epsilon^\dagger)_{mn}.$$

Now $(\epsilon^\dagger)_{mn} = (\epsilon^*)_{nm}$ and we have that

$$(\epsilon)_{mn}\exp(-2i\delta_n) = (\epsilon^*)_{nm}\exp(2i\delta_m).$$

In the absence of angular momentum the $S$-matrix is symmetric. Our system contains angular momentum, but nonetheless the $S$-matrix can be made symmetric by the correct choice of the representation of the incoming and outgoing waves (Hamilton, 1959b). Assuming that this choice has been made, we have $(\epsilon)_{mn} = (\epsilon)_{nm}$, and multiplying the last equation above by $\exp[i(\delta_n - \delta_m)]$, we have that

$$(\epsilon)_{mn}\exp[-i(\delta_n + \delta_m)] = (\epsilon^*)_{mn}\exp[i(\delta_n + \delta_m)].$$

We see immediately that this is an equality between real quantities; therefore

$$(\epsilon)_{mn} = \rho_{mn}\exp[i(\delta_n + \delta_m)]$$

where $\rho_{mn}$ is a real quantity. This relation applies quite generally to weak links between channels and we use it to fill in the photoproduction $S$-matrix elements. These elements contain an isotopic spin assignment and are therefore constrained by the analysis introduced early in this section. If $(\epsilon)_{mn}$ leads to an isotopic spin state $t = \tfrac{3}{2}$, then we have relations of the following type:

$$i(\epsilon)_{mn} = \sqrt{2}\,V_3.$$

If $(\epsilon)_{mn}$ leads to a $t = \tfrac{1}{2}$ state, then

$$i(\epsilon)_{mn} = S_1 \pm V_1/2.$$

We therefore have to extend this nomenclature and we write the matrix element $(\epsilon)_{mn}$ in the form indicated in Table 7.9.

TABLE 7.9

THE PHOTOPRODUCTION $S$-MATRIX ELEMENTS

| Channels (linked by conservation of parity and angular momentum) | | | $S$-matrix elements |
|---|---|---|---|
| Photon–nucleon | Meson–nucleon Angular momentum | Total isotopic spin | $\rho_{mn} \exp\left[i(\delta_n + \delta_m)\right]$ |
| Electric dipole | $S_{1/2}$ | $\frac{1}{2}$ $\frac{3}{2}$ | $\frac{1}{2}(E_1 \pm \Delta E_1) \exp(i\delta_1)$ $\sqrt{2}\,E_3 \exp(i\delta_3)$ |
| Magnetic dipole | $P_{1/2}$ | $\frac{1}{2}$ $\frac{3}{2}$ | $\frac{1}{2}(M_{11} \pm \Delta M_{11}) \exp(i\delta_{11})$ $\sqrt{2}\,M_{31} \exp(i\delta_{31})$ |
| Magnetic dipole | $P_{3/2}$ | $\frac{1}{2}$ $\frac{3}{2}$ | $\frac{1}{2}(M_{13} \pm \Delta M_{13}) \exp(i\delta_{13})$ $\sqrt{2}\,M_{33} \exp(i\delta_{33})$ |
| Electric quadrupole | $P_{3/2}$ | $\frac{1}{2}$ $\frac{3}{2}$ | $\frac{1}{2}(E_{13} \pm \Delta E_{13}) \exp(i\delta_{13})$ $\sqrt{2}\,E_{33} \exp(i\delta_{33})$ |

Note that the subscripts in the last column *do not* correspond to the $m$ and $n$ on $\rho_{mn}$ but to the $2t$ and $2j$ of the final meson–nucleon state. Thus the quantities in the last column of the table correspond to the quantities $S_1$, $V_1$, and $V_3$. For example, $\frac{1}{2}i(E_1 \pm \Delta E_1)\exp i\delta_1 = S_1 \pm \frac{1}{2}V_1$ and $i\sqrt{2}\,E_3 \exp(i\delta_3) = \sqrt{2}\,V_3$ for electric dipole absorption. The quantities fill in the appropriate elements left blank in our discussion of the top right rectangle of the $S$-matrix. This completes our reduction of the 32 real quantities to 12, namely $E_1, \Delta E_1, E_3, \ldots$, etc.

We now return to actual photoproduction cross sections. These represent the observation of charge states, not of isotopic spin states, and we therefore combine the formalism of Table 7.9 with that of Eqs. (7.35)–(7.38) to give transition matrix elements for various multipole transitions to the states $\pi^+ n$, $\pi^0 p$, $\pi^- p$, $\pi^0 n$. Consider the first only. We can substitute into Eq. (7.35) to define

$$E_d^+ = \sqrt{\tfrac{1}{3}}\,i\,\{\sqrt{2}\,E_3 \exp i\delta_3 + \sqrt{\tfrac{1}{2}}\,(E_1 + \Delta E_1) \exp i\delta_1\}, \qquad (7.39)$$

$$M_{d1}^+ = \sqrt{\tfrac{1}{3}}\,i\,\{\sqrt{2}\,M_{31} \exp i\delta_{31} + \sqrt{\tfrac{1}{2}}(M_{11} + \Delta M_{11}) \exp i\delta_{11}\}, \qquad (7.40)$$

$$M_{d3}^+ = \sqrt{\tfrac{1}{3}}\,i\,\{\sqrt{2}\,M_{33} \exp i\delta_{33} + \sqrt{\tfrac{1}{2}}\,(M_{13} + \Delta M_{13}) \exp i\delta_{13}\}, \qquad (7.41)$$

$$E_q^+ = \sqrt{\tfrac{1}{3}}\,i\,\{\sqrt{2}\,E_{33} \exp i\delta_{33} + \sqrt{\tfrac{1}{2}}\,(E_{13} + \Delta E_{13}) \exp i\delta_{13}\}. \qquad (7.42)$$

These four equations give the matrix elements for the four operative multipole absorptions in the reaction

$$\gamma + p \to \pi^+ + n.$$

The notation on the left-hand side of Eqs. (7.39)–(7.42) is such that the capital letter refers to the nature of the multipole transition. The subscript $d$ or $q$ refers to dipole or quadrupole and any extra number refers to $2j$ if a further distinction must be made. The superscript is the charge of the photoproduced mesons. The matrix elements for the reaction

$$\gamma + n \to \pi^- + p,$$

are obtained by changing the sign of the terms $\Delta E_1, \Delta M_{11}, \ldots$, etc. We can obtain the similar matrix elements for the reaction

$$\gamma + p \to \pi^0 + p,$$

by substituting into Eq. (7.36). Then we have

$$E_d^0 = \frac{i}{\sqrt{3}} \{2E_3 \exp i\delta_3 - \tfrac{1}{2}(E_1 + \Delta E_1) \exp i\delta_1\}, \tag{7.43}$$

$$M_{d1}^0 = \frac{i}{\sqrt{3}} \{2M_{31} \exp i\delta_{31} - \tfrac{1}{2}(M_{11} + \Delta M_{11}) \exp i\delta_{11}\}, \tag{7.44}$$

$$M_{d3}^0 = \frac{i}{\sqrt{3}} \{2M_{33} \exp i\delta_{33} - \tfrac{1}{2}(M_{13} + \Delta M_{13}) \exp i\delta_{13}\}, \tag{7.45}$$

$$E_q^0 = \frac{i}{\sqrt{3}} \{2E_{33} \exp i\delta_{33} - \tfrac{1}{2}(E_{13} + \Delta E_{13}) \exp i\delta_{13}\}. \tag{7.46}$$

The corresponding matrix elements for the reaction

$$\gamma + n \to \pi^0 + n$$

can be obtained by changing the sign of the terms $\Delta E_1, \Delta M_{11}, \ldots$, etc.

We can now calculate the angular distribution; this applies to any of the reactions so we use the matrix elements $E_d$, $M_{d1}$, $M_{d3}$, and $E_q$ without specifying the charge states. The addition of a superscript to those elements and a substitution from Eqs. (7.39) to (7.46) will give the distribution for the appropriate reaction. We proceed exactly as in Section 7.10. The angular momentum wave functions $\gamma(l_\gamma, l_{\gamma z})$ of the incoming photon are

$$\gamma(1, \pm 1) \text{ for electric and magnetic dipole,}$$

$$\gamma(2, \pm 1) \text{ for electric quadrupole.}$$

These have to be combined with the spin function representing a proton having spin $\tfrac{1}{2}$ directed along the $z$ axis. We decompose these states into eigenfunctions of total angular momentum $\phi(j, j_z)$. Thus

$$\psi(1, +1)\chi(\tfrac{1}{2}, \tfrac{1}{2}) = \phi(\tfrac{3}{2}, \tfrac{3}{2}) \qquad \text{magnetic dipole,} \tag{7.47}$$

$$\psi(1, -1)\chi(\tfrac{1}{2}, \tfrac{1}{2}) = \sqrt{\tfrac{1}{3}}\,\phi(\tfrac{3}{2}, -\tfrac{1}{2}) - \sqrt{\tfrac{2}{3}}\,\phi(\tfrac{1}{2}, -\tfrac{1}{2}), \qquad \begin{array}{l}\text{electric and magnetic}\\ \text{dipole,} \qquad\qquad\text{(7.48)}\end{array}$$

$$\psi(2, +1)\chi(\tfrac{1}{2}, \tfrac{1}{2}) = \sqrt{\tfrac{4}{5}}\,\phi(\tfrac{5}{2}, \tfrac{3}{2}) - \sqrt{\tfrac{1}{5}}\,\phi(\tfrac{3}{2}, \tfrac{3}{2}), \qquad \begin{array}{l}\text{electric quadrupole,}\\ \qquad\qquad\qquad\quad\text{(7.49)}\end{array}$$

$$\psi(2, -1)\chi(\tfrac{1}{2}, \tfrac{1}{2}) = \sqrt{\tfrac{2}{5}}\,\phi(\tfrac{5}{2}, -\tfrac{1}{2}) - \sqrt{\tfrac{3}{5}}\,\phi(\tfrac{3}{2}, -\tfrac{1}{2}), \qquad \begin{array}{l}\text{electric quadrupole.}\\ \qquad\qquad\qquad\quad\text{(7.50)}\end{array}$$

The states having $j_z = \tfrac{3}{2}$ are incoherent with those of $j_z = -\tfrac{1}{2}$ if the incoming photon beam is unpolarized and we therefore consider them separately. First, states having $j_z = \tfrac{3}{2}$; the initial states having this value of the $z$ component of angular momentum can only contribute to meson–nucleon state $P_{3/2}$. It follows that the outgoing wave amplitude in the $P_{3/2}$ state is

$$\{\sqrt{3}\,M_{d3} - E_q\}\,\phi(1, \tfrac{3}{2}, \tfrac{3}{2}). \tag{7.51}$$

Each multipole matrix element is multiplied by its appropriate weight $\sqrt{(2l_\gamma + 1)}$ from the plane wave expansion of the electromagnetic field [Eq. (4.31)] and by the weight with which it contributes to states of different total angular momentum [Eqs. (7.47)–(7.40)]. We have replaced $\phi(j, j_z)$ by $\phi(l, j, j_z)$ to indicate to which outgoing partial wave the amplitude belongs, as in Eqs. (3.10) to (3.14).

The initial states having $j_z = -\tfrac{1}{2}$ can contribute to all the pi-meson nucleon states; as above, we find the outgoing wave is

$$-\sqrt{2}\,E_d\,\phi(0, \tfrac{1}{2}, -\tfrac{1}{2}) + (M_{d3} - \sqrt{3}\,E_q)\,\phi(1, \tfrac{3}{2}, -\tfrac{1}{2}) - \sqrt{2}\,M_{d1}\,\phi(1, \tfrac{1}{2}, -\tfrac{1}{2}). \tag{7.52}$$

The intensity of the final state is the sum of the intensities represented by these waves. Equation (7.52) contains two noninterfering amplitudes, one due to transitions in which the nucleon spin has flipped, the other due to transitions in which nucleon spin remains unchanged. As usual, we decompose the total angular momentum eigenfunctions into orbital and spin functions (using Table 2.1) and substitute the spherical harmonics [Eq. (2.46)]. As formulated, each term is a matrix element which must be substituted in the transition rate formula [Eqs. (5.2) and (5.3)]. Therefore the differential cross section is of the form

$$\frac{1}{W}\frac{d\sigma}{d\Omega} = A + B\cos\theta + C\cos^2\theta$$

where $W$ is the density of states and other factors of no immediate interest, and

$$A = |E_d|^2 + |X|^2 + |Y|^2, \tag{7.53}$$

$$B = -2\,\mathrm{Re}\,(E_d^* K), \tag{7.54}$$

$$C = |K|^2 - |X|^2 - |Y|^2, \tag{7.55}$$

where

$$K = M_{d3} - \sqrt{3}\,E_q - M_{d1}, \tag{7.56}$$

$$Y = \tfrac{1}{2}\{M_{d3} - \sqrt{3}\,E_q\} + M_{d1}, \tag{7.57}$$

$$X = \tfrac{3}{2}M_{d3} - \sqrt{\tfrac{3}{4}}\,E_q. \tag{7.58}$$

This result deviates slightly from that given by Watson *et al.* (1956) due to a difference in the definition of the matrix element. These equations apply to all the photoproduction reactions if the correct matrix elements are substituted from Eqs. (7.39) to (7.46) or their variants. This procedure gives all the angular distributions in terms of the twelve real quantities and six phase shifts. The final expressions are very clumsy and we do not calculate them.

The experimental work determines the quantities $A^+$, $B^+$, $C^+$, $A^0$, $B^0$, and $C^0$. This has been done at many energies up to 450 Mev. At any one energy it is obvious that we have an over-sufficient number of parameters to fit the observed coefficients. However, we wish to make the fit with the minimum number of nonzero matrix elements; such a fit has been given by Watson *et al.* (1956), and we will briefly consider their procedure and results. They have to make one over-all assumption, namely, that the $P$-wave contributions are mainly due to transitions to the $t = \tfrac{3}{2}$, $j = \tfrac{3}{2}$ pi-meson–nucleon state. They call this the $(3,3)$ enhancement model and it implies that the $M_{33}$ and $E_{33}$ matrix elements predominate. In Section 7.10 we have shown that a preliminary analysis indicates that electric dipole transitions to the $S_{1/2}$ state in charged meson production and magnetic dipole transitions to the $P_{3/2}$ states are the most important; this information justifies the first step in the analysis of Watson *et al.* which is to assume that only the matrix elements

$$M_{33} \text{ and } E_d^+ = \sqrt{\tfrac{1}{3}}\,i\,[\sqrt{2}\,E_3\exp i\delta_3 + \sqrt{\tfrac{1}{2}}\,(E_1 + \Delta E_1)\exp i\delta_1]$$

are nonzero. This is called the magnetic dipole model and it fails to agree consistently with the experimental data. The authors' next step is to add $E_{33}$ to the nonzero elements and they call this "the simple enhancement" model. Although it agrees more consistently with the data, there are still discrepancies which are much larger than can be accounted by the experimental errors. This leads to the "general enhancement model" in which all the remaining $P$-waves are added as a first-order correction. This means that only the matrix elements $M_{33}, E_{33}, E_d^+$ appear quadratically; all the others appear linearly multiplied by one of these "strong" matrix elements. This still leaves an embarrassingly large number of parameters which can be adjusted to fit the data, but this can be avoided by grouping the terms so that they are described by their actual action in the cross section. Thus the authors define the following contributions to the differential cross sections:

$A_s$ is the $S$-wave contribution to the $\pi^+$ production cross section;

$A_{x0}$ is the $P$-wave contribution from the enhanced matrix elements $M_{33}$ and $E_{33}$ which does not interfere with the $S$-wave;

$A_{k0}$ is the $P$-wave contribution from $M_{33}$ and $E_{33}$ which does interfere with the $S$-wave;

$A_\Delta$ is the $P$-wave contribution from all other matrix elements which does not interfere with the $S$-wave.

$A_s$ is identically the term $|E_d^+|^2$ in Eq. (7.53). The interference between $S$- and $P$-waves is expressed in the $B$ coefficient, which is $-2\,\mathrm{Re}\,(E_d^* K)$; thus the $P$-wave contribution $A_{k0}$ which interferes with the $S$-wave is $K$ with $M_{d1}, E_{13}, \Delta E_{13}, M_{13}$, and $\Delta M_{13}$ dropped [Eq. (7.56)]. The $A_{x0}$ is essentially the terms $|X|^2 + |Y|^2$ again with these matrix elements dropped. $A_\Delta$ arises from cross terms in $|X|^2 + |Y|^2$ due to products of the unenhanced $P$-wave matrix elements with the enhanced matrix elements $M_{33}$ and $E_{33}$. Other terms in $E_d^* K$ due to the products of $E_d$ with the unenhanced matrix elements are shown to be small, so the authors neglect this interference between the $S$-wave and the unenhanced $P$-wave.

The final expressions for the coefficients are:

$$
\left.
\begin{aligned}
A^+ &= A_s + A_{x0} + \tfrac{1}{4}A_{k0} + A_\Delta \cos\delta_{33}, \\
B^+ &= -\tfrac{2}{3}(A_s A_{k0})^{1/2}\{\cos(\delta_{33} - \delta_3) + 2\cos(\delta_3 - \delta_1)\}, \\
C^+ &= \tfrac{3}{4}A_{k0} - A_{x0} - A_\Delta \cos\delta_{33}, \\
A^0 &= 2(A^+ - A_s) - 3A_\Delta \cos\delta_{33}, \\
C^0 &= 2C^+ + 3A_\Delta \cos\delta_{33}.
\end{aligned}
\right\}
\qquad (7.59)
$$

$B_0$ is known to be small and is therefore disregarded. Watson *et al* (1956) find that it is possible to make a consistent fit of the experi mental values for the five cross-section coefficients with the four quantities enumerated above. The phase shifts are given the value: determined from the experimental results of meson–nucleon scattering The authors also make theoretical predictions for the energy variation of these quantities and find that $A_\Delta \cos \delta_{33}$ as determined experi mentally via Eq. (7.59) changes sign at an incident photon energy o 280 Mev which is lower than would be expected (330 Mev) from the energy variation of the phase shift $\delta_{33}$. This effect is ascribed to the appearance of a $D$-wave in the final meson–nucleon state at these energies. The authors' final conclusion is that the photoproduction cross sections can be satisfactorily interpreted in terms of $S$- and $P$-wave final states for incident photon energies between threshold and 300 Mev. We note that the analysis is based upon an assumption concerning the importance of the pi-meson–nucleon state having $t = \frac{3}{2}$ $j = \frac{3}{2}$, and the results are therefore consistent with conclusions drawn from other experimental results.

The partial wave analysis made by Watson *et al.* fails to take into account one term which occurs in the interaction between the electro magnetic field and the particles involved in photoproduction. This term has been discussed by Moravcsik (1956, 1957) and he shows that it leads to terms in the expression for the differential cross section containing factors of $(1 - \beta \cos \theta)^{-1}$ or $(1 - \beta \cos \theta)^{-2}$, where $\beta$ is the velocity of the outgoing meson. The true origin of the term is in the interaction between the electromagnetic field of the absorbed photon and the electric current of the outgoing meson; consequently, it has an effect only on the photoproduction of charged mesons. The powers of $(1 - \beta \cos \theta)$ occurring in the denominator of the expressions for the differential cross section have the same effect as would occur if all partial waves were present in the outgoing wave; an analysis assuming $S$- and $P$-waves only and an angular distribution $A + B \cos \theta + C \cos^2 \theta$ is therefore incorrect. Moravcsik suggests that the observed angular distributions be multiplied by $(1 - \beta \cos \theta)^2$ and analysed assuming that the result of this operation is a quartic in $\cos \theta$:

$$\frac{d\sigma}{d\Omega} (1 - \beta \cos \theta)^2 = A + B \cos \theta + C \cos^2 \theta + D \cos^3 \theta + E \cos^4 \theta.$$

The predicted effect of this interaction is a minimum in the angular distribution of photoproduced pi-mesons at about 20° in the laboratory system, for an incident photon energy of 260 Mev. This minimum has been observed by Uretsky and co-workers (1958) (see Fig. 7.8). In spite of this qualification, the main conclusions of Watson *et al.* concerning the enhancement of the $\frac{3}{2}, \frac{3}{2}$ matrix elements are unaltered.

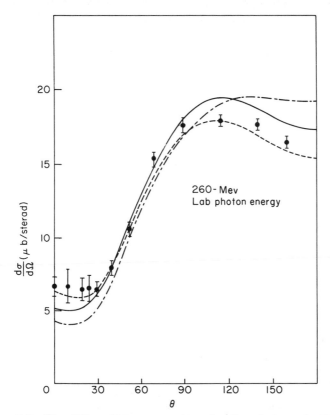

FIG. 7.8. The differential cross section for the photoproduction of positive pi-mesons from hydrogen at 260 Mev as a function of centre-of-mass production angle. The solid and broken lines are theoretical predictions for various choices of the small meson–nucleon scattering phase shifts (Uretsky *et al.*, 1958).

The Chew–Low (1956b) theory predicts a closer relationship between photoproduction and scattering than that available from the analysis of Watson *et al.* It concerns the photoproduction of neutral mesons and the elastic scattering of neutral mesons by protons; the relation is

$$\sigma = \left(\frac{\mu_p - \mu_n}{2}\right)^2 \frac{\sigma_0}{4\pi f^2 \beta} \tag{7.60}$$

where $\sigma$ is the total cross section for the reaction $\gamma + p \to \pi^0 + p$, $\sigma_0$ is the total cross section for the elastic scattering $\pi^0 + p \to \pi^0 + p$, $f^2$ is the coupling constant mentioned in our discussion of meson scattering (Section 7.9), $\beta$ is the velocity of the meson in the centre of mass and $\mu_p$ and $\mu_n$ are the magnetic moments of the proton and neutron respectively. This equation is expressed in the system of units which

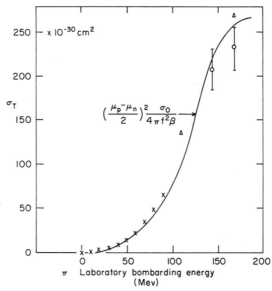

FIG. 7.9. Graph showing the relation between the total cross section for neutral pi-meson production from hydrogen and meson scattering at the same centre-of-mass total energy. The solid line is the prediction of the Chew–Low theory using the known scattering phase shifts. The points are measured cross sections from the Universities of Illinois and Cornell and from the California Institute of Technology (Koester and Mills, 1957).

has $\hbar = c = m_\pi = 1$ (see Appendix C). The relation applies to cross sections at the same total energy in the centre-of-mass system. Strictly it applies only to the $P$-wave contributions to the total cross section but since these predominate in both reactions, the relation should be correct to within 5% for energies below the resonance maximum. Koester and Mills (1957) have made measurements of $\sigma$, and in Fig. 7. we reproduce the graph which compares their results with the cross sections predicted by Eq. (7.60). The authors took $f^2 = 0.087$ and calculated $\sigma_0$ from the phase shifts deduced from experiments on the observable pi-meson–proton scattering reactions. The good agreement is another success for the Chew–Low theory.

## 7.12 The Consistency of the Low-Energy Parameters of Pi-Meson Physics

A measurement of the Panofsky ratio allows us to make a test of the internal consistency of our interpretation of pi-meson physics. We can see this by referring to Fig. 7.10. In each box is written a reaction and a description which serves to indicate the energy conditions under which the reaction is observed. Connecting each pair of neighbouring boxes is a line which is labelled with the assumption or method by which the two reactions are connected. In addition, we have marked on the figure the places at which information obtained experimentally can be put into the scheme. All this data should be consistent if our assumptions are correct; the most important of these is charge independence, but the value of the scheme as a check on this postulate is marred by factors which will be discussed at the end of this section.

We will briefly discuss the scheme. Starting at the top of the figure, we see that all the scattering data will yield phase shifts and their energy dependence which should permit an extrapolation to an appropriate energy and hence a calculation of the transition rate $(\omega_0)$ for mesonic absorption (box 4). From the bottom we can proceed by using the positive pi-meson photoproduction data and the $\pi^-/\pi^+$ photoproduction ratio from deuterium to arrive at a transition rate $(\omega_\gamma)$ for the radiative absorption. Then $\omega_0$ and $\omega_\gamma$ should stand in the same ratio as the observed Panofsky ratio.

We shall proceed by obtaining formulae for $\omega_0$ and $\omega_\gamma$ in terms of the data mentioned. We will then present the relevant data, evaluate the two transition rates, and compare their ratio with the observed Panofsky ratio. Finally, the results will be discussed in the light of our assumptions and their validity.

Let us start by extrapolating the scattering cross-section formula to low energy and transforming from a cross section to a transition rate for mesonic absorption. The same reaction at positive kinetic energies is charge-exchange scattering for which Eq. (7.22) holds. Since absorption takes place from an $S$-state of relative orbital motion, we need only consider the $S$-waves; thus Eq. (7.22) reduces to

$$\frac{d\sigma}{d\Omega} = \frac{2}{9k^2}|\alpha_3 - \alpha_1|^2.$$

The total cross section is given by

$$\sigma = \frac{8\pi}{9k^2}|\alpha_3 - \alpha_1|^2. \tag{7.61}$$

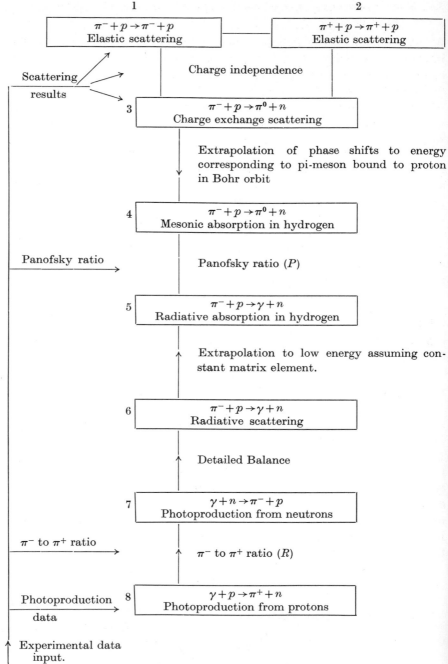

FIG. 7.10. Diagram illustrating the connection between the various reactions of low-energy pi-meson physics.

At low energies the incoming $\pi^-$ meson has an appreciably smaller velocity $(v_-)$ than the outgoing $\pi^0$ (velocity $v_0$) and it is necessary to correct Eq. (7.61) for this difference in channel velocities. In Eq. (3.2) the scattered wave is $(1/r)e^{ikr}f(\theta)$. We rearrange this outgoing wave by writing it as

$$\frac{e^{ikr}}{r(v_0)^{\frac{1}{2}}}(v_0)^{\frac{1}{2}}f(\theta).$$

If we compare this with Eq. (5.9), we see that it corresponds to an outgoing flux of $v_0|f(\theta)|^2$ neutral pi-mesons per steradian per second. To find the cross section we must divide by the incident velocity $v_-$ and we find

$$\frac{d\sigma}{d\Omega} = \frac{v_0}{v_-}|f(\theta)|^2.$$

Thus, in Eq. (7.22), the differential cross section is modified by the factor $v_0/v_-$ and we must do the same to Eq. (7.61)

$$\sigma = \frac{8\pi}{9k^2}\frac{v_0}{v_1}(\delta_3 - \delta_1)^2. \tag{7.62}$$

In addition we have put $|\alpha_3 - \alpha_1|^2 = (\delta_3 - \delta_1)^2$, an approximation justified by the known smallness of the phase shifts at low energy.

From Eq. (5.3) we know that the cross section $\sigma$ is the transition rate $\omega$ divided by the relative velocity in the initial state, which is $v_-[1 + (m_\pi/m_p)]$; hence,

$$\omega = \frac{8\pi v_0}{9k^2}(\delta_3 - \delta_1)^2\left(1 + \frac{m_\pi}{m_p}\right). \tag{7.63}$$

This equation applies to free negative mesons; for a meson bound to a proton in a Bohr-like orbit the relative motion is that of an $S$-state, and the $\pi^-$ density at the proton is higher than it is for the plane wave $e^{ikz}$ by a factor $L^3/\pi a^3$, where $a$ is the "Bohr radius" of the $S$-orbit of $\pi^-$ meson and $L^3$ is the normalization volume [Eq. (5.3)]. In deriving Eq. (7.63) we have tacitly taken $L^3 = 1$ so that it follows that the transition rate $\omega_0$ for $\pi^-$ absorption in hydrogen to give a $\pi^0$ is given by

$$\omega_0 = \frac{8v_0}{9k^2a^3}(\delta_3 - \delta_1)^2\left(1 + \frac{m_\pi}{m_p}\right). \tag{7.64}$$

We now make the second extrapolation from the photoproduction data to low energies. We examine the reaction

$$\gamma + p \rightarrow \pi^+ + n,$$

in order to relate it to the radiative absorption

$$\pi^- + p \to \gamma + n.$$

Let us put $\sigma_+$ as the total cross section for $\pi^+$ photoproduction from protons and $\sigma_-$ as the total cross section for $\pi^-$ photoproduction from neutrons. Near threshold we put

$$R = \frac{\sigma_-}{\sigma_+}.$$

$R$ is the famous $\pi^-/\pi^+$ ratio which can only be measured by observing the production ratio from deuterium. We shall use the observed $R$ and $\sigma_+$ to obtain $\sigma_-$:

$$\sigma_- = R\sigma_+.$$

We want to know the average matrix element $M$ for the total $\pi^-$ photoproduction so that we can use it to calculate the transition rate for the radiative absorption. Now

$$\sigma_- = \frac{2\pi}{\hbar} \frac{1}{v} |M|^2 \frac{dN}{dE}$$

where the symbols have their usual meaning [cf. Eq. (5.2)] and $v$ is the relative velocity of the incident photon and the target neutron in the centre of mass; it is $c[1 + (\epsilon_\gamma/m_n c^2)]$. We shall use $\epsilon$ with an appropriate subscript to indicate the total energy of a particle, $p$ to indicate momentum, and $m$ to indicate mass; $c$ is the velocity of light. Using Eq. (B.6), we have

$$\frac{dN}{dE} = \frac{4\pi p_\pi \epsilon_\pi}{(2\pi\hbar)^3 c^2 [1 + (\epsilon_\pi/\epsilon_p)]},$$

hence

$$\sigma_- = \frac{2\pi}{\hbar} |M|^2 \frac{4\pi}{(2\pi\hbar)^3 c^3} \frac{2p_\pi \epsilon_\pi}{[1 + (\epsilon_\pi/\epsilon_p)][1 + (\epsilon_\gamma/m_n c^2)]}.$$

An extra factor of 2 is included so that the two possible spin orientations of the proton are correctly included in the density of available final states. In this equation the only factor which varies rapidly with energy near threshold is $p_\pi$. Hence we use the following approximations which are valid near threshold

$$\epsilon_\pi = m_\pi c^2 \quad \text{and} \quad \epsilon_p = m_p c^2;$$

then

$$\sigma_- = \frac{16\pi^2}{\hbar c (2\pi\hbar)^3} |M|^2 \frac{p_\pi m_\pi}{\left(1 + \dfrac{m_\pi}{m_p}\right)\left(1 + \dfrac{\epsilon_\gamma}{m_n c^2}\right)}. \tag{7.65}$$

By detailed balancing we suppose that the same matrix element $M$ is applicable to the inverse reaction

$$\pi^- + p \to \gamma + n.$$

The fact that $\sigma_+$ is observed to be proportional to $p_\pi$ (Beneventano et al., 1956) indicates that $M$ is almost independent of energy, and we can therefore assume that it applies to this reaction when it occurs during the absorption of a $\pi^-$ from a Bohr orbit about the proton. The transition rate $\omega_\gamma$ for this process is

$$\omega_\gamma = \frac{32\pi}{\hbar c (2\pi\hbar)^3} \frac{|M|^2}{a^3} \frac{p_\gamma^2}{1 + (\epsilon_\gamma/\epsilon_n)}. \tag{7.66}$$

In this equation we have included a factor of 2 for the two neutron spin states and another 2 for the two possible photon polarization states; there is also a $1/\pi a^3$ factor for the meson density at the proton. We put $\epsilon_n = m_n c^2$ and compare Eqs. (7.65) and (7.66):

$$\frac{\omega_\gamma \pi a^3}{2 p_\gamma^2} = \frac{\sigma_-}{p_\pi m_\pi}\left(1 + \frac{m_\pi}{m_p}\right);$$

hence

$$\omega_\gamma = R\sigma_+ \frac{2}{\pi a^3} \frac{p_\gamma^2}{p_\pi m_\pi}\left(1 + \frac{m_\pi}{m_p}\right). \tag{7.67}$$

Taking the ratio of Eq. (7.64) to Eq. (7.67), we have a predicted value of the Panofsky ratio $\omega_0/\omega_\gamma$. As a first trial we use the experimental data available in 1957 to calculate $\omega_0$ and $\omega_\gamma$:

$$\delta_1 - \delta_3 = (0.27 \pm 0.02) p_\pi/m_\pi c \text{ radians (Orear, 1955)}, \tag{7.68}$$

$$v_0 = (0.204 \pm 0.005) c \text{ (Cassels et al., 1957)}, \tag{7.69}$$

$$\sigma_+ = (1.43 \pm 0.06) \times 10^{-28} p_\pi/m_\pi c \text{ cm}^2 \text{ (Beneventano et al., 1956)}. \tag{7.70}$$

The Bohr radius $(a)$ of the pi-meson orbit around the proton is calculated from the Bohr radius $(a_e)$ of the analogous orbit of an electron around an infinitely heavy nucleus of unit electric charge. The relation is

$$a = a_e\left(\frac{1}{m_\pi} + \frac{1}{m_p}\right)$$

where $m_\pi$ and $m_p$ are expressed in electron masses. The result is

$$a = 2.244 \times 10^{-11} \text{ cm}.$$

Other data are obtained from Appendix D.

We proceed by rearranging Eq. (7.67) into a form suitable for simple evaluation

$$\omega_\gamma = R \frac{\sigma_+}{p_\pi/m_\pi c} \left(\frac{2}{\pi a^3}\right) \left(\frac{p_\gamma c}{m_\pi c^2}\right)^2 c \left(1 + \frac{m_\pi}{m_p}\right),$$

which gives

$$\omega_\gamma = 2.40 \times 10^{14} R \, \text{sec}^{-1} \text{ (standard error about 4\%)}.$$

Rearranging Eq. (7.64),

$$\omega_0 = \frac{8c}{9a^3} \frac{v_0}{c} \left(\frac{\hbar}{m_\pi c}\right)^2 \left(\frac{\delta_1 - \delta_3}{p_\pi/m_\pi c}\right)^2 \left(1 + \frac{m_\pi}{m_p}\right),$$

$$= 8.11 \times 10^{14} \, \text{sec}^{-1} \text{ (standard error about 16\%)}.$$

These are essentially zero energy absorption rates predicted from the positive energy data. In addition we can predict the product of the Panofsky ratio ($P$) and of the $\pi^-/\pi^+$ ratio ($R$)

$$RP = \frac{\omega_0 R}{\omega_\gamma} = 3.38 \text{ (standard error about 17\%)}.$$

The observed values of $P$ and $R$ are:

$$P = 1.50 \pm 0.11 \text{ (Cassels et al., 1957)},$$

$$R = 1.87 \pm 0.13 \text{ (Beneventano et al., 1956)},$$

which have

$$RP = 2.80 \pm 0.28.$$

Although the agreement between the value predicted by the positive energy data for $RP$ and the value found from the zero energy experiments appears to be satisfactory, the existing difference is still in the same direction as that existing for earlier results of zero energy experiments. For example, before 1956,

$$R = 1.35 \text{ (Bethe and de Hoffmann, 1955)},$$

$$P = 0.94 \pm 0.20 \text{ (Panofsky et al., 1951)},$$

giving $RP = 1.27 \pm 0.27$.

This value of $RP$ cannot agree with the positive energy data. The origin of the discrepancy was not understood although it was attributed to a failure of charge independence at very low energies. The more recent values appear to close the gap but the value of 1.87 for $R$ appears to be very high and based on a doubtful interpretation of the data, particularly when the value expected theoretically is 1.3 to 1.4.

In 1958 several papers appeared which critically examined this low-energy analysis and the experimental data. Baldin (1958) examined the extrapolation to low energies of the $\pi^-/\pi^+$ ratio observed from deuterium and the relation of this extrapolated ratio to that which would exist if the nucleons were free. He took into account the kinematics of the deuteron, the final state interaction, and the Coulomb corrections which are different in the two cases of $\pi^-$ and $\pi^+$ photoproduction. He finds that the observed ratios are entirely consistent with a ratio of 1.4 for photoproduction cross sections from free nucleon targets. This result makes discrepancy greater and forces us to examine the extrapolation of the positive energy data; this was done by Cini et al. (1958) using dispersion relations and the model used by Chew and Low (1956a) to describe meson phenomena. The result is to raise the value of the coefficient in the equation for $\sigma_+$ (7.70) from 1.43 to $1.87 \times 10^{-28}$ cm$^2$ and to reduce the phase shift coefficient [Eq. (7.68)] from 0.27 to 0.24 radian. Taking these adjusted values, we recalculate

$$\omega_\gamma = 3.14 \times 10^{14} R \sec^{-1},$$

$$\omega_0 = 6.38 \times 10^{14} \sec^{-1},$$

and

$$PR = 2.04.$$

If we insert Baldin's value of 1.4 for $R$, we predict that the Panofsky ratio $P$ will be 1.46, in excellent agreement with the experimental value of Cassels et al. (1957). These values are closely supported by new data and analyses reported by Bernardini (1959).

Moravcsik, also in 1958, suggested that the experimental evidence indicated a breakdown in the postulate of charge independence. Such a breakdown is expected at pi-meson kinetic energies comparable to the mass difference between charged and neutral mesons (4.4 Mev) since this mass difference is a charge-dependent effect. Thus the application of extrapolated phase shifts to this region is of doubtful validity. Moravcsik takes the experimental values for the charge exchange scattering cross section [$\sigma$ of Eq. (7.62)] to calculate $\omega_0$, rather than Orear's data; he finds

$$RP = 1.4 \pm 1.3.$$

The error is due to the experimental error in the cross section. This result encompasses all the experimental values. Moravcsik urges that the low-energy charge exchange scattering cross sections be determined more accurately in order to test charge independence in this region.

The weaknesses in this low-energy meson roundabout are obvious. The standing of charge independence is not known and the theoretical jump from $\pi^-/\pi^+$ ratios observed in photoproduction from deuterium targets to a ratio for photoproduction from free nucleons is beset with difficulties. The agreement amongst the data is as good as can be expected in view of our imperfect knowledge of the pi-meson–nucleon interaction.

## 7.13 Conclusions

We can now sum up this chapter on the pi-meson–nucleon interaction. We recall that our analysis has been conducted on the assumption that, up to 200-Mev pi-meson kinetic energy, the interaction is only important in the $S$ and $P$ states of relative orbital motion, and that charge independence is valid. These assumptions lead to a consistent interpretation in which the state having $t = \frac{3}{2}$ and $j = \frac{3}{2}$ is the most important. That this would be so had been predicted by strong coupling theory (Bethe and de Hoffmann, 1955). However, above 300 Mev the experimental data do not yield to a simple phenomenological analysis and we are not in a position to discuss this energy region; interested readers are referred to a review by Lindenbaum (1957). We have mentioned several times the Chew–Low theory and its successes; however, this theory applies primarily to the $P$-wave interaction. In fact, the experimental data and any existing phenomenological interpretation at all energies still await a theory which describes these results as fully and precisely as quantum electrodynamics describes phenomena which are the effects of the electromagnetic interaction.

# CHAPTER VIII

# THE POLARIZATION
# OF ELEMENTARY PARTICLES

## 8.1 Introduction

Polarization is a phenomenon of considerable importance in elementary particle physics. Its existence implies that observations may be made on the properties of individual states which normally occur mixed with other states, all appearing degenerate to our crude measuring devices. Thus further details of the properties of systems are revealed.

We shall discuss polarization at length, not only for its intrinsic importance but because it illustrates some features of quantum mechanics which are of great importance. In the first few sections we consider some examples of polarization in elementary particle physics in order to orient our later discussion. In Section 8.6 we introduce the formalism required to describe partially polarized states and thereafter apply the technique to nucleon–nucleus and nucleon–nucleon scattering. The chapter finishes with a brief review of polarization involving electrons, positrons, and photons. In all parts our discussion is restricted to the polarization of free particles and hence mainly to the polarization of beams of particles at high energies, i.e., kinetic energy $\gg kT$.

## 8.2 Definition of Polarization

The polarization of a beam of particles in an eigenstate of linear momentum is defined in the centre-of-mass frame of the particles. A statement that the beam is polarized indicates that there exists a net angular momentum in this frame; such an angular momentum can only be due to spin and will be the result of a nonuniform and asymmetric population of the spin states. (These statements must be modified for photons which have no centre-of-mass frame.) It is self-evident that particles having zero spin cannot be polarized.

The polarization of particles of spin $\hbar/2$ is an important phenomenon. The polarization of a spin state represented by the wave function $\chi$ is the expectation value of the operator $\mathbf{S}$ (Section 2.4) in units of $\hbar/2$. This is identical to the expectation value of the Pauli spin operator $\boldsymbol{\sigma}$ (Section 2.9). Thus throughout this chapter the polarization of the $r$th beam of particles in a pure spin state $\chi_r$ is

$$\langle \boldsymbol{\sigma} \rangle_r = (\chi_r | \boldsymbol{\sigma} | \chi_r). \tag{8.1}$$

If the particles in the beam are not all in the same spin state, then the polarization is the expectation value averaged over all the particles in the beam. Since this is usually the case we do not make any distinction in notation for beam polarization between polarization for a "pure" beam and for a "mixed" beam. The polarization is a vector and the net angular momentum in any direction in units of $\hbar/2$ is the component of $\langle \boldsymbol{\sigma} \rangle$ in that direction; thus the $z$ component of the spin polarization is $\langle \sigma_z \rangle$. An individual measurement on one particle of the spin angular momentum component in a particular direction can only yield one of the two values, $+\hbar/2$ or $-\hbar/2$. Suppose $N_+ + N_-$, such measurement are made on that number of particles in the beam where $N_+$ is the number of measurements which yield $+\hbar/2$ and $N_-$ is the number yielding $-\hbar/2$; then the component of $\langle \boldsymbol{\sigma} \rangle$ is that direction $k$ is

$$\langle \sigma_k \rangle = \frac{N_+ - N_-}{N_+ + N_-}. \tag{8.2}$$

This is an imprecise definition of $\langle \sigma_k \rangle$ since $N_+$ and $N_-$ suffer from statistical fluctuations. If we define $N_+$ and $N_-$ to mean the probability of a measurement yielding $+\hbar/2$, $-\hbar/2$, respectively, then the equation  becomes exact. A statement about the magnitude of the polarization when the direction is not defined uses $|\langle \boldsymbol{\sigma} \rangle|$ where

$$|\langle \boldsymbol{\sigma} \rangle|^2 = (\chi | \boldsymbol{\sigma} | \chi) \cdot (\chi | \boldsymbol{\sigma} | \chi).$$

The polarization of particles having spin greater than $\hbar/2$ presents a more complicated situation. The polarization is again the expectation value of the operator $\mathbf{S}$ in units of the spin, but the number of parameters required to describe the state of polarization of a beam of such particles is considerable (see Section 8.7). We shall deal later with techniques for describing the polarization but at this point we wish to draw the reader's attention to the possibility of "alignment" which exists for particles of spin $\hbar$ and greater (except photons). Consider an assembly of particles, each having spin $\hbar$, which has no net angular momentum. This can happen in several ways, for example: (1) All spin states are equally populated so that a measurement of spin component in a fixed direction yields the values $\hbar$, 0, and $-\hbar$ with equal probability; this is an entirely unpolarized assembly. (2) The zero spin component state is unoccupied so that measurements yield spin components $+\hbar$ and $-\hbar$ with equal probability but never yield the 0 result; this is complete alignment. The alignment will be incomplete if a measurement can yield the zero result but with a probability less than the probability that it yields the result $+\hbar$ or $-\hbar$. (3) The $+\hbar$ and $-\hbar$ spin component states are unoccupied or have equal populations which are smaller than that in the zero spin component state. It is obvious that alignment does not produce a net angular momentum. We shall not be concerned with alignment in this book although it can be treated by the same methods as we shall use (Blin-Stoyle *et al.*, 1953).

The polarization of photons is defined in a manner depending on the problem. In Chapter V we have given the multipole representation and have indicated how the "spin" of the photon behaves. Although this spin is $\hbar$, its polarization properties are closer to those of particles of spin $\hbar/2$. This happens because there are only two possible orientations of the spin of a photon and, although polarization is possible, alignment is not.

We must stress one important point which we do by discussing one example. A fully polarized assembly of electrons does not have all the spin angular momentum vectors pointing the same way; the magnitude of the spin is $\hbar\sqrt{s(s+1)} = \sqrt{3}\,\hbar/2$, whereas the maximum value to the spin which can be observed is a component $\hbar/2$. Thus the direction of polarization is not the direction in which all the spins point but the direction in which every measurement of spin component yields the value $\hbar/2$. Of course, the uncertainty principle allows no meaning to be placed on any statement as to the direction in which the spin points. Readers are warned not to over-interpret statements about spin direction which are made with regard to conciseness rather than to preciseness.

## 8.3 Examples of Specific Polarization Problems

In this section we treat three problems in meson physics as an illustration of the methods which can be used, and to provide a background to later sections of this chapter. These problems have been treated in the literature (Fermi, 1953; Feld, 1954). One of them provides a means of deciding which is the correct set of meson scattering phase shifts of those proposed (Section 7.9). However, until 1958 no experimental techniques existed which could take advantage of this possibility.

We deal first with the polarization of protons recoiling from $\pi^+$ scattering on hydrogen. In Eq. (3.18) we have given the amplitude of the outgoing wave from an initial state in which the target proton had its spin directed in the $z$ direction. We relabel this amplitude $f_{+1/2}(\theta,\phi)$ to distinguish it from $f_{-1/2}(\theta,\phi)$, which is the corresponding amplitude from the initial state having the proton spin directed in the $-z$ direction. For an unpolarized target the two amplitudes are incoherent and have equal weight in averaging over the initial states; hence the differential cross section is

$$\frac{d\sigma}{d\Omega} = \tfrac{1}{2}\{|f_{+1/2}(\theta,\phi)|^2 + |f_{-1/2}(\theta,\phi)|^2\}.$$

Now parity conservation requires

$$|f_{+1/2}(\theta,\phi)|^2 = |f_{-1/2}(\theta,\phi)|^2 = |f(\theta)|^2, \qquad (8.3)$$

as discussed in Section 3.6, and we obtain the differential cross section given in Eq. (3.19). (We have added the independent variable $\phi$, the azimuthal angle in polar coordinates, as we shall be deriving expressions which depend on $\phi$.) In these circumstances it is possible for the recoiling protons to be polarized with the polarization vector directed perpendicularly to the plane of scattering. We proceed by finding the expectation values $\langle\sigma_x\rangle = 2\langle S_x\rangle/\hbar$ and $\langle\sigma_y\rangle = 2\langle S_y\rangle/\hbar$ for the scattered wave. Thus

$$\langle\sigma_x\rangle = \frac{1}{\hbar}\left\{\frac{(f_{+1/2}(\theta,\phi)|S_x|f_{+1/2}(\theta,\phi))}{(f_{+1/2}(\theta,\phi)|f_{+1/2}(\theta,\phi))} + \frac{(f_{-1/2}(\theta,\phi)|S_x|f_{-1/2}(\theta,\phi))}{(f_{-1/2}(\theta,\phi)|f_{-1/2}(\theta,\phi))}\right\}.$$

$$(8.4)$$

and similarly for $\langle\sigma_y\rangle$. The integration implied in the expectation values is over spin space, hence the denominators are equal to $d\sigma/d\Omega$. Now $f_{+1/2}(\theta,\phi) = f(\theta)$ of Eq. (3.18), and by repeating the analysis of Section 3.6 with the initial state proton spin reversed we can find $f_-(\theta,\phi)$. Using a simplification of Eq. (3.18), we have

$$kf_{+1/2}(\theta,\phi) = (A + B\cos\theta)\chi(\tfrac{1}{2},\tfrac{1}{2}) + C\sin\theta\chi(\tfrac{1}{2},-\tfrac{1}{2})e^{+i\phi}, \qquad (8.5)$$

$$kf_{-1/2}(\theta,\phi) = (A + B\cos\theta)\chi(\tfrac{1}{2},-\tfrac{1}{2}) - C\sin\theta\chi(\tfrac{1}{2},\tfrac{1}{2})e^{-i\phi}, \qquad (8.6)$$

where $A = \alpha_3$, $B = \alpha_3 + 2\alpha_{33}$, and $C = \alpha_{31} - \alpha_{33}$. We have used the amplitude and subscript convention of Section 7.7. We substitute in Eq. (8.4) and use the matrix elements of Eqs. (2.26) and (2.27) with

$j = s$, etc. Then

$$k^2 \frac{d\sigma}{d\Omega} \langle \sigma_x \rangle = \tfrac{1}{2} \{ (A + B \cos \theta)^* \, C \sin \theta \, e^{i\phi} + C^* \sin \theta (A + B \cos \theta) \, e^{-i\phi}$$

$$- (A + B \cos \theta)^* \, C \sin \theta \, e^{-i\phi} - C^* \sin \theta (A + B \cos \theta) \, e^{+i\phi} \}$$

$$= - 2 \sin \phi \, \mathrm{Im} \, \{ (A + B \cos \theta)^* \, C \sin \theta \};$$

similarly,

$$k^2 \frac{d\sigma}{d\Omega} \langle \sigma_y \rangle = + 2 \cos \phi \, \mathrm{Im} \, \{ (A + B \cos \theta)^* \, C \sin \theta \},$$

and

$$\langle \sigma_z \rangle = 0.$$

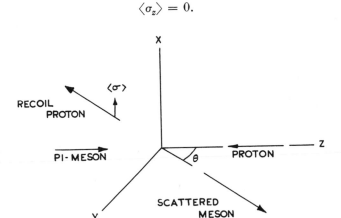

FIG. 8.1. Diagram showing the geometry of a pi-meson scattering at a proton as discussed in the text.

If we orient the $x$ and $y$ axes so that $\phi = 90°$, the reaction takes place in the $zy$ plane (see Fig. 8.1), and we see that

$$[(N_+ - N_-)/(N_+ + N_-)] = \langle \boldsymbol{\sigma} \rangle = \langle \sigma_x \rangle$$

where $N_+$ will be the probability that the proton spin is found pointing up (along the $x$ axis) and $N_-$ is the probability that the spin is pointing down (along the $-x$ axis). For this case we can write

$$k^2 \frac{d\sigma}{d\Omega} \langle \boldsymbol{\sigma} \rangle = 2 \, \mathrm{Im} \, \{ AC^* \sin \theta + BC^* \sin \theta \cos \theta \}, \qquad (8.7)$$

where

$$AC^* = \alpha_3 (\alpha_{31} - \alpha_{33})^*,$$

$$BC^* = (\alpha_{31} + 2\alpha_{33}) \, (\alpha_{31} - \alpha_{33})^*.$$

Expressions for the polarization of the recoiling nucleon in elastic and charge exchange $\pi^-$ scattering can be obtained in the same way.

The Fermi set of phase shifts discussed in Section 7.9 has only the phase shifts $\delta_3$, $\delta_1$, and $\delta_{33}$ nonzero so that the term $BC^* = -2\alpha_{33}\alpha_{33}^*$ is real, leaving the polarization due to the term $2\,\mathrm{Im}\{\alpha_3^*\,\alpha_{33}\sin\theta\}$. If the Yang set of phase shifts is correct, there is always a $\delta_{31}$ phase shift and both terms $AC^*$ and $BC^*$ contribute to give a polarization which will be different from that in the Fermi set. We can give a numerical example: at a pi-meson energy near 120 Mev the relevant Fermi phase shifts are

$$\delta_{33} = 30°, \quad \delta_3 = -7.5°.$$

Solving Eqs. (7.26) and (7.27), we find the Yang set

$$\delta_{33}' = 21.8°, \quad \delta_{31}' = 51.8°, \quad \delta_3 = -7.5°.$$

Substituting in Eq. (8.7), we have

$$k^2\frac{d\sigma}{d\Omega}\langle\boldsymbol{\sigma}\rangle = -1.05\sin\theta, \quad \text{for the Fermi set,}$$

$$k^2\frac{d\sigma}{d\Omega}\langle\boldsymbol{\sigma}\rangle = -0.72\sin\theta - 2.17\sin\theta\cos\theta, \quad \text{for the Yang set.}$$

A measurement of the polarization would therefore determine the correct set of phase shifts. A measurement of the corresponding polarization in $\pi^-$ scattering has been made and the result favours the Fermi set (Kunze et al., 1960).

As a matter of interest we now examine the effect on the angular distribution of polarizing the target protons in the case of positive pi-meson scattering. A first case is that in which the initial state protons are polarized with their spin angular momentum vector parallel (or antiparallel) to the incident meson momentum. This leads to an outgoing amplitude $f_{+1/2}(\theta,\phi)$ [or $f_{-1/2}(\theta,\phi)$] [Eqs. (8.5) or (8.6)]. These cases give angular distributions and polarizations which are identical with those from unpolarized targets. This result is expected from reasons of symmetry. In either case the initial state is invariant under rotations around the $z$ axis and therefore there can be no azimuthal variation in the scattered intensity. In addition, these states of initial polarization do not affect the scattered distribution as a function of polar angle ($\theta$) if parity is conserved in the interaction which causes the scattering. This is the argument used in Section 3.6 and implied in Eq. (8.3). Also, the polarization of the recoiling nucleons is equal in magnitude and direction in these two cases.

A more important case is that in which the target protons have their polarization vector perpendicular to the momentum of the incident pi-meson beam. Let us suppose that all the proton spins have

$x$ component $+\hbar/2$. Such a spin state is fully polarized and can be expressed as a coherent sum, with correct amplitudes and phases, of the two eigenstates $\chi(\frac{1}{2}, \frac{1}{2})$ and $\chi(\frac{1}{2}, -\frac{1}{2})$ with which we have previously started calculating pi-meson proton scattering (Section 3.6). Let us represent this transverse polarized spin state by the function $\psi$; it is an eigenfunction of the operator $S_x$; thus

$$S_x \psi = \frac{\hbar}{2} \psi.$$

By the principle of superposition of states (Section 1.3) $\psi$ can be expressed as the linear sum of $\chi(\frac{1}{2}, \frac{1}{2})$ and $\chi(\frac{1}{2}, -\frac{1}{2})$

$$\psi = d\chi(\tfrac{1}{2}, \tfrac{1}{2}) + e\chi(\tfrac{1}{2}, -\tfrac{1}{2}). \tag{8.8}$$

$d$ and $e$ are generally complex, so we require four equations to find these coefficients. The first is one of normalization,

$$(\psi | \psi) = 1,$$

which gives

$$d^* d + e^* e = 1.$$

The other three equations are obtained by requiring that $\psi$ has expectation values $\hbar/2, 0, 0$ to the operators $S_x$, $S_y$, and $S_z$, respectively. Using the matrix elements of Eqs. (2.26) to (2.29), we find

$$d^* e + e^* d = 1,$$

$$d^* e - e^* d = 0,$$

$$d^* d - e^* e = 0.$$

Solving, we find

$$d = e = 1/\sqrt{2}.$$

It is now evident that the outgoing wave consists of the two coherent parts $f_{+1/2}(\theta, \phi)$ and $f_{-1/2}(\theta, \phi)$ with relative phases and amplitudes which are the same as those in Eq. (8.8). Hence the total outgoing amplitude is

$$f(\theta, \phi) = \frac{1}{\sqrt{2}} [f_{+1/2}(\theta, \phi) + f_{-1/2}(\theta, \phi)],$$

and the differential cross section is

$$\frac{d\sigma}{d\Omega} \bigg| = |f(\theta, \phi)|^2 = \frac{d\sigma}{d\Omega} + \text{Re}\,\{f^*_{+1/2}(\theta, \phi) f_{-1/2}(\theta, \phi)\},$$

where $\dfrac{d\sigma}{d\Omega}\Big|$ is the differential cross section observed with polarized target

and $\dfrac{d\sigma}{d\Omega}$ is that observed with an unpolarized target. Using Eqs. (8.5) and (8.6) and employing the orthonormal property of the spin functions, we find that

$$\frac{d\sigma}{d\Omega}\bigg| = \frac{d\sigma}{d\Omega} + \frac{\sin\phi}{k^2} 2\,\mathrm{Im}\left\{(A+B\cos\theta)\,C^*\sin\theta\right\}. \qquad (8.9)$$

The $\sin\phi$ factor gives an azimuthal variation of intensity to the scattered beam which has its maximum and minimum at azimuthal directions perpendicular to the direction of the initial polarization. It is usual to call these directions left and right and the scattering asymmetry $\epsilon$ is defined as

$$\epsilon = \frac{\dfrac{d\sigma}{d\Omega}\bigg|_{\mathrm{L}} - \dfrac{d\sigma}{d\Omega}\bigg|_{\mathrm{R}}}{\dfrac{d\sigma}{d\Omega}\bigg|_{\mathrm{L}} + \dfrac{d\sigma}{d\Omega}\bigg|_{\mathrm{R}}}, \qquad (8.10)$$

where all cross sections refer to the same angle ($\theta$) of scattering. If we evaluate Eq. (8.10), using Eq. (8.9), and compare the result with Eq. (8.7). we find that

$$\epsilon = |\langle\boldsymbol{\sigma}\rangle|.$$

Thus the scattering asymmetry in scattering from a fully transversely polarized proton target is equal to the magnitude of the recoil proton polarization generated at the same scattering angle from an unpolarized target. This is a particular case of a general property of polarization experiments which will be discussed in detail.

We will complete this section by an example of the effects in meson photoproduction due to polarized photons. Such effects have been observed (Mozley et al., 1958). As in the last case no variation in production with azimuthal angle occurs unless the incident beam is transversely polarized. Let us consider photoproduction of a meson in a $P_{3/2}$ state by magnetic dipole absorption of a plane polarized photon; such a plane polarized state $\xi$ is the superposition of two states of circular polarization [Eq. (4.22)]

$$\xi = \frac{1}{\sqrt{2}}[\gamma(1,1) + \gamma(1,-1)].$$

If the target is unpolarized, the initial state is an incoherent sum of the two states (distinguished by choice of sign)

$$\psi_{\pm 1/2} = \frac{1}{\sqrt{2}} \chi(\tfrac{1}{2}, \pm \tfrac{1}{2}) [\gamma(1,1) + \gamma(1,-1)],$$

which can be expressed as eigenfunctions of total angular momentum $\phi(j, j_z)$ (do not confuse with azimuthal angle $\phi$)

$$\psi_{\pm 1/2} = \frac{1}{\sqrt{2}} \{ \phi(\tfrac{3}{2}, \pm \tfrac{3}{2}) + \sqrt{\tfrac{1}{3}} \, \phi(\tfrac{3}{2}, \mp \tfrac{1}{2}) \mp \sqrt{\tfrac{2}{3}} \, \phi(\tfrac{1}{2}, \mp \tfrac{1}{2}) \}.$$

We are interested only in the $j = \tfrac{3}{2}$ states; we obtain two incoherent outgoing amplitudes

$$f_{\pm 1/2}(\theta, \phi) = \frac{1}{\sqrt{2}} \{ \psi(1, \pm 1) \chi(\tfrac{1}{2}, \pm \tfrac{1}{2}) + \tfrac{1}{3} \psi(1, \mp 1) \chi(\tfrac{1}{2}, \pm \tfrac{1}{2})$$
$$+ \frac{\sqrt{2}}{3} \psi(1,0) \chi(\tfrac{1}{2}, \mp \tfrac{1}{2}) \}.$$

The intensity of the outgoing mesons is given by

$$I(\theta, \phi) = \tfrac{1}{2} \{ |f_{+1/2}(\theta, \phi)|^2 + |f_{-1/2}(\theta, \phi)|^2 \}.$$

The two terms are identical, and we find

$$I(\theta, \phi) = \frac{1}{12\pi} \sin^2 \theta (5 - 3\cos 2\phi) + \frac{3}{18\pi} \cos^2 \theta.$$

Thus the distribution depends on $\cos 2\phi$. The dependence must be $\cos 2\phi$ rather than $\cos \phi$ since the photon polarization defines a plane and not a direction (i.e., we do not know the phase of the electromagnetic vectors) and therefore the production distribution must be symmetric for reflections in a plane containing the $z$ direction and the plane of the photon polarization.

The case of the polarization of the nucleons recoiling from normal photoproduction has been discussed by Feld (1954); he takes into account the absorption of all multipoles leading to the final states having $j = \tfrac{1}{2}$ and $j = \tfrac{3}{2}$. His paper also covers some other polarization effects of interest in pi-meson physics.

## 8.4 A General Discussion of Polarization Experiments

In the previous section we have discussed three examples involving polarization in meson reactions. We notice that the experimental conditions were not discussed in that we did not say how the polarization of reaction products was measured or how the polarized beams and targets were produced; in fact, these matters are of great importance in polarization experiments. We do not consider the polarization of targets, as this appears to be a rather remote possibility at the present time. There exists a close analogy between the experimental conditions of a polarization experiment in nuclear or elementary particle physics and the conditions of simple polarization experiments in optics. Such optical experiments consist of two or three parts. The general three-part experiment consists of:

(1) A polarizer, e.g., a Nicol prism.
(2) An intermediary element which may cause a change in the polarization of the light beam emerging from (1). An example is an optically active material which rotates the plane of plane polarization.
(3) An analyser, e.g., a second Nicol prism.

The examples given make up one simple experiment to investigate the optical activity of the material under part 2. More complex examples can easily be found and in general the parts 1 and 3 are not identical. We notice that the interpretation of these experiments requires a knowledge of the behaviour of parts 1 and 3. This knowledge can be obtained by making parts 1 and 3 identical and omitting item 2. For example, the relative intensities of light transmitted through crossed and uncrossed Nicol prisms gives the polarization of the light transmitted by the first. The second Nicol can then be replaced by another type of analyser and a determination of its transmission plus the previously obtained knowledge of the polarization of the light serves to determine the behaviour of the new analyser. We are finally in a position to do the general experiment with the three parts. Such an experiment serves to determine some of the properties of the part 2 with respect to polarized light; a full determination of its properties might require several experiments with different qualities of polarization. Once this is done the result may indicate that this item has properties which make it a good analyser or polarizer, and it is then ready to play such roles.

Experiments on particle polarization in nuclear physics often follow this pattern and we shall be speaking of nuclear reactions or scattering which serve to polarize a beam of product particles and of reactions which can be employed to analyse the polarization. Triple scattering experiments have been performed which correspond to the three-part optical experiment and which obviously serve to determine the properties of the second scatter.

We wish now to develop the techniques for describing nucleon polarization experiments. Firstly, we wish to describe what happens to the polarization in part 2 of the three-part experiment. This will be done by considering the scattering of a fully polarized beam of nucleons. However, it is almost impossible to generate fully polarized beams and it will be necessary to describe the techniques required to deal with partially polarized beams. These techniques will be applied to the scattering of nucleons by spinless and nonzero spin target nuclei and by protons.

We will complete this section by giving the notation to be employed in describing the geometry of the scattering of polarized particles. Although triple scattering experiments are considered, we do not need to consider the geometry of the polarizing and analysing experiments; we need only give the geometry of the important middle scattering. If we are considering simple analysing or polarizing scatters again we have to give the geometry of one scattering alone. All momenta are in the centre of mass and the scattered particle has momentum $\mathbf{p}_1$ before and $\mathbf{p}_2$ after scattering. The actual scatter is characterized by a subscript $a$; if it is necessary to characterize a further scattering which follows $a$, it is by the subscript $b$. The plane of scatter at $a$ is defined by the unit normal vector $\mathbf{n}_a = \mathbf{k}_1 \times \mathbf{k}_2$ where $\mathbf{k}_1$ and $\mathbf{k}_2$ are unit vectors in the directions of $\mathbf{p}_1$ and $\mathbf{p}_2$. The angle of scattering is given by

$$\cos \theta_a = \mathbf{k}_1 \cdot \mathbf{k}_2.$$

## 8.5 The Polarization and Scattering of Particles of Spin $\frac{1}{2}$ (I)

In this section we consider the scattering of a fully polarized beam of particles having spin $\hbar/2$; the spin state $\chi_1$ of one particle is represented by a column matrix with two elements

$$\chi_1 = \begin{bmatrix} d_1 \\ e_1 \end{bmatrix},$$

where $|d_1|^2 + |e_1|^2 = 1$ is a normalization requirement. The matrix is called a spinor and if the spin is oriented so that $\chi_1$ is an eigenfunction of one of the operators $S_x$, $S_y$, or $S_z$, then the spinor $\chi_1$ is an eigenfunction of the corresponding Pauli spin matrix [Eqs. (2.50) to (2.52)]. If the spin points in a direction given by the polar coordinates $\theta_1, \phi_1$, then we have, according to Eq. (2.59a), that

$$\chi_1 = \begin{bmatrix} \cos \dfrac{\theta_1}{2} \exp \dfrac{i\phi_1}{2} \\[2ex] \sin \dfrac{\theta_1}{2} \exp \dfrac{-i\phi_1}{2} \end{bmatrix}. \tag{8.11}$$

This is entirely consistent with the spin eigenfunctions determined for the polarized target example in Section 8.3; the coefficients $d$ and $e$ of Eq. (8.8) are the elements of the matrix describing the polarized state having $\theta_1 = 90°$ and $\phi_1 = 0°$.

The pure spin state described by $\chi_1$ is fully polarized with polarization given by Eq. (8.1). We will now consider the scattering of a beam of such particles by a target of spinless nuclei. There exists the possibility of altering the spin orientation by means of any spin-orbit force which may occur between the incident particles and the target nuclei. The total incident plus scattered wave of Eq. (3.2) becomes

$$\psi = \begin{bmatrix} d_1 \\ e_1 \end{bmatrix} \exp(ikz) + M_a \begin{bmatrix} d_1 \\ e_1 \end{bmatrix} \cdot \frac{\exp(ikr)}{r}. \tag{8.12}$$

We are using the subscripts 1, 2, and $a$ to distinguish quantities belonging to the incident, scattered beam, and to the scattering process. The scattered wave amplitude is now $M_a \begin{bmatrix} d_1 \\ e_1 \end{bmatrix}$, which is a two-element column matrix or spinor formed by operating upon the spinor $\begin{bmatrix} d_1 \\ e_1 \end{bmatrix}$ with a two-by-two matrix $M_a$. Any arbitrary two-by-two matrix such as $M_a$ is a linear sum of the unit matrix 1 and the three Pauli spin matrices; thus

$$M_a = g1 + h_x \sigma_x + h_y \sigma_y + h_z \sigma_z = g + \mathbf{h} \cdot \boldsymbol{\sigma}, \tag{8.13}$$

where we have dropped the unit matrix. The coefficients are complex numbers which are functions of the scattering process under discussion, of the angle at which the scattering is observed, and of the energy. Since parity appears to be conserved in all observable scattering processes, $M_a$ cannot contain any terms which change sign on applying the parity transformation. Now $\boldsymbol{\sigma}$ is an axial vector, so if we require $M_a$ to be scalar, $\mathbf{h}$ must also be an axial vector. $M_a$ cannot be a function either of the incident or of the scattered wave polarization axial vector and we are left to find another axial vector to relate to $\mathbf{h}$. The only axial vector available is $\mathbf{n}_a = \mathbf{k}_1 \times \mathbf{k}_2$, the vector representing the normal to the plane of scattering. The most general $M_a$ is now

$$M_a = g + h\mathbf{n}_a \cdot \boldsymbol{\sigma}. \tag{8.14}$$

The scattered wave amplitude becomes

$$\chi_2 = \begin{bmatrix} d_2 \\ e_2 \end{bmatrix} = (g + h\mathbf{n}_a \cdot \boldsymbol{\sigma}) \begin{bmatrix} d_1 \\ e_1 \end{bmatrix}.$$

We have oriented our Cartesian coordinates so that the $z$ axis is along the vector $\mathbf{p}_1$; hence $\mathbf{n}_a$ lies in the $xy$ plane and the scattered wave amplitude can be written

$$(g + h\sigma_x \sin \phi_a + h\sigma_y \cos \phi_a) \begin{bmatrix} d_1 \\ e_1 \end{bmatrix},$$

where $\phi_a(\cos \phi_a = \mathbf{n}_a \cdot \mathbf{x})$ is the azimuthal scattering angle at the scattering $a$. Then

$$\chi_2 = \begin{bmatrix} d_2 \\ e_2 \end{bmatrix} = \left\{ g + hi \begin{bmatrix} 0 & -\exp(i\phi_a) \\ \exp(-i\phi_a) & 0 \end{bmatrix} \right\} \begin{bmatrix} d_1 \\ e_1 \end{bmatrix},$$
$$= \begin{bmatrix} gd_1 - e_1\, hi \exp(i\phi_a) \\ ge_1 + d_1\, hi \exp(-i\phi_a) \end{bmatrix}. \tag{8.15}$$

The differential scattering cross section $d\sigma_a/d\Omega|$ is given by

$$\frac{d\sigma_a}{d\Omega}\bigg| = \chi_2^\dagger \chi_2 = |d_2|^2 + |e_2|^2. \tag{8.16}$$

The vertical line distinguishes a cross section for a polarized incident beam from a cross section for an unpolarized beam. If we suppose that the initial polarization vector $\langle \boldsymbol{\sigma} \rangle_1$ is oriented in a direction with polar angles $\theta_1, \phi_1$, we can substitute for $d_1$ and $e_1$ in Eq. (8.15) and thence evaluate (8.16). This gives

$$\frac{d\sigma_a}{d\Omega}\bigg| = |g|^2 + |h|^2 - \sin \theta_1 \sin(\phi_1 - \phi_a)\, 2\, \mathrm{Re}\, g^* h, \tag{8.17}$$

$$= |g|^2 + |h|^2 + \mathbf{n}_a \cdot \langle \boldsymbol{\sigma} \rangle_1\, 2\, \mathrm{Re}\, g^* h. \tag{8.18}$$

Thus the differential scattering cross section for a fully polarized beam contains a factor depending on the cosine of the azimuthal scattering angle. A partially polarized beam will behave in the same way; only the azimuthal dependence will be less marked. We can derive $d\sigma/d\Omega$ for an unpolarized beam by averaging over two equally likely and incoherent initial spin states, one of which is represented by Eq. (8.11) and the other the same with the spin direction reversed; the result is

$$\frac{d\sigma_a}{d\Omega} = |g|^2 + |h|^2, \tag{8.19}$$

hence

$$\frac{d\sigma_a}{d\Omega}\bigg| = \frac{d\sigma_a}{d\Omega}(1 + P_a \mathbf{n}_a \cdot \langle \boldsymbol{\sigma} \rangle_1), \tag{8.20}$$

where

$$P_a = \frac{2\,\mathrm{Re}\,g^*\,h}{|g|^2+|h|^2}. \tag{8.21}$$

We can put

$$g+h = \left[\frac{d\sigma_a}{d\Omega}(1+P_a)\right]^{1/2}\exp\left[i\left(\alpha-\frac{\beta}{2}\right)\right], \tag{8.22}$$

$$g-h = \left[\frac{d\sigma_a}{d\Omega}(1-P_a)\right]^{1/2}\exp\left[i\left(\alpha+\frac{\beta}{2}\right)\right]. \tag{8.23}$$

We shall show in Section 8.8 that $\beta$ is the angle by which the projection of $\langle\sigma\rangle_1$ on the scattering plane is rotated during the scatter. We can define $\gamma_1$ to be the angle between $\langle\sigma\rangle_1$ and $n_a$, and $\gamma_2$ to be the angle between $n_a$ and $\langle\sigma\rangle_2$; that is,

$$\cos\gamma_1 = n_a\cdot\langle\sigma\rangle_1, \quad \cos\gamma_2 = n_a\cdot\langle\sigma\rangle_2.$$

We shall also show in Section 8.8 that

$$\cos\gamma_2 = \frac{P_a+\cos\gamma_1}{1+P_a\cos\gamma_1}. \tag{8.24}$$

This indicates that the incident beam polarization vector is rotated towards or away from the normal to the scattering plane, according to the sign of $P_a$.

If the incident beam is unpolarized, that is, it has the average value of $\langle\sigma\rangle$ equal to zero, then the scattered beam will in general be polarized. This polarization can be found by calculating the expectation value of $\sigma$ for the scattered beam and averaging over two initial spin states, as was done to obtain Eq. (8.4). This gives

$$\langle\sigma\rangle_2 = P_a n_a. \tag{8.25}$$

This is a completely general result; the scattering of an unpolarized beam produces a polarization vector in the scattered beam which is directed perpendicularly to the plane in which the scattering is observed.

## 8.6 Density Matrix Formalism

It is now evident that we require a technique to deal with the description of partially polarized beams. Equation (8.25) shows that it is possible to generate polarized beams, but unless $P_a = 1$ this polarization is only partial. The required technique is that of the density matrix (Fano, 1957).

We examine this technique by returning to some of the basic concepts of quantum mechanics, in particular to the concept of a state of a system. Since the results of measurements are the most important aspects, we consider the result of making a measurement on one state. If there exists a measurement which always yields the same result, then the state is said to be a "pure state". All the particles in a fully polarized beam of monoenergetic particles are in a pure spin state, since repeated measurement of the component of spin angular momentum of a particle in the direction of polarization always yields the same result. In addition, the same result is obtained for all the particles on which the measurement is performed. The measurement which always yields this unique result is called a "complete experiment". To such a complete experiment there will correspond an operator and the pure state is represented by an eigenfunction of this operator; this eigenfunction is called a wave function or state function. However, it is not always convenient to represent the pure state by such an eigenfunction but to invoke the principle of superposition and to represent the pure state as a linear sum of the eigenfunctions of a complete set. The choice of the complete set is a matter of convenience; thus in Section 8.3 we represented a target of protons all in a pure state of spin which was an eigenfunction of the operator $S_x$ as a linear sum of eigenfunctions of the operator $S_z$ [Eq. (8.8)]. Such procedure does not affect the purity of the state. A more general example was given in Section 1.3 to illustrate the principle of superposition.

There can exist systems for which no measurement yields the same result for all members of the system. Thus there is no orientation of a perfect Nicol prism which will permit the transmission of every photon of a partially transverse polarized beam of photons. Such systems are said to be in a "mixed state". These mixed states can be described by data which are sufficient to predict the probability of a particular result to any measurement. Mixed states can be represented as an incoherent sum of pure states. This must be compared with the representation of a pure state as a linear sum of other pure states; the sum implied is a coherent one.

We consider a pure state represented by the state function $\psi_n$. Let us expand this state vector as a linear sum of eigenfunctions $\phi_m$ of some operator:

$$\psi_n = \sum_m a_{nm} \phi_m. \tag{8.26}$$

Then the expectation value $\langle Q \rangle_n$ of an operator $Q$ is

$$\langle Q \rangle_n = (\psi_n | Q | \psi_n) = \sum_{l,m} a_{nl}^* a_{nm} q_{lm} \tag{8.27}$$

where

$$q_{lm} = (\phi_l | Q | \phi_m).$$

A mixed state is an incoherent sum of pure states such as $\psi_n$ each occurring with statistical weight $\omega_n$; the operator $Q$ has an expectation value for such a mixed state which is given by

$$\langle Q \rangle = \sum_n \omega_n \langle Q \rangle_n$$
$$= \sum_n \sum_m \sum_l \omega_n a_{nm} a_{nl}^* q_{lm}$$
$$= \sum_l \sum_m q_{lm} \sum_n \omega_n a_{nl}^* a_{nm}. \tag{8.28}$$

We define the density matrix $\rho$ by

$$\rho_{ml} = \sum_n \omega_n a_{nl}^* a_{nm}. \tag{8.29}$$

Therefore

$$\langle Q \rangle = \sum_l \sum_m q_{lm} \rho_{ml}.$$

$q_{lm}$ is a matrix element of the operator $Q$, hence

$$\langle Q \rangle = \operatorname{Tr} Q\rho \tag{8.30}$$

where Tr is a contraction for "Trace" which means the sum of the diagonal elements of the following matrix, $Q\rho$ in this case. This $Q$ in Eq. (8.30) is the matrix representation of the operator $Q$, that is, the $lm$ element of $Q$ is $q_{lm}$ of Eq. (8.27).

The density matrix provides a convenient description of a mixed state since the results of any measurement can be predicted by the use of Eq. (8.30).

We must give the properties of the density matrix and we do so with a view to its application to the polarization experiments. Under these circumstances the matrix refers to mixed spin states of a mono-energetic beam of particles. If the beam were not monoenergetic then there would be a density matrix to describe the mixture of momentum states and each element of this matrix would be itself a density matrix describing the mixed spin state of the beam. We are not considering this possibility and all our discussion will refer to the polarization applications.

The important properties of the density matrix are as follows.

(1) The density matrix is Hermitian. This follows from the fact that $\langle Q \rangle$ is a real quantity and $Q$ is a Hermitian operator; therefore

$$\rho_{lm} = \rho_{ml}^*.$$

(2) Since any particle of a system must be in one of the available states, we require

$$\operatorname{Tr} \rho = 1.$$

Later we shall be using two matrices $\rho_1$ and $\rho_2$ which represent the spin states of a beam of incident particles and a beam of scattered particles respectively. We shall see that it is a matrix $M_a$ [Eq. (8.12)] which transforms $\rho_1$ into $\rho_2$, in which case we require

$$\text{Tr}\,\rho_1 = 1$$

which represents a beam of flux $\hbar k/m$ particles per cm² per sec, and

$$\text{Tr}\,\rho_2 = \frac{d\sigma}{d\Omega}.$$

(3) In view of the normalization undertaken in (2) we have to modify the expectation value of Eq. (8.29) to

$$\langle Q \rangle = \frac{\text{Tr}\,Q\rho}{\text{Tr}\,\rho}. \tag{8.31}$$

(4) By a comparison of Eq. (8.26) and the statements made in Section 1.3 we see that the diagonal elements of the density matrix are the probability of finding any member of the system in a pure state described by one of the state functions like $\phi_n$. Thus the diagonal elements of the matrix are positive definite or zero

$$\rho_{nn} \geqslant 0.$$

(5) A matrix with $N$ rows and $N$ columns requires $2N^2$ real quantities; the Hermitian density matrix therefore requires $N^2$ and if $\text{Tr}\,\rho = 1$, $N^2 - 1$ parameters suffice.

We cannot discuss fully the properties and applications of the density matrix; readers who are interested are referred to literature on the subject (Fano, 1957, and his bibliography).

## 8.7 The Application of the Density Matrix to Polarization

We shall examine the specification of mixed spin states of a beam of spin $s\hbar$ particles. It is usual to quantize the $z$ component of a single particle spin and there are $(2s+1)$ such states to choose from. Any other pure spin state can be expressed as a coherent sum of these $(2s+1)$ states and thus there are that number of terms in a sum like that of Eq. (8.26). The density matrix describing a system of such particles in a mixed state will have $N = 2s+1$ and requires $(2s+1)^2$ real numbers to describe the state completely; if the intensity of a beam of such particles is of no consequence, then the state of polarization is described by $(2s+1)^2 - 1$ real numbers.

Let us consider the procedure of Section 8.5 and find how it fits with the density matrix formalism. We commence with a pure spin state represented by the spinor $\chi_1$. Let its expansion in terms of eigenfunctions of $S_z$ [Eqs. (2.47), (2.48)] be

$$\chi_1 = \sum_{s_z} a_{s_z} \chi(s, s_z); \tag{8.32}$$

for example, in Eq. (8.11) we have

$$a_{+1/2} = \cos\frac{\theta}{2} e^{i\phi/2}, \quad a_{-1/2} = \sin\frac{\theta}{2} e^{-i\phi/2}.$$

We can write $\chi_1$ as a column matrix which has as elements the coefficients $a_{s_z}$:

$$\begin{bmatrix} a_s \\ a_{s-1} \\ \vdots \\ a_{-s} \end{bmatrix}$$

Then if a beam of particles in this pure spin state has intensity $\hbar k/m$ particles/cm$^2$/sec (a plane wave $e^{ikz}$), we put

$$\chi_1^\dagger \chi_1 = 1.$$

The density matrix for this beam of particles which are all in this pure spin state is

$$\rho_1 = \chi_1 \chi_1^\dagger; \tag{8.33}$$

this follows from the definition of Eq. (8.29). The spin state and amplitude of a scattered beam is given by operating on $\chi_1$ with a matrix $M_a$:

$$\chi_2 = M_a \chi_1.$$

By Eq. (8.16) the differential scattering cross section is given by

$$\left.\frac{d\sigma_a}{d\Omega}\right| = \chi_2^\dagger \chi_2.$$

The density matrix $\rho_2$ for the scattered wave spin states is

$$\rho_2 = \chi_2 \chi_2^\dagger = M_a \chi_1 \chi_1^\dagger M_a^\dagger = M_a \rho_1 M_a^\dagger.$$

Now

$$\frac{d\sigma_a}{d\Omega} = \chi_2^\dagger \chi_2 = \mathrm{Tr}\, \rho_2 = \mathrm{Tr}\, M_a \rho_1 M_a^\dagger.$$

If the initial state is a mixed state then it is specified by the density matrix $\rho_1$ where

$$\rho_1 = \sum_r \omega_r \chi_{1r} \chi_{1r}^\dagger \tag{8.33a}$$

which follows from Eq. (8.29). The sum is performed over all the different pure spin states $\chi_{1r}$ which occur in the incident beam. The matrix $M_a$ is independent of $r$; thus it follows that

$$\rho_2 = M_a \rho_1 M_a^\dagger, \tag{8.34}$$

$$\frac{d\sigma_a}{d\Omega} = \mathrm{Tr}\, M_a \rho_1 M_a^\dagger, \tag{8.35}$$

$$\langle Q \rangle_1 = \mathrm{Tr}\, Q \rho_1 / \mathrm{Tr}\, \rho_1, \tag{8.36}$$

as for the pure state.

Let us now examine the scattering of particles of spin $\hbar/2$ by target nuclei without spin, in more detail. $\chi_1$ and $\chi_2$ are now two-column matrices and $M_a$ is a two-by-two matrix. We have seen already that the general form of $M_a$ is given by Eq. (8.14); by the same arguments used to derive Eq. (8.13) we can write the density matrices $\rho_1$ and $\rho_2$ in terms of the unit matrix and the Pauli spin matrices,

$$\rho_n = l_n + \mathbf{m}_n \cdot \boldsymbol{\sigma} \quad (n = 1, 2). \tag{8.37}$$

We normalize so that $\mathrm{Tr}\, \rho_1 = 1$ and $\mathrm{Tr}\, \rho_2 = \dfrac{d\sigma_a}{d\Omega}\bigg|$. To evaluate these traces we use the Pauli matrices [Eqs. (2.50) to (2.52)] and recall that $l_n$ is multiplied by an implied unit matrix. Hence

$$l_1 = \tfrac{1}{2}, \quad l_2 = \frac{1}{2} \frac{d\sigma_a}{d\Omega}\bigg|.$$

The polarization of either of these beams is the expectation value of $\boldsymbol{\sigma}$

$$\langle \boldsymbol{\sigma} \rangle_n = \frac{\mathrm{Tr}\, \boldsymbol{\sigma} \rho_n}{\mathrm{Tr}\, \rho_n} = \frac{\mathrm{Tr}\, [l_n \boldsymbol{\sigma} + \boldsymbol{\sigma}(\mathbf{m}_n \cdot \boldsymbol{\sigma})]}{\mathrm{Tr}\, \rho_n},$$

whence

$$\langle \boldsymbol{\sigma} \rangle_n = \frac{2\mathbf{m}_n}{\mathrm{Tr}\, \rho_n}.$$

Thus for beam 1 having the density matrix $\rho_1$, normalized $\mathrm{Tr}\, \rho_1 = 1$, and having polarization $\langle \boldsymbol{\sigma} \rangle_1$, we have

$$\rho_1 = \tfrac{1}{2}\{1 + \langle \boldsymbol{\sigma} \rangle_1 \cdot \boldsymbol{\sigma}\}. \tag{8.38}$$

Similarly, the scattered beam density matrix is given by

$$\rho_2 = \frac{1}{2}\frac{d\sigma_a}{d\Omega}\bigg|\{1 + \langle\sigma\rangle_2\cdot\sigma\}. \qquad (8.39)$$

Now we have that

$$\rho_2 = M_a\,\rho_1\,M_a^\dagger.$$

Therefore

$$\frac{1}{2}\frac{d\sigma_a}{d\Omega}\bigg|\{1 + \langle\sigma\rangle_2\cdot\sigma\} = \tfrac{1}{2}(g + h\mathbf{n}_a\cdot\sigma)(1 + \langle\sigma\rangle\cdot\sigma)(g^* + h^*\,\mathbf{n}_a\cdot\sigma). \qquad (8.40)$$

To evaluate Eq. (8.40) we use the commutation and anticommutation relations of the Pauli spin matrices [derived from Eq. (2.52a)] and the following vector relation:

$$(\mathbf{A}\cdot\sigma)(\mathbf{B}\cdot\sigma) = \mathbf{A}\cdot\mathbf{B} + i(\mathbf{A}\times\mathbf{B})\cdot\sigma.$$

The first result of interest occurs if $\langle\sigma\rangle_1 = 0$ for which we find

$$\frac{d\sigma_a}{d\Omega}(1 + \langle\sigma\rangle_2\cdot\sigma) = |g|^2 + |h|^2 + \mathbf{n}_a\cdot\sigma\,2\,\mathrm{Re}\,g^*\,h.$$

Therefore

$$\frac{d\sigma_a}{d\Omega} = |g|^2 + |h|^2, \qquad (8.41)$$

and

$$\langle\sigma\rangle_2 = P_a\mathbf{n}_a \qquad (8.42)$$

which confirms the result of Eq. (8.19) and proves the result stated in Eq. (8.25).

The complete evaluation of Eq. (8.40) gives

$$\rho_2 = \frac{1}{2}\frac{d\sigma_a}{d\Omega}\bigg\{1 + P_a\langle\sigma\rangle_1\cdot\mathbf{n}_a + \bigg[P_a\mathbf{n}_a + (\langle\sigma\rangle_1\cdot\mathbf{n}_a)\,\mathbf{n}_a + \frac{2\,\mathrm{Im}\,g^*\,h}{|g|^2 + |h|^2}(\langle\sigma\rangle_1\times\mathbf{n}_a)$$
$$+ \frac{|g|^2 - |h|^2}{|g|^2 + |h|^2}\mathbf{n}_a\times(\langle\sigma\rangle_1\times\mathbf{n}_a)\bigg]\cdot\sigma\bigg\}. \qquad (8.43)$$

$d\sigma_a/d\Omega$ is the differential scattering cross section for an unpolarized incident beam. The differential cross section for a polarized beam is found by comparing Eqs. (8.43) and (8.39); we find

$$\frac{d\sigma_a}{d\Omega}\bigg| = \frac{d\sigma_a}{d\Omega}(1 + P_a\langle\sigma\rangle_1\cdot\mathbf{n}_a), \qquad (8.44)$$

which thereby concludes a more general proof of Eq. (8.20). The polarization of the scattered beam is

$$\langle\boldsymbol{\sigma}\rangle_2 = \frac{1}{(1+P_a\langle\boldsymbol{\sigma}\rangle_1\cdot\mathbf{n}_a)}\left\{P_a\mathbf{n}_a + (\langle\boldsymbol{\sigma}\rangle_1\cdot\mathbf{n}_a)\mathbf{n}_a + \frac{2\,\mathrm{Im}\,g^*h}{|g|^2+|h|^2}(\langle\boldsymbol{\sigma}\rangle_1\times\mathbf{n}_a)\right.$$
$$\left. + \frac{|g|^2-|h|^2}{|g|^2+|h|^2}\mathbf{n}_a\times(\langle\boldsymbol{\sigma}\rangle_1\times\mathbf{n}_a)\right\}. \tag{8.45}$$

In the next section we shall examine the consequences of these relations, Eqs. (8.44) and (8.45), in detail.

## 8.8 The Polarization and Scattering of Particles of Spin $\frac{1}{2}$ (II)

We will now examine in detail the properties of a scattered beam as expressed by the density matrix $\rho_2$ of Eq. (8.43). The differential cross section of a polarized beam has important experimental consequences; therefore, we shall start by discussing Eq. (8.44).

Let us consider a beam polarized with the direction of $\langle\boldsymbol{\sigma}\rangle_1$ pointing vertically upwards. We describe the scattering of this beam from the view of an upright observer looking in the direction of the beam. We are not interested in the variation of $d\sigma_a/d\Omega$ with the scattering angle $\theta_a(\cos\theta_a = \mathbf{k}_1\cdot\mathbf{k}_2)$ which is therefore held constant in the following discussion, fixed by the orientation of the detector. The variation with azimuthal scattering angle $\phi_a(\cos\phi_a = \mathbf{n}_a\cdot\langle\boldsymbol{\sigma}\rangle_1)$ is interesting;‡ in fact,

$$\frac{d\sigma_a}{d\Omega}\bigg| = \frac{d\sigma_a}{d\Omega}(1+|\langle\boldsymbol{\sigma}\rangle_1|\,P_a\cos\phi_a).$$

To the observer there are four important directions of azimuthal scattering: 1, up and down ($\phi_a = 90°$ and $270°$ respectively); 2, left (L) and right (R) ($\phi_a = 0°$ and $180°$ respectively). Obviously the differential cross sections for up and down scattering are equal. The cross sections for left and right scattering stand in the ratio

$$\frac{\dfrac{d\sigma_a}{d\Omega}\bigg|_{\mathrm{L}}}{\dfrac{d\sigma_a}{d\Omega}\bigg|_{\mathrm{R}}} = \frac{1+P_a|\langle\boldsymbol{\sigma}\rangle_1|}{1-P_a|\langle\boldsymbol{\sigma}\rangle_1|},$$

or

$$P_a|\langle\boldsymbol{\sigma}\rangle_1| = \frac{\dfrac{d\sigma_a}{d\Omega}\bigg|_{\mathrm{L}} - \dfrac{d\sigma_a}{d\Omega}\bigg|_{\mathrm{R}}}{\dfrac{d\sigma_a}{d\Omega}\bigg|_{\mathrm{L}} + \dfrac{d\sigma_a}{d\Omega}\bigg|_{\mathrm{R}}} = \epsilon_a.$$

‡ $\phi_a$ is now defined as the angle between $\mathbf{n}_a$ and $\langle\boldsymbol{\sigma}\rangle_1$, in contrast to previous usage, for example in Eqs. (8.9) and (8.15).

$\epsilon_a$ is called the left-right scattering asymmetry. Let us apply this result to two successive scatterings of an initially unpolarized beam of spin $\frac{1}{2}$ particles. The incident beam is unpolarized; hence

$$\langle \sigma \rangle_1 = 0.$$

After the first scatter $a$, the beam will be polarized according to Eq. (8.45)

$$\langle \sigma \rangle_2 = P_a \mathbf{n}_a. \tag{8.46}$$

At the second scatter $b$, there will be a left-right asymmetry $\epsilon_b$ given by

$$\begin{aligned} \epsilon_b &= P_b |\langle \sigma \rangle_2 |, \\ &= P_b P_a. \end{aligned} \tag{8.47}$$

If the two scattering events are identical, apart from the azimuthal scattering angle, then $P_a = P_b = |\langle \sigma \rangle_2|$, and we have that

$$\epsilon_b = |\langle \sigma \rangle_2|^2 = P_a^2. \tag{8.48}$$

Thus the square root of the left-right asymmetry at the second of two identical scatters will be equal to the magnitude of the polarization of the beam after the first scatter and to the property of the scattering $P_a$. A determination of $P_a$ using this property corresponds to the optical experiment of using two identical Nicols to discover their analysing and polarizing powers, as described in Section 8.4.

Once $P_a$ is known, we have a scattering reaction which can be used as polarizer or analyser of known power. The first ability is expressed in Eq. (8.46). The polarization vector is always perpendicular to the plane in which the scattering is observed and has a magnitude $P_a$. The second ability is expressed in Eq. (8.47). If $P_a$ is known, then a measurement of the left-right asymmetry will determine the transverse component of the polarization $\langle \sigma \rangle_1$ of an incident beam; the plane of maximum asymmetry is perpendicular to the vector $\langle \sigma \rangle_1$. It is impossible to measure or detect a longitudinal component to $\langle \sigma \rangle_1$ (see, however, Section 8.10).

We now wish to examine the actual change in the polarization vector during the scattering; to do this we consider three cases.

I. Suppose $\langle \sigma \rangle_1$ lies perpendicular to the plane in which the scattering is observed, so that $\langle \sigma \rangle_1 \cdot \mathbf{n}_a = |\langle \sigma \rangle_1|$ and $\langle \sigma \rangle_1 \times \mathbf{n}_a = 0$. Using Eq. (8.45), we find

$$\langle \sigma \rangle_2 \frac{d\sigma_a}{d\Omega} \bigg| = [|\langle \sigma \rangle_1|(|g|^2 + |h|^2) + 2 \operatorname{Re} g^* h] \mathbf{n}_a$$

or

$$\langle\boldsymbol{\sigma}\rangle_2\cdot\mathbf{n}_a = \frac{|\langle\boldsymbol{\sigma}\rangle_1|+P_a}{1+|\langle\boldsymbol{\sigma}\rangle_1|P_a}. \tag{8.49}$$

Thus the scattered beam has a polarization which is increased or decreased according to the value of $P_a$. This case can be generalized by considering the initial polarization vector to lie at an angle $\gamma_1$ to $\mathbf{n}_a$; if the polarization of the scattered beam lies at an angle $\gamma_2$ to the direction $\mathbf{n}_a$, then by generalizing the arguments in Eq. (8.49) we have

$$|\langle\boldsymbol{\sigma}\rangle_2|\cos\gamma_2 = \frac{|\langle\boldsymbol{\sigma}\rangle_1|\cos\gamma_1+P_a}{1+P_a|\langle\boldsymbol{\sigma}\rangle_1|\cos\gamma_1}.$$

If this incident beam is fully polarized, then $|\langle\boldsymbol{\sigma}\rangle_1| = 1$ and from Eq. (8.45) $|\langle\boldsymbol{\sigma}\rangle_2| = 1$ also; it follows that

$$\cos\gamma_2 = \frac{P_a+\cos\gamma_1}{1+P_a\cos\gamma_2}$$

which proves Eq. (8.24). If $P_a>0$, the polarization vector is rotated towards $\mathbf{n}_a$; if $P_a<0$, the polarization vector is rotated towards $-\mathbf{n}_a$.

II. Consider an incident beam longitudinally polarized, so that $\langle\boldsymbol{\sigma}\rangle_1$ is in the direction of the incident momentum. Substituting in Eq. (8.45) we can extract the components of $\langle\boldsymbol{\sigma}\rangle_2$ along three directions, as follows:

$$\text{component along } \mathbf{n}_a \quad = P_a;$$

$$\text{component along } \mathbf{k}_1\times\mathbf{n}_a = \frac{2\,\mathrm{Im}\,g^*h}{|g|^2+|h|^2}|\langle\boldsymbol{\sigma}\rangle_1|;$$

$$\text{component along } \mathbf{k}_1 \quad = \frac{|g|^2-|h|^2}{|g|^2+|h|^2}|\langle\boldsymbol{\sigma}\rangle_1|.$$

The projection of $\langle\boldsymbol{\sigma}\rangle_2$ on the plane of scattering is at an angle $\beta_a$ with respect to $\langle\boldsymbol{\sigma}\rangle_1$, where

$$\tan\beta_a = -\frac{2\,\mathrm{Im}\,g^*h}{|g|^2-|h|^2}.$$

This $\beta_a$ is then identical to the $\beta$ of Eqs. (8.22) and (8.23). The sign of $\beta_a$ is positive if a right-handed rotation around $\mathbf{n}_a$ moves $\langle\boldsymbol{\sigma}\rangle_1$ towards the projection of $\langle\boldsymbol{\sigma}\rangle_2$.

III. Consider an incident beam transversely polarized so that $\langle\boldsymbol{\sigma}\rangle_1$ is in the direction $\mathbf{k}_1\times\mathbf{n}_a$. The components of $\langle\boldsymbol{\sigma}\rangle_2$ after scattering are as follows:

$$\text{component along } \mathbf{n}_a \quad = P_a;$$

$$\text{component along } \mathbf{k}_1 \times \mathbf{n}_a = -\frac{|g|^2 - |h|^2}{|g|^2 + |h|^2} |\langle \boldsymbol{\sigma} \rangle_1|; \qquad (8.50$$

$$\text{component along } \mathbf{k}_1 \quad = -\frac{2 \operatorname{Im} g^* h}{|g|^2 + |h|^2} |\langle \boldsymbol{\sigma} \rangle_1|. \qquad (8.51$$

Once again the projection of the polarization is rotated through an angle $\beta_a$ around the $\mathbf{n}_a$ direction. We have displayed this rotation for two components in the plane of scattering; it is, therefore, a general property of this scatter to rotate the polarization vector in this manner

It is convenient to resolve the two components of Eqs. (8.50) and (8.51) into components along the directions $\mathbf{k}_2$ and $\mathbf{k}_2 \times \mathbf{n}_a$; the latter is the interesting component since it is transverse to the momentum and can be measured by the "left-right" asymmetry in a suitable oriented plane at a subsequent analysing scatter. The component in the direction $\mathbf{k}_2 \times \mathbf{n}_a$ is

$$-\frac{1}{|g|^2 + |h|^2} \{(|g|^2 - |h|^2) \cos \theta + 2 \operatorname{Im} g^* h \sin \theta\} |\langle \boldsymbol{\sigma} \rangle_1|,$$

where $\theta$ is the scattering angle to which the discussion applies. Substituting from Eqs. (8.22) and (8.23), this becomes

$$(1 - P_a)^{1/2} \cos (\beta - \theta) |\langle \boldsymbol{\sigma} \rangle_1|. \qquad (8.52$$

This applies to an incident beam polarized in the $\mathbf{k}_1 \times \mathbf{n}_a$ direction with polarization vector magnitude $|\langle \boldsymbol{\sigma} \rangle_1|$. The observation of this quantity is obviously a part of a triple-scattering experiment in which the scattering under discussion is the second item; it is preceded by a polarizing reaction and followed by an analysing reaction, all the scattering planes being oriented so that polarizations are generated in the right direction and so that the correct polarization components are measured.

We can now enumerate the experiments which determine matrices of the kind $M_a$. Of the four real quantities in Eqs. (8.22) and (8.23) it is possible to find three by straightforward experiments.

(1)
$$\frac{d\sigma_a}{d\Omega} = |g|^2 + |h|^2$$

is determined in a straightforward single-scattering experiment of an unpolarized beam.

(2)
$$P_a = \frac{2 \operatorname{Re} g^* h}{|g|^2 + |h|^2}$$

is determined in a double-scattering experiment most simply by looking at the left-right asymmetry after successive identical scatters of the kind under investigation; see Eq. (8.48). Other methods can be used if a polarized beam is already available from another scattering reaction or if it is more convenient to use a different analyser.

$$(3) \qquad \beta = \cos^{-1} \frac{|g|^2 - |h|^2}{(|g|^2 + |h|^2)(1 - P_a^2)^{1/2}}$$

is determined in a triple-scattering experiment. The target in which the scattering occurs is bombarded with a polarized beam and the polarization of the scattered beam is analysed so as to measure the component derived in Eq. (8.52). The planes in which these scatters are observed have to be arranged so that each is perpendicular to the plane of the previous scatter.

(4) The common phase $\alpha$ in Eqs. (8.22) and (8.23) can be determined by measuring the interference between nuclear and Coulomb scattering. This is difficult except at angles at which the two are comparable (cf. Section 7.9).

## 8.9 The Polarization and Scattering of Particles of Spin $\frac{1}{2}$ (III)

A target of spinless nuclei can polarize a beam of particles with spin through the action of a spin orbit force, proportional to $\mathbf{L} \cdot \mathbf{S}$. The measurement of polarization phenomena serves to explore the magnitude and shape of the corresponding potential. The connection between a postulated potential and the parameters $g$ and $h$ is established by using either the Born approximation (Fermi, 1955) or the optical model (Heckrotte, 1956). A spin-orbit force appears to occur with all nuclei but has been most investigated with proton scattering from carbon (Chamberlain et al., 1956; Chesnut et al., 1956; Dickson et al., 1955). As a function of the energy of the incident protons, the polarization in the scattered protons increases rapidly from zero at about 80 Mev to almost 100% at about 150 Mev for favourable scattering angles; further increase in energy brings a decrease in polarization. Over this whole range the greatest polarization appears among those particles scattered at about 10° to 20° (it must be zero at 0° scattering), the maximum occurring at an angle which decreases with increasing energy. A smooth angular variation of polarization is not expected at the minima in the diffraction scattering cross section. Such effects occur because, of the particles scattered in directions near the diffraction minima, those with spin up will see a potential different from that seen by those with spin pointing down. Such a difference makes the diffracting nucleus of different size to the two sets of particles and it follows that their diffraction minima are at different angles and there is a quick fluctuation of polarization with scattering angle. These effects have been observed (Chamberlain *et al.*, 1956) but not in carbon. They may not always be obvious, probably due to swamping by inelastic scattering. It appears that proton scattering from helium shows large polarization effects at lower energies than does carbon (Brockman, 1958; Gammel and Thaler, 1958). Proton–helium scattering is therefore an excellent polarizing or analysing reaction.

It is evident that pi-meson–proton scattering is a transformed example of the scattering of spin $\frac{1}{2}$ particles by a spinless target. It follows that we should be able to derive the matrix $M$ for positive meson scattering from the relations derived in Sections 3.6 and 8.3. We compare Eqs. (3.19) and (8.41) to find

$$|g|^2 + |h|^2 = \frac{1}{k^2}\{|A + B\cos\theta|^2 + |C\sin\theta|^2\},$$

where $g$ and $h$ are the coefficients associated with the appropriate $M$, and where we have contracted the amplitudes as in Eqs. (8.5) and (8.6). Comparing Eqs. (8.7) and (8.25), we find

$$\mathrm{Re}\, g^* h = \frac{1}{k^2}\,\mathrm{Im}\,(AC^*\sin\theta + BC^*\sin\theta\cos\theta),$$

$$= \frac{1}{k^2}\,\mathrm{Re}\,i(A^*C\sin\theta + B^*C\sin\theta\cos\theta).$$

If we calculate $\langle\sigma_z\rangle$ for a longitudinally polarized target, i.e., amplitude $f_{-1/2}(\theta,\phi)$ only, we find after comparing with Eq. (8.45) that

$$|g|^2 - |h|^2 = \frac{1}{k^2}|A + B\cos\theta|^2 - |C\sin\theta|^2.$$

We can see a solution to these equations immediately:

$$g = A + B\cos\theta, \tag{8.53}$$

$$h = iC\sin\theta. \tag{8.54}$$

Another solution occurs if we multiply the right-hand side of these equations by $-i$. The correct solution is found by applying the optical theorem [Eq. (3.7)]

$$\frac{4\pi}{k}\,\mathrm{Im}\,f_{\pm1/2}(\theta = 0) = \text{total cross section, } \sigma.$$

$f_{\pm 1/2}(\theta = 0)$ is the scattering amplitude at a scattering angle of zero; in this position $M \equiv g$ as there is no means of defining $\mathbf{n}_a$. Therefore

$$\mathrm{Im}\, g = \frac{k\sigma}{4\pi}.$$

From Eq. (3.21) (modifying the subscripts to include the isotopic spin specification) it follows that our solution must satisfy

$$\mathrm{Im}\, g = \frac{1}{k}\{\sin^2 \delta_3 + \sin^2 \delta_{31} + 2\sin^2 \delta_{33}\}.$$

If we substitute for $A$, $B$ in Eq. (8.53) and put $\theta = 0$, we can confirm that $g$ of Eq. (8.53) satisfies this equation. Hence our solution, Eqs. (8.53) and (8.54), is correct, and the full matrix $M$ for positive pi-meson–proton scattering is

$$M = \{[\alpha_3 + (\alpha_{31} + 2\alpha_{33})\cos\theta] + [i(\alpha_{31} - \alpha_{33})\sin\theta]\mathbf{n}\cdot\boldsymbol{\sigma}\}.$$

This equation holds in the centre of mass. The amplitudes $\alpha$ are related to the phase shifts as indicated in Section 7.8. The second example worked out in Section 8.3 was the scattering of pi-mesons at a polarized proton target. The result, Eq. (8.9), follows immediately on applying Eq. (8.44), using the value of $P_a$ for this process (after allowing for change in convention concerning the azimuthal angle $\phi$).

## 8.10 Scattering from Targets with Spin

The polarization effects which will occur during the scattering of spin $\frac{1}{2}$ particles from targets with spin are obviously more complicated than those which occur during scattering from a spinless target. The technique of Section 8.7 can be reformulated to deal with this problem. Let $s_1$ be the spin of the particles in the incident beam 1, and let $s_a$ be the spin of the target $a$ nuclei, both in units of $\hbar$. A pure spin state of the system (beam + target) is represented by a linear superposition of $(2s_1 + 1)(2s_a + 1)$ basic states. Equation (8.32) now consists of that number of terms:

$$\chi_1 = \sum_{s_{1z}}\sum_{s_{az}} a_{s_{1z}\,s_{az}} \chi_1(s_1, s_{1z})\chi_a(s_a, s_{az}). \tag{8.55}$$

The density matrix $\rho_1$ for this pure spin state is defined exactly as in the simpler case, Eq. (8.33). Similarly, a mixed state has a density matrix defined as in Eq. (8.33a); this matrix has $(2s_1 + 1)(2s_a + 1)$ rows and columns. The expectation value of an operator $Q$ is given by Eq. (8.36).

If we allow $Q_\mu$ to be a complete set of $(2s_1+1)^2(2s_a+1)^2$ basic Hermitian matrices having $\mathrm{Tr}\,Q_\mu Q_\nu = (2s_1+1)(2s_a+1)\delta_{\mu\nu}$, then it is possible to expand the matrix $\rho_1$ as a linear sum of $Q_\mu$:

$$\rho_1 = \sum_\mu A_\mu Q_\mu.$$

If we operate with $Q_\mu$ and take the trace of both sides, we find that

$$\langle Q_\mu \rangle_1 = (2s_1+1)(2s_a+1)A_\mu \mathrm{Tr}\,\rho_1;$$

hence

$$\rho_1 = \frac{\mathrm{Tr}\,\rho_1}{(2s_1+1)(2s_a+1)} \sum_\mu \langle Q_\mu \rangle_1 Q_\mu. \tag{8.56}$$

Equation (8.38) is an example of such an expansion.

$\rho_1$ is Hermitian and contains $(2s_1+1)^2(2s_a+1)^2$ real numbers; if the intensity is known, the polarization is fully described by the remaining $(2s_1+1)^2(2s_a+1)^2-1$ real numbers. This is to be compared with $2(2s_1+1)(2s_a+1)-1$ real numbers required to describe the pure spin state which is fully polarized, Eq. (8.55). We have implied that $\rho$ applies to an incident beam and target; after scattering, a matrix $\rho$ applies to the scattered beam and recoiling nucleus for the scattering angle under discussion. As before,

$$\rho_2 = M_a \rho_1 M_a^\dagger. \tag{8.34}$$

The measurable quantities in this scattered state are found by applying the appropriate operator and taking the trace [Eq. (8.36)].

Let us apply this technique to the scattering of spin $\tfrac{1}{2}$ particles by a heavy target. We consider only the normal experimental situation in which the target is unpolarized and the polarization of the recoiling nucleus is unobserved. The incident state can be represented by the right-hand side of Eq. (8.38) standing with a density matrix representing the target spin space. Since the target is unpolarized, only the unit matrix has an expectation value and we can use Eq. (8.56) to show that the density matrix for the unpolarized target is

$$\frac{1_a}{(2s_a+1)}$$

where $1_a$ is a unit matrix of $(2s_a+1)$ rows and columns; hence

$$\rho_1 = \frac{1_a}{2(2s_a+1)}(1+\langle \boldsymbol{\sigma} \rangle_1 \cdot \boldsymbol{\sigma}). \tag{8.57}$$

The matrix $M_a$, which transforms $\rho_1$ into $\rho_2$, can be considered to be like $M_a$ of Eq. (8.14), only $g$ and $h$ are now four matrices of $(2s_a+1)$ rows and columns each. These matrices operate on $1_a/(2s_a+1)$ to transform it into the density matrix describing the spin state of the recoiling nucleus. We do not observe this spin state; hence, in taking the expectation value of $\boldsymbol{\sigma}$ for the scattered beam by evaluating $\mathrm{Tr}\,\boldsymbol{\sigma}\rho_2$, it is necessary to take the trace over the matrix products such as $gh^\dagger$, $hg^\dagger$, ..., etc. which will occur in the expression for $\rho_2$. The evaluation is complicated and we will not discuss it here (see Wolfenstein, 1949 or Oehme, 1955). The differential cross section is

$$\frac{d\sigma_a}{d\Omega}\bigg| = \frac{d\sigma_a}{d\Omega}(1+P_a\langle\boldsymbol{\sigma}\rangle_1\cdot\mathbf{n}_a).$$

The polarization of the scattered beam is best expressed as components along orthogonal Cartesian axes $\mathbf{n}_a$, $\mathbf{k}_2$, and $\mathbf{n}_a\times\mathbf{k}_2$ thus:

$$\frac{d\sigma_a}{d\Omega}\langle\boldsymbol{\sigma}\rangle_2 = \frac{d\sigma_a}{d\Omega}\{(P_a+D_a\langle\boldsymbol{\sigma}\rangle_1\cdot\mathbf{n}_a)\mathbf{n}_a$$
$$+[A_a\langle\boldsymbol{\sigma}\rangle_1\cdot\mathbf{k}_1+R_a\langle\boldsymbol{\sigma}\rangle_1\cdot(\mathbf{k}_1\times\mathbf{n}_a)]\mathbf{k}_2\times\mathbf{n}_a$$
$$+[A'_a\langle\boldsymbol{\sigma}\rangle_1\cdot\mathbf{k}_1+R'_a\langle\boldsymbol{\sigma}\rangle_1\cdot(\mathbf{k}_1\times\mathbf{n}_a)]\mathbf{k}_2\}. \qquad (8.58)$$

This expression gives the polarization components along the direction of momentum of the scattered beam and in two transverse directions in terms of similar components of the incident beam polarization. That Eq. (8.58) is the most general possible equation can be proved by recalling that $\langle\boldsymbol{\sigma}\rangle_2$ is an axial vector and by observing that the right-hand side contains all the independent axial vectors which can be made from $\langle\boldsymbol{\sigma}\rangle_1$, $\mathbf{n}_a$, $\mathbf{k}_1$, and $\mathbf{k}_2$. The coefficients $d\sigma_a/d\Omega$, $P_a$, $D_a$, $A_a$, $A'_a$, $R_a$, and $R'_a$ depend upon the parameters of the matrix $M_a$. However, they are not entirely independent. Wolfenstein (1954) applies the requirement of invariance under time reversal to show that there are only six independent quantities among these seven. For a spinless target there are only three independent quantities and we have

$$\frac{d\sigma_a}{d\Omega} = |g|^2+|h|^2, \quad P_a = \frac{2\,\mathrm{Re}\,g^*h}{|g|^2+|h|^2},$$

$$D_a = 1,$$
$$R_a = -(1-P_a^2)^{1/2}\cos(\theta_a-\beta),$$
$$R'_a = (1-P_a^2)^{1/2}\sin(\theta_a-\beta),$$
$$A_a = (1-P_a^2)^{1/2}\sin(\beta+\theta_a),$$
$$A'_a = (1-P_a^2)^{1/2}\cos(\beta+\theta_a),$$

where

$$\beta = \cos^{-1}\left(\frac{|g|^2 - |h|^2}{\dfrac{d\sigma_a}{d\Omega}(1 - P_a^2)^{1/2}}\right).$$

We have already described in Section 8.8 how the three essential parameters for this case can be determined.

Returning to the scattering from a target with spin we can now discuss the determination of the independent quantities of Eqs. (8.44) and (8.58). The measurement of $d\sigma_a/d\Omega$ and $P_a$ are as before. The measurement of $D_a$ requires a determination of the $\mathbf{n}_a$ components of $\langle \boldsymbol{\sigma} \rangle_1$ and $\langle \boldsymbol{\sigma} \rangle_2$. Thus

$$\langle \boldsymbol{\sigma} \rangle_2 \cdot \mathbf{n}_a = \frac{P_a + D_a \langle \boldsymbol{\sigma} \rangle_1 \cdot \mathbf{n}_a}{1 + P_a \langle \boldsymbol{\sigma} \rangle_1 \cdot \mathbf{n}_a}.$$

The determination of $A_a$, $A_a'$, $R_a$, and $R_a'$ is done by setting the orientation of analyser and polarizer so that the polarization component detected and the polarization of the incoming beam make all but one of the corresponding terms in Eq. (8.58) equal to zero. We leave to the reader the formulation of these experiments but point out that it is necessary to produce longitudinally polarized beams and to detect longitudinal polarization. We have seen that this is impossible by direct scattering. However, in the case of nucleons, longitudinal components may be turned into transverse polarization components and vice versa by passing the beam of particles through a suitably oriented magnetic field; the fact that the Larmor frequency is greater than the cyclotron frequency for both protons and neutrons causes the polarization vector to rotate faster than does the momentum vector and polarization components can be shuffled as required. Hence longitudinally polarized beams can be generated from the transverse polarization of scattering and the longitudinal components turned into transverse components suitable for measurement by the scattering asymmetry.

## 8.11 Nucleon–Nucleon Scattering

The two-nucleon problem is of great importance. At the present time the objective is to find a potential which correctly predicts all the properties of this system from the structure of the deuteron to the very high energy scattering. However, this is a very ambitious programme and may not be very meaningful as a potential is a non-relativistic concept; an alternative procedure is to find the phase shifts and mixing parameters (Section 6.5) from the scattering data and in this respect polarization experiments are an essential part of the determination. This is analogous to the situation in pi-meson scattering where a polarization experiment is required to resolve the Fermi–Yang ambiguity.

We can start by considering nucleon–nucleon scattering as a special case of scattering from a spinning target; hence Eqs. (8.44) and (8.58) hold if the target is unpolarized and the polarization of the recoiling nucleon is unobserved. There is a relation between the coefficients in Eq. (8.58) which is, in the nonrelativistic approximation, given by

$$\frac{A + R'}{A' - R} = \tan \frac{\theta}{2}. \tag{8.59}$$

$\theta$ is the centre-of-mass scattering angle (Wolfenstein, 1956a).

However, the nature of high-energy nucleon–nucleon scattering gives us the possibility of detecting the polarization of the recoiling

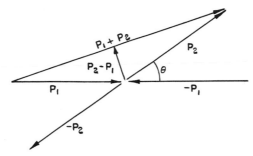

FIG. 8.2. Diagram showing the geometry of nucleon–nucleon scattering.

nucleon as well as that of the scattered nucleon; such correlation measurements give further information on the appropriate scattering matrix $M$ and on the phase shifts in nucleon–nucleon scattering. We shall now briefly examine this situation.

The geometry of the polarization is best described with respect to a set of orthogonal axes based upon the momenta in the centre-of-mass system. Figure 8.2 shows the direction of the momentum vectors involved. To keep in line with our convention the incident nucleon has initial and final momenta represented by $\mathbf{p}_1$ and $\mathbf{p}_2$, whilst the target nucleon has initial and final momenta $-\mathbf{p}_1$ and $-\mathbf{p}_2$. The two vectors $\mathbf{p}_2 + \mathbf{p}_1$ and $\mathbf{p}_2 - \mathbf{p}_1$ define perpendicular directions which we represent by the unit vectors $\mathbf{p}_a$ and $\mathbf{k}_a$; with the unit vector $n_a = \mathbf{p}_a \times \mathbf{k}_a$ they form a convenient set of orthogonal axes. In the laboratory system $\mathbf{p}_2 + \mathbf{p}_1$ is in the direction of motion of the scattered nucleon and $-(\mathbf{p}_2 - \mathbf{p}_1)$ is in that of the recoil nucleon.

The density matrix formalism is the same as that in Section 8.10 with $s_1 = s_a = \frac{1}{2}$. There is a choice of basic states. The first is the four possible combinations of eigenfunctions of the operators $S_{1z}$ and $S_{az}$; this is analogous to the representation implied in the sum of Eq. (8.57); the other possibility is the set of four basic states which are eigen-functions of the total spin z-component operator $S_z = S_{1z} + S_{az}$ and $S^2 = (\mathbf{S}_1 + \mathbf{S}_a)^2$ which in fact correspond to the three triplet and one singlet total spin states. The density matrices $\rho_1$ and $\rho_1'$ in the two representations are connected by a unitary transformation (Skarsvag, 1958). We find that the first representation is of more interest since the measurement of the polarization of the outgoing nucleons can only give the polarization of the nucleons independently and not in terms of the polarization of the triplet and fraction of the singlet state present. In this representation the matrix $M_a$ is the form

$$M_a = BS + C(\boldsymbol{\sigma}_1 + \boldsymbol{\sigma}_a) \cdot \mathbf{n}_a + \left\{ N(\boldsymbol{\sigma}_1 \cdot \mathbf{n}_a)(\boldsymbol{\sigma}_a \cdot \mathbf{n}_a) + \frac{G}{2}[(\boldsymbol{\sigma}_1 \cdot \mathbf{k}_a)(\boldsymbol{\sigma}_a \cdot \mathbf{k}_a) \right.$$

$$\left. + (\boldsymbol{\sigma}_1 \cdot \mathbf{p}_a)(\boldsymbol{\sigma}_a \cdot \mathbf{p}_a)] + \frac{H}{2}[(\boldsymbol{\sigma}_1 \cdot \mathbf{k}_a)(\boldsymbol{\sigma}_a \cdot \mathbf{k}_a) - (\boldsymbol{\sigma}_1 \cdot \mathbf{p}_a)(\boldsymbol{\sigma}_a \cdot \mathbf{p}_a)] \right\} T. \quad (8.60)$$

Wolfenstein and Ashkin (1952) and Wolfenstein (1956a) show that this is the most general scattering matrix which conserves parity and is invariant under time reversal; Wolfenstein and Ashkin's $M$ includes a term $(\boldsymbol{\sigma}_1 - \boldsymbol{\sigma}_a) \cdot \mathbf{n}_a$ which does not conserve isotopic spin and has therefore been omitted. $B$, $C$, $N$, $G$, and $H$ are energy-dependent functions of the scattering angle $\theta_a$. $S = \frac{1}{4}(1 - \boldsymbol{\sigma}_1 \cdot \boldsymbol{\sigma}_a)$ and $T = \frac{1}{4}(3 + \boldsymbol{\sigma}_1 \cdot \boldsymbol{\sigma}_a)$ are the singlet and triplet spin state projection operators respectively. This means that the $N$, $G$, and $H$ terms only operate on triplet spin states whilst the $B$ term acts only on the singlet state. This is a convenient division of $M_a$ if we require that the coefficients be related to the phase shifts and mixing parameters. This can be seen if we note that the phase shifts and mixing parameters are defined for states of given total and orbital angular momentum and of parity, which is a repre-sentation in which total spin is a good quantum number. From the matrix $M_a$ we can derive expressions for various observable quantities of the kind already discussed in earlier sections of this chapter. In addition there exist the spin correlation measurements which we now describe.

A correlation coefficient $C(\mathbf{l}, \mathbf{m})$ is the expectation value $\langle \sigma_l \rangle_2 \langle \sigma_m \rangle_a$; that is, the product of the $\mathbf{l}$ component of the polarization of the scattered nucleon 2 and of the $\mathbf{m}$ component of the polarization of the recoiling nucleon, $a$. The measurement of this correlation requires an analysis in coincidence of the polarization of the scattered and recoil nucleons. If l and **m** are directions perpendicular to the scattered and recoil nucleon momenta respectively, then $\langle\sigma_l\rangle_2$ and $\langle\sigma_m\rangle_a$ can be found by left-right scattering asymmetries at an analysing scatter. The measurement of $C(\mathbf{l}, \mathbf{m})$ means operating both these analysing scattering detectors in coincidence so as to measure four rates:

LL: both scattered and recoil nucleons scattered to left at analyser;

RR: both nucleons scattered to right;

LR: scattered nucleon scattered to left, recoil nucleon to right;

RL: scattered nucleon scattered to right, recoil nucleon to left.

Then, if $P_b$ is the analysing (= polarizing) power of the analysers, we have:

$$C(l, m) = \frac{1}{P_b^2} \frac{LL + RR - LR - RL}{LL + RR + LR + RL}.$$

If $l$ or $m$ lie in the direction of momentum of the corresponding particle, then it will be necessary to employ a magnetic field to turn this longitudinal polarization into a transverse polarization suitable for analysis.

We can now examine the case of proton–proton scattering. The $p$–$p$ system is in a state of total isotopic spin 1, so we label the coefficients $B$, $G$, etc. of Eq. (8.60) with the subscript 1. There is no physical interest in the derivation of equations for the observable quantities such as $d\sigma_a/d\Omega$, $P_a$, $D_a$, ..., etc. and in fact we will only quote three results: readers who require a formula for other quantities are referred to articles by Kanellopoulos and Brown (1957a, b), where they are given in a very convenient form. For unpolarized incident states,

$$\frac{d\sigma_a}{d\Omega} = \frac{1}{4}[\,|B_1|^2 + 8\,|C_1|^2 + |G_1 - N_1|^2 + 2\,|N_1|^2 + 2\,|H_1|^2], \qquad (8.61)$$

$$P_a \frac{d\sigma_a}{d\Omega} = 2\,\mathrm{Re}\,C_1^*\,N_1, \qquad (8.62)$$

$$C(\mathbf{n}_a, \mathbf{n}_a)\frac{d\sigma_a}{d\Omega} = \frac{1}{4}[-|B_1|^2 + 8\,|C_1|^2 - |G_1 - N_1|^2 + 2\,|N_1|^2 + 2\,|H_1|^2]. \qquad (8.63)$$

Then Eqs. (8.42) and (8.44) hold. The identity of the two protons restricts the nature of the coefficients of Eq. (8.60). They are, in fact, functions of $\cos\theta_a$ where $\theta_a$ is the angle of scattering; by applying the requirement of antisymmetry it is possible to decide whether these functions are even or odd in $\cos\theta_a$. We consider $\chi_1$ to represent the spin state of the system before the scattering, and $M_a\chi_1(e^{ikr}/r)$ to represent the total wave function of the final state, which must be antisymmetric under interchange of the two final state protons. This interchange is done by replacing $\mathbf{p}_2$ by $-\mathbf{p}_2$, which causes

$$\theta \to \pi - \theta,$$

$$\mathbf{k}_a \to \mathbf{p}_a,$$

$$\mathbf{p}_a \to \mathbf{k}_a,$$

$$\mathbf{n}_a \to -\mathbf{n}_a.$$

We apply this to Eq. (8.60), bearing in mind that $S$ and $T$ pick out antisymmetric and symmetric spin states respectively. We find

$$B_1(\pi - \theta) = B_1(\theta), \qquad H_1(\pi - \theta) = H_1(\theta),$$

$$G_1(\pi - \theta) = -G_1(\theta), \qquad N_1(\pi - \theta) = -N_1(\theta);$$

hence $B_1$ and $H_1$ are even functions of $\cos\theta_a$ and $G_1$ and $N_1$ are odd. The coefficient $C_1$ has to be examined differently. We notice that $P_a = 2\,\mathrm{Re}\,C_1^* N_1$, so that if $P_a$ is odd then $C_1$ is even and vice versa. In the scattering of unpolarized protons on an unpolarized hydrogen target, the final protons must have identical polarization, i.e., $P_a\mathbf{n}_a$ is unchanged if $\mathbf{p}_2 \to -\mathbf{p}_2$; but $\mathbf{n}_a$ changes sign as $\mathbf{p}_2 \to -\mathbf{p}_2$, and it follows that $P_a$ is odd and $C_1$ even. In addition, $P_a = 0$ if $\theta = 0$ or $\pi$, so that $C_1$ is an even function of $\cos\theta_a$ multiplied by $\sin\theta_a$.

We note that $C_1(\boldsymbol{\sigma}_1 + \boldsymbol{\sigma}_a)\cdot\mathbf{n}_a$ is antisymmetric under exchange of the final state nucleons; thus it only acts upon triplet states. The polarization effects in the scattering of an unpolarized incident beam depend upon $C_1$ and therefore only occur in the triplet state. This can be seen from elementary principles applied to the singlet state. Such a state cannot be polarized and, since total spin is conserved and the spin states are incoherent, there can be no net polarization of any particle in a singlet final state and the correlation along parallel axis will always be $-1$ for these states. There is no need to put a triplet projection operator $T$ in this term since it picks out these terms automatically. This is in contrast to the $G_1$, $H_1$, $N_1$ terms in Eq. (8.60) which do not do this; since they are allowed to act on triplet states only they must contain $T$. The corresponding terms that would act on singlet states have coefficients such that the net effect can be contained in the $B_1$ term.

There is obviously a very large variety of polarization experiments which can be performed on this proton–proton system; their value will be in their contribution to determining the phase shifts and mixing parameters. The coefficients $B_1, G_1, \ldots$, etc. have been given in terms of these quantities by Wright (1955). Kanellopoulos and Brown (1957a, b) have discussed the experiments which determine the coefficients. We can give one simple example to illustrate this application. Consider the correlation $C(\mathbf{n}_a, \mathbf{n}_a)$ for unpolarized proton scattering at $\vartheta_a = 90°$. At this angle $G_1 = N_1 = 0$ and we find from Eqs. (8.61) and (8.63) that

$$C(\mathbf{n}_a, \mathbf{n}_a) = -1$$

if singlet spin state scattering alone is effective and $+1$ if triplet scattering alone is effective. The departure of this quantity from $-1$ indicates the admixture of triplet scattering which can only be due to noncentral forces at this angle. Measurements have been made at 380-Mev laboratory energy (Ashmore et al., 1958) giving

$$C(\mathbf{n}_a, \mathbf{n}_a) = 0.416 \pm 0.084,$$

indicating that the triplet scattering cross section is about 71% and the singlet cross section 29% of the total. This is in fair agreement with the value calculated at 300 Mev for the Signell–Marshak potential. Readers are referred to a second paper by Kanellopoulos and Brown (1957b) for a general discussion of the properties of the correlation coefficients. In contrast to these authors, Skarsvåg (1958) gives results in terms of the elements of the matrix $M_a$ in the singlet–triplet representation.

Neutron–proton scattering takes place through both singlet and triplet isotopic spin states, $t = 0$ and 1 respectively (Section 6.4). Therefore $M_a$ for $n$–$p$ scattering is divided into two parts,

$$M_a = \tfrac{1}{2}(M_{a0} + M_{a1}). \tag{8.64}$$

$M_{a1}$ is precisely the same as for the $p$–$p$ scattering and operates only on the triplet isotopic spin states. $M_{a0}$ is similar with coefficients $B_0, C_0, G_0, H_0, N_0$. This applies to the singlet isotopic spin states which have symmetrical orbital and spin functions; therefore these coefficients are even or odd in the opposite way to the corresponding coefficients in $M_{a1}$. $B_0$ and $H_0$ are odd, $G_0$ and $N_0$ even, and $C_0$ is an odd function of $\cos \theta_a$ multiplied by $\sin \theta_a$. The use of this scattering matrix [Eq. (8.64)] proceeds as in the $p$–$p$ case, only the initial state must be expressed as eigenfunctions of the total isotopic spin. Application of $M_a$ gives final states in the same representation, and these must be converted into observable $n$–$p$ states. The results can be obtained by replacing the coefficients $B_1, C_1$, etc. in the $p$–$p$ results by the coefficients $\tfrac{1}{2}(B_0 + B_1)$, etc. Aspects of the $n$–$p$ and $p$–$n$ scattering have been discussed by Wolfenstein (1956b).

Before closing this section we wish to return to consider the completeness of $M_a$. First we note that it is indeed invariant under the parity transformation $P$ and under time reversal $T$. This can be checked by noting that under these transformations the vectors change as follows

$P$: $\mathbf{p}_1, \mathbf{p}_2, \mathbf{p}_a, \mathbf{k}_a$ change sign; $\mathbf{n}_a, \boldsymbol{\sigma}_1, \boldsymbol{\sigma}_a$ do not change sign.

$T$: $\mathbf{p}_1 \to -\mathbf{p}_2, \mathbf{p}_2 \to -\mathbf{p}_1, \mathbf{p}_a \to -\mathbf{p}_a$; $\boldsymbol{\sigma}_1$ and $\boldsymbol{\sigma}_a$ change sign; $\mathbf{k}_a$ does not change sign.

If the terms of the matrix expansion (8.60) are chosen so as to be invariant, then all but one of all independent terms are contained in this equation (Wolfenstein, 1954); the missing term $(\boldsymbol{\sigma}_1 - \boldsymbol{\sigma}_a) \cdot \mathbf{n}_a$ is not invariant under rotations in isotopic spin space. The recent interest in the nonconservation of parity in certain interactions has been extended to the nucleon–nucleon interaction. The possible effects of noninvariance under $P$ (and $T$) are calculated by adding terms to $M_a$ which are not invariant; this has been done by Woodruff (1959). We cannot discuss his results in detail but notice some simple results. If the interaction is not invariant under $P$, then polarized nucleons can scatter with an up-down asymmetry and unpolarized nucleons can scatter with a nonzero polarization component in the scattering plane. These statements may be checked by requiring a reaction and its mirror image to be equally likely if parity is conserved. A consequence of time reversal invariance is that the transverse polarization $P_a$ generated in unpolarized nucleon–nucleon scattering is equal to the scattering asymmetry $\epsilon_a$ if a fully transverse polarized beam is scattered from an unpolarized target at the same energy and angle. The polarization-asymmetry equality breaks down if the interaction is not invariant under $T$ (Bell and Mandl, 1958) independently of whether parity is conserved or not. Equation (8.59) also breaks down. Woodruff gives other more complex examples.

## 8.12 Review of Experimental Results for Nucleon–Nucleon Scattering

At the time of writing (1959) the situation is obscure. The experimental observations have taken us very little of the way to finding phase shifts and mixing parameters although in general the data do agree with the Signell–Marshak potential. By 1958, measurements had been made for $p$–$p$ scattering of $d\sigma/d\Omega$ and $P$ as a function of energy and angle from 45 Mev to 420 Mev, of $D$ at 146 Mev and of $D, R$, and $A$ at 310 Mev, and of $C(\mathbf{n}, \mathbf{n})$ at 90 and 382 Mev. The results indicate that $F$ waves are important even at 140 Mev and thus there must be at least 8 phase shifts and one mixing parameter in any analysis at one energy. There are less data available on $n$–$p$ scattering. For a compilation of references on the experimental work, readers are referred to a review by Hess (1958).

## 8.13 Relativistic Nucleon Polarization

It is obvious that our treatment of nucleon polarization has been non-relativistic; fortunately, this suffices up to the greatest energies at which experiments have been done (380 Mev). Stapp (1956) has given the relativistic treatment corresponding to the one given here. His results are a slight modification of the results we have presented, due to the rotation of polarization vectors during the transformations between various centre-of-mass coordinates in double and triple scattering experiments, and to other relativistic effects.

## 8.14 Electron Polarization

The electron possesses spin and can therefore be polarized. The situation is similar to the case of nucleon polarization except that the treatment must be relativistic, *ab initio*. In fact, double scattering experiments for electrons were suggested and performed many years before the corresponding nucleon experiments. The density matrix formalism can be used to describe electron (or positron) polarization as long as care is taken to make the theory compatible with the full Dirac electron theory. This is discussed in a comprehensive review by Tolhoek (1956) on the subject of electron polarization. He uses the formalism in a discussion of the double electron Coulomb scattering; this is an extension of the work described by Mott and Massey (1949) using the Dirac theory. It appears that there is an effective spin-orbit force in the interaction which scatters electrons and positrons in the electric field of a nucleus and which leads to a polarization of the scattered beam. As usual, this polarization may be detected in a second scattering; as before, if the scatters are identical, the scattering asymmetry is the square of the polarization. This polarization is only appreciable for heavy nuclei and in the energy range up to about 2 Mev. It is greater for electrons than for positrons as the latter are repelled from the nucleus and feel the influence of the spin-orbit force less. This Coulomb scattering has been used to detect and measure the polarization of beta particles emitted from radioactive materials. This polarization is longitudinal and must be transformed into transverse polarization before it can be detected by a scattering asymmetry; this can be done by passing the beam through an electric field which deflects the beam by 90° but does not turn the polarization, or through crossed electric and magnetic fields which turn the spin but not the beam. (Magnetic fields alone cannot be used as the cyclotron and Larmor frequency are almost the same.) For an example of this work readers are referred to the paper by Cavanagh et al. (1957).

Electron–electron (Møller) scattering, positron–electron (Bhabba) scattering, and positron annihilation in flight can all show effects due to polarization. There is a fortunate aspect to these reactions in that even at present it is possible to have polarized targets; the electron polarization in magnetically saturated soft iron is about 8%. In addition, many of the asymmetries and cross-section ratios are large for different polarizations of the incident particles. There are a large number of polarization measurements which are possible but which we shall not attempt to discuss. It seems that at present there is no difficulty in measuring transverse or longitudinal polarization of low-energy ($< 4$ Mev) electrons (or positrons). In principle, the measurement of the longitudinal polarization at all energies of electrons or positrons can be done by a determination of the differential cross sections for Møller or Bhabba scattering on polarized electrons; the difficulty lies in the dilution of the desired effect among competing processes. The measurement of the transverse polarization of higher-energy electrons is not easy and it is not possible to transform the transverse into a longitudinal polarization. For more details the reader is referred to articles by Stehle (1958), by Ford and Mullin (1957), by Bouchial and Michel (1958), by Grodzins (1959), and by Page (1959).

### 8.15 Photon Polarization

From our knowledge of classical light polarization we know that there are two convenient representations for the description of polarized light, either in terms of two perpendicular plane polarizations or in terms of two circular polarizations. This situation has already been discussed to illustrate the principle of superposition in Section 1.3. Whichever representation is chosen, the pure state of polarization can be described by a function $\chi$ which is a linear superposition of two states of polarization represented by orthogonal wave functions

$$\chi = c_1 \chi_1 + c_2 \chi_2. \tag{8.65}$$

The density matrix for this pure state is

$$\rho = \begin{bmatrix} c_1 c_1^* & c_1 c_2^* \\ c_1^* c_2 & c_1 c_2^* \end{bmatrix}.$$

For a beam of photons the complete density matrix is the average over all photons. It is a $2 \times 2$ matrix and can be expressed

$$\rho = \tfrac{1}{2}(1 + \boldsymbol{\xi} \cdot \boldsymbol{\sigma}),$$

as for the electron polarization. However, there is an important distinction between the interpretation of the two matrices. In the photon case $\boldsymbol{\sigma}$ is the three Pauli matrices, only we label them $\sigma_1, \sigma_2, \sigma_3$, where $\sigma_1 \equiv \sigma_x, \dots$, etc.; this is done in order to destroy any connection with directions in real space. The three components of $\boldsymbol{\xi}$ describe the polarization in what is sometimes called Poincaré space; the connection with ordinary space is determined by the properties of $\chi_1$ and $\chi_2$ in Eq. (8.65). If we choose these to represent vertically and horizontally plane polarized light, then the components of $\boldsymbol{\xi}$ can have the following extreme values which represent the polarization described:

$\xi_3 = \mathrm{Tr}\,\sigma_3 \rho = +1$ (or $-1$) for fully vertical (or horizontal) plane polarization;

$\xi_2 = \mathrm{Tr}\,\sigma_2 \rho = +1$ (or $-1$) for fully plane polarization at $45°$ to right (or left) of vertical;

$\xi_1 = \mathrm{Tr}\,\sigma_1 \rho = +1$ (or $-1$) for fully right (or left) circular polarization.

If $\boldsymbol{\xi}$ is a unit vector, the beam is fully polarized and the components indicate the nature of the polarization, e.g., plane, elliptical, etc. If $|\boldsymbol{\xi}| < 1$, the beam is not fully polarized but again the components indicate the type of partial polarization.

This description is closely connected with the Stokes parameters (Stokes, 1852). A full discussion of this representation and its connection with these parameters is given by Fano (1949, 1957), McMaster (1954), and Tolhoek (1956). These authors also discuss applications, in particular to the Compton effect. These photon polarization descriptions are invariant with respect to transformations between frames stationary or moving in the line of motion of the photon; thus there is no need for the polarization to be described with respect to a special frame, the centre of mass in the case of particles having rest mass. In fact, nature works the other way: since no centre-of-mass frame exists for a photon, it can only have a polarization which is described in an invariant fashion. This has the result that there are only two linearly independent states of photon polarization instead of the three usually associated with a particle carrying an intrinsic angular momentum of $\hbar$.

The photon manifests itself by interacting with electrons or nuclei and therefore photon polarization experiments will involve the scattering or absorption of photons by nuclei or by atomic electrons. This leads to a large variety of polarization phenomena which we do not discuss here, apart from mentioning some of the possibilities in the field of fast electrons ($\beta \simeq 1$), and hard photons ($> 100$ kev).

### a. *Compton Scattering*

In general, the scattered photon and recoiling electron will be polarized and this polarization may be detected at a second scatter. The scattering of polarized photons differs with the direction of polarization of the target electrons; these properties can be used to measure various kinds of photon polarization. These methods are most useful at lower energies ($< 10$ Mev). For a full discussion, readers are referred to Tolhoek (1956), to Lipps and Tolhoek (1954a, b), to Wightman (1948), to Fagg and Hanna (1959), and to Grodzins (1959).

### b. *Pair Production and Bremsstrahlung*

At high energies it appears that the polarization of the incident particle tends to be transferred to the most energetic of the final particles in these two processes. Thus during the development of a cascade shower the highest energy component tends to have the polarization of the incident particle. This phenomenon allows the energy of polarized radiation to be degraded sufficiently to permit a polarization measurement to be made using the Compton scattering in magnetically saturated iron (for example, see Holt *et al.*, 1959) For a theoretical discussion of this effect and the magnitudes involved readers are referred to the following works: Olsen and Maximon (1959) Banerjee (1958), and McVoy (1958).

There are also polarization effects in the nuclear interaction of photons. Unpolarized photons will eject polarized nucleons from nuclei; the polarization of nucleons recoiling from meson photoproduc tion is an example of this (Section 8.3). Polarized photons will eject nucleons asymmetrically from nuclei. This is not a widely investi gated field owing to the lack of polarized photons and the smallness of the cross sections involved.

### 8.16 Conclusion

We have covered a few aspects of polarization by giving examples and introducing techniques as required; readers are reminded that the most important of these, the density matrix formalism, is not restricted to polarization problems. For a review we refer readers to the article by Fano (1957); he discusses many applications and gives a full biblio graphy to earlier work.

# CHAPTER IX

# FIELD THEORY

## 9.1 Introduction

This chapter is intended to introduce the reader to the vocabulary of field theory. For the grammar of the subject we refer readers to more specialized works, such as those of Bogoliubov and Shirkov (1959), of Jauch and Rohrlich (1955), of Schweber et al. (1955), of Thirring (1958), and of Umezawa (1956). We shall attempt to make familiar the ideas of field quantization, of annihilation and creation operators, and of Feynman diagrams, without the full mathematical formalism which makes these subjects rigorous. We shall illustrate our description by referring to quantum electrodynamics and justify the subject by referring to its successes. We end the chapter by indicating the present status of quantum mesodynamics.

## 9.2 First Quantization

The formulation of a simple wave mechanics corresponds to the process of first quantization, for such a process implies the incorporation of Planck's constant into the equations. The simplest wave mechanics were formulated in such a way that the equations of motion represented the motion of a single particle, free or under the influence of a field. There are three outstanding equations of this nature.

The Schrödinger equation:
(a) for a free particle

$$-\frac{\hbar^2}{2m}\nabla^2\psi = i\hbar\frac{\partial\psi}{\partial t};$$

(b) for a particle in an electromagnetic field

$$-\frac{\hbar^2}{2m}\sum_{l=1}^{3}\left(\frac{\partial}{\partial x_l} - \frac{ie}{\hbar c}A_l\right)^2\psi = i\hbar\frac{\partial\psi}{\partial t} - ec\phi.$$

The Dirac equation for an electron:
(a) free

$$-i\hbar c \sum_{l=1}^{3} \alpha_l \frac{\partial \psi}{\partial x_l} + mc^2 \beta \psi = i\hbar \frac{\partial \psi}{\partial t};$$

(b) in an electromagnetic field

$$-i\hbar c \sum_{l=1}^{3} \alpha_l \left( \frac{\partial}{\partial x_l} - \frac{ie}{\hbar c} A_l \right) \psi + mc^2 \beta \psi = i\hbar \frac{\partial \psi}{\partial t} - ec\phi.$$

The Klein–Gordon equation:
(a) for a free particle

$$-\hbar^2 \nabla^2 \psi + m^2 c^2 \psi = -\frac{\hbar^2}{c^2} \frac{\partial^2 \psi}{\partial t^2};$$

(b) for a particle in an electromagnetic field

$$-\hbar^2 \sum_{l=1}^{3} \left( \frac{\partial}{\partial x_l} - \frac{ie}{\hbar c} A_l \right)^2 \psi + m^2 c^2 \psi = -\frac{\hbar^2}{c^2} \left( \frac{\partial}{\partial t} + \frac{iec\phi}{\hbar} \right)^2 \psi.$$

$A_l$ ($l = 1, 2, 3$) are the three components of the vector potential [Eq. (4.16)] and $\phi$ is the static electric potential. The quantities $\alpha_l$ ($l = 1, 2, 3$) and $\beta$ which occur in the Dirac equations are four-by-four Hermitian matrices satisfying the following relations:

$$\alpha_l \alpha_m + \alpha_m \alpha_l = 2\delta_{lm} \quad (l, m = 1, 2, 3), \tag{9.1}$$

$$\alpha_l \beta + \beta \alpha_l = 0, \tag{9.2}$$

$$\beta^2 = 1. \tag{9.3}$$

These equations are used by solving for the function $\psi$ and by interpreting this function according to the postulates of quantum mechanics as described in Section 1.2. In particular there are functions of $\psi$ which satisfy a continuity equation

$$\frac{\partial \rho}{\partial t} + \operatorname{div} \mathbf{j} = 0 \tag{9.4}$$

where $\rho$ is a probability density and $\mathbf{j}$ a current associated with the particle. For example, in the case of the free-particle Schrödinger equation, this equation is satisfied by

$$\rho = \psi^* \psi, \tag{9.5}$$

$$\mathbf{j} = \frac{\hbar}{2mi} (\psi^* \nabla \psi - \psi \nabla \psi^*). \tag{9.6}$$

The corresponding quantities for the free-particle Dirac equation are

$$\rho = \psi^\dagger \psi, \tag{9.7}$$

$$j_l = c\psi^\dagger \alpha_l \psi \quad (l = 1, 2, 3). \tag{9.8}$$

Finding quantities for the free-particle Klein–Gordon equation creates difficulty; if **j** is taken as in (9.6), then to satisfy (9.4) we must have

$$\rho = \frac{i\hbar}{2mc^2} \left( \psi^* \frac{\partial \psi}{\partial t} - \frac{\partial \psi^*}{\partial t} \psi \right),$$

which can have negative values. This fact defeats any efforts to make a consistent one-particle theory from the Klein–Gordon equation. However, Pauli and Weisskopf (1934) showed how the equation could be reinterpreted as the equation of motion for a field which represented the behaviour of many particles of all electric charges so that negative probability density is connected with an excess of negatively charged over positively charged particles; that is, we consider the probability density to be a charge density.

Although the Dirac theory is satisfactory as a one-particle theory, and as such successfully predicts the energy levels of the hydrogen atom, it fails to predict the fine structure. The trouble was recognized as being due to the difficulty of making the single-particle theory into a many-particle theory which remained Lorentz covariant. This difficulty can be overcome by interpreting the equation as being the equation of motion of a field which can contain many particles; that is, a many-particle theory, *ab initio*. This theory is very successful and correctly predicts the fine structure of the hydrogen atom energy levels and the anomalous magnetic moment of the electron.

The process of interpreting these theories as many-particled theories is called second quantization.

## 9.3 The Covariant Notation

It is convenient to introduce and discuss the notation employed in this chapter; it places all four components of four vectors on precisely the same footing. We wish to avoid the use of contravariant and covariant notation (Margenau and Murphy, 1943), so our fourth component has to be imaginary. Previously we have indicated three-dimensional vectors by boldface type (e.g., **x**); we continue this convention and indicate four vectors by lightface type (e.g., $x$). Components of a three-dimensional vector are indicated by roman subscripts, for example $x_l$ $(l = 1, 2, 3)$, whilst the components of a four vector are indicated by

Greek subscripts, thus: $x_\lambda$ ($\lambda = 1, 2, 3, 4$). The fourth component of the coordinates of a point is $x_4 = ict$ (Section 1.3).

Repeated indices in mathematical expressions implies summation over the four or three values of the index. Thus for the scalar products

$$\mathbf{a \cdot b} = \sum_{l=1}^{3} a_l b_l = a_l b_l,$$

$$a \cdot b = \sum_{\lambda=1}^{4} a_\lambda b_\lambda = a_\lambda b_\lambda.$$

There are two important four vectors connected with the electromagnetic field and its interaction with electric charges. The first is the vector potential $A$ which has the three-dimensional vector potential $\mathbf{A}$ as spacelike components and $ic\phi$, where $\phi$ is the static potential, as its fourth component. The second is the current vector $j$ which combines the normal three-dimensional current vector with $ic\rho$, where $\rho$ is the charge density.

In this chapter we shall follow field theory convention and use the natural system of units in which $\hbar = c = 1$; this is described more fully in Appendix C. The unit of electric charge is defined in a rationalized system and we have therefore that

$$e \simeq \sqrt{\frac{4\pi}{137}}.$$

We shall use the symbols $p$ and $k$ to represent the four momenta of electrons or positrons and of photons or mesons respectively. In this natural system all components of these four vectors have the dimensions of $cm^{-1}$; that is, they are $2\pi$ times reciprocal wavelengths. It follows that $m$, the symbol for mass, has the same quality.

For real particles we have that

$$k^2 = k \cdot k = \mathbf{k}^2 - k_0^2 = \begin{cases} 0 & \text{(photons)}, \\ -m^2 & \text{(mesons)}, \end{cases}$$

$$p^2 = p \cdot p = \mathbf{p}^2 - p_0^2 = -m^2 \text{ (positrons and electrons)},$$

where $ip_0 = p_4$ and $ik_0 = k_4$. $k_0$ and $p_0$ are the total energies of the particles in the appropriate units.

The volume element $dx\,dy\,dz$ is contracted to $d\mathbf{x}$, the space–time element $dx\,dy\,dz\,dict$ to $d^4x$, and similarly for elements in momentum space.

The differential operators can also be expressed in covariant notation; for example,

$$\nabla^2 - \frac{1}{c^2}\frac{\partial^2}{\partial t^2} = \frac{\partial^2}{\partial x_\lambda \, \partial x_\lambda} = \Box \, .$$

## 9.4 The Lagrangian Formalism

A relativistic many-particle theory is set up by defining the dynamical field variables $\psi(x)$ which are operators and are functions of the space–time coordinates $x_\lambda$ ($\lambda = 1, 2, 3, 4$). The field variables exist at all points in space–time and can have more than one component at each point. The behaviour of the field is described by the Lagrangian density which is assumed to be a fuctinon of the field variables $\psi^\kappa(x)$ ($\kappa = 1, 2, ..., n$ for an $n$-component field) and of their derivatives $\psi_\lambda^\kappa(x) = \partial \psi^\kappa / \partial x_\lambda$ ($\lambda = 1, 2, 3, 4$). Thus:

$$\mathscr{L} = \mathscr{L}(\psi^\kappa, \psi_\lambda^\kappa).$$

This implies that $\mathscr{L}$ is a function of the coordinates. The total Lagrangian or action is the density integrated over a suitable space–time volume $\Omega$:

$$L = \frac{1}{i} \int_\Omega \mathscr{L}(\psi^\kappa, \psi_\lambda^\kappa) \, d^4 x. \tag{9.9}$$

An action principle is used to predict the behaviour of physically permissible systems. This principle requires that $L$ be stationary for variations of the field variables at values they have when representing physical systems; it follows that the equations of motion are

$$\frac{\partial \mathscr{L}}{\partial \psi^\kappa} - \frac{\partial}{\partial x_\lambda} \frac{\partial \mathscr{L}}{\partial \psi_\lambda^\kappa} = 0.$$

Other information about the field may be found by making other variations such as displacements of the boundary of $\Omega$. The usual procedure is to use the $\mathscr{L}$ which gives the required equations of motion. We shall illustrate the information given in this section by giving the scalar field as example. This field has Lagrangian density given by

$$\mathscr{L} = -\frac{1}{2}\left\{ \frac{\partial \phi}{\partial x_\lambda} \frac{\partial \phi}{\partial x_\lambda} + m^2 \phi^2 \right\},$$

when $\phi$ is here the field variable for the scalar field. This leads to the equation of motion

$$\Box \phi + m^2 \phi = 0$$

which is the Klein–Gordon equation in covariant notation. Once the Lagrangian is known it is possible to find the commutators of the field variables and it is this step which is the essential part of second quantization. We shall not quote the commutators at this stage but proceed to the next stage, which is to make a Fourier expansion of the field variables in terms of plane waves of fixed momentum. The Fourier coefficients must be operators and their commutation relations can be derived from the commutation relations for the field variables. For the scalar field

$$\phi(x) = \frac{1}{(2\pi)^{3/2}} \int_{-\infty}^{+\infty} \frac{d\mathbf{k}}{(2k_0)^{1/2}} \{a_k e^{ik \cdot x} + a_k^\dagger e^{-ik \cdot x}\}, \qquad (9.9a)$$

where $+(\mathbf{k}^2 + m^2)^{1/2} = k_0$. The volume of integration $\Omega$ has been taken to infinity. The operators $a_k, a_k^\dagger$ satisfy the commutation rules:

$$[a_k, a_{k'}] = [a_k^\dagger, a_{k'}^\dagger] = 0, \quad [a_k, a_{k'}^\dagger] = \delta(k - k'). \qquad (9.10)$$

The field variables obey the Heisenberg equation of motion

$$i\frac{d\phi}{dt} = [\phi, H],$$

where $H$ is the Hamiltonian. This is an operator equation and we can find its matrix elements between two states represented by state vectors $\Phi_1$ and $\Phi_2$ which are eigenfunctions of $H$ with eigenvalues $E_1$ and $E_2$. Then

$$\left(\Phi_2 \left| i\frac{d\phi}{dt} \right| \Phi_1\right) = (\Phi_2 | \phi H - H\phi | \Phi_1).$$

We can pick out one Fourier component $a_k e^{ik \cdot x}$ and we have

$$(\Phi_2 | k_0 a_k e^{ik \cdot x} | \Phi_2) = (E_1 - E_2)(\Phi_2 | a_k e^{ik \cdot x} | \Phi_1).$$

Therefore

$$k_0 = E_1 - E_2 \quad \text{if} \quad (\Phi_2 | a_k e^{ik \cdot x} | \Phi_1) \neq 0.$$

This equation states that the total energy in the field represented by state vector $\Phi_1$ is greater than that in the field $\Phi_2$ by $k_0$ if the matrix element of $a_k e^{ik \cdot x}$ between these states is nonzero. Thus this operator only has matrix elements between states which differ in energy by $k_0 = \sqrt{(\mathbf{k}^2 + m^2)}$. This is a quantum condition and implies that the field of plane waves of momentum $k$ can only contain an integral number of energy units $k_0$. Therefore the operator $a_k$ operates on $\Phi_1$ to produce a state $\Phi_2$ which has an energy which is less by $k_0$; that is, it has the effect of removing one quantum of momentum $k$ from the field; and as such it is called an annihilation operator. Similarly,

$a_k^\dagger$ only has matrix elements between $\Phi_2$ and $\Phi_1$ if $E_2 - E_1 = k_0$; it follows that $a_k^\dagger$ has the effect of creating a quantum and is consequently called a creation operator.

We can define a vacuum state which contains no particle by the equation

$$a_k \Phi_0 = 0 \text{ for all } k. \tag{9.11}$$

Let us put

$$a_k^\dagger \Phi_0 = \Phi_1,$$

and

$$a_k^\dagger a_k^\dagger \Phi_0 = a_k^\dagger \Phi_1 = \Phi_2;$$

that is,

$$(a_k^\dagger)^n \Phi_0 = \Phi_n.$$

We wish to consider the operator $a^\dagger a$ where we have dropped the subscript $k$, since all the following discussion is independent of $k$ as long as the same subscript is implied throughout.

We have that

$$\Phi_n = a^\dagger \Phi_{n-1}.$$

Therefore

$$a^\dagger a \Phi_n = a^\dagger a a^\dagger \Phi_{n-1}$$

$$= a^\dagger (1 + a^\dagger a) \Phi_{n-1}$$

$$= \Phi_n + (a^\dagger)^2 a a^\dagger \Phi_{n-2}$$

$$= \Phi_n + (a^\dagger)^2 (1 + a^\dagger a) \Phi_{n-2}$$

$$= 2\Phi_n + (a^\dagger)^3 a \Phi_{n-2}.$$

Repeating the procedure in these steps, we find that

$$a^\dagger a \Phi_n = r\Phi_n + (a^\dagger)^{r+1} a \Phi_{n-r};$$

when $r = n$, we have

$$a^\dagger a \Phi_n = n \Phi_n. \tag{9.12}$$

Now $n$ is the number of quanta having the momentum of interest in the field and is the eigenvalue of the operator $a^\dagger a$. The Hamiltonian for this free scalar field can be found from the Lagrangian by the quantum analogue of the classical formalism; this Hamiltonian can be expanded into a function of creation and annihilation operators. The result is

$$H = \int k_0 a_k^\dagger a_k \, d\mathbf{k},$$

$$= \int k_0 n_k \, d\mathbf{k}.$$

We expect the total energy to be the eigenvalue of the Hamiltonian and this is satisfied by this equation.

If we require the action [Eq. (9.9)] to be invariant under Lorentz transformations, then there exist combinations of the field variables and their derivatives which do not vary with time. These conservation laws are the same as the conservation laws discussed in Section 1.2, and the list of transformations with their equivalent conserved qualities (Table 1.1) applies in the Lagrangian formalism. In this formalism, the requirement of invariance under inhomogeneous Lorentz transformations without rotations draws attention to the importance of a tensor $T_{\lambda\mu}$ given by

$$T_{\lambda\mu} = \frac{\partial \mathscr{L}}{\partial \psi_\lambda^\kappa} \psi_\mu^\kappa - \mathscr{L}\delta_{\lambda\mu}.$$

The fourth column components can be integrated over all three-dimensional space to give a four vector $P_\lambda$ which is constant

$$\frac{dP_\lambda}{dx_4} = \frac{d}{dx_4} \int T_{\lambda 4}\, d\mathbf{x} = 0.$$

$P_\lambda$ can be identified as the total momentum-energy four vector and the conservation of energy and momentum is assured by the invariance of the Lagrangian density. Similarly, Lorentz rotations generate the angular momentum tensor having components which can be connected with the components of orbital angular momentum and of spin. The conserved quantity is the total angular momentum. In the case of the one-component scalar field the spin is found to be zero, as expected.

There is one important transformation which can be applied to fields described by complex field variables (non-Hermitian operators)— the gauge transformation. Let us consider a complex scalar field for which the Lagrangian density is

$$\mathscr{L} = -\frac{1}{2}\left\{\frac{\partial \phi^\dagger}{\partial x_\lambda}\frac{\partial \phi}{\partial x_\lambda} + m^2\phi^\dagger\phi\right\}.$$

If $\phi$ and $\phi^\dagger$ are linearly independent, this gives two field equations:

$$\Box\,\phi + m^2\phi = 0, \quad \Box\,\phi^\dagger + m^2\phi^\dagger = 0.$$

The gauge transformation changes the phase of the field variables

$$\phi \to \phi\, e^{-i\alpha} \quad \text{and} \quad \phi^\dagger \to \phi^\dagger\, e^{i\alpha}$$

and it is evident that the Lagrangian is invariant. In addition there is an associated tensor of unit rank

$$j_\lambda = ie\left(\phi^\dagger \frac{\partial\phi}{\partial x_\lambda} - \frac{\partial\phi^\dagger}{\partial x_\lambda}\phi\right), \tag{9.13}$$

which satisfies the continuity equation

$$\frac{\partial j_\mu}{\partial x_\mu} = 0$$

and has a fourth component with a space integral which is conserved

$$\frac{d}{dx_4}\int j_4\, d\mathbf{x} = 0. \tag{9.14}$$

The tensor $j_\lambda$ is a four vector and is normally taken to be the four vector of current and charge density. The conservation equation (9.14) expresses the over-all conservation of electric charge. The same four vector appears on the application of gauge transformation to Lagrangians describing other charged particle fields. Equation (9.13) makes it evident that this four vector does not exist for the real scalar field and we deduce that such a field cannot describe charged particles. We expect that Lagrangians are invariant under other gauge transformations associated with the conservation of leptons (Section 11.2) and of baryons (Section 12.2). The Fourier expansion of the complex scalar field is

$$\phi(x) = \frac{1}{(2\pi)^{3/2}}\int \frac{d\mathbf{k}}{(2k_0)^{1/2}}\{a_k e^{ik\cdot x} + b_k^\dagger e^{-ik\cdot x}\},$$

$$\phi^\dagger(x) = \frac{1}{(2\pi)^{3/2}}\int \frac{d\mathbf{k}}{(2k_0)^{1/2}}\{a_k^\dagger e^{-ik\cdot x} + b_k e^{ik\cdot x}\},$$

where $k_0 = +(\mathbf{k}^2+m^2)^{1/2}$ and the operators $a_k$, $b_k$, $a_k^\dagger$, and $b_k^\dagger$ satisfy commutation relations similar to those of Eq. (9.10). From our definition of the current operator [Eq. (9.13)] it follows that $a$ and $a^\dagger$ annihilate and create particles of charge $e$ whilst $b$ and $b^\dagger$ annihilate and create particles of charge $-e$.

The scalar fields have been used in this section to exemplify the usefulness of the Lagrangian formalism in quantum field theory and to indicate how the insertion of commutation relations gives the field the required quantized structure. In the next two sections we discuss two rather more involved fields.

## 9.5 The Electromagnetic Field

The equations of the electromagnetic field have been given in Section 4.4. We regard $\mathbf{E}$ and $\mathbf{H}$ to be the observables and the four vector $A_\mu$ to be the field variables

$$\mathbf{B} = \operatorname{curl} \mathbf{A},$$

$$\mathbf{E} = -\frac{\partial \mathbf{A}}{\partial t} - \operatorname{grad} \phi,$$

where $i\phi = A_4$. The equations do not determine $A_\mu$ uniquely, for the observables are unaffected by the gauge transformation

$$A_\mu \to A_\mu + \frac{d\chi}{dx_\mu},$$

where $\chi$ is a scalar quantity. It is usual to apply the Lorentz subsidiary condition to the field, which in covariant notation reads [Eq. (4.19)]

$$\frac{\partial A_\mu}{\partial x_\mu} = 0, \tag{9.15}$$

in which case the field variables satisfy Eq. (4.20)

$$\Box\, A_\mu = 0 \tag{9.16}$$

and the uncertainty in $A$ becomes due to the special gauge transformation

$$A_\mu \to A_\mu + \frac{\partial \chi_0}{\partial x_\mu}$$

where $\chi_0$ satisfies

$$\Box\, \chi_0 = 0.$$

A rigorous quantum theory of the electromagnetic field runs into several difficulties which are connected with its invariance under gauge transformations and its zero rest mass. However, we shall not do more than mention these difficulties as we proceed by stating what is done in quantizing the field. A suitable Lagrangian is

$$\mathscr{L} = -\frac{1}{4}\left(\frac{\partial A_\mu}{\partial x_\lambda} - \frac{\partial A_\lambda}{\partial x_\mu}\right) - \frac{1}{2}\left(\frac{\partial A_\mu}{\partial x_\mu}\right)^2,$$

which gives the required field equations (9.16) if the Lorentz condition (9.15) is satisfied. This condition conflicts with the commutation relations which are derived, and has to be modified to be a condition on the expectation value of the operator; that is,

$$\left\langle \frac{\partial A_\mu}{\partial x_\mu} \right\rangle = 0.$$

As usual the field can be expanded in terms of annihilation and creation operators

$$A_\mu(x) = \frac{1}{(2\pi)^{3/2}} \int \frac{d\mathbf{k}}{(2k_0)^{1/2}} \{A_{k\mu} e^{ik \cdot x} + A_{k\mu}^\dagger e^{-ik \cdot x}\}, \qquad (9.17)$$

where $k_0 = |\mathbf{k}|$. The $A_{k\mu}$ annihilates and the $A_{k\mu}^\dagger$ creates a photon of momentum $k$ and polarization $\mu$. These properties are derived as usual from the commutation properties of the field variables. It appears in this theory that a photon can have four degrees of freedom with respect to polarization, when we know that there are two degrees only. Thus there are two superfluous states of polarization in Eq. (9.17). Formally it is found that the subsidiary condition and other properties of the field cause the four states to be linearly dependent; resolving this difficulty is a matter of some complexity and we shall not discuss it here. However, it turns out in practice that the inclusion of all four polarization states leads to consistent results as the two superfluous states always give cancelling contributions. The connection between the four polarizations and the observable states is discussed in Bogoliubov and Shirkov (1959).

## 9.6 The Dirac Field

The Dirac field is described by field variables which have four components and which transform as do spinors. The field contains quanta which carry an intrinsic angular momentum of $\hbar/2$ and it appears that all such spin $\frac{1}{2}$ particles in the free field situation are described by a Dirac field.

We proceed by reforming the Dirac equation into covariant notation. We define four matrices by the equations

$$\gamma_k = -i\beta\alpha_k \quad (k = 1, 2, 3), \qquad (9.18)$$

$$\gamma_4 = \beta, \qquad (9.19)$$

where $\beta$ and $\alpha_k$ are given by the relations of Eqs. (9.1) to (9.3). From these commutation relations for the matrices $\boldsymbol{\alpha}$ and $\beta$ we find that

$$\gamma_\rho \gamma_\sigma + \gamma_\sigma \gamma_\rho = 2\delta_{\rho\sigma} I \quad (\rho, \sigma = 1, 2, 3, 4). \qquad (9.20)$$

When defined as in Eqs. (9.18) and (9.19) the $\gamma$ matrices are Hermitian:

$$\gamma_\rho^\dagger = \gamma_\rho.$$

It is not normally necessary to use an explicit representation of the $\gamma$ matrices. Such a representation in its irreducible form will be a set of four-by-four matrices; see, for example, Bogoliubov and Shirkov (1959). Substituting Eqs. (9.18) and (9.19) into the free particle Dirac equation (Section 9.2), we find that the free field equation is

$$\gamma_\rho \frac{\partial \psi}{\partial x_\rho} + m\psi = 0. \tag{9.21}$$

$\psi$ is a four-component wave function which is readily represented by a column matrix of four elements; therefore the Dirac equation, as expressed in Eq. (9.21), contains four equations. A second field variable, called the adjoint function $\bar{\psi}$, is given by

$$\bar{\psi} = \psi^\dagger \gamma_4$$

and satisfies

$$\frac{\partial \bar{\psi}}{\partial x_\rho} \gamma_\rho - m\bar{\psi} = 0.$$

The Lagrangian density which generates these field equations is

$$\mathscr{L} = -\bar{\psi} \left( \gamma_\rho \frac{\partial}{\partial x_\rho} + m \right) \psi. \tag{9.22}$$

Let us now consider the plane wave solutions to Eq. (9.21)

$$\psi(x) = u(p)\, e^{ip \cdot x},$$

where

$$p \cdot x = \mathbf{p} \cdot \mathbf{x} - p_0 x_0.$$

The spinor $u(p)$ satisfies the equation

$$(\gamma_\rho p_\rho - im)\, u(p) = 0.$$

There are four solutions for a given value of $\mathbf{p}$, two having $p_0 = +(\mathbf{p}^2 + m^2)^{1/2}$ and the others having $p_0 = -(\mathbf{p}^2 + m^2)^{1/2}$. The four solutions form an orthogonal set. However, it is more convenient to make use of another orthogonal set, namely the four solutions $u_r(p)$ and $v_r(p)$, where $r = 1, 2$, which have $\mathbf{p}$ and $p_0$ positive for $u_r(p)$ whilst $\mathbf{p}$ and $p_0$ are negative for $v_r(p)$. These solutions satisfy

$$(\gamma_\rho p_\rho - imc)\, u_r(p) = 0,$$

$$(\gamma_\rho p_\rho + imc)\, v_r(p) = 0.$$

The solutions $u_r(p)$ go with plane waves $e^{+ip \cdot x}$ and the solutions $v_r(p)$ with the plane waves $e^{-ip \cdot x}$.

We can now make a Fourier expansion of $\psi(x)$

$$\psi(x) = \int \frac{d\mathbf{p}}{(2\pi)^{3/2}} \left(\frac{m}{p_0}\right)^{1/2} \sum_{r=1}^{2} \{a_{pr}\, u_r(p)\, e^{ip\cdot x} + b_{pr}^{\dagger}\, v_r(p)\, e^{-ip\cdot x}\},$$

where $p_0 = +(\mathbf{p}^2 + m^2)^{1/2}$. There is a similar expansion for the adjoint function if we define the adjoint spinors

$$\bar{u}_r(p) = u_r^{\dagger}(p)\gamma_4 \quad \text{and} \quad \bar{v}_r(p) = v_r^{\dagger}(p)\gamma_4,$$

$$\bar{\psi}(x) = \int \frac{d\mathbf{p}}{(2\pi)^{3/2}} \left(\frac{m}{p_0}\right)^{1/2} \sum_{r=1}^{2} \{a_{pr}^{\dagger}\, \bar{u}_r(p)\, e^{-ip\cdot x} + b_{pr}\, \bar{v}_r(p)\, e^{+ip\cdot x}\}.$$

The normal method of second quantization would be to derive the commutation relations for the field variables of this Dirac field; however, in this case commutation relations lead to physical inconsistencies which can only be avoided by having the field variables obey anticommutation relations. The result is that the operators $a$, $a^{\dagger}$, $b$, and $b^{\dagger}$ also satisfy anticommutation relations. These are

$$\{a_{pr}, a_{p'r'}^{\dagger}\} = \delta(p-p')\delta_{rr'},$$

$$\{b_{pr}, b_{p'r'}^{\dagger}\} = \delta(p-p')\delta_{rr'},$$

where we have used the notation

$$\{A, B\} = AB + BA.$$

All other combinations of these operators anticommute.

As in the case of the previous fields, these operators can be interpreted as creation and annihilation operators:

$a_{pr}$ annihilates a particle of momentum $\mathbf{p}$ and energy $p_0$,

$a_{pr}^{\dagger}$ creates a particle of momentum $\mathbf{p}$ and energy $p_0$,

$b_{pr}$ creates a particle of momentum $-\mathbf{p}$ and energy $-p_0$,

$b_{pr}^{\dagger}$ annihilates a particle of momentum $-\mathbf{p}$ and energy $-p_0$.

The subscript $r$ refers to the spin orientation of the particle concerned. Physically the creation of a particle of momentum $-\mathbf{p}$ and energy $-p_0$ is equivalent to the destruction of a particle of momentum $\mathbf{p}$ and energy $p_0$ and of opposite electric charge. Thus, applied to the electron–positron field, we have

$$\left.\begin{array}{l} a_{pr} \text{ annihilates electrons} \\[6pt] a^{\dagger}_{pr} \text{ creates electrons} \\[6pt] b_{pr} \text{ annihilates positrons} \\[6pt] b^{\dagger}_{pr} \text{ creates positrons} \end{array}\right\} \begin{array}{l} \text{all of momentum } \mathbf{p} \\ \text{ and energy } p_0. \end{array}$$

Thus, for this field,

$\psi(x)$ annihilates electrons or creates positrons at the point $x$,

$\bar{\psi}(x)$ creates electrons or annihilates positrons at the point $x$.

Let us consider the properties of these creation and annihilation operators in more detail. We define the vacuum state $\Phi_0$ by

$$a\Phi_0 = b\Phi_0 = 0$$

where we have dropped the subscripts on the operators; in the following argument all operators refer to particles in the same state, that is, momentum $\mathbf{p}$ and spin $r$. Let us create a one-electron state $\Phi_1$

$$\Phi_1 = a^{\dagger}\Phi_0.$$

We now try to create a second electron having the same momentum and spin as the first:

$$\Phi_2 = a^{\dagger}\Phi_1 = a^{\dagger}a^{\dagger}\Phi_0 = 0.$$

The last equality follows from the fact that $a^{\dagger}$ anticommutes with itself, that is,

$$\{a^{\dagger}, a^{\dagger}\} = 0.$$

This zero that appears when we try to create electrons of the same momentum and spin is interpreted to mean that it is impossible to have two electrons of the same momentum and spin in the same field. This result is gratifying as it means that the implications of the Pauli exclusion principle appear as a consequence of the anticommuting properties of the field variables and that the principle does not have to be put directly into the theory as a postulate.

It is possible to construct an operator which has eigenvalues equal to the number of quanta of specified momentum and spin in the field.

It is $N_{pr} = a_{pr}^\dagger a_{pr}$. It has the property

$$N_{pr}(N_{pr} - 1) = 0,$$

so that

$$N_{pr} = 1 \text{ or } 0,$$

as required for a field which obeys the exclusion principle. $M_{pr} = b_{pr}^\dagger b_{pr}$ is the operator which has eigenvalues equal to the number of anti-particles in the field. The $b$ operators behave in the same way as the $a$ operators and the antiparticles also obey the exclusion principle, but have charge opposite to that of the particle.

We can now discuss the other quantities which can be derived once the Lagrangian density is known. These are the current four vector, the energy-momentum tensor, and the angular momentum tensor. The current four vector is

$$j_\rho = ie\bar{\psi}\gamma_\rho \psi. \tag{9.22a}$$

Taking the fourth component, integrating over space, and substituting the Fourier expansion, we obtain an expression for the conserved total charge of the field; it is

$$Q = e \sum_{r=1}^{2} \int d\mathbf{p}(a_{pr}^\dagger a_{pr} - b_{pr}^\dagger b_{pr}),$$

which confirms our assignment of one charge to the particle whose number operator is $a^\dagger a$ and opposite charge to the antiparticle whose number operator is $b^\dagger b$. The energy-momentum tensor leads to an expression for the total momentum four vector

$$P_\mu = \int d\mathbf{p}\, p_\mu \sum_{r=1}^{2} \{a_{pr}^\dagger a_{pr} + b_{pr}^\dagger b_{pr}\}.$$

The fourth component is related to the energy and indicates that this quantity is a positive definite quantity which is equal to the total energy of particles and antiparticles in the field. The angular momentum tensor can be used to find the component of spin angular momentum along the direction of motion. We pick out quanta of one momentum $p$ and we find that the required component is

$$s = \tfrac{1}{2}\{a_{p1}^\dagger a_{p1} - a_{p2}^\dagger a_{p2} - b_{p1}^\dagger b_{p1} + b_{p2}^\dagger b_{p2}\}.$$

This result allows us to complete our interpretation of the $a$ and $b$ operators. All the particles created or annihilated have spin $\tfrac{1}{2}$; the component of this spin is $\pm\tfrac{1}{2}$ along the direction of $\mathbf{p}$ according to:

$r = 1$ for particle or $r = 2$ for antiparticle with spin component $+\tfrac{1}{2}$,

$r = 2$ for particle or $r = 1$ for antiparticle with spin component $-\tfrac{1}{2}$.

## 9.7 Second Quantization and the Commutation Relations

The subjects described in the last section did not include a detailed consideration of the commutation relations although these relations were stated to be the source of the commutation relations for the annihilation and creation operators. The commutation properties of the field variables are the real reason for the quantized nature of the field and thus the essential part of second quantization is the determination of these properties. We shall not discuss the procedure for doing this but refer readers to more detailed work; the method is due to Peierls (1952) and is described by Gunn (1955), for example. The commutation relations and their expectation values, which are also important in the theory, can be expressed as complex integrals which are solutions of the field equations with δ-function sources. A discussion of these so-called Green's functions is also beyond our scope and readers are referred to the literature: for example, Bogoliubov and Shirkov (1959) and Jauch and Rohrlich (1955).

We shall take a brief look at one commutation relation—that for a scalar field

$$[\phi(x), \phi(y)] = -iD(x - y)$$

where

$$D(x) = \frac{-i}{(2\pi)^3} \int_{-\infty}^{+\infty} e^{ik \cdot x} \delta(k^2 + m^2) \, \epsilon(k_0) \, d^4 k, \qquad (9.23)$$

and where

$$\epsilon(k_0) = \begin{cases} +1 \text{ for } k_0 > 0, \\ -1 \text{ for } k_0 < 0. \end{cases}$$

If $x$ and $y$ are spacelike points, that is, if $\mathbf{x} - \mathbf{y} > (x_4 - y_4)/i$, which means $x$ and $y$ cannot be connected by a light signal, then $\phi(x)$ and $\phi(y)$ must commute and $D(x - y) = 0$. Hence $D(x)$ must be zero if $x$ is a spacelike point with respect to the origin. We can test this by putting $x_4 = 0$ in Eq. (9.23) from which we find $D(x) = 0$. This particular equal-time case can be transformed into any spacelike separation by a Lorentz transformation. This leaves $D(x)$ unchanged and it is therefore zero for all spacelike points.

## 9.8 Interaction and the S-Matrix

In earlier sections of this chapter we have discussed free fields. In practice the fields are not free but interacting continuously and this has several effects. One of these is to change "bare" particles into "dressed" particles; for example, an electron is in continuous interaction with the electromagnetic field, emitting and reabsorbing virtual photons, and this causes a change in mass, electric charge, and magnetic moment from the unobservable values for a bare electron to the observed values for a dressed electron. A second effect of the interaction is to cause an interchange of energy between interacting fields so that particles are created, or destroyed, or change energy; these particle reactions only take place if energy and momentum are conserved. It is this second feature of interacting fields which interests us in this section and we shall discuss quantum electrodynamics as an example of the interaction properties.

Let us consider two interacting fields, 1 and 2, which have free field Lagrangian densities $\mathscr{L}_1$ and $\mathscr{L}_2$. The total Lagrangian density is given by

$$\mathscr{L} = \mathscr{L}_1 + \mathscr{L}_2 + \mathscr{L}_I,$$

where $\mathscr{L}_I$ is the contribution from the interaction energy. Many formal difficulties appear in the theory when this term is added and satisfactory progress can only be made in a perturbation theory in which solutions appear as a power series in the coefficient which occurs in $\mathscr{L}_I$. This perturbation theory must be set up in the "interaction representation" (see works cited in Section 9.1), which we do not discuss here.

$\mathscr{L}_I$ is able to cause transitions from an initial state represented by a state function $\Phi_\alpha$ to a final state of the same energy and momentum represented by $\Phi_\beta$. $\Phi_\alpha$ and $\Phi_\beta$ are defined at times distant in the past and future respectively; let us suppose at $t_\alpha = -\infty$ and $t_\beta = +\infty$. Then the probability amplitude for finding the state $\Phi_\beta$ at $t_\beta = +\infty$ is

$$(\Phi_\beta \,|\, S \,|\, \Phi_\alpha).$$

$S$ is the unitary $S$-matrix and it is this operator which we wish to relate to $\mathscr{L}_I$. There is no relation in closed form but $S$ can be expressed as a power series

$$S = \sum_{n=0}^{\infty} \frac{(-i)^n}{n!} \int_{-\infty}^{+\infty} d^4 x_1 \int_{-\infty}^{+\infty} d^4 x_2 \ldots \int_{-\infty}^{+\infty} d^4 x_n$$
$$P\{\mathscr{L}_I(x_1)\mathscr{L}_I(x_2)\ldots\mathscr{L}_I(x_n)\}. \quad (9.24)$$

This is the necessary perturbation expansion, and will depend for its success upon the smallness of the coefficient contributed by $\mathscr{L}_I$. $P$ is the chronological ordering operator which puts all operators following into order of increasing time from right to left.

Let us examine the effects of $S$ for the case of quantum electrodynamics for which $\mathscr{L}_1$ and $\mathscr{L}_2$ are the free electron–positron and electromagnetic field Lagrangians respectively. The interaction is

given by
$$\mathscr{L}_I(x) = -ie\bar{\psi}(x)\,\gamma_\mu\,\psi(x)\,A_\mu(x).\tag{9.25}$$

We count the terms in the expansion of $S$ by the order $n$. The zeroth term is unity and of no interest.

Let us consider the first term of the $S$-matrix with $\mathscr{L}_I$ as given in Eq. (9.25):

$$S_1 = -e\int_{-\infty}^{+\infty} d^4x\{\bar{\psi}(x)\,\gamma_\mu\,\psi(x)\,A_\mu(x)\}.$$

It is evident that this operator is able to create and destroy photons, electrons, and positrons at the point $x$. The number of particles involved is one photon $[A_\mu(x)]$ and two particles of the electron–positron field $[\bar{\psi}(x)$ and $\psi(x)]$ with the restriction that gauge invariance of $\mathscr{L}_I$ limits the effective operators in $S_1$ to those that conserve charge in the process occurring at the point $x$.

There are no reactions involving one photon and two particles of the electron–positron field alone which conserve energy and momentum. Therefore $S_1$ has no matrix elements except for electron or positron scattering by a fixed field such as that due to a heavy nucleus. In Coulomb scattering, for example, $\psi(x)$ [or $\bar{\psi}(x)$] destroys the incoming electron (or positron) and $\bar{\psi}(x)$ [or $\psi(x)$] creates the outgoing electron (or positron); $A_\mu(x)$ describes the virtual photon exchanged between the scattered particle and the Coulomb field.

There is a graphical representation of the $S_1$-matrix as operating at the point $x$. In a diagram we draw a line from the edge of the diagram

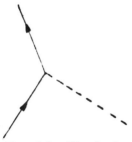

directed to the point $x$ for the term $\psi(x)$. From the point $x$ we draw a directed line towards the edge of the diagram for the term $\bar{\psi}(x)$. We draw a dotted line between $x$ and the edge for the term $A_\mu(x)$. This basic diagram is shown in Fig. 9.1 and is called a vertex. If we place a time axis on the diagram we can draw our lines with any orientation we please with respect to the axis: two examples are shown in Figs. 9.2a and 9.2b. We choose to interpret the lines pointing into the vertex as electrons moving into or positrons moving away from $x$, and the lines pointing out of the vertex as electrons moving away from or positrons moving into $x$. It follows that our time axis immediately enables us to label the process in diagrams 9.2a and 9.2b as electron and positron scattering at a fixed field respectively. We must note that the diagrams are really only representations of terms in the

Fig. 9.1. The basic vertex of the Feynman graphs.

S-matrix; that we can put coordinates on to the diagram and interpret them as pictures of what is actually happening is a concept due to Feynman. He used such diagrams in his method of calculating problems in quantum electrodynamics (1949a, b).

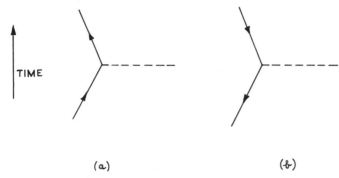

(a)                                    (b)

FIG. 9.2. The Feynman diagrams for (a) electron scattering by a fixed field, and (b) positron scattering by a fixed field.

Let us now examine the second term in the $S$-matrix and learn how to draw the Feynman diagrams associated with it:

$$S_2 = \frac{e^2}{2} \int_{-\infty}^{+\infty} d^4 x_1 \int_{-\infty}^{+\infty} d^4 x_2 \, P\{\bar{\psi}(x_1)\, \gamma_\lambda\, \psi(x_1)\, A_\lambda(x_1)\, \bar{\psi}(x_2)\, \gamma_\mu\, \psi(x_2)\, A_\mu(x_2)\}.$$

$$(9.26)$$

It is evident that this contains terms corresponding to Feynman diagrams with two vertices ($x_1$ and $x_2$) and up to six incoming or outgoing particles. The lines corresponding to the operators behind $P$ do not all have to reach to the boundary of the diagram from a vertex. Some lines can start at one vertex, where they represent one operator, and end at the other vertex, where they represent another operator of the same field. When we interpret the diagrams containing one or more internal lines, then the number of ingoing and outcoming particles will be four or less. For example, of particular interest are the cases of two-particle initial state and two-particle final state reactions such as electron–electron scattering by the exchange of a virtual photon. It is evident that $S_1$ has all the necessary creation and annihilation operators and therefore that $S_1$ will have matrix elements for such processes. Our intention is to make a logical decomposition of $S_1$ into different terms each of which is represented by a Feynman diagram with which we can associate a physical process; the terms are called "normal constituents" and each constituent only has matrix elements for the physical processes associated with its diagram. We must stress at this point that $S_2$ is not normally the only term in $S$ which has matrix elements for such physical processes and contributions can come from higher-order terms. These contributions are the radiative corrections to be discussed in Section 9.9.

Let us now examine the normal constituents. We proceed by describing the normal ordering operator $N$. It has the effect of rearranging any arbitrary product of annihilation and creation operators so that the creation operators stand to the left and the annihilation operators stand to the right. Any normal constituent has a factor containing sufficient normally ordered operators to annihilate the initial state and to create the final state. Such a grouping of operators in a normal constituent of one term of the $S$-matrix will in general leave unused some of the operators occurring in that term. There will be an even number of operators for each field and they occur in the normal constituent as the vacuum expectation value of pairs of such operators. By vacuum expectation value we mean the matrix element for such pairs between vacuum states [e.g., $\Phi_0$ in Eq. (9.11)]. The pairs of operators occurring in a normal constituent are called factor pairs. Summarizing, we find that each normal constituent contains one set of normally ordered operators and a number of vacuum expectation values of factor pairs.

Let us represent by $O$ the factor in $S_n$ which contains the field variables thus, for $S_2$ we have

$$O = \bar{\psi}(x_1)\,\psi(x_1)\,A_\lambda(x_1)\,\bar{\psi}(x_2)\,\psi(x_2)\,A_\mu(x_2).$$

Then any $O$ can be represented as a sum of all possible normal constituents $O_m$, where $O_m$ can be expressed as we have described:

$$O_m = \pm\,\langle PQ\rangle_0\,\langle RS\rangle_0 \ldots N(UVW\ldots).$$

$P, Q, R, S, \ldots, U, V, W, \ldots$ are the field variables and

$$\langle PQ\rangle_0 = (\Phi_0\,|\,PQ\,|\,\Phi_0),$$

etc. There is a $+$ or $-$ sign, depending upon the even or odd number of permutations of electron–positron field variables made in proceeding from the order of these operators in $O$ to the order in the normal constituent.

We can generate all the $O_m$ by writing down every possible way of choosing any number of factor pairs from $O$. The vacuum expectation value of many of these pairs is zero and the corresponding normal constituent is zero. The only nonzero expectation values are of the kind

$$\langle\bar{\psi}(x_1)\,\psi(x_2)\rangle_0, \quad \langle\psi(x_1)\,\bar{\psi}(x_2)\rangle_0, \quad \text{and} \quad \langle A_\lambda(x_1)\,A_\lambda(x_2)\rangle_0.$$

These expectation values are zero if the pairs of operators within the bracket are normally ordered. This property is evident if we remember that normal ordering in this case has an annihilation operator acting on the vacuum which gives zero [Eq. (9.11)].

The decomposition into normal constituents must now be applied to the chronologically ordered operators in $S_n$. We give a list of the nonzero constituents of the chronologically ordered operators in $S_2$ Eq. (9.26)]:

$$O_1 = \pm N[\bar{\psi}(x_1)\,\psi(x_1)\,A_\lambda(x_1)\,\bar{\psi}(x_2)\,\psi(x_2)\,A_\mu(x_2)],$$

$$O_2 = \pm \langle P[\psi(x_1)\,\bar{\psi}(x_2)]\rangle_0\,N[\bar{\psi}(x_1)\,A_\lambda(x_1)\,\psi(x_2)\,A_\mu(x_2)],$$

$$O_3 = \pm \langle P[\bar{\psi}(x_1)\,\psi(x_2)]\rangle_0\,N[\psi(x_1)\,A_\lambda(x_1)\,\bar{\psi}(x_2)\,A_\mu(x_2)],$$

$$O_4 = \pm \langle P[A_\lambda(x_1)\,A_\mu(x_2)]\rangle_0\,N[\bar{\psi}(x_1)\,\psi(x_1)\,\bar{\psi}(x_2)\,\psi(x_2)],$$

$$O_5 = \pm \langle P[\bar{\psi}(x_1)\,\psi(x_2)]\rangle_0\,\langle P[A_\lambda(x_1)\,A_\mu(x_2)]\rangle_0\,N[\psi(x_1)\,\bar{\psi}(x_2)],$$

$$O_6 = \pm \langle P[\psi(x_1)\,\bar{\psi}(x_2)]\rangle_0\,\langle P[A_\lambda(x_1)\,A_\mu(x_2)]\rangle_0\,N[\bar{\psi}(x_1)\,\psi(x_2)],$$

$$O_7 = \pm \langle P[\psi(x_1)\,\bar{\psi}(x_2)]\rangle_0\,\langle P[\bar{\psi}(x_1)\,\psi(x_2)]\rangle_0\,N[A_\lambda(x_1)\,A_\mu(x_2)],$$

$$O_8 = \pm \langle P[\psi(x_1)\,\bar{\psi}(x_2)]\rangle_0\,\langle P[\bar{\psi}(x_1)\,\psi(x_2)]\rangle_0\,\langle P[A_\lambda(x_1)\,A_\mu(x_2)]\rangle_0.$$

We now draw a Feynman diagram for each normal constituent. For the operators under $N$ we draw lines between a vertex and the edge of the diagram, as described earlier for $S_1$. For the expectation values $\langle P[\bar{\psi}(x)\,\psi(y)]\rangle_0$ and $\langle P[\psi(y)\,\bar{\psi}(x)]\rangle_0$ we draw a directed line from vertex $x$ to vertex $y$. For the expectation values $\langle P[A_\lambda(x)\,A_\mu(y)]\rangle_0$ we draw a dotted line between $x$ and $y$. The diagrams corresponding to $O_1$ to $O_8$ are shown in Fig. 9.3. For full details of the derivation of normal constituents we refer readers to Bogoliubov and Shirkov (1959), to Schweber et al. (1955), or to Wick (1950). The type of process for which each normal constituent has matrix elements can be found immediately from an examination of the corresponding graph. The external lines, that is lines reaching the edge, continue to be interpreted as described for the diagrams we drew in connection with $S_1$ (Fig. 9.2). Thus solid lines directed into the diagrams are electrons in the initial state or positrons in the final state and vice versa for lines directed out of the diagram; external dotted lines represent photons in the initial or final state. The internal lines connecting vertices represent virtual intermediate state particles. With these properties

in mind let us give seven re-drawings of $O_3$ and identify them with
physical processes.  In Fig. 9.4 the orientation of the external lines with

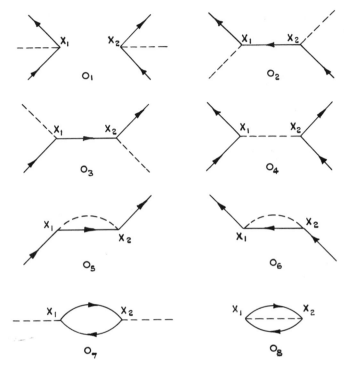

FIG. 9.3. The Feynman diagrams for the normal constituents of $S_2$.

respect to the time axis fixes the physical process to which the diagram applies.  Therefore the normal constituent $O_3$ has matrix elements for the processes:

> Compton effect;
> photon–positron scattering;
> positron–electron annihilation;
> electron bremsstrahlung;
> positron bremsstrahlung;
> pair production;
> photoelectric effect.

Wherever a nuclear electric field is involved a photon line has been
drawn perpendicular to the time axes; this is a virtual photon which

transfers the momentum unbalance to the participating nucleus. We note that other diagrams of second order may contribute to any of these physical processes.

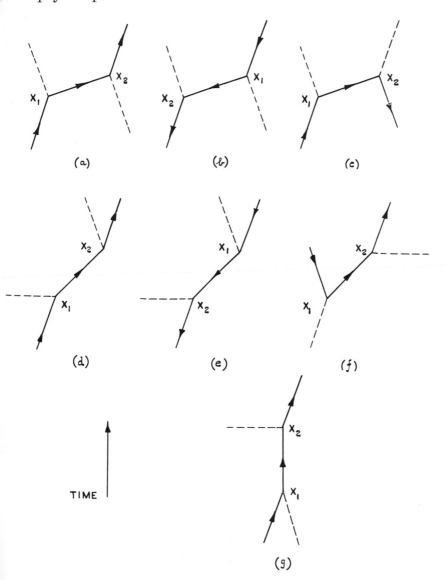

FIG. 9.4. Some Feynman diagrams of the $O_3$ type. (a), Compton scattering; (b), photon–positron scattering; (c), positron–electron annihilation; (d), electron bremsstrahlung; (e), positron bremsstrahlung; (f), pair production; (g), photoelectric effect.

The Feynman diagrams of Fig. 9.3 are apparently only convenient ways of representing the normal constituents of the $S$-matrix. However, as we have mentioned earlier, Feynman interpreted these diagrams as representing the actual physical process. Thus in Fig. 9.4a an incoming electron radiates a real photon at $x_1$, and propagates as a virtual electron to $x_2$ where it absorbs the incoming photon to become a real electron. We shall be drawing many Feynman diagrams in the later chapters and will interpret them in this manner. Fermi–Dirac particles will be drawn with an arrow giving the direction of propagation of the particle; lines directed backward in time represent the antiparticle propagating forward in time.

The next step is to examine how all this adds up to a usable theory. Suppose we are interested in calculating the cross section for some process; we can proceed by one of two routes having the same destination. The first involves the analytic evaluation of the $S_2$-matrix element for the process in question. This involves extracting the correct normal constituents, substituting for the vacuum expectation values of the factor pairs, and making a Fourier transformation of the normally ordered operators. Various integrations and summations have to be performed and the result is a matrix element summed over final states and averaged over initial states. This element can be substituted into the transition rate formula [Eq. (5.2)] after some manipulation of a $\delta$-function of four momentum which remains in the matrix element. The second method is to draw the Feynman diagrams and use the rules given by Feynman for writing down the matrix elements directly. These elements must be summed and averaged and thereafter treated in the same way as the elements appearing in the first method.

Feynman's rules can be derived from the formal theory of the $S$-matrix; essentially they enumerate the factors which must be written down for each diagram. These rules apply in momentum space: each external positron or electron line contributes a normalized spinor; each external photon contributes a normalized polarization vector; each vertex contributes a $\gamma$-matrix and a momentum $\delta$-function. The internal lines contribute factors which can be called propagators which correspond to the terms $\langle P(\psi\bar{\psi})\rangle_0$ and $\langle P(AA)\rangle_0$ in the normal constituents of the $S$-matrix. An internal photon line labelled with four momentum $k$ contributes the propagator

$$\frac{1}{k^2}.$$

An internal electron line labelled with four momentum $p$ contributes

he propagator

$$\frac{i\gamma_\mu p_\mu - m}{p^2 + m^2}.$$

We notice that these internal lines represent virtual states, so that $k^2 \neq 0$ for the internal photons and $p^2 + m^2 \neq 0$ for the virtual electrons. We also note that energy and momentum are conserved at each vertex and as three particles are involved, one at least of these must be a virtual particle and be represented on a Feynman diagram by a line which ends at another vertex.

We have attempted in this section to describe the meaning of the Feynman diagrams and to give the background to calculations in modern quantum electrodynamics. It is obviously beyond the scope of this book to give any fuller treatment and we refer readers to other authors (see Section 9.1).

## 9.9 Renormalization and the Radiative Corrections

We have already noted that terms of the $S$-matrix higher than $S_2$ can contribute to processes which receive their simplest contribution from $S_2$. Thus Compton effect has fourth-order contributions of the kind shown in Fig. 9.5; these are only a few of the contributions from this

FIG. 9.5. The Feynman diagrams for three fourth-order contributions to Compton scattering.

order. Formal calculation of higher-order diagrams normally yields an infinite contribution, a result which is disturbing in view of the fact that the lowest-order calculation alone gives results which are normally within experimental error of observed values. A careful investigation shows that higher-order infinities are due to three basic types of diagram which are shown in Fig. 9.6. Figure 9.6a shows a correction to an electron external line or propagator; 9.6b is a correction to a photon external line or propagator; 9.6c is a correction to a vertex.

Let us consider Fig. 9.6a, which is called the electron self-energy term, for it has the effect of altering the electron energy. A formal calculation shows that the change in energy is infinite and this difficulty is analogous to that which occurs in the classical theory of the

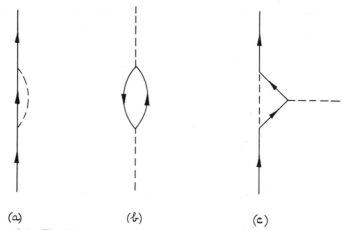

(a)                    (b)                    (c)

FIG. 9.6. The Feynman diagrams for the nonzero primitive divergent contributions.

electron. In that theory a point electron has infinite self-energy; if the self-energy is reduced to a finite value by giving the electron structure in the form of a spread-out charge, the theory leads to results which are inconsistent with the special theory of relativity. The change of energy in quantum theory is equivalent to a change in rest mass and this gives rise to doubts as to the value of the mass that we should put into the Lagrangian density. We suppose that the observed mass $m$ is the sum of the unobservable bare electron mass $m_0$ plus the unobservable self-energy $\delta m$:

$$m = m_0 + \delta m,$$

or

$$m_0 = m - \delta m.$$

We would expect the free-field Lagrangian to contain $m_0$ and not $m$, and in this spirit we can replace $m$ [in Eq. (9.22), for example] by $m_0 = m - \delta m$; thus another term $+\delta m \bar{\psi} \psi$ appears in our stated Lagrangian density for the electron–positron field. When we put this field into interaction with the electromagnetic field we can shift this term into the interaction Lagrangian, to give

$$\mathscr{L}_I = -ie\bar{\psi}\gamma_\mu \psi A_\mu + \delta m \bar{\psi} \psi.$$

The theory is the same as before apart from this extra term. When the electron self-energy term is calculated, we can cancel the normal infinity due to the first term of the interaction by the contribution from the $\delta m \bar{\psi} \psi$ if $\delta m$ is given the correct value. This value is, of course, related to the divergent integral which produces the infinity, and is itself infinite, but this causes no difficulty as $\delta m$ is unobservable. This procedure is called mass renormalization; the essence of renormalization is the correct recognition of the divergent parts of the integrals involved. Once this has been done the resulting infinity can be dropped and the renormalized theory gives the correct result if everywhere that $m$ occurs we use the value of the observed mass. By correct recognition of divergent integrals we mean those parts which disappear if the term $\delta m \bar{\psi} \psi$ is included in the interaction Lagrangian.

Charge renormalization is required when we consider the effect of diagram b in Fig. 9.6. This effect is called vacuum polarization and increases the apparent coupling constant $e$ by an infinite factor. Charge renormalization involves redefining the electric charge so as to absorb this infinite factor. We assume the electron has a bare charge $e_0$ which is unobservable; the infinities in the theory occur multiplied by some power of $e_0$, and we take this product to be the observable charge to the same power. Thus if the charge $e$ occurring in the theory is taken to have the value observed and if we correctly factor out the infinities, we are left with a finite contribution. The polarization of the vacuum has no effect upon the mass of the photon which must be zero by gauge invariance; however, it does have an effect upon physical processes involving photons in interaction with charged particles, and after charge renormalization the remaining finite contributions are a part of the radiative corrections.

We can now give an example to show how renormalization is applied to remove the divergences which occur in an actual problem. Let us consider the subtraction of infinities from the higher-order corrections to the scattering of an electron in the Coulomb field of a nucleus. The lowest order which has matrix elements for this process is $S_1$ and the Feynman diagram is shown in Fig. 9.7a. The radiative corrections which interest us are some of the processes which have $S_3$ matrix elements; those of interest are shown in Fig. 9.7b–9.7e If we renormalize the mass by adding the term $\delta m \bar{\psi} \psi$ to the interaction Lagrangian, the effects of graphs 9.7b, 9.7c, and 9.7d are finite. Charge renormalization removes the effect of diagram 9.7e. The result is a cross section for the scattering which includes the radiative corrections due to diagrams 9.7b to 9.7e. There are some other contributions of order 2 and 3 due to second- and third-order scattering in the Coulomb field—diagrams f and g of Fig. 9.7. These give a finite contribution only if the Coulomb field is modified for screening due to the atomic electrons (Jauch and Rohrlich, 1955). A final difficulty remains due to the "infrared" divergence which is the contribution due to the radiation of virtual and real photons of very long wavelengths. It can be shown that if the calculations are done to all orders these effects cancel and the

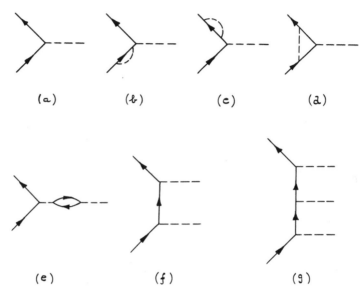

$(a)$          $(b)$          $(c)$          $(d)$

$(e)$          $(f)$          $(g)$

Fig. 9.7. The Feynman diagrams for the Coulomb scattering of electrons (a), with second-order radiative corrections (b) to (e). Diagrams (f) and (g) show the diagram for second- and third-order scattering in the Coulomb field.

result is a value for the only kind of cross section that can be measured, namely that for elastic plus inelastic scattering with the radiation of a photon of energy less than some value set by the resolution of the measuring equipment.

The foregoing discussion applies to scattering in the electric field of a nucleus; the same procedure can be applied to the behaviour of an electron in a fixed magnetic field. After renormalization the radiative corrections indicate that the electron behaves as if it had an anomalous magnetic moment in addition to the magnetic moment of one Bohr magneton predicted by the one-particle Dirac theory. Calculations to fourth order (Sommerfeld, 1957) indicate that the magnetic moment is

1.0011596 Bohr magnetons.

The measured value (Koenig *et al.*, 1952) is

$$1.001146 \pm 0.000012 \text{ Bohr magnetons.}$$

The second problem to which the renormalization technique has been applied concerns the energy levels of the hydrogen atom. In the simple Dirac theory the $2S_{1/2}$ and $2P_{1/2}$ excited states are degenerate; in the many-particle quantum electrodynamics these levels split. The energy difference can be predicted by calculation of the radiative corrections to the motion of the bound electron. Such calculations have been made to fourth order. There are many contributions but the most important are two: the first is due to renormalization of the electron self-energy diagrams and it raises the $2S_{1/2}$ level relative to the $2P_{1/2}$ by 1079 Mc/s; the second is due to vacuum polarization and it depresses the $2S_{1/2}$ level by 27 Mc/s. These effects and others are tabulated in Jauch and Rohrlich (1955); the total calculated effect is to raise the $2S_{1/2}$ relative to the $2P_{1/2}$ level by $1057.19 \pm 0.2$ Mc/s. The measured value of this energy difference is $1057.77 \pm 0.10$ Mc/s (Triebwasser *et al.*, 1953). The difference can probably be attributed to higher-order corrections.

These successes of modern quantum electrodynamics are seen to be truly remarkable when we remember that these predictions are the radiative corrections which remain once the infinities have been removed from the theory. It is in this way that the renormalization procedure is justified.

We wish to stress one fact about renormalization: basically it is the process of correctly identifying and ignoring the infinities; if this is done the theory gives a finite result and this procedure is seen to be equivalent to the renormalization of charge and mass. That renormalization can be carried out to all orders in the perturbation expansion for quantum electrodynamics was proved by Dyson (1949) and this means that the $S$-matrix has finite matrix elements between any two states involving photons, electrons, and positrons. However, the labour involved in performing the calculations prevents evaluation of any but a few of the lowest orders.

Throughout this discussion we have implied that, after renormalization, the finite contributions from each term of the series expansion of the $S$-matrix form a convergent series. That this appears to be the case is due to the smallness of the parameter $e = \sqrt{4\pi/137}$ which occurs with increasing power in successive terms. However, it appears that the series may not be convergent (Dyson, 1952). No successful solution to this problem has been presented.

## 9.10 Quantum Mesodynamics

Insofar as the field theory and the perturbation expansion are a good approximation, the interaction between the electromagnetic field and the electron–positron field is well understood and explored. In contrast, the interaction between the pi-meson field and the nucleon field is less well understood.

Let us examine the types of interaction that can occur between a meson field and the nucleon field. We assume that in the absence of other fields the nucleons obey the Dirac equation and that the field is represented by spinor field variables. From these field variables it is possible to construct the following spinor covariants which have the given transformation properties

$$\bar{\psi}\psi \qquad\qquad \text{scalar (S)},$$

$$i\bar{\psi}\gamma_5\gamma \qquad\qquad \text{pseudoscalar (P)},$$

$$i\bar{\psi}\gamma_\mu\psi \qquad\qquad \text{vector (V)},$$

$$i\bar{\psi}\gamma_5\gamma_\mu\psi \qquad\qquad \text{pseudo (or axial) vector (A)},$$

$$i\bar{\psi}(\gamma_\mu\gamma_\nu-\gamma_\nu\gamma_\mu)\psi \quad \text{antisymmetric tensor (T)},$$

where $\gamma_5 = \gamma_1\gamma_2\gamma_3\gamma_4$.

For a single-component meson field we have the following covariant quantities:

$$\phi \qquad\qquad \text{scalar (S) or pseudoscalar (P) according to } \phi,$$

$$\partial\phi/\partial x_\mu \quad \text{vector (V) or axial vector (A) according to } \phi.$$

The interaction of this meson field with the nucleon field is represented by a scalar quantity, the interaction Lagrangian density $\mathscr{L}_I$. The permitted interactions have $\mathscr{L}_I$ equal to:

$$G\bar{\psi}\psi\phi \qquad\qquad \text{for a scalar meson with scalar coupling (SS)},$$

$$iG\bar{\psi}\gamma_5\psi\phi \qquad\qquad \text{for a pseudoscalar meson with pseudoscalar coupling (PP)},$$

$$\frac{iF}{m}\bar{\psi}\gamma_\mu\psi\frac{\partial\phi}{\partial x_\mu} \qquad \text{for a scalar meson with vector coupling (SV)},$$

$$\frac{iF}{m}\bar{\psi}\gamma_5\gamma_\mu\psi\frac{\partial\phi}{\partial x_\mu} \quad \text{for a pseudoscalar meson with axial vector coupling (PA)}.$$

The pi-meson is pseudoscalar and its interaction with nucleons is believed to be through the pseudoscalar coupling. Although of no immediate interest, we mention that the vector meson field variable has four components, and three possible interactions are:

$iG\bar{\psi}\gamma_\mu\psi\phi_\mu$          for a vector meson with vector coupling (VV),

$iG\bar{\psi}\gamma_5\gamma_\mu\psi\phi_\mu$       for a pseudovector meson with axial vector coupling (AA),

$\dfrac{iF}{m}\bar{\psi}(\gamma_\mu\gamma_\nu-\gamma_\nu\gamma_\mu)\psi\left(\dfrac{\partial\phi_\mu}{\partial x_\nu}-\dfrac{\partial\phi_\nu}{\partial x_\mu}\right)$ for a vector meson with tensor coupling (VT),

and so on. $G$ and $F$ are coupling constants and the interactions are given so that the constants are real and have the same dimensions.

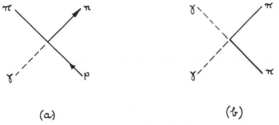

(a)                (b)

FIG. 9.8. The Feynman diagrams for the "catastrophic transition" (a) in meson photoproduction; (b) the term $\phi^\dagger\phi A_\rho A_\rho$ in a meson electromagnetic interaction.

$m$ is the reciprocal of the Compton wavelength of the pi-meson. Extra factors of $i$ occur to make the interaction operator Hermitian. As given above, the meson fields are real and therefore apply only to uncharged mesons; it is necessary to add isotopic spin operators and to consider the nucleon field to be described by eight-component spinors if we wish to describe the interaction of charged mesons. These complications are omitted as they obscure the essential parts of the interaction (see, however, Bethe and de Hoffmann, 1955).

The photoproduction of mesons from nucleons involves three fields interacting together. The interaction Lagrangian density for this circumstance depends upon the meson–nucleon interaction; if this is of the type which involves derivatives of the meson field variables, then it contains a term of the kind $\bar{\psi}\gamma_\mu\psi A_\mu\phi$. Evidently this gives rise to a special Feynman diagram in which four particles interact at one vertex; this is shown in Fig. 9.8a. Marshak (1952) calls this the "catastrophic transition" and discusses its contribution to photo production; however, we note that it does not occur in the favoured meson–nucleon interaction.

Vertices with four interacting particles also occur in the interaction of charged bosons (e.g., $\pi$-mesons) with the electromagnetic field and in the Fermi theory of $\beta$ decay (Section 11.3). In the former case the interaction Lagrangian contains terms such as $\phi^\dagger \phi A_\mu A_\mu$ (Fig. 9.8b) and in the latter case terms such as $(\bar{\psi}_\mu\psi)(\bar{\psi}_\mu\psi)$ (Fig. 11.7).

Formally, we can use the perturbation expansion for the solution of problems in mesodynamics. This procedure leads to an analysis of the terms of the $S$-matrix into normal constituents and from there to the Feynman diagrams representing those constituents. There is nothing new in this above what we found in electrodynamics and we do not find it necessary to describe these diagrams. However, the use of perturbation theory leads to the problems of renormalization and convergence. Dyson has shown (Matthews and Salam, 1951) that the nonderivative couplings are renormalizable; in addition, it appeared that derivative couplings were not renormalizable but recent work has indicated that this is probably incorrect. Although the pseudoscalar coupling theory is renormalizable, the perturbation series does not converge; this is due to the size of the coupling constant which is no longer small as in electrodynamics. This divergence defeats our efforts to obtain sensible results from a straightforward perturbation theory. Various attempts have been made to avoid this difficulty, such as the Tamm–Dancoff method, but their success is far from complete; we refer readers to the work of Bethe and de Hoffmann (1955) for an account of these methods.

Let us briefly examine the values of the coupling constants which occur in mesodynamics; for orientation we return to quantum electrodynamics and recall that the coupling constant which occurs is $e$, the magnitude of the electron charge in units which are rationalized and have $\hbar = c = 1$. The value of $e$ is approximately $\sqrt{4\pi/137}$ and is dimensionless. Many readers will find these units unfamiliar, so let us return to the cgs and es units. We put $e'$ to represent the electron charge in electrostatic units, then we have

$$\frac{e'^2}{\hbar c} \simeq \frac{1}{137}.$$

This is the square of the constant which appears in the interaction Lagrangian density divided by $4\pi$. It is the smallness of this quantity which makes the perturbation expansion an apparently convergent series after renormalization. We now put the coupling constants $G$

and $F$ into more familiar form; as they occur they are rationalized and dimensionless. If we rewrite our expressions in cgs units in which the coupling constants are $G'$ and $F'$, then we have to make the following replacements

$$G^2 \to \frac{4\pi G'^2}{\hbar c}, \quad F^2 \to \frac{4\pi F'^2}{\hbar c} \quad \left(\text{cf. } e^2 \to \frac{4\pi e'^2}{\hbar c}\right).$$

In the pseudoscalar coupling the value of $G'$ is such that, very approximately,

$$\frac{G'^2}{\hbar c} \simeq 15.$$

An alternative presentation of the coupling constant is given by

$$f^2 = \frac{f'^2}{\hbar c} = \left(\frac{m_\pi}{2m_n}\right)^2 \frac{G'^2}{\hbar c} \simeq 0.08.$$

This is the coupling constant to which reference has been made in Section 7.9. $m_\pi$ and $m_n$ are the pi-meson and nucleon mass respectively.

## 9.11 Conclusion

It will be evident to the reader that this chapter has done no more than attempt to make field theory a more familiar subject. We have, for example, stopped short of attempting to describe how the $S$-matrix elements can be evaluated for particular processes, but we hope that readers will not take this to mean that they are to be deterred from discovering how this is done. In fact, the intention has been to reduce for the uninitiated the apparent formidableness of the subject and to encourage further reading.

# CHAPTER X

# PARITY, TIME REVERSAL, AND CHARGE CONJUGATION

## 10.1 Introduction

Throughout much of this book we have been concerned with the implications of the symmetry laws of quantum mechanics. We have made use of two important symmetry properties which elementary particles and their strong interactions appear to possess, those of invariance under the parity transformation (Section 1.7) and time reversal (Section 1.8). In this chapter we explore these symmetries in more detail and introduce a third, that of invariance under charge conjugation. We shall discuss the implications of these symmetries and of their breakdown.

## 10.2 Parity

If this section were our first introduction to parity, it would contain the matter of Section 1.7. To avoid repetition readers may find it helpful to read that section before proceeding.

First, we have to prove that the parity of a one-component function is the eigenvalue of the unitary operator $P$ which describes the effects of a parity coordinate transformation. Consider the function $f(\mathbf{x})$; let us apply the coordinate transformation which changes the sign of the space coordinates of each space–time point. The function of the new coordinates, $\mathbf{x}'$, which has the same numerical value at a point as $f(\mathbf{x})$ at that point is $f'(\mathbf{x}')$, where

$$f'(\mathbf{x}') = f(\mathbf{x}),$$

and

$$\mathbf{x}' = -\mathbf{x}.$$

$f'(\mathbf{x}')$ defines a function $f'(\mathbf{x}) = Pf(\mathbf{x})$. Now the point with coordinates $\mathbf{x}$

in the transformed system had coordinates $-x$ in the untransformed system; therefore

$$Pf(\mathbf{x}) = f'(\mathbf{x}) = f(-\mathbf{x}),$$

but

$$f(-\mathbf{x}) = \pm f(\mathbf{x}),$$

for functions having even $(+)$ or odd $(-)$ parity. Therefore

$$Pf(\mathbf{x}) = \pm f(\mathbf{x}),$$

and $f(\mathbf{x})$ is an eigenfunction of $P$ with eigenvalues $+1$ or $-1$ for even or odd parity.

We shall now stop talking about the coordinate transformation in the context of parity and devote our attention to the active parity transformation; the results of any mathematical analysis are independent of these two views of the transformation. The active transformation inverts the physical system so that what was at point $\mathbf{x}$ is now at the point $-\mathbf{x}$, etc.; this procedure reverses the direction of all vectors (linear momentum, etc.) but leaves the direction of all pseudo-vectors (e.g., angular momentum, spin, etc.) unchanged. Thus if the physical system is described by a wave function which is an eigenfunction of momentum and total angular momentum with eigenvalues $\mathbf{p}$, $j$, and $j_z$, then the parity-transformed function is an eigenfunction with eigenvalues $-\mathbf{p}, j, j_z$, i.e.,

$$P\psi(\mathbf{p},j,j_z) = \eta\psi(-\mathbf{p},j,j_z).$$

$\eta$ is a constant such that $\eta^2 = 1$, as can be seen by operating twice with $P$. Therefore $\eta = \pm 1$. Now it is evident that $\psi(\mathbf{p},j,j_z)$ is not an eigenfunction of $P$, since its momentum eigenvalue is not invariant. Thus we deduce that the parity eigenvalue only exists for systems having total linear momentum zero, i.e., for systems observed in their centre of mass.

In Section 1.7 we suggested that the Schrödinger Hamiltonian is invariant under the passive parity transformation; it is also invariant under the active transformation for we expect the total energy of the system to be unchanged under the inversion. It follows that $H$ and $P$ commute. $H$ contains the energy of interaction between particles in the system, which induces particle reaction, and it follows that the parity of the complete system is conserved whatever reaction it undergoes. Therefore the statement that the (Hamiltonian of the) system is invariant under the parity transformation is identical in meaning to the statement that the parity of the system is conserved.

## 10.3 Parity Conservation

Parity conservation places restraints upon nuclear or particle reactions which must be maintained in any theoretical investigation of the reactions; this permits us to make tests of the validity of proposed interactions or reactions. There are several ways of making these tests which we will now discuss.

The first method of testing requires that the initial and final state wave functions have the same parity. We have used this method in several places; for example, in Section 6.5 it was employed to decide which states of different orbital but of the same total angular momentum cannot mix in nucleon–nucleon scattering, where parity is conserved. In Section 7.4 we deduced the intrinsic parity of the negative pi-meson by considering the before and after total wave-function parities for $\pi^-$ absorption in deuterium.

We can now introduce a second method which is of great use in making simple tests on reactions involving polarization and which uses the invariance under the active parity transformation. Consider a simple nuclear or elementary particle reaction. If the system is invariant under $P$, then any reaction and its parity transform will occur with equal probability and therefore with equal cross section. Let us see how to apply this. The parity transformation reverses the space coordinates of point and this is identical to reversing one co-ordinate and rotating through 180° around the axis of that coordinate; since the conservation of angular momentum is almost beyond doubt the system is invariant under the final rotation and parity invariance reduces to invariance under reversal of one coordinate. A simple pictorial way of making such a reversal is to take a mirror image of the system to be transformed. There is no difficulty in taking the mirror image of vectors; axial or pseudovectors such as magnetic field or angular momentum are more difficult and the easiest way is to consider the corresponding vector, e.g., a loop of electric current for the examples mentioned. The result is that the pseudovector components parallel to the mirror surface reverse their direction in going from object to image whilst pseudovector components perpendicular to the mirror are unchanged. A 180° rotation of the image in the plane of the mirror turns a pseudovector image into its object, thus confirming that the parity transformation leaves pseudovectors unchanged. Let us apply this to meson–proton scattering to show that the differential cross section is independent of any proton polarization in the direction of the incident pi-meson. We refer to Fig. 10.1, which has a mirror set in the plane containing the $x$ and $z$ axes. In the foreground a stationary target proton awaits the arrival of a $\pi$-meson with momentum $\mathbf{p}_\pi$

parallel to the $z$ axis; the meson scatters from the proton with final momentum $\mathbf{p}'_\pi$ at an angle $\theta$ to $\mathbf{p}_\pi$ and in the $zy$ plane. The mirror image of this system is seen in the mirror on the far side. The object has the proton spin $\boldsymbol{\sigma}_p$ pointing along the $-z$ direction, whilst the image points along the $+z$ direction. A simple 180° rotation around $\mathbf{p}_\pi$ will transform the image into the same form as the object apart from the proton spin. If the interaction responsible for scattering is invariant under the parity transformation, these two reactions will have equal

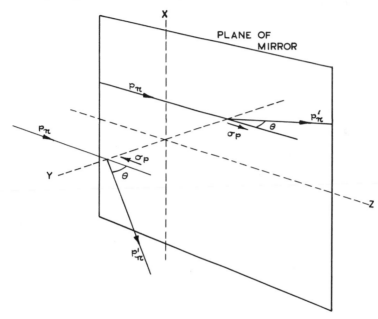

FIG. 10.1. A diagram of a meson–nucleon scattering and its mirror image to illustrate the parity transformation.

probability. Thus the differential cross section at a given scattering angle is independent of any polarization of the target protons in the direction of the incident pi-mesons. This fact was used in the partial wave analysis of positive meson scattering made in Section 3.5 and in other places in this book. The differential cross section is, in fact, independent of any proton polarization in the scattering plane. However, it does depend upon a polarization of the target protons in a direction perpendicular to the scattering plane. Taking a mirror image of a scatter generates an exactly identical system (identical after a simple rotation), so there is nothing to tell us how its cross section is related to that for an opposite proton polarization, and there can be a difference in cross sections; it is this difference that we have called the left-right scattering asymmetry in Chapter VIII. By drawing similar diagrams of hypothetical reactions we can show that a parity conserving interaction can only polarize reaction products in a direction perpendicular to the plane of the reaction; this applies to two-body products from unpolarized initial states. These results are in complete accord with those derived in Chapter VIII.

The third method of examining the effects of parity invariance concerns the structure of the Hamiltonian for a system. The Hamiltonian of a system must be invariant and the terms it contains describing the interaction between the particles present must likewise be invariants. These terms will be operators which must have scalar observables; the parity of the wave function cancels and the scalar properties of the operator can be found by inspection. Examples have been discussed in earlier parts of the book, viz.

$$\mathbf{L} \cdot \boldsymbol{\sigma} \qquad \text{(spin–orbit coupling)},$$

$$\boldsymbol{\sigma}_1 \cdot \boldsymbol{\sigma}_2 \qquad \text{(spin–spin coupling for two nucleons)},$$

$$\frac{3(\boldsymbol{\sigma}_1 \cdot \mathbf{r})(\boldsymbol{\sigma}_2 \cdot \mathbf{r})}{r^2} - \boldsymbol{\sigma}_1 \cdot \boldsymbol{\sigma}_2 \qquad \text{(noncentral tensor force between two nucleons)}.$$

There could also be terms depending upon the linear momentum of the particles involved; for example, in the case of meson–nucleon scattering there may be more specific terms such as

$$\mathbf{p}_\pi \cdot \mathbf{p}_\pi', \tag{10.1}$$

$$(\mathbf{p}_\pi \times \mathbf{p}_\pi') \cdot \boldsymbol{\sigma}_p. \tag{10.2}$$

All these examples are scalars. For the meson–nucleon scattering the two vectors $\mathbf{p}_\pi, \mathbf{p}_\pi'$ and the pseudovector $\boldsymbol{\sigma}_p$ can be combined to form only two independent scalars, namely (10.1) and (10.2). Thus the only dependence on $\boldsymbol{\sigma}_p$ is via the scalar $(\mathbf{p}_\pi \times \mathbf{p}_\pi') \cdot \boldsymbol{\sigma}_p$ which is zero unless the proton polarization has a component perpendicular to the scattering plane. It follows that the scattering cross section cannot depend upon the presence of any initial state polarization in the scattering plane. Thus we can apply parity conservation by requiring that the Hamiltonian, the transition rate, and the cross section depend upon scalar quantities alone. We have already made this kind of restriction by requiring that $M_a$ of Eqs. (8.13) and (8.60) be a scalar operator.

There is an interesting consequence of parity conservation which we can mention at this point. First, we notice that a reaction proceeding from a state of no defined parity (e.g., a plane wave) gives final states of different parity (e.g., partial waves) which can interfere; hence, states of opposite parity can be coherent. Nuclear and particle reactions can sometimes be analysed in terms of intermediate or compound states of defined parity and total angular momentum. If only one of such states is involved, then the outgoing waves must have the same parity; that is, only all even or all odd $l$ spherical harmonics are present in the final state amplitude. This has the result that the reaction differential cross section is symmetrical about $90°$ in the centre of mass. Reversing the argument, we can say that reactions not having this symmetry must have at least two states (partial waves) of opposite parity operative.

However, we cannot say anything about reactions having this symmetry except that if states of opposite parity are operative, they are incoherent; for example, proton–proton scattering.

## 10.4 The Intrinsic Parity of Elementary Particles

In this section we review briefly the situation on intrinsic parities and discuss the concept of parity as applied to particles with spin. We have seen that particles described by a one-component wave function have an intrinsic parity which is the parity of the wave function representing the particle at rest, or more correctly, of the dynamical field variable; such one-component particles have no spin and are bosons. They are said to be scalar if the parity is even and pseudoscalar if it is odd. The intrinsic parity of spin $\frac{1}{2}$ particles, which are fermions, is complex and unobservable; this is connected with the fact that the wave function of a spin $\frac{1}{2}$ particle is two-valued since it is found that rotation through $360°$ reproduces the original state multiplied by $-1$. This complexity is of no importance since the parity of fermion plus antifermion is odd and the number of fermions less the number of antifermions appears to be conserved, which leaves the parity of any unpaired fermion a quantity which cancels from all parity equalities (Yang and Tiomono, 1950; Kemmer et al., 1959). Spin 1 particles: there are no known elementary particles having spin 1 apart from the photon; its parity depends upon its multipolarity and nature as discussed in Section 4.4. At present we know of no elementary particles having spin $3/2$ or greater, and we shall not discuss the parity properties of their fields.

## 10.5 Parity Nonconservation

Let us briefly consider the situation which leads to the discovery of the nonconservation of parity. In 1956 there appeared to be two kinds of $K$ meson which were, within experimental accuracy, identical in mass, charge, and lifetime; their difference was in their decay:

$$\theta^+ \to \pi^+ + \pi^0, \tag{10.3}$$

$$\tau^+ \to \pi^+ + \pi^+ + \pi^-. \tag{10.4}$$

Dalitz (1957) showed that these two decays were not alternative channels for one particle and hence the $\theta$ and $\tau$ were different particles; his argument goes as follows (we assume that the $\pi$-meson is pseudo-scalar). If the spin of the $\theta$ is $s_\theta$ in units of $\hbar$, then the relative orbital angular momentum of the two $\pi$ mesons must be $s_\theta$ and the final state parity is $(-1)^{s_\theta}$; therefore, if parity is conserved, the parity of the $\theta$ meson is $\rho_\theta = (-1)^{s_\theta}$. Consider now the $\tau$ decay; in the final state we divide the motion into two parts, that of the $2\pi^+$ mesons about their centre of mass (angular momentum $l$) and that of the $2\pi$ centre of mass relative to the $\pi^-$ (angular momentum $L$). We have

$$|l - L| \leqslant s_\tau \leqslant l + L$$

and

$$\rho_\tau = (-1)^3 (-1)^l (-1)^L.$$

The identity of the two $\pi^+$ mesons requires their relative wave function to be symmetric, which means $l$ is even; hence

$$\rho_\tau = -(-1)^L.$$

Let us suppose the $\theta$ and $\tau$ are identical and work through various spin assignments until we can obtain the same parity

$$s_\theta = s_\tau = 0 \quad \text{gives} \quad \rho_\theta = +1 \quad \text{but} \quad \rho_\tau = -1 \quad (l = L).$$

$$s_\theta = s_\tau = 1 \quad \text{gives} \quad \rho_\theta = -1 \quad \text{and} \quad \rho_\tau = \mp 1,$$

as $L$ is even (negative sign) or odd (positive sign). $L$ is even ($\rho_\tau = -1$) in the following combinations: $l = 2$, $L = 2$; $l = 4$, $L = 4$; etc. $L$ is odd ($\rho_\tau = +1$) in the following combinations: $l = 0$, $L = 1$; $l = 2$, $L = 1$ or 3; $l = 4$, $L = 3$ or 5; etc. Thus if $\theta \equiv \tau$, the lowest assignments are $s_\theta = s_\tau = 1$, $\rho_\theta = \rho_\tau = -1$ and $l = L = 2$. These orbital motions in the $\tau$ decay mode would give the $\pi^-$ an anisotropic distribution with respect to the direction of relative momentum of the $2\pi^+$, which is not observed, and would inhibit the decay mode very strongly on account of angular momentum barrier. In addition, this assignment is not favoured if we try to include $\theta^0$, the neutral counterpart of the $\theta^+$ in the scheme. It is observed to be able to decay into $2\pi^0$ mesons and this it can do only if it has even spin and even parity. Higher $\tau$ and $\theta$

spins can be matched, but similar contrary arguments apply and it is therefore difficult to reconcile the apparent identity of the $\theta$ and $\tau$ mesons with the conservation of angular momentum and parity (Dalitz, 1957).

These difficulties led Lee and Yang (1956) to a final suggestion that parity was not conserved in certain interactions. They examined the field of $\beta$-decay and found that no experiments had ever been done which indicated that parity was conserved in the $\beta$-interaction. They suggested experiments which would test their suggestion and these were performed immediately. It was found that parity was not conserved either in $\beta$-decay (Wu et al., 1957) or in the decay of the $\pi$ and $\mu$ mesons (Garwin et al., 1957). The responsibility for nonconservation was placed upon the properties of the neutrino which is involved in all these processes; this did not resolve the $\tau$–$\theta$ puzzle which does not involve neutrinos. The answer appears to be that parity is not conserved in reactions in which four fermions interact at a single vertex and that such vertices with virtual fermions are involved in the $\tau$ and $\theta$ decays (Section 12.11).

Let us now examine the experiment which first showed parity was not conserved. It is evident that nonconservation makes it possible for an elementary particle reaction to depend upon a pseudoscalar combination of observables. We apply this to the intensity of $\beta$ particles emitted from a radioactive specimen in which the nuclei have been polarized; this polarization is described by the expectation value of $\mathbf{J}$, namely $\langle \mathbf{J} \rangle$, which is an axial vector. Let the vector $\mathbf{p}$ be the momentum of the outgoing electrons. The quantity $\langle \mathbf{J} \rangle \cdot \mathbf{p}$ is pseudoscalar and if parity is not conserved the intensity of the electrons can be a function of this quantity, among others. This leads to an electron distribution proportional to $1 + \alpha \cos \theta$ where

$$\cos \theta = \frac{\langle \mathbf{J} \rangle \cdot \mathbf{p}}{|\langle \mathbf{J} \rangle| |\mathbf{p}|},$$

that is, the cosine of the angle between the polarization and the emitted electron. The electrons are therefore emitted preferentially along the polarization vector ($\alpha > 0$) or against ($\alpha < 0$). Such asymmetry was found in the decay of a polarized specimen of $Co^{60}$ (Wu et al., 1957) and was unequivocal proof of the nonconservation of parity.

We find it convenient at this point to illustrate some of the effects of parity nonconservation by considering the decay of the $\Lambda^0$ hyperon:

$$\Lambda^0 \rightarrow \pi^- + p + 37 \text{ Mev.}$$

We do this because we are used to dealing with the meson–nucleon system and can avoid obscuring the essential properties in the field-theoretical language used in $\beta$-decay. We treat the decay in the rest system of the $\Lambda^0$ and assume that the intrinsic parity of the $\Lambda^0$ is even (or odd) with respect to that of the proton. If parity was conserved, the meson–nucleon system would have to be in a $P$ (or $S$) state of relative orbital motion. If parity is not conserved, both states $S$ and $P$ can occur, with respective amplitudes $a_S$ and $a_P$. We have to construct the total outgoing amplitudes for the two possible spin orientations of the $\Lambda^0$, $s_z = j_z = \pm \frac{1}{2}$; using the same notation as in Eqs. (3.14) and (3.15), we have:

$S$ wave: $\phi(0, \frac{1}{2}, \pm \frac{1}{2}) = \psi(0, 0)\chi(\frac{1}{2}, \pm \frac{1}{2})$;

$P$ wave: $\phi(1, \frac{1}{2}, \pm \frac{1}{2}) = \pm \sqrt{\frac{2}{3}}\psi(1, \pm 1)\chi(\frac{1}{2}, \mp \frac{1}{2}) \mp \sqrt{\frac{1}{3}}\psi(1, 0)\chi(\frac{1}{2}, \pm \frac{1}{2})$.

We can substitute the usual spherical harmonics and combine these two waves to give the total outgoing wave:

$$\psi_{\pm 1/2} = \frac{a_S}{\sqrt{4\pi}}\chi(\tfrac{1}{2}, \pm \tfrac{1}{2}) \mp \frac{a_P}{\sqrt{4\pi}}\sin \theta \exp(\pm i\phi)\chi(\tfrac{1}{2}, \mp \tfrac{1}{2})$$

$$\mp \frac{a_P}{\sqrt{4\pi}}\cos \theta \, \chi(\tfrac{1}{2}, \pm \tfrac{1}{2}). \qquad (10.5)$$

In the $z$ direction the amplitude is

$$\psi_{\pm 1/2}(\cos \theta = 1) = \frac{1}{\sqrt{4\pi}}(a_S \mp a_P)\chi(\tfrac{1}{2}, \pm \tfrac{1}{2}).$$

Now suppose the $\Lambda^0$ were fully polarized in a direction making polar angles $\theta'$ and $\phi'$ with the $z$ axis; this state appears to be a linear sum of the two spin states having $s_z = +\frac{1}{2}$ and $s_z = -\frac{1}{2}$ with weights and phases

$$\cos \frac{\theta'}{2}\exp\left(\frac{+i\phi'}{2}\right) \quad \text{and} \quad \sin \frac{\theta'}{2}\exp\left(\frac{-i\phi'}{2}\right),$$

respectively [Eq. (2.59a)]. Thus this polarized state gives an outgoing amplitude along the $z$ axis which is the same linear combination of the two waves $\psi_{\pm 1/2}(\cos \theta = 1)$:

$$\psi = \frac{1}{\sqrt{4\pi}}\Bigg\{(a_S - a_P)\cos \frac{\theta'}{2}\exp \frac{i\phi'}{2}\chi(\tfrac{1}{2}, +\tfrac{1}{2})$$

$$+ (a_S + a_P)\sin \frac{\theta'}{2}\exp \frac{-i\phi'}{2}\chi(\tfrac{1}{2}, -\tfrac{1}{2})\Bigg\}.$$

Then the total proton intensity per unit solid angle in a direction $\theta'$ to the $\Lambda^0$ polarization is given by

$$I = |\psi|^2 = \frac{1}{4\pi}\{|a_S|^2 + |a_P|^2 - 2\operatorname{Re} a_S^* a_P \cos\theta'\} \qquad (10.6)$$

or

$$I \propto (1 + \alpha\cos\theta'), \qquad (10.7)$$

where

$$\alpha = \frac{-2\operatorname{Re} a_S^* a_P}{|a_S|^2 + |a_P|^2}.$$

If the $\Lambda^0$ are only partially polarized, Eq. (10.7) becomes

$$I \propto (1 + \alpha|\langle\boldsymbol{\sigma}\rangle_\Lambda|\cos\theta').$$

Thus the protons are produced preferentially along or against the direction of the $\Lambda^0$ polarization. Such an asymmetry has been observed (Crawford et al., 1958a).

Let us look at the $z$ component of the polarization of outgoing protons as given by the expectation value of $\sigma_z$

$$\langle\sigma_z\rangle_p = \frac{(\psi\,|\,\sigma_z\,|\,\psi)}{(\psi\,|\,\psi)}$$

from which

$$
\begin{aligned}
I\langle\sigma_z\rangle_p = &\left\{(a_S - a_P)^* \cos\frac{\theta'}{2}\exp\left(\frac{-i\phi'}{2}\right)\chi^\dagger(\tfrac{1}{2}, +\tfrac{1}{2})\right.\\
&\left. + (a_S + a_P)^* \sin\frac{\theta'}{2}\exp\left(\frac{+i\phi'}{2}\right)\chi^\dagger(\tfrac{1}{2}, -\tfrac{1}{2})\right\}\\
&\times\left\{(a_S - a_P)\cos\frac{\theta'}{2}\exp\left(\frac{+i\phi'}{2}\right)\chi(\tfrac{1}{2}, +\tfrac{1}{2})\right.\\
&\left. - (a_S + a_P)\sin\frac{\theta'}{2}\exp\left(\frac{-i\phi'}{2}\right)\chi(\tfrac{1}{2}, -\tfrac{1}{2})\right\}\\
= &\,(|a_S|^2 + |a_P|^2)\cos\theta' - 2\operatorname{Re} a_S^* a_P. \qquad (10.8)
\end{aligned}
$$

If the $\Lambda^0$ hyperons are unpolarized, there can be no $\cos\theta'$ term and Eq. (10.8) becomes

$$\langle\sigma_z\rangle_p = \frac{-2\operatorname{Re} a_S^* a_P}{|a_S|^2 + |a_P|^2} = \alpha. \qquad (10.9)$$

In this circumstance $\langle\sigma_y\rangle_p$ and $\langle\sigma_x\rangle_p$ are both zero.

This is longitudinal polarization of the proton and implies that the decay rate depends upon the pseudoscalar $\boldsymbol{\sigma}_p \cdot \mathbf{p}_p$ where $\mathbf{p}_p$ is the momentum of the proton. This polarization has been observed (Boldt et al., 1958a, Appendix A.6).

We note that in deriving these relations we could have obtained Eq. (10.6) directly from Eq. (10.5) without considering the state polarized along an axis other than $z$. However, in deriving the polarization [Eq. (10.9)] we prefer to orient our axes with respect to the direction of the final state proton rather than with respect to the initial state, and this requires the procedure employed.

We notice that the asymmetry and the proton polarization require that both $a_S$ and $a_P$ are nonzero and thus depend upon interference between decay channels of opposite parity. If the initial state and final state are of the same or completely opposite parity no such effects would occur. These statements apply generally to parity non-conserving interactions.

The discovery of parity nonconservation in the decay of particles cast doubt upon the parity invariance of the strong interactions, such as those responsible for nuclear forces. This invariance has now been tested to a considerable degree of accuracy (Wilkinson, 1958; Jones *et al.*, 1958; and Crawford *et al.*, 1959a) and we now have considerable confidence in its validity.

## 10.6 Time Reversal

The laws of classical mechanics and of electromagnetism are invariant under the time-reversal transformation; that is, a system can develop backwards in time in the same way as it normally does forwards in time. There is no reason, however, why this should also be true for elementary particle physics. We shall briefly investigate the time-reversal transformation and examine the requirements invariance or noninvariance (Wick, 1958; Kemmer *et al.*, 1959; Sachs, 1953; Wigner, 1932).

We consider firstly the time-dependent Schrödinger equation (1.1)

$$i\hbar \frac{\partial}{\partial t} \psi(\mathbf{x}, t) = \left\{ -\frac{\hbar^2}{2m} \nabla^2 + V(\mathbf{x}) \right\} \psi(\mathbf{x}, t),$$

$$= H\psi(\mathbf{x}, t). \tag{10.10}$$

Let us take the complex conjugate of this equation

$$-i\hbar \frac{\partial}{\partial t} \psi^*(\mathbf{x}, t) = H^* \psi^*(\mathbf{x}, t)$$

or

$$i\hbar \frac{\partial}{\partial(-t)} \psi^*(\mathbf{x}, t) = H^* \psi^*(\mathbf{x}, t). \tag{10.11}$$

By comparing Eqs. (10.10) and (10.11) it is evident that $\psi^*(\mathbf{x}, t)$ represents a system which is developing backwards in time in the same way as $\psi(\mathbf{x}, t)$ develops forwards if $H$ is real and if the two functions have the same initial conditions. Thus, in this rather restricted representation the system is invariant under time reversal if $H$ is real.

Time reversal alters the sign of the expectation of value of linear and angular momentum operators; as far as the former is concerned, the complex conjugate of a function has the reversed expectation value. The expectation value of orbital and spin angular momentum operators will only change sign if other things happen to the wave functions apart from complex conjugation. Thus we introduce the operator $T$ which engenders the required changes

$$\psi \to \psi' = T\psi,$$

$$H \to H' = THT^{-1}.$$

Now $T$ is not a unitary operator as it is not linear; this is manifest in the fact that $T$ causes coefficients to change to their complex conjugates in any expansion of a wave function in terms of orthonormal functions, an effect a linear operator cannot have. However, $T$ can be broken into two parts,

$$T = UK, \tag{10.12}$$

where $U$ is a unitary operator and $K$ is the operator which changes a quantity into its complex conjugate. $T$ is sometimes called anti-unitary.

We can now consider the Heisenberg picture in which the time variation of the operator is the necessary equation of motion

$$i\hbar \frac{dQ}{dt} = [Q, H].$$

Apply time reversal,

$$-i\hbar \frac{d}{dt} TQT^{-1} = [TQT^{-1}, THT^{-1}],$$

put $Q' = TQT^{-1}$, and if we have invariance under time reversal, then $H' = THT^{-1} = H$; hence

$$i\hbar \frac{dQ'}{d(-t)} = [Q', H]$$

and we see that $Q'$ has the same equation of motion backwards in time as has $Q$ forwards in time. The expectation values of $Q$ and $Q'$ are very often simply related; for example, if $Q$ is the position operator, then $\langle Q \rangle = \langle Q' \rangle$ and the particle traverses its normal path in reverse. If $Q$ is the operator of linear momentum, angular momentum, or spin then $\langle Q' \rangle = - \langle Q \rangle$ and the particle moves so that at any instant — its expectation values are vectors of the same magnitude but oppositely directed to those at time $t$ in the normal motion.

If our systems are invariant under time reversal, then we have that

$$THT^{-1} = H.$$

This implies that any coefficients in $H$ are real and any operators it may contain are combined in such a way that the combination is a scalar under time reversal. Thus terms containing $\mathbf{p}$, $\mathbf{J}$, $\mathbf{L}$, or $\boldsymbol{\sigma}$ alone would not be allowed nor would terms such as $\mathbf{x} \cdot \boldsymbol{\sigma}$, which is pseudo scalar under time reversal. However, scalar combinations can be accommodated; for example,

$$\mathbf{L} \cdot \mathbf{S}, \ \mathbf{p}^2, \text{ etc.}$$

We have used such requirements in restricting the possible terms in the scattering matrix of Eq. (8.60).

In Section 5.6 we applied the idea of time-reversal invariance to develop the reciprocity properties of the simple $S$-matrix. Any conclusions drawn from these properties can be used as a test of the invariance of physical systems under time reversal. Several such tests have been made on the strong interactions responsible for nuclear reactions (Hillman *et al.*, 1958; Abashian and Hafner, 1958; Rosen and Brolley, 1958; Bodansky *et al.*, 1959). The results indicate that there are no significant effects due to any noninvariance. Other tests have been proposed in connection with the weak interactions of $\beta$ decay (Henley and Jacobsohn, 1957; Morita and Morita, 1957; Jackson *et al.* 1957), but no results are yet available; we shall return to this point later.

## 10.7 Charge Conjugation

The operation of charge conjugation transforms particles into anti-particles and vice versa; thus electrons transform into positrons, positrons into electrons, and so on. Perhaps a more correct name for this operation is particle–antiparticle conjugation as there is not always a change in electric charge (e.g., neutron $\rightleftharpoons$ antineutron); however, present usage favours the name charge conjugation. We notice that this operation is not a Lorentz transformation as are the parity transformation and time reversal; charge conjugation changes the nature of the particles involved, but leaves unchanged their linear and angular momenta, and positions. In the Schrödinger wave mechanics, the wave

'unction does not necessarily specify the nature of the particles involved; however, in order to satisfy a continuity equation for charge
ınd current the wave function must be complex, and it is found that
he particle represented by the complex conjugate wave function has
opposite charge and current densities. Thus it appears that under
charge conjugation

$$\psi \to \psi' = C\psi = \psi^*.$$

This is also true for the Dirac equation in one representation of the
γ matrices (see Wick, 1958; Corinaldesi, 1958). Scalar and pseudoscalar particles are represented by functions of one component $\phi$; if the
particle is charged, then the transformation is

$$\phi \to \phi' = C\phi = \phi^*.$$

$\phi$ can be put as the sum of two real functions

$$\phi = \phi_1 + i\phi_2$$

so that

$$C\phi = \phi_1 - i\phi_2$$

and the components transform

$$C\phi_1 = \phi_1 \quad \text{and} \quad C\phi_2 = -\phi_2.$$

Uncharged particles can be represented by real fields for which

$$C\phi = \pm \phi.$$

The positive sign is usually chosen for $\pi^0$ mesons for reasons connected
with the interaction Hamiltonian for the meson–nucleon interaction.
This Hamiltonian is constructed to be invariant under rotation in
isotopic spin space (charge independence) and is charge conjugation
invariant only if

$$C\phi = +\phi \tag{10.13}$$

for the $\pi^0$ field (Pais and Jost, 1952).

The field functions for the electromagnetic field must change sign
under charge conjugation; thus the components of the vector potential
transform

$$CA_\rho(x) = -A_\rho(x) \quad (\rho = 1, 2, 3, 4). \tag{10.14}$$

We now turn our attention towards the properties of some electrically
neutral systems under charge conjugation. These divide themselves
into two categories:

(1) systems which transform into antisystems—for example, the
neutron, the hydrogen atom, mesonium;

(2) systems which transform into themselves—for example, photons, neutral pi-mesons, positronium. These are called self-conjugate.

Systems of the first kind are of no immediate interest; they are not self-conjugate and must be described by complex functions. The complex functions are important for they can be described by real functions which are eigenfunctions of $C$.

Now we postulate the invariance of many physical systems under charge conjugation, from which it follows that the eigenvalue of $C$ is a conserved quantity. The self-conjugate systems decay or interact under the influence of selection rules required by charge conjugation invariance. Let us consider some examples. From Eq. (10.14) it is evident that a state representing a system containing $n$ photons is an eigenfunction of $C$ with eigenvalue $(-1)^n$. The interaction which causes the decay of $\pi^0$ meson into two photons is believed to be charge conjugation invariant, so that the $\pi^0$ field function is an eigenfunction of $C$ with eigenfunction $+1$, as already required in Eq. (10.13). Another interesting example is the system consisting of a positive and a negative pi-meson considered in their centre-of-mass coordinates. We could construct a total wave function which contains space plus isotopic spin functions and which must be symmetric because the two bosons $\pi^+ \pi^-$ are indistinguishable in the absence of the electromagnetic field. It follows that the isotopic function is symmetric (antisymmetric) under interchange of charge coordinates as the space function is symmetric (antisymmetric) under interchange of space coordinates. The operation of charge conjugation is the same as interchange of the charge coordinates and we find that the eigenvalue of $C$ is the isotopic function symmetry which is $(-1)^l$, where $l$ is the quantum number of relative angular momentum of the two pi-mesons. This last example leads us naturally to the case of positronium, the hydrogenlike atom consisting of positron and electron bound together. If we place charge coordinates on the total wave function for the system, the wave function for these two fermions must be antisymmetric under simultaneous interchange of space, spin, and charge coordinates. The symmetry under space + spin interchange is $-(-1)^{l+s}$ where $s$ is the total spin (0 for singlet, 1 for triplet spin states); it follows that the symmetry under interchange of charge coordinates and the charge conjugation eigenvalue is $(-1)^{l+s}$.

The electromagnetic interaction which is responsible for the decay of positronium into photons is invariant under charge conjugation and we find that positronium will decay into

(a) an even number of photons from triplet spin, $l$ odd states and from singlet, $l$ even states, or into

(b) an odd number of photons from triplet spin, $l$ even states and from singlet, $l$ odd states.

The $\pi^0$ decay takes place via strong interactions which are believed o be invariant under charge conjugation and we can deduce from the bserved two-photon decay that decay into an odd number of photons lone is forbidden.

Charge conjugation invariance breaks down in the weak interactions, s we shall find in the next section. There is no evidence at present or a breakdown of this symmetry in strong interactions.

## 0.8 The TCP Theorem

There exists a very important theorem which relates the properties of article fields under proper Lorentz transformations with their pro- erties under the improper transformations and charge conjugation Lüders, 1954; Pauli, 1956). The theorem states that the interaction agrangian (or Hamiltonian) for locally interacting fields, which is Iermitian and invariant under proper Lorentz transformations, will ommute with any of the six operators which can be formed by the roduct of $T$, $C$, and $P$ taken in any order. This theorem is true as ong as certain arbitrary phases are chosen correctly and this can lways be done. This theorem has some very important consequences vhich we will now discuss.

We have seen that the weak interactions are not invariant under he parity transformation. Since the interaction must be invariant nder the transformation $TCP$ (since $H$ commutes with $TCP$), the nteraction must also be noninvariant under at least one of the two ransformations, $T$ and $C$. When the postulate of nonparity conserva- ion was experimentally demonstrated, it became obvious from the heory of $\beta$ decay that the responsible weak interaction was not nvariant under $C$ (Lee and Yang, 1956); no conclusions could be lrawn as to the invariance, or otherwise, of the interaction under $T$. A question that arises immediately is why, if $C$ invariance breaks lown, are the mass and lifetime of any elementary particle and its ntiparticle identical? For example, the lifetimes of the free $\mu^+$ and $\mu^-$ ppear to be identical, although the decay interaction is not invariant nder $C$ or $P$ (see Section 11.8). That these quantities will be invariant s a consequence of the $TCP$ theorem, as we will now show.

(1) To show that particle and antiparticle have the same mass. The transformation $TCP$ applied to a free particle generates an anti- article with the same total energy and momentum, and therefore of he same rest mass. This rather trivial proof fails to be precise about he meaning of the mass of a particle; the correct proof has been given

by Lüders and Zumino (1957), and it contains a proof of the equality of lifetimes. This happens because the rest mass is truly a complex quantity having the observed rest mass as the real part and $\hbar$ multiplied by the reciprocal of the lifetime as the complex part. However, we give another proof of the lifetimes equality due to Lee et al. (1956).

(2) To show the equality of lifetimes for particle and antiparticle. We consider particle $A$ and its decay products $B$ to be represented by eigenfunctions $\psi_a$ and $\psi_b$ of the Hamiltonian $H_S$. The complete Hamiltonian is, in fact, $H_S + H_\omega$ where $H_\omega$ is due to the interaction responsible for the transition from $A \to B$; $H_\omega$ is negligible compared to $H_S$ and its presence does not affect the eigenfunctions of $H_S$. We assume $H_S$ is invariant under $T$, $C$, and $P$ separately; $H_\omega$ must be invariant under $TCP$ or permutations thereof. If the initial and final states are contained in a normalization volume, we find that the eigenfunctions $\psi_a$ and $\psi_b$ are stationary states, in which case

$$T\psi_a = \psi_{-a} \quad \text{and} \quad T\psi_b = \psi_{-b} \tag{10.15}$$

where $\psi_{-a}$ and $\psi_{-b}$ represent the stationary states $\psi_a$ and $\psi_b$ with spins reversed, i.e., with opposite eigenvalue to the operator $J_z$. We need one other property of the operator $T$. Consider a matrix element like $(\psi_1 | \psi_2)$; this can be developed as follows:

$$\begin{aligned}(T\psi_1 | T\psi_2) &= (U\psi_1^* | U\psi_2^*), \\ &= (\psi_1^* | U^{-1}U | \psi_2^*), \\ &= (\psi_1 | \psi_2)^*.\end{aligned}$$

We have used the separation of $T$ into a unitary operator $U$ and $K$, the operator which causes complex conjugation [Eq. (10.12)]. We apply this result to the matrix elements of $H_\omega$:

$$\begin{aligned}(\psi_b | H_\omega | \psi_a)^* &= (\psi_b | H_\omega \psi_a)^*, \\ &= (T\psi_b | TH_\omega \psi_a), \\ &= (T\psi_b | TH_\omega T^{-1} | T\psi_a). \tag{10.16}\end{aligned}$$

Now the operator $PCT$ commutes with $H_\omega$; therefore

$$PCTH_\omega T^{-1}C^{-1}P^{-1} = H_\omega,$$

or

$$TH_\omega T^{-1} = C^{-1}P^{-1}H_\omega PC. \tag{10.17}$$

Substitute Eq. (10.17) into Eq. (10.16):

$$\begin{aligned}(\psi_b | H_\omega | \psi_a)^* &= (T\psi_b | C^{-1}P^{-1}H_\omega PC | T\psi_a), \\ &= (C\psi_{-b} | P^{-1}H_\omega P | C\psi_{-a}). \tag{10.18}\end{aligned}$$

In general, $H_\omega$ is not invariant under $P$ and we can divide it into two parts: one parity conserving, the other parity nonconserving

$$H_\omega = H_1 + H_2$$

where

$$PH_1 P^{-1} = H_1,$$

$$PH_2 P^{-1} = -H_2.$$

$H_1$ only has nonzero matrix elements between states $\psi_a$ and $\psi_b$ of the same parity, whilst $H_2$ only has nonzero matrix elements between states of opposite parity. Equation (10.18) can now be written

$$|(\psi_b|H_1|\psi_a) + (\psi_b|H_2|\psi_a)|^2 = |(C\psi_{-b}|H_1|C\psi_{-a}) - (C\psi_{-b}|H_2|C\psi_{-a})|^2. \tag{10.19}$$

The left-hand side is the required matrix element for the decay $A \to B$, whilst the right-hand side is the squared matrix element for the corresponding antiparticle decay $\bar{A} \to \bar{B}$. The transition rate for the decay is found by summing over all states of $J_z$ and all accessible eigenstates of $B$ and finally integrating over all directions. In this final integration the interference terms between states of opposite parity go to zero and the effect of the opposite sign between the matrix elements on left and right disappears. The equality of Eq. (10.19) leads to the equality of lifetimes of particle and antiparticle; we have not required $H_\omega$ to be invariant under $C$.

There is a third theorem of importance concerning the effects of charge conjugation invariance.

(3) To show that the parity conserving and parity nonconserving final states cannot interfere if $H_\omega$ is invariant under charge conjugation. We use the notation employed in the previous proof but must restrict ourselves to decay without spin in initial or final states. In this case Eq. (10.15) reduces to

$$T\psi_a = \psi_a,$$

$$T\psi_b = \psi_b.$$

We have that $CPT$ commutes with $H_\omega$; hence

$$TH_\omega T^{-1} = P^{-1}C^{-1}H_\omega CP = P^{-1}H_\omega P, \tag{10.20}$$

since we are investigating the effects of invariance under $C$.

Substitute Eq. (10.20) into (10.16):

$$(\psi_b|H_\omega|\psi_a)^* = (\psi_b|P^{-1}H_\omega P|\psi_a). \tag{10.21}$$

Let us divide $\psi_b$ into two parts: $\psi_{b+}$, which has the same parity as $\psi_a$ and $\psi_{b-}$, which has opposite parity. We can rewrite Eq. (10.21) thus

$$(\psi_{b+}|H_1|\psi_a)^* + (\psi_{b-}|H_2|\psi_a)^* = (\psi_{b+}|H_1|\psi_a) - (\psi_{b-}|H_2|\psi_a).$$

(10.22)

It follows from Eq. (10.22) that the matrix element $(\psi_{b+}|H_1|\psi_a)$ is entirely real and that $(\psi_{b-}|H_2|\psi_a)$ is entirely imaginary. The actual outgoing waves are the outgoing parts of $\psi_b$ multiplied by the appro priate matrix element. The outgoing parts of $\psi_{b+}$ and $\psi_{b-}$ have real relative amplitudes if the products $B$ are free particles and it follows that the actual outgoing waves of opposite parity have imaginary relative amplitudes; this condition forbids interference between out going waves of opposite parity. This is the required result. This result does not hold if there is any interaction between the decay products. The more general proof for decay, including spin, has been given by Coester (1957).

We can conclude from the foregoing theorem that, in the absence of final state interactions, it is impossible to observe the interference effects due to the nonconservation of parity if the decay interaction is invariant under charge conjugation. In the case of the $\beta$-decay asym metry observed by Wu and collaborators, the final state interaction which is between the charge of the residual nucleus and the charge of the $\beta$ particle, is too small to account for the observed asymmetry and it becomes evident that the $\beta$-decay interaction is not invariant under charge conjugation. In the case of the $\Lambda^0$ decay, there is a considerable interaction in the final state, but again it is insufficient to account for the observed asymmetry, and we must conclude that the decay interaction is not invariant under charge conjugation. The case of $K^+$ meson decay is different: if we assume that the $\theta^+$ and $\tau^+$ have spin zero, the apparent nonconservation of parity is detected by the appearance of decay states having opposite parity; this is not an interference effect and we can draw no conclusions about the invariance of the decay interaction under $C$.

## 10.9 Conclusion

In this chapter we have discussed some of the implications of three important discontinuous symmetry transformations. Our treatment is far from exhaustive and readers are referred to the reviews and their accompanying bibliographies by Wick (1958) and by Kemmer et al. (1959).

# CHAPTER XI

# BETA DECAY

## 11.1 Introduction

We devote a chapter to $\beta$-decay since this subject has been one of the most fruitful fields of application of the symmetry laws discussed in the last chapter; fruitful, not because the symmetry laws applied, but because some of the laws did not apply.

## 11.2 The Description of Beta Decay

$\beta$-decay is the name given to the manifestation of the following fundamental decay reactions:

$$n \rightarrow p + e^- + \bar{\nu}, \tag{11.1}$$

$$p \rightarrow n + e^+ + \nu. \tag{11.2}$$

For the time being we assume neutrino ($\nu$) and antineutrino ($\bar{\nu}$) are different, and define them by these reactions. The second reaction is energetically forbidden for the free proton and can only be observed in certain complex nuclei. Other reactions involving the $\beta$-interaction can be found by rearranging the particles in reactions (11.1) and (11.2) (i.e., by charge conjugating a particle and changing the side on which it appears), for example,

$$e^- + p \rightarrow n + \nu \tag{11.3}$$

is the reaction which takes place in nucleon capture of an electron from a $K$ orbit, and

$$\bar{\nu} + p \rightarrow n + e^+ \tag{11.4}$$

is the antineutrino absorption reaction observed by Reines and Cowan (1959). Antinucleons are supposed to be able to undergo $\beta$-decay, although this has not been observed:

$$\bar{p} \to \bar{n} + e^- + \bar{\nu}, \tag{11.5}$$

$$\bar{n} \to \bar{p} + e^+ + \nu. \tag{11.6}$$

The antiproton decay can only occur in complex antinuclei. Other particles are also involved in interactions which are very like the $\beta$-interaction in quality and strength; for example, the decay of the $\mu$ meson

$$\mu^{\pm} \to e^{\pm} + \nu + \bar{\nu}, \tag{11.7}$$

or the forced decay of the $\mu^-$ meson

$$\mu^- + p \to n + \nu. \tag{11.8}$$

This last reaction (11.8) has an immediate similarity to $K$ capture, reaction (11.3).

We note at this point that our definition of the neutrino and antineutrino is in line with the concept of the conservation of leptons. Lepton is the generic name for all the fermions having a mass less than that of the proton. The class is divided into leptons and antileptons:

$$\text{leptons:} \quad \mu^-, e^-, \nu,$$

$$\text{antileptons:} \ \mu^+, e^+, \bar{\nu}.$$

The law of the conservation of leptons states that the number of leptons, less the number of antileptons, is a constant. This rather empirical law cannot receive more justification until we come to discuss the two-component neutrino theory.

We also note that the interactions required to give the observed reaction rates for the reactions (11.1), (11.7), and (11.8) have almost equal strengths, suggesting that a universal interaction is operating. This has been called the Fermi interaction.

## 11.3 The Theory of Beta Decay

We proceed in the language of field theory by writing down an interaction Lagrangian density

$$\mathscr{L}_I = \sum_r C_r (\bar{\psi}_p O_r \psi_n) (\bar{\psi}_e O'_r \psi_\nu) + \text{Hermitian conjugate.} \tag{11.9}$$

The $C_r$ are constants which determine the strength of the interaction. The $O_r, O'_r$ are operators whose form we shall examine shortly. The remaining quantities are field operators which have the property of creating or destroying particles, thus:

$\psi_\nu$ destroys a neutrino or creates an antineutrino,

$\bar\psi_e$ creates an electron or destroys a positron,

$\psi_n$ destroys a neutron or creates an antineutron,

$\bar\psi_p$ creates a proton or destroys an antiproton.

Thus these four terms taken together will form a term in an $S$-matrix which has matrix elements between a state consisting of neutron plus neutrino and a state consisting of proton plus electron, and which indicates that a transition from the first to the second state is possible; that is

$$n + \nu \to p + e^-,$$

which is just reaction (11.1). This last statement can be checked by using the alternative property $\psi_\nu$ has of creating antineutrinos. It is evident that such a term also has matrix elements between the states (antiproton + positron) and (antineutron + antineutrino); i.e., for the reactions

$$\bar p + e^+ \to \bar n + \bar\nu \quad \text{or} \quad \bar p \to \bar n + e^- + \bar\nu. \tag{11.5}$$

The Hermitian conjugate term is of the form

$$\sum_r \epsilon_r C_r (\bar\psi_n O_r^\dagger \psi_p)(\bar\psi_\nu O_r^\dagger \psi_e) \tag{11.10}$$

where $\epsilon_r$ is $\pm 1$, depending upon $O_r$ and $O_r'$, and

$\psi_e$ destroys an electron or creates a positron,

$\bar\psi_\nu$ creates a neutrino or destroys an antineutrino,

$\psi_p$ destroys a proton or creates an antiproton,

$\bar\psi_n$ creates a neutron or destroys an antineutron.

This term has matrix elements for the reactions

$$p \to e^+ + n + \nu, \tag{11.2}$$

$$\bar n \to \bar p + e^+ + \nu. \tag{11.6}$$

It is now obvious that the interaction of Eq. (11.9) covers all the reactions (11.1) to (11.6).

There are certain symmetry restrictions placed upon the operators $O_r$. At present our knowledge of $\beta$-decay is such that we believe that the interaction is invariant under proper Lorentz transformations, and hence under the $TCP$ transformation, and we know that it is not invariant under $C$ or $P$. Let us examine the restrictions upon the $O_r$ due to Lorentz invariance. The Lagrangian density must be scalar (under proper Lorentz transformations); the bilinear forms $(\bar{\psi}O_r\psi)$ in Eq. (11.9) are scalars, four vectors, axial vectors, tensors, or pseudo-scalars according to the operator $O_r$ and to make a scalar out of two such covariants requires that $O_r = O'_r$ and that a sum is performed over indices. In Fermi's original theory of the $\beta$-decay (Fermi, 1934) the $O_r$ were chosen so that the covariants were four vectors. We need not make such a restriction and we will consider all the independent forms of $O_r$. We do not, however, consider interactions containing derivatives of the field operators as such interactions give obvious contradictions with experimental observation. The five independent $O_r$ are:

$$
\begin{aligned}
O_\text{S} &= 1 & \text{scalar,} \\[4pt]
O_\text{V} &= i\gamma_\rho & \text{vector,} \\[4pt]
O_\text{A} &= i\gamma_5\gamma_\rho & \text{axial vector,} \\[4pt]
O_\text{P} &= i\gamma_5 & \text{pseudoscalar,} \\[4pt]
O_\text{T} &= \frac{i}{2\sqrt{2}}(\gamma_\rho\gamma_\sigma - \gamma_\sigma\gamma_\rho) & \text{tensor.}
\end{aligned}
\qquad (11.11)
$$

The covariants $\bar{\psi}O_r\psi$ transform as shown opposite each operator. The factors $i = \sqrt{-1}$ have been included to make the space components of the covariants Hermitian. Thus Fermi's original proposal for the inter-action was

$$
\mathscr{L}_I = C_\text{V}(\bar{\psi}_p\gamma_\rho\psi_n)(\bar{\psi}_e\gamma_\rho\psi_\nu)
$$

where, as always, a sum is implied over repeated indices, $\rho$ in this case. This term is the scalar product of two four vectors.

We know that the $\beta$-interaction must contain a part which is parity nonconserving; this, in turn, implies that there are terms in $\mathscr{L}_I$ which are pseudoscalar. We can construct a further five terms having this property by having $O'_r = O_r\gamma_5$. Thus for every term

we can add

$$
C_r(\bar{\psi}_p O_r\psi_n)(\bar{\psi}_e O_r\psi_\nu) + \text{h.c.}
$$

$$
C'_r(\bar{\psi}_p O_r\psi_n)(\bar{\psi}_e O_r\gamma_5\psi_\nu) + \text{h.c.}\ddagger
$$

‡ Where h.c. stands for Hermitian conjugate.

These extra terms are pseudoscalar and have matrix elements between states of opposite parity. We notice that we have followed convention and put the extra $\gamma_5$ into the lepton covariant $(\bar{\psi}_e O_r \gamma_5 \psi_\nu)$; the interaction is specified by the transformation properties of the nucleon covariant $(\bar{\psi}_p O_r \psi_n)$ which is scalar, vector, etc., as $O_r = O_S, O_V, \ldots$, etc. The complete interaction Lagrangian now reads

$$\mathscr{L}_I = \sum_r (C_r(\bar{\psi}_p O_r \psi_n)(\bar{\psi}_e O_r \psi_\nu) + C'_r(\bar{\psi}_p O_r \psi_n)(\bar{\psi}_e O_r \gamma_5 \psi_\nu)) + \text{h.c.}$$

$$(11.12)$$

We can now state the values of $\epsilon_r$ of Eq. (11.10), which can be used to write out the Hermitian conjugate explicitly if required:

$\epsilon_r = 1$     if   $O_r = O'_r$,   i.e., for all the parity conserving terms,

$\epsilon_r = 1$     if   $O'_r = O_r \gamma_5$   and   $r = $ V, A,

$\epsilon_r = -1$   if   $O'_r = O_r \gamma_5$   and   $r = $ S, T, or P.

Before proceeding, let us examine the effects on $\mathscr{L}_I$ if it is invariant under charge conjugation, time reversal, and the parity transformation separately.

$P$ invariance requires $\mathscr{L}_I$ to be scalar and in Eq. (11.12) all $C'_r$ would have to be zero. $T$ invariance requires $\mathscr{L}_I$ to be real, just as it required $H$ to be real (Section 10.6); hence all the $C_r$ and $C'_r$ would have to be real apart from a common phase factor which has no effect. $C$ invariance has the result that the parity conserving matrix elements and the parity nonconserving matrix elements have relative amplitudes which are imaginary, if there is no interaction in the final state. There is no such interaction in a first-order calculation with this simple Lagrangian; hence, if the $C_r$ are real, the $C'_r$ are imaginary, and vice versa. We do not impose these conditions but keep them in mind so that we can observe the effect of any postulated invariance.

The object of all experimental investigation in $\beta$-decay is to confirm, or otherwise, this theory of $\beta$-decay and to ascertain the values of the coupling constants $C_r$ and $C'_r$.

This theory is not renormalizable; however, the lowest order of an $S$-matrix perturbation expansion gives results which appear to agree closely with observation if suitable values of the coupling constants are employed. At present there is no solution to the problem of the divergences which remain in higher orders.

## 11.4 The Classification of Beta Decays

We will now briefly consider the evaluation of matrix elements of the interaction Lagrangian and show how this leads to a classification of the transitions by the changes in parity and angular momentum between the initial and final nucleus and by the degree of forbiddenness.

The first term of a perturbation expansion is found to give meaningful results; this term gives the transition rate $\omega$ in the form

$$d\omega = \frac{2\pi}{\hbar} \Sigma \, | \, (\Psi_\beta | S_1 | \Psi_\alpha) \, |^2 \, d\left(\frac{dN}{dE}\right), \qquad (11.13)$$

where $\Psi_\alpha$ and $\Psi_\beta$ are the initial and final state wave functions and $S_1$ is the first term in the $S$-matrix expansion [Eq. (9.24)]. A sum is to be taken over all unobserved final particle spins and an average over all initial spin states. As shown, the transition rate is a differential quantity for the rate into an interval around the configuration given by $\Psi_\beta$. The complete transition rate is found by an integration over all the independent dynamic variables, electron energy and direction, and neutrino direction.

The matrix element $(\Psi_\beta | S_1 | \Psi_\alpha)$ includes integration over all the space variables of the particles involved; the outgoing leptons have wave functions of a simple form, plane wave for the neutrino, a Coulomb function (Blatt and Weisskopf, 1952) for the electron (or positron), and their integration over space is in principle straightforward. In contrast to this, the integration over the nucleon wave functions can be a very complex matter. At the moment only one free baryon $\beta$-decay is fully observable (cf. Section 12.10),

$$n \to p + e^- + \bar{\nu},$$

and this is the only $\beta$-decay which does not involve nuclear structure effects, although it does not follow that we can have full confidence in the calculation of the nucleon part of the matrix element. All other cases of $\beta$-decay take place in complex nuclei and the integration requires a knowledge of nuclear structure; this problem occurs with varying degrees of difficulty according to the nucleus. Often the reverse procedure is applied: a knowledge of the properties of a given $\beta$-decay serves to give the nuclear matrix element and information on the structure of the nuclei involved.

The nuclear matrix element contains a factor $e^{-i\mathbf{p}\cdot\mathbf{r}}$ where $\mathbf{p}$ is the momentum of the recoiling nucleus. In performing the space integration of the nucleon wave functions, it is convenient to expand this exponential as a power series in $\mathbf{p}\cdot\mathbf{r}$. Each term in the expansion contributes to the matrix element an amount which is about 1/100 of the previous term, so that only the first few terms have to be considered. In addition, each term imposes certain selection rules upon the nuclear transition. If the selection rules are such that a given transition allows the first term to have a matrix element, the transition is said to be allowed; if the selection rules are such that the first nonzero matrix element is that of $(\mathbf{p} \cdot \mathbf{r})^n$, the transition is said to be a forbidden transition of order $n$. In Table 11.1 we have listed the selection rules

TABLE 11.1

CLASSIFICATION OF NUCLEAR $\beta$-DECAY

| Order of forbiddenness | Change in parity | Change in angular momentum. $\Delta j$ | Interaction |
|---|---|---|---|
| Allowed | No | 0 | S or V |
| | No | 0 or 1 but not $0 \to 0$ | T or A |
| 1st forbidden | Yes | 1 | S |
| | Yes | 1 | V |
| | Yes | 0, 1, 2 | T |
| | Yes | 0, 1, 2 | A |
| | Yes | 0 | P |

for the first two orders. These rules concern the change in parity and the change in angular momentum ($\Delta j = |j_\beta - j_\alpha|$) from the initial nucleus to the final nucleus. Thus a nucleus $(Z, A)$ which is energetically able to undergo $\beta$-decay to the nucleus $(Z \pm 1, A)$ will do so by the lowest order transition allowed by the required change in parity and nuclear angular momentum. If the lowest choice is anything but allowed, the number of interactions which can be involved is large and it becomes difficult to interpret the experimental data. In addition, the contribution of the pseudoscalar interaction is almost certainly very small (Konopinski, 1954) and we can therefore confine our discussion to the S, T, A, and V interactions in allowed transitions.

Fermi's original theory was based upon the V interaction alone, for which $\Delta j = 0$; however, there are many $\Delta j = 1$ transitions indicating that there must also be some T and/or A interaction present. It is usual to classify the transitions into "Fermi" (S and V) and "Gamow–Teller" (T and A) after the authors who suggested these interactions (Fermi, 1934; Gamow and Teller, 1936). The nuclear parts of the matrix element are represented by $M_F$ or $M_{GT}$; we can make this generalization because in the nonrelativistic limit, which applies to the nuclear matrix element, $|M_F|^2$ is independent of whether the interaction is S or V and $|M_{GT}|^2$ is independent of whether the interaction is T or A (Rose, 1958).

## II.5 Beta Decay: Pre-1956

We can now examine the results of pre-1956 measurements which
were made in an effort to determine what interactions are present and
their strengths. These experiments were all interpreted under the
assumption that the interaction was invariant under $P$, $C$, and $T$
separately. The first experimental data concern the energy spectrum
of beta particles (electrons or positrons) emitted from a radioactive
source. Using the interaction of Eq. (11.12), with all $C_r' = 0$, we expect
the spectrum to be given by

$$N_\pm(E)\,dE$$

$$= \frac{dE}{2\pi^3\hbar^7 c^5}\underbrace{pE(E_0-E)^2}_{1}\underbrace{F(\mp Z,E)}_{2}$$

$$\times \underbrace{\left\{|M_{\mathrm{F}}|^2|C_{\mathrm{F}}|^2 + |M_{\mathrm{GT}}|^2|C_{\mathrm{GT}}|^2 \pm \frac{2m_e c^2}{E}\left[1-\left(\frac{Z}{137}\right)^2\right]^{1/2}(b_{\mathrm{F}}+b_{\mathrm{GT}})\right.}_{3}$$

$$(11.14)$$

$N_\pm(E)\,dE$ is the probability that a beta particle is emitted in one
second with total energy in the range $E$ to $E+dE$. $E$ and $p$ are the
total energy and momentum of the emitted beta particle (upper sign
for positron, lower for electron). $E_0$ is the maximum permissible
energy of the beta particle, $m_e$ is the electron mass, (1) is the density
of states factor and other numerical factors, (2) is the factor which
indicates the effect of the Coulomb distortion of the outgoing electron
wave (as shown, it is a function of $E$ and of the nuclear charge $Z$, of
the final nucleus), (3) is the summed square of the matrix element
having $M_{\mathrm{F}}$ and $M_{\mathrm{GT}}$, as already discussed, and

$$|C_{\mathrm{F}}|^2 = |C_{\mathrm{S}}|^2 + |C_{\mathrm{V}}|^2, \tag{11.15}$$

$$|C_{\mathrm{GT}}|^2 = |C_{\mathrm{T}}|^2 + |C_{\mathrm{A}}|^2, \tag{11.16}$$

$$b_{\mathrm{F}} = 2\,\mathrm{Re}\,C_{\mathrm{S}}\,C_{\mathrm{V}}^*|M_{\mathrm{F}}|^2, \tag{11.17}$$

$$b_{\mathrm{GT}} = 2\,\mathrm{Re}\,C_{\mathrm{T}}\,C_{\mathrm{A}}^*|M_{\mathrm{GT}}|^2. \tag{11.18}$$

We have written these formulas as if the $C_r$ could be imaginary. This
is not so if $T$ invariance holds. $b_{\mathrm{F}}$ and $b_{\mathrm{GT}}$ are the Fierz interference
terms; they are due to interference between the S and V interactions
in Fermi transitions and between T and A in Gamow–Teller transitions.
Experimental evidence indicates that these interference terms are
absent (Gerhart, 1958; Allen et al., 1955; Sherr and Miller, 1954)

It follows that the quantities $C_S C_V^*$ and $C_T C_A^*$ are purely imaginary or zero; they cannot be imaginary if T invariance holds, and we find that they must be zero. Thus the Fermi interaction is S or V but not both, and the Gamow–Teller interaction is T or A but not both.

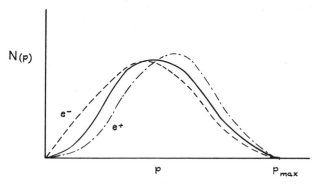

FIG. 11.1. The momentum spectrum of electrons and positrons emitted in $\beta$-decay. The solid line is the density of states factor [(1) in Eq. (11.14)]. Broken lines include the effect of $F(\pm Z, E)$.

Figure 11.1 is a sketch of the spectrum of $\beta$-particles: apart from the term $F(\pm Z, E)$, the spectrum depends only upon the statistical factors in the density of states. The shape of the end point of the spectrum for tritium decay has been used to check that the neutrino mass is zero, as is assumed in deriving Eq. (11.14). The result is $n_\nu < 0.0010 m_e$ (Hamilton $et\ al.$, 1953).

A convenient way of plotting the spectrum is by the "Kurie plot". From Eq. (11.14) we have that

$$\sqrt{\frac{N_\pm(E)}{pEF(\mp Z, E)}} = K(E_0 - E), \tag{11.19}$$

where $K$ is a constant independent of energy. A graph of the left-hand side of (11.19) against energy $E$, should yield a straight line intersecting the $E$ axis at $E_0$. We can integrate Eq. (11.14) to obtain the total transition rate $\omega = (\ln 2)/t$, where $t$ is the half-life of the decaying nucleus

$$\omega = \frac{|C_F|^2 |M_F|^2 + |C_{GT}|^2 |M_{GT}|^2}{2\pi^3 \hbar^7 c^5} f,$$

where

$$f = \int_{E = m_e c^2}^{E_0} Ep(E_0 - E)^2 F(\pm Z, E)\, dE,$$

or

$$ft = \frac{2\pi^3 \hbar^7 c^5 \ln 2}{|C_F|^2 |M_F|^2 + |C_{GT}|^2 |M_{GT}|^2}. \tag{11.20}$$

The values of $\log_{10}ft$ fall very roughly into two groups: favoured transitions have $\log_{10}ft$ about 2.9 to 3.7 and are transitions between corresponding states in mirror nuclei or between even–even and odd–odd nuclei; unfavoured transitions have $\log_{10}ft$ values of about 5 to 6. Forbidden transitions have $\log_{10}ft$ values which are even higher.

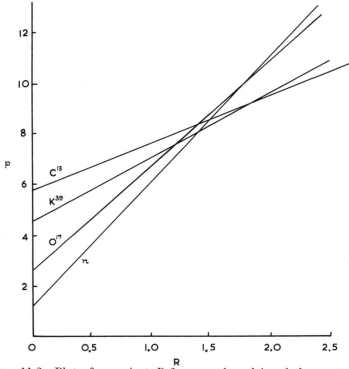

Fig. 11.2. Plot of $p$ against $R$ for several nuclei and the neutron. The vertical scale is in units $10^{-36}$ cgs.

The value of $ft$ will give the values of $C_F$ and $C_{GT}$ if the nuclear matrix elements are known. A systematic analysis of this kind has been given by Kofoed-Hansen and Winther (1956). Let us put

$$R = \frac{|C_{GT}|^2}{|C_F|^2}$$

$$p = \frac{2\pi^3\hbar^7 c^5 \ln 2}{|C_F|^2}.$$

Then substituting in Eq. (11.20), we have

$$\{|M_F|^2 + R|M_{GT}|^2\}ft = p.$$

We plot a graph of $p$ against $R$ for every transition for which $M_F$ and $M_{GT}$ can be calculated and for which $ft$ is known. There will be a straight line for each transition and all the lines should intersect at one point which will give values for $R$ and $p$ for which values of $|C_{GT}|^2$ and $|C_F|^2$ can be obtained. Figure 11.2 shows such a graph for several nuclei. The lines do not all pass through one point, presumably due to the errors in calculating $M_F$ and $M_{GT}$. Kofoed-Hansen and Winther give a least-squares analysis which yields

$$\frac{|C_{GT}|^2}{|C_F|^2} = 1.27 \pm 0.10$$

$$(|C_F|^2 + |C_{GT}|^2)\frac{m^5 c^4}{\hbar^7} = 1.53 \times 10^{-2}\,\text{sec}^{-1},$$

which gives $|C_F|^2 = 1.39 \times 10^{-49}\,\text{erg cm}^3$. The identification of the two interactions can be determined, in principle, from electron–neutrino correlation experiments (for example, Alford and Hamilton, 1957), but these are very difficult and do not give decisive results; what evidence there was suggested that the Fermi interaction was scalar (S) and that the Gamow–Teller was tensor (T). This is how $\beta$-decay knowledge stood at the end of 1956.

## 11.6 Beta Decay: Post-1956

The nonconservation of parity was discovered late in 1956 and its experimental manifestation was first observed in the $\beta$-decay of cobalt-60 (Wu *et al.*, 1957). This discovery entails a complete re-examination of the theory of $\beta$-decay. We relax the requirement that the Lagrangian is invariant under $P$ and it becomes the full expression given in Eq. (11.12). In addition, Eqs. (11.15) to (11.18) become

$$|C_F|^2 = |C_V|^2 + |C_V'|^2 + |C_S|^2 + |C_S'|^2, \tag{11.21}$$

$$|C_{GT}|^2 = |C_A|^2 + |C_A'|^2 + |C_T|^2 + |C_T'|^2, \tag{11.22}$$

$$b_F = 2\,\text{Re}\,(C_S C_V^* + C_S' C_V'^*)\,|M_F|^2, \tag{11.23}$$

$$b_{GT} = 2\,\text{Re}\,(C_A C_T^* + C_A' C_T'^*)\,|M_{GT}|^2. \tag{11.24}$$

Equation (11.14) remains unchanged if the notation of Eqs. (11.21) to (11.24) replaces that of Eqs. (11.15) to (11.18). The subscripts S, V, A, T now refer to the Lorentz properties of the nuclear covariant. The absence of Fierz interference terms is no longer strong evidence that the Fermi interaction is S or V; $b_F$ could easily be close to zero without requiring that $C_S = C'_S = 0$ or that $C_V = C'_V = 0$. The same argument applies to any conclusions regarding the Gamow–Teller interaction.

We can now examine some of the physically observable quantities associated with parity nonconservation. Let us consider the asymmetry in the emission of $\beta$-particles from polarized radioactive nuclei. The relevant factor in the angular distribution of $\beta$-particles is

$$\left\{ 1 + \frac{ac}{E} \langle \sigma \rangle \cdot \mathbf{p} \right\}$$

where $E$ is the electron total energy, $\mathbf{p}$ is the electron momentum, and $\langle \sigma \rangle$ is the polarization of the decaying nucleus; the asymmetry factor $a$ is given by

$$a = \frac{\mathrm{Re}\,[\,\mp\,|M_{GT}|^2 \lambda_{jj'}(C_T^* C'_T - C_A^* C'_A) + 2\delta_{jj'}\{j/(j+1)\}^{1/2}|M_F||M_{GT}|(C_T^* C'_S + C_T'^* C_S - C_A^* C'_V - C_A'^* C_V)]}{|M_F|^2|C_F|^2 + |M_{GT}|^2|C_{GT}|^2}$$

$$(11.25)$$

The sign is $-$ for positrons and $+$ for electrons, and we have neglected some small terms depending upon $Z$, the nuclear charge. The quantity $\lambda_{jj'}$ depends upon the nuclear angular momentum and its change

$$\lambda_{jj'} = +1 \qquad \text{for} \quad j \to j' = j - 1,$$

$$= \frac{1}{j+1} \qquad j \to j' = j,$$

$$= \frac{-j}{j+1} \qquad j \to j' = j + 1,$$

where $j$ is the angular momentum quantum number. We observe that if parity were conserved all $C'_r = 0$ and $a = 0$. Alternatively, if the interaction were charge conjugation invariant, all $C_r$ would be real and all $C'_r$ would be imaginary, in which case $a = 0$. Thus the observation of an asymmetry indicates that the interaction is not invariant under $C$ or $P$. The observations made upon $Co^{60}$ indicated that $a = -1$ for this transition which is a pure Gamow–Teller with $j = 5$ and $j' = 4$. From Eq. (11.25) we see that this result is consistent with either

$$C_T = -C'_T \quad \text{and} \quad C_A = C'_A = 0,$$

or

$$C_A = C'_A \quad \text{and} \quad C_T = C'_T = 0.$$

The nonconservation of parity allows the emitted $\beta$-particles to be longitudinally polarized, that is, the decay rate depends upon $\boldsymbol{\sigma} \cdot \mathbf{p}$, where $\boldsymbol{\sigma}$ is the polarization vector of the $\beta$-particle and $\mathbf{p}$ is its momentum

$$\frac{\boldsymbol{\sigma} \cdot \mathbf{p}}{|\mathbf{p}|} = \mp \frac{v}{c} \frac{2 \operatorname{Re}\left[\,|M_{\mathrm{F}}|^2 (C_{\mathrm{S}} C_{\mathrm{S}}'^* - C_{\mathrm{V}} C_{\mathrm{V}}'^*) + |M_{\mathrm{GT}}|^2 (C_{\mathrm{T}} C_{\mathrm{T}}'^* - C_{\mathrm{A}} C_{\mathrm{A}}'^*)\right]}{|M_{\mathrm{F}}|^2 |C_{\mathrm{F}}|^2 + |M_{\mathrm{GT}}|^2 |C_{\mathrm{GT}}|^2}.$$

$v$ is the velocity of the $\beta$-particle. The sign is again $-$ for a positron and $+$ for an electron. The experimental results of the longitudinal polarization of electrons emitted in $\beta$-decay indicate that it is $-v/c$. The negative sign indicates that the spin is directed against the momentum (Deutsch et al., 1958; Alder et al., 1957). This result requires that either

$C_r = C_r'$ and only V and A interactions are acting,

$C_r = -C_r'$ and only T and S interactions are acting.

Both these choices agree with the Co$^{60}$ asymmetry and the absence of Fierz interference terms.

The neutrinos or antineutrinos emitted in $\beta$-decay can also be longitudinally polarized. By considering Eqs. (11.9) and (11.10) and comparing the positions of the particle creation and destruction operators, we can expect that a neutrino [due to (11.10)] will be emitted with the same direction of polarization as an electron [due to (11.9)], unless $\epsilon_r = -1$. It follows that the neutrino polarization has the same polarization direction as an electron if the interaction is V or A but opposite if the interaction is S or T. Thus a measurement of the polarization of neutrinos emitted from a $\beta$-active material which is emitting positrons or capturing $K$-electrons serves to decide between the V and A interaction and the S and T interaction. This measurement has been made in a most elegant manner by Goldhaber and collaborators (1958). The results indicate that the polarization directions are indeed the same. All the experimental results are therefore consistent with

$$C_{\mathrm{V}} = C_{\mathrm{V}}' \quad \text{and} \quad C_{\mathrm{A}} = C_{\mathrm{A}}',$$

$$C_{\mathrm{S}} = C_{\mathrm{S}}' = C_{\mathrm{T}} = C_{\mathrm{T}}' = C_{\mathrm{P}} = C_{\mathrm{P}}' = 0.$$

The nonzero coupling constants can be complex but one of the phases involved may be removed as it is unobservable. Let us put $C_{\mathrm{V}}$ real; then $C_{\mathrm{A}}$ is also real if the interaction is invariant under time reversal. A measurement of the decay asymmetry for polarized neutrons determines, in principle, the relative phase between $C_{\mathrm{V}}$ and $C_{\mathrm{A}}$ and thus tests time reversal invariance. Burgy and collaborators (1958) find that, if $|C_A|^2/|C_V|^2 = 1.27$, the relative phase is about $160°$ with a standard error of about $20°$. This is consistent with $C_A = -1.13C_V$, which has been accepted as correct until such time as more sensitive tests of time reversal invariance can be made.

The $\beta$-interaction Lagrangian density is now

$$\mathscr{L}_I = (\bar{\psi}_p \gamma_\rho (C_V - C_A \gamma_5) \psi_n)(\bar{\psi}_e \gamma_\rho (1 + \gamma_5) \psi_\nu) + (\bar{\psi}_n (C_V + C_A \gamma_5) \gamma_\rho \psi_p) \\ \times (\bar{\psi}_\nu (1 - \gamma_5) \gamma_\rho \psi_e), \tag{11.26}$$

with $C_V \simeq 10^{-49}$ erg cm³ and $C_A = -1.13C_V$. The coefficient $C_A$ has a change of sign in this compact expression to allow for two missing $i$ in the A interaction.

It appears that $C_V$ and $C_A$ owe their inequality to the effect of the meson fields associated with the nucleons; i.e., the contribution of the Feynman diagram of Fig. 11.3 depends upon the interaction at the four-fermion vertex (see Section 12.11).

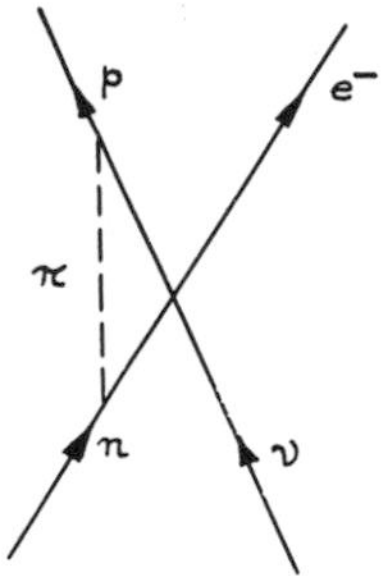

FIG. 11.3. The Feynman diagram for the effect of the meson field on the $\beta$-decay interaction.

It is evident that our discussion has not been able to cover all the experimental results now available which are in favour of our interpretation of the $\beta$-decay interaction. The abstracts of papers presented at the conference on weak interactions held at Gatlinburg in 1958 (Gatlinburg, 1959; Wu, 1959) present an excellent picture of the results available at that time. For a complete account of $\beta$-decay experiments readers are referred to the contribution of Deutsch and Kofoed-Hansen (1959).

The interaction of Eq. (11.26) is said to give maximum parity nonconservation; by this we mean that the interaction connects states of the same or of opposite parity impartially.

## 11.7 The Two-Component Theory of the Neutrino

So far we have discussed the theory of $\beta$-decay as if the neutrino was a particle which was described by the Dirac equation as is the electron. Such a description requires a four-component wave function; however, if the neutrino is massless it is possible to simplify the Dirac equation and describe the neutrino by a two-component wave function (Lee and Yang, 1957; Salam, 1957; Landau, 1957). This theory is not invariant under the C and P transformations separately and has several features which suggest that it is the correct interpretation of the $\beta$-decay.

Let us consider the Dirac equation in its covariant form:

$$\left(\gamma_\rho \frac{\partial}{\partial x_\rho} + \frac{mc}{\hbar}\right)\psi_\nu = 0.$$

If this applies to a massless neutrino, it reduces to

$$\gamma_\rho \frac{\partial \psi_\nu}{\partial x_\rho} = 0,$$

or

$$\gamma_4 \frac{\partial \psi_\nu}{\partial x_4} = -\gamma_l \frac{\partial \psi_\nu}{\partial x_l}. \tag{11.27}$$

In the original Dirac theory (Dirac, 1947) the matrices employed were $\alpha_l$ and $\beta$, from which the $\gamma$ matrices are defined thus:

$$\gamma_l = -i\beta\alpha_l, \quad \gamma_4 = \beta.$$

Thus Eq. (11.27) can be written

$$\frac{\partial \psi_\nu}{\partial x_4} = +i\alpha_l \frac{\partial \psi_\nu}{\partial x_l}$$

or, in a more easily interpreted form,

$$i\hbar \frac{\partial \psi_\nu}{\partial t} = -i\hbar c\alpha_l \frac{\partial \psi_\nu}{\partial x_l}. \tag{11.28}$$

The $\alpha$ matrices also have the following property,

$$\alpha_l = -\gamma_5\sigma_l = -\sigma_l\gamma_5, \tag{11.29}$$

where $\sigma_l$ is a $4 \times 4$ matrix formed from the Pauli matrix $\sigma_l$ (Section 2.9); thus

$$\sigma_l = \begin{bmatrix} \sigma_l & \begin{matrix} 0 & 0 \\ 0 & 0 \end{matrix} \\ \begin{matrix} 0 & 0 \\ 0 & 0 \end{matrix} & \sigma_l \end{bmatrix}.$$

Substitute either of the equations implied in Eq. (11.29) into Eq. (11.28) and we find that

$$i\hbar \frac{\partial}{\partial t}\gamma_5\psi_\nu = i\hbar c\,\sigma_l \frac{\partial \psi_\nu}{\partial x_l}, \tag{11.30}$$

or

$$i\hbar \frac{\partial \psi_\nu}{\partial t} = i\hbar c\, \sigma_l \frac{\partial}{\partial x_l} \gamma_5\, \psi_\nu. \tag{11.31}$$

By adding Eqs. (11.30) and (11.31) we get

$$i\hbar \frac{\partial}{\partial t} (1+\gamma_5)\,\psi_\nu = i\hbar c\, \sigma_l \frac{\partial}{\partial x_l} (1+\gamma_5)\,\psi_\nu, \tag{11.32}$$

and by subtracting we get

$$i\hbar \frac{\partial}{\partial t} (1-\gamma_5)\,\psi_\nu = -i\hbar c\, \sigma_l \frac{\partial}{\partial x_l} (1-\gamma_5)\,\psi_\nu. \tag{11.33}$$

If $(1+\gamma_5)\,\psi_\nu$ and $(1-\gamma_5)\,\psi_\nu$ represent plane waves they are eigenfunctions of energy and momentum and we can write these equations:

$$E = -\boldsymbol{\sigma}\cdot\mathbf{p}c \text{ for the function } (1+\gamma_5)\,\psi_\nu,$$

$$E = +\boldsymbol{\sigma}\cdot\mathbf{p}c \text{ for the function } (1-\gamma_5)\,\psi_\nu.$$

These are massless particles, hence $E = pc$. Let us consider the $(1+\gamma_5)\,\psi_\nu$ particle

$$p = -\boldsymbol{\sigma}\cdot\mathbf{p}.$$

If we call the positive energy state of this particle the neutrino, we observe that the neutrino spin vector must be directed antiparallel to the momentum. If we call the negative energy state the antineutrino, it follows that the antineutrino has its spin directed parallel to its momentum. The spin antiparallel corresponds to left-hand polarization for the photon and in this context is often called negative helicity; the spin parallel case corresponds to right-hand polarization or positive helicity. In the language of field theory we find that

> $(1+\gamma_5)\,\psi_\nu$ destroys neutrinos with negative helicity
>
> > or
>
> creates antineutrinos with positive helicity.

If we take the complex conjugate of Eq. (11.32) we find that

> $\bar{\psi}_\nu(1-\gamma_5)$ creates neutrinos with negative helicity
>
> > or
>
> destroys antineutrinos with positive helicity.

We can make similar statements about the state function which obeys Eq. (11.33). If we now look at Eq. (11.26), we see that this $\beta$-interaction always creates negative helicity neutrinos and positive helicity anti-neutrinos. However, the interaction was suggested to be of the form of Eq. (11.26) in order that the theory agree with the experimental observation that neutrinos from $\beta$-decay have negative helicity. We have merely confirmed in this section that it is the $(1+\gamma_5)$ operator which is responsible for this. The two-component theory goes further by noticing that, although both Eqs. (11.32) and (11.33) appear each to contain four equations, one for each component of $(1+\gamma_5)\psi_\nu$ or $(1-\gamma_5)\psi_\nu$, they are in fact twofold degenerate and each contains only two independent equations so that $(1+\gamma_5)\psi_\nu$ or $(1-\gamma_5)\psi_\nu$ can be reduced to two independent functions. If we choose Eq. (11.32), then the neutrino has negative helicity and the antineutrino has positive helicity, always. If we choose Eq. (11.33), then the neutrino has positive helicity and the antineutrino negative helicity. Nature appears to have made the first choice and consequently requires that the coupling constants obey

$$C_r = C_r'.$$

To nullify Eq. (11.33) the neutrino state function must obey $\gamma_5\psi_\nu = \psi_\nu$. The two-component theory has been further extended by means of certain postulates to the point where the theory allows only V–A inter-action (Feynman and Gell-Mann, 1958).

We can show that the two-component theory can apply only to massless particles. Suppose we require that the neutrino always has negative helicity from all inertial frames. It follows that unless its velocity is that of light we can always find a frame for which the helicity is opposite; for example, a frame that is moving so as to overtake the neutrino from which we would observe the momentum reversed but the spin unchanged. The neutrino mass must be zero if its velocity is to be that of light.

This theory is not invariant under the parity transformation or under charge conjugation separately. $P$ changes the direction of the momentum of a neutrino, leaves the spin unchanged, and leaves the neutrino a neutrino; it therefore changes the allowed negative helicity neutrino into a positive helicity neutrino which is not an allowed state. Similarly, $C$ changes the allowed negative helicity neutrino into a negative helicity antineutrino which is also not allowed. Thus the theory is not invariant under $C$ or $P$; however, the simultaneous operation $CP$ connects allowed states and the theory is invariant under the $CP$ transformation (and consequently under time reversal).

There is a clear physical picture which shows immediately why the two-component theory leads to asymmetry in $\beta$-decay. Let us illustrate this by considering the decay of $Co^{60}$:

$$Co^{60} \to Ni^{60} + e^- + \bar{\nu}.$$

This is an allowed Gamow–Teller with $j \to j' = j - 1$ where $j = 5$ and $j' = 4$. We refer to Fig. 11.4, where we have indicated the angular

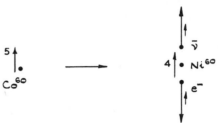

FIG. 11.4. Diagram showing a preferred configuration of spins and momenta in the $\beta$-decay of $Co^{60}$. (The large arrows indicate momenta, the small arrows indicate spins. The unattached horizontal arrow indicates the direction of the decay reaction.)

momentum vector of one $Co^{60}$ nucleus in a fully polarized specimen having $j_z = 5$. The final state consists of a $Ni^{60}$ nucleus with electron and antineutrino which we have considered as ejected along the $+$ or $-z$ axis. If the antineutrino has positive helicity, the most likely configuration to conserve angular momentum will have the electron moving along the $-z$ axis with negative helicity (left-hand polarization) and the antineutrino moving along the $+z$ axis. It follows that the electrons ejected from a polarized specimen of $Co^{60}$ tend to emerge against the direction of the nuclear spin polarization. Next we consider an unpolarized specimen of $Co^{60}$. The observation of electrons in a particular direction picks out decays from nuclei that had nuclear spins preferentially aligned in the opposite direction; this gives the electrons a longitudinal polarization (in this case a negative helicity) which is in agreement with observation. Similarly, positron emitters give positrons which are longitudinally polarized with positive helicity. We note that this discussion relies upon the definition of neutrinos and antineutrinos as particles which are emitted with positrons and electrons respectively; this is in line with the conservation of leptons.

There is further evidence which supports the hypothesis of lepton conservation in as far as it suggests that the light neutral particle ($\bar{\nu}$) emitted in neutron $\beta$-decay is different from that ($\nu$) emitted in proton $\beta$-decay. This is in contrast to the Majorana theory that $\bar{\nu} \equiv \nu$. The evidence concerns a few nuclei for which the following transition is energetically possible: two neutrons in the nucleus simultaneously undergo $\beta$-decay with the emission of two electrons but without emitting neutrinos

$$n + n \to p + p + e^- + e^-,$$

for example,

$$Sn_{50}^{124} \to Te_{52}^{124} + 2e^-.$$

This process is called double $\beta$-decay and is supposed to proceed by the emission and reabsorption of a neutrino. The reactions are, from Eqs. (11.1) and (11.2),

$$n \to p + e^- + \bar{\nu},$$

followed by

$$n + \nu \to p + e^-.$$

These equations have been written maintaining the defined nature of the neutrinos involved. It is evident that reabsorption of the neutrino from reaction (11.1) is only possible if neutrino and antineutrino are identical ($\nu \equiv \bar{\nu}$). The nonobservation double $\beta$-decay will be evidence for the $\nu \neq \bar{\nu}$. The only other way double $\beta$-decay can occur is via the accidental coincidence, within the experimental resolving time, of two ordinary $\beta$-decays. At the present time the observations indicate that the double $\beta$-decay happens at a rate which is several orders of magnitude slower than that predicted by the Majorana theory ($\nu \doteq \bar{\nu}$) and the conclusion is that, as already defined, the neutrino is not the same as the antineutrino. This lends support to the hypothesis of lepton conservation. We notice that the two-component neutrino theory without lepton conservation would permit double $\beta$-decay. A full discussion of all the neutrino possibilities and of the double $\beta$-decay observations is given in the review by Primakoff and Rosen (1959).

The antineutrino absorption experiment [Eq. (11.4)] yields a cross section which supports the two-component neutrino theory rather than the four-component theory. However, the error on the observed cross section is considerable:

observed cross section: $(6.7 \pm 1.5) \times 10^{-43}$ cm$^2$/fission,

2-component theory predicts: $(6.1 \pm 1) \times 10^{-43}$ cm$^2$/fission,

4-component theory predicts: $(3.05 \pm 0.5) \times 10^{-43}$ cm$^2$/fission

(Reines and Cowan, 1959; Carter et al., 1959). The cross sections are expressed with respect to a fission product neutrino source and the theoretical uncertainties include a lack of knowledge concerning the antineutrino energy spectrum and the average number of antineutrinos emitted per fission. There is another neutrino absorption experiment which supports lepton conservation: according to our lepton assignments fission products emit antineutrinos which should be incapable of inducing the following neutrino absorption reaction

$$Cl^{37}_{17} + \nu \to A^{37}_{18} + e^-.$$

Davis (1956) has searched for this reaction using fission product antineutrinos and finds a cross section $0.5 \pm 0.6 \times 10^{-45}$ cm$^2$. If the Majorana theory is correct ($\nu \equiv \bar{\nu}$) the expected cross section is $2.5 \times 10^{-45}$ cm$^2$.

## 11.8 Meson Decays

In this section we discuss the decay of the free $\pi$ and $\mu$ mesons:

$$\pi^+ \to \mu^+ + \nu, \tag{11.34}$$

$$\pi^- \to \mu^- + \bar{\nu}, \tag{11.35}$$

$$\mu^\pm \to e^\pm + \nu + \bar{\nu}. \tag{11.7}$$

These equations are written to comply with the conservation of leptons assuming the $\mu^-$ is the lepton and the $\mu^+$ the antilepton. At the time that tests were being made on parity nonconservation in nuclear $\beta$-decay similar tests were made upon the decay of $\mu$-mesons. A beam of $\mu^+$ mesons was stopped in a block of graphite and the angular distribution of positrons emitted on decay was measured with respect to the direction of incidence (given by the momentum vector $\mathbf{p}_\mu$). There was a marked correlation, the positrons being emitted preferentially in the $-\mathbf{p}_\mu$ direction (Garwin et al., 1957). This decay asymmetry indicates that parity is not conserved in the decay interaction. This result follows from the statement that a fully polarized spin $\frac{1}{2}$ particle, which is decaying by a parity conserving interaction, gives decay products which are isotropically distributed. The only explanation of the observed asymmetry is that parity is not conserved in the decay. In addition, the observed distribution depends upon the scalar $\mathbf{p}_\mu \cdot \mathbf{p}_e$ ($\mathbf{p}_e$ is momentum vector of the decay positron) whereas, in fact, it must depend upon a pseudoscalar. The only possibility is that the $\mu$-mesons were longitudinally polarized and that the distribution depends upon the pseudoscalar $\mathbf{s}_\mu \cdot \mathbf{p}_e$. Thus two results appear from this observation: the $\mu$-mesons were longitudinally polarized and parity is not conserved in $\mu$-meson decay. In addition, the longitudinal polarization indicates that parity is not conserved in the $\pi^+$ decay, which is the source of the observed $\mu^+$ mesons.

We will now follow through the decay sequence assuming the two-component neutrino theory. Let us consider

$$\pi^+ \to \mu^+ + \nu,$$

as observed in the centre of mass of the $\pi$-meson. In Fig. 11.5 the momentum and spin orientations of the decay products are shown: the neutrino ($\nu$) must have negative helicity, and to conserve angular momentum about the direction $\mathbf{p}_\mu$, the $\mu$-meson must also have negative helicity. This $\mu^+$ meson longitudinal polarization appears to be strongly maintained in the slowing-down process and in some materials (electrical conductors, mainly) is maintained until decay; thus the depolarization time must be long compared with the decay lifetime. The observed decay asymmetry is such that if the two-component theory is correct, the positron from $\mu^+$ decay is emitted preferentially in the direction of $\mathbf{s}_\mu$.

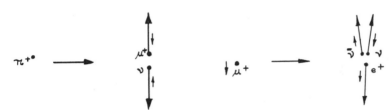

FIG. 11.5. Diagram showing the configuration of spins and momenta in positive pi-meson decay. (The large arrows indicate momenta, the small arrows indicate spins. The unattached horizontal arrow indicates the direction of the decay reaction.)

FIG. 11.6. Diagram showing a preferred configuration of spins and momenta in mu-meson decay. (The large arrows indicate momenta, the small arrows indicate spins. The unattached horizontal arrow indicates the direction of the decay reaction.)

The positron spectrum of $\mu^+$ decay is strongly peaked towards the maximum energy so that most likely decay configuration is for the positron to be emitted in the direction $\mathbf{s}_\mu$, whilst the neutrino and antineutrino are both emitted in the opposite direction, $-\mathbf{s}_\mu$. This momentum configuration is shown in Fig. 11.6. The neutrino and antineutrino spins cancel, if the two-component theory is correct, and the positron is emitted with positive helicity. In fact, the positron helicity is opposite to the helicity of the neutrino emitted in the original $\pi^+$ decay and a measurement of the positron helicity will be a measure of that neutrino helicity, assuming the conservation of leptons and the two-component theory. Two results are available, due to Macq et al. (1958) and to Culligan et al. (1959). They find that the positron is right-hand polarized (positive helicity) and consequently that the neutrino has negative helicity. The fact that this agrees with the neutrino helicity assignment of Goldhaber et al. (Section 11.6) adds considerable weight to the validity of the assumptions we have made in performing this analysis. Similar considerations apply to the decay chain

$$\pi^- \to \mu^- + \bar{\nu},$$

$$\mu^- \to e^- + \nu + \bar{\nu}.$$

The electron has $\mp$ helicity as the antineutrino has $\pm$ helicity. The electron is observed to be left-hand polarized ($-$ helicity) (Macq et al. 1958; Culligan et al., 1959) so that the antineutrino has positive helicity.

We can briefly examine the interaction Lagrangian density for the $\mu$-meson decay:

$$\mathscr{L}_I = \sum_r \{ D_r(\bar{\psi}_\nu O_r \psi_\mu)(\bar{\psi}_e O_r \psi_\nu) + D'_r(\bar{\psi}_\nu O_r \psi_\mu)(\bar{\psi}_e O_r \gamma_5 \psi_\nu) \}$$
$$+ \text{Hermitian conjugate.} \tag{11.36}$$

The terms under the summation are responsible for $\mu^-$ decay as $\psi$ destroys the $\mu$-lepton. The Hermitian conjugate terms are responsible for the $\mu^+$ decay.

The two-component theory of the neutrino requires that $D_r = D$ and causes the S, T, and P interactions to be zero (Lee and Yang 1957). The Lagrangian reduces to

$$\mathscr{L}_I = (\bar{\psi}_\nu \gamma_\rho (D_V - D_A \gamma_5) \psi_\mu)(\bar{\psi}_e \gamma_\rho (1 + \gamma_5) \psi_\nu)$$
$$+ \text{Hermitian conjugate.} \tag{11.37}$$

The two-component theory, which we signify by (a), is a rather considerable restriction to place upon the interaction. Several other neutrino possibilities have been considered (Larsen et al., 1957; Kinoshita and Sirlin, 1957):

(b) Two-component neutrino with nonconservation of leptons:

$$\mu^\pm \to e^\pm + \nu + \nu,$$

or

$$\mu^\pm \to e^\pm + \bar{\nu} + \bar{\nu}.$$

(c) Four-component neutrino with conservation of leptons, and all interactions:

$$\mu^\pm \to e^\pm + \nu + \bar{\nu}.$$

(d) Four-component neutrino with nonconservation of leptons and all interactions. Decay equation as under (b).

All these theories predict various observable properties of the $\mu$-decay process.

(1) The spectrum of electrons or positrons emitted in all directions
is given by

$$N(x)\,dx = \frac{12x^2\,dx}{\tau}\left\{(1-x)+\frac{2}{9}\rho(4x-3)\right\}$$

$x = \dfrac{E}{E_0}$ = electron energy divided by maximum electron energy
$\qquad (E_0 \simeq 53 \text{ Mev})$,

$\tau$ = mean life of $\mu$-meson,

$N(x)\,dx$ = number of electrons emitted per second in energy range
$\qquad x \to x + dx$,

$\rho$ = Michel parameter (Michel, 1950); it has the following
$\qquad$ values according to the four theories:

(a) $\rho = \frac{3}{4}$,

(b) $\rho = 0$,

(c) $0 \leqslant \rho \leqslant 1$,

(d) $0 \leqslant \rho \leqslant \frac{3}{4}$.

The observed value is $0.741 \pm 0.027$ (Dudziak *et al.*, 1959); the closeness
of this value to that required by (a) is strong evidence for the two-
component theory.

(2) The second quantity of interest is the decay asymmetry averaged
over all electron energies:

$$N(\Omega)\,d\Omega = \frac{1}{\tau}\frac{d\Omega}{4\pi}\left(1 \pm |\langle\boldsymbol{\sigma}\rangle_\mu|\frac{\xi}{3}\cos\theta\right). \tag{11.38}$$

$N(\Omega)\,d\Omega$ is the number of electrons (upper sign) or positrons (lower
sign) emitted per second into a solid angle $d\Omega$ about direction $\Omega$ which
makes an angle $\theta$ with the direction of the polarization. The theories
predict:

(a) and (b) $\qquad \xi = \dfrac{2\,\mathrm{Re}\,D_V^* D_A}{|D_V|^2 + |D_A|^2}$, that is, $0 \leqslant |\xi| \leqslant 1$;

(b) $\qquad 0 \leqslant |\xi| \leqslant 3 - \frac{2}{3}\rho$;

(c) $\qquad 0 \leqslant |\xi| \leqslant 3 - \frac{8}{3}\rho$.

The observed value of $|\langle \sigma \rangle_\mu| \xi/3$ is $0.325 \pm 0.015$ (Bardon *et al.*, 1959) which gives $|\xi| \geqslant 0.97 \pm 0.05$. The sign of the decay asymmetry is not immediately known with respect to the $\mu$-meson spin direction measurements show that electron or positron are preferentially ejected against the direction of incidence of the $\mu$-meson (Garwin *et al.*, 1957) The two-component theory predicts that the $\mu$-meson from $\pi$-decay will have:

$\mu^+$ negative helicity,

$\mu^-$ positive helicity.

Combining this with the signs in Eq. (11.38), we find that the equation predicts the observed asymmetry if $\xi$ is negative. Hence if the interaction is time reversal invariant, we find that

$$D_A \simeq - D_V.$$

This is the same property as is possessed by the nuclear $\beta$-decay coupling constants.

The two-component theory predicts that the helicity of positrons (or electrons) from an unpolarized source of $\mu$-mesons is $-\xi$ ($+\xi$). The polarization measurements we have quoted show that if this theory is correct, $\xi$ is indeed negative, but the accuracy of the measurements is insufficient to check that $|\xi| = 1$, as required by the theory.

(3) A third quantity of interest is the parameter $\delta$ which describes the variation of decay asymmetry with energy:

$$N(x, \Omega)\, dx\, d\Omega = \frac{3x^2\, dx\, d\Omega}{\tau} \left\{ (1-x) + \frac{2\rho}{9}(4x-3) \mp \frac{\xi}{3}\cos\theta \right.$$
$$\left. \times \left[ (1-x) + \frac{2\delta}{3}(4x-3) \right] \right\}. \tag{11.39}$$

The symbols have the same meaning as before with $N(x, \Omega)$ now the electron intensity, differentiated with respect to energy and solid angle. In the four theories $\delta$ has the values:

(a) $\delta = \frac{3}{4}$;

(b) $\delta = 0$;

(c) and (d) $|\xi\delta| \leqslant \rho$.

At the time of writing most of the experimental results are very inaccurate. However, Kruger and Crowe (1958) find $\delta = 0.65$ ($+0.05$ $-0.10$) and Plano (Kiev Conf., 1959) finds $\delta = 0.78 \pm 0.02$. These results are close to that required by the two-component theory.

(4) The final quantity of interest is the actual lifetime of the free $\mu$-meson, but this can only be calculated if some value is inserted for the coupling constants $D_A$ and $D_V$. We can assume, for the present, the existence of a universal $\beta$-decay interaction characterized by a certain coupling constant. If the interaction involves nucleons, this constant must be renormalized as indicated in Section 11.6, but this only affects $C_A$; hence we put

$$ -D_A = D_V = C_V. $$

A value for $C_V$ is found from the pure Fermi transition

$$ O^{14} \rightarrow N^{14} + e^+ + \nu. $$

It is $\sqrt{2}\,C_V = (1.41 \pm 0.01) \times 10^{-49}$ erg cm$^3$ (Gerhart, 1954). This gives a value for the mean life of the free $\mu$-meson (Kinoshita and Sirlin, 1959)

$$ \tau = (2.27 \pm 0.04) \times 10^{-6} \text{ sec.} $$

The observed lifetime is (Fischer et al., 1959; Swanson et al., 1959)

$$ \tau = (2.22 \pm 0.02) \times 10^{-6} \text{ sec.} $$

The agreement is good and is the basis for the concept of a universal interaction discussed in the next section.

In the preceding discussion we have neglected the effects of radiative corrections to these parameters: the electromagnetic interaction causes the real parameters to deviate slightly from the values predicted by the simple theory. These effects have been discussed by Berman (1958) and by Kinoshita and Sirlin (1959); as an example they find that $\mu$-meson lifetime will be 2.31 $\mu$sec if calculated from the $O^{14}$ results. The discrepancy, if any, with the observed lifetime has still to be clarified.

Taken all together the $\mu$-meson decay properties are good evidence for the two-component neutrino theory and lepton conservation. A reliable measurement of the helicity of $\mu$-mesons from $\pi$-meson decay would help to confirm, or otherwise, these hypotheses. A measurement by Love et al. (1959) suggests that the $\mu^-$ has positive helicity as required by the two-component theory.

## 11.9 The Universal Fermi Interaction (I)

At the end of the last section we found that the coupling constants of $\beta$-decay were very close to the coupling constants of $\mu$-meson decay. This gives rise to the concept of a universal V–A interaction which couples four fermion fields with a strength which is independent of the type of Fermi particles involved, apart from some renormalization effects due to strong interactions. Further evidence for this concept comes from data on the forced decay of the negative $\mu$-meson

$$\mu^- + p \to n + \nu.$$

This has been extensively observed in complex nuclei but it is difficult to interpret as the nuclear matrix elements are not known in most cases due to the transition taking place to excited nuclear states. However, the coupling constant is almost certainly of the same magnitude as that in the $\beta$-decay interaction. There is one reaction which does permit a direct comparison with the $\beta$-decay interaction,

$$\mu^- + C^{12} \to B^{12} + \nu,$$

followed by

$$B^{12} \to C^{12} + e^- + \bar\nu.$$

There are no excited states of $B^{12}$ and at first sight it appears that the nuclear matrix elements are the same; however, the neutrino emitted after $\mu^-$ absorption has a very short wavelength and higher-order transitions become important. If this effect is neglected, it is found that (Argo *et al.*, 1959)

$$|C_{\mathrm{GT}}|_\beta = |C_{\mathrm{GT}}|_\mu,$$

where $|C_{\mathrm{GT}}|_\mu$ is the magnitude of a coupling constant appropriate to the forced decay of the $\mu$-meson. The Lagrangian density for the universal interaction is

$$\mathscr{L}_I = C(\bar\psi_3 \gamma_\rho (1 + \gamma_5)\psi_1)(\bar\psi_4 \gamma_\rho (1 + \gamma_5)\psi_2) + \text{Hermitian conjugate}$$

FIG. 11.7. The Feynman diagram for the four-fermion interaction.

where $C$ is of the order of $10^{-49}$ erg cm³. The Feynman diagram is shown in Fig. 11.7 and the reaction is

$$1 + 2 \to 3 + 4,$$

which must be consistent with the conservation of leptons and of nucleons. The effect of other interactions between the particles involved will be to alter the coupling constant; thus in ordinary $\beta$-decay $|C_{\mathrm{GT}}| \neq |C_{\mathrm{F}}|$, due to meson interactions between the two nucleons involved. Apart from such effects this universal interaction correctly describes the following reactions and their variants:

$$n \to p + e^- + \nu,$$

$$p \to n + e^+ + \bar{\nu},$$

$$\mu^\pm \to e^\pm + \nu + \bar{\nu},$$

$$\mu^- + p \to n + \nu.$$

This list does not exhaust the reactions which the universal interaction can cause. The charged $\pi$-meson decay is believed to be due to this interaction operating on the virtual nucleon–anti-nucleon state into which the $\pi$-meson dissociates. A first-order Feynman diagram is shown in Fig. 11.8. The decay rate is zero unless the four-fermion interaction is P or A. The actual calculation is done in perturbation theory and the series is found to be divergent: a finite result is obtained if a cutoff is applied but this result is good only in as far as this procedure has meaning (Gell-Mann and Rosenfeld, 1957). A more important property of $\pi$-mesons concerns their decay:

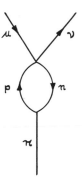

$$\pi^+ \to e^+ + \nu,$$

$$\pi^- \to e^- + \bar{\nu}.$$

FIG. 11.8. A Feynman diagram for $\pi^+$-meson decay.

A corresponding Feynman diagram is the same as that of Fig. 11.7 with $\mu^\pm$ replaced by $e^\pm$. Again, it is not possible to calculate the decay rate but is possible to calculate the ratio for the decay rates

$$R = \frac{\omega(\pi^+ \to e^+ + \nu)}{\omega(\pi^+ \to \mu^+ + \nu)},$$

and the result is independent of the order to which perturbation calculation is carried and therefore of any cutoff which is applied (Ruderman and Finkelstein, 1949). The results are:

V–A interaction, $R = 1.28 \times 10^{-4}$;

P interaction, $R = 5.48.$

The observed rate is $1.22 \pm 0.30 \times 10^{-4}$ (Ashkin et al., 1959a), which is in excellent agreement with the universal interaction. The P interaction

result is wrong by almost five orders of magnitude which confirm
our neglect of this interaction.

As postulated, the universal interaction neither conserves parity no
makes restrictions as to the type of fermions involved. These usefu
properties allow us to extend the scope of the interaction so as t
include the decay of strange particles in which parity is not conserved
we shall discuss this situation in detail in Section 12.12. However, th
interaction does not necessarily include neutrinos and the two
component theory becomes superfluous; in fact, the interaction i
specified as $O_r = O'_r = \gamma_\rho (1 + \gamma_5)$ rather than as V–A with a two
component neutrino $(1 + \gamma_5)\psi_\nu$. This interaction is such that an

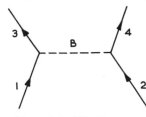

FIG. 11.9. The Feynman
diagram for the four-
fermion interaction via the
intermediary of a vector
boson $B$.

neutrinos (antineutrinos) which are involve
always have negative (positive) helicity whic
gives us the observed two-component natur
to the massless neutrino. The same woul
be true for the electrons and positrons pro
duced in $\beta$-decay if they were massless; w
would always observe negative helicit
electrons and positive helicity positrons
Thus all the consequences of a two
component neutrino theory are still valid bu
the theory is redundant apart from its us
in making simple deductions concerning th

helicities of the particles produced in various decays. The clarificatio
of the status of a universal interaction awaits an understanding of th
mechanisms which are operating in strange particle decays.

The universal interaction predicts several reactions which have no
been observed; for example,

$$\mu^\pm \to e^\pm + e^+ + e^-, \tag{11.40}$$

$$\mu^- + p \to e^- + p. \tag{11.41}$$

There is no apparent reason for the suppression of these reactions
They do not occur if we require that each covariant in the interactio
Lagrangian contains only one charged particle field variable.

We note before leaving this section that the four-fermion inter
action could be due to the exchange of a very heavy boson—as i
Fig. 11.9. This boson would have to be very much heavier than th
proton. If this is the true state of affairs, this boson will be produce
at very high energies or will manifest itself in very high-energy reac
tions due to the universal interaction. The cross sections for thes
reactions increases as the square of the momentum of the final-stat

articles in the centre of mass, probably up to about $10^{-38}$ cm$^2$ at Gev; above that energy it is likely that form factor effects will prevent further increase (Lee and Yang, 1960). For example, at very high energies the reaction

$$e^- + p \rightarrow n + \nu$$

would be more likely than elastic electromagnetic scattering in some lepton scattering angle ranges. A measurement of cross sections might detect the presence of a heavy boson exchange. If this boson has no

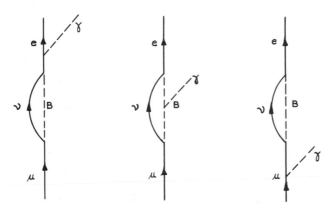

FIG. 11.10. Feynman diagrams for the decay $\mu^+ \rightarrow e^+ + \gamma$. $B$ indicates the intermediate vector boson.

uncharged member, the reactions of Eqs. (11.40) and (11.41) cannot take place as required. However, the charged intermediate boson does not prevent the decay

$$\mu^+ \rightarrow e^+ + \gamma,$$

which is not observed (Ashkin *et al.*, 1959b). This decay occurs in lowest order by the Feynman diagrams of Fig. 11.10. By considering the nature of the neutrinos involved we see that it is forbidden if the $\mu^+$ meson is a lepton instead of an antilepton. The $\mu$-decay is then

$$\mu^+ \rightarrow e^+ + 2\nu.$$

This is not supported by the observed value of the Michel parameter. These difficulties serve to indicate the problems associated with weak interactions which still remain to be resolved and perhaps to draw attention to that unusual particle, the $\mu$-meson.

## 11.10 Time Reversal Invariance in Beta Decay

The only appreciable interaction among the final-state products of $\beta$-decay is the Coulomb interaction; if we can neglect this force, the

observation of a decay rate depending upon a quantity which is odd
under time reversal serves to detect the effect of any noninvariance
under $T$. All angular and linear momenta change sign under $T$ and
odd quantities are such as

$$\boldsymbol{\sigma} \cdot (\mathbf{p}_1 \times \mathbf{p}_2),$$

$$\mathbf{p} \cdot (\boldsymbol{\sigma}_1 \times \boldsymbol{\sigma}_2).$$

For example, $\boldsymbol{\sigma} \cdot (\mathbf{p}_1 \times \mathbf{p}_2)$ could be a correlation between the spin direction $\boldsymbol{\sigma}$ of a decaying nucleus and the plane $(\mathbf{p}_e \times \mathbf{p}_N)$ defined by the
decay electron and recoil nucleus. The correlation is proportional to
terms such as $\mathrm{Im}\, C_V^* C_A$ which are zero for a time-reversal invariant
interaction. (We recall that the coupling constants are all real, apart
from a common phase factor, in such an interaction.) The experiment
of Burgy et al. (1958) mentioned in Section 11.5 is of this kind. Other
experiments have been proposed and discussed by Jackson et al. (1957)

If we include the effects of the final-state Coulomb interaction we
find that terms depending on any complex part of the coupling constants (e.g., $\mathrm{Im}\, C_V^* C_A$) appear in expressions for the decay asymmetries
and for the lepton helicities, although these are connected with quantities which are even under time reversal. However, these terms are
proportional to $Z/137$ and are certainly small, facts which make the
detection of imaginary parts of the coupling constants very difficult.
On the other hand, the Coulomb interaction causes the appearance of
terms odd under $T$, e.g., $\boldsymbol{\sigma} \cdot (\mathbf{p}_1 \times \mathbf{p}_2)$ even though the coupling constants
are real (Gell-Mann and Rosenfeld, 1957); again, any noninvariance
under $T$ is small and to separate such an effect from the effects of the
Coulomb interaction requires a high degree of experimental accuracy
in measurements renowned for their difficulty. At the time of writing
there exists no evidence for a noninvariance under time reversal.

For lack of evidence to the contrary we have taken the interaction
to be invariant under $T$. Since it must be invariant under $CPT$, it is
also invariant under $CP$, although we know that it is not invariant
under $C$ or $P$ separately. The $CP$ invariance allows us to make the
following type of statement: although the mirror image of a system
of particles is not a permitted state ($P$ noninvariance), the mirror
image of the system in antiparticles is a permitted state. Thus the
preferred decay of a $Co^{60}$ nucleus ejects an electron against the direction
of the nuclear spin angular momentum, whilst the preferred decay of
an anti-$Co^{60}$ nucleus would eject a positron along the direction of the
nuclear spin. Similar statements can be made concerning meson
decays.

## 11.11 Conclusion

At the time of writing our knowledge of weak interactions is far from complete. We have mentioned that it appears that weak interactions are involved in the decay of strange particles and in this field there are several problems to be resolved. This chapter therefore continues in Section 12.12 where this subject is discussed in detail; in addition, we shall introduce some recent speculations upon weak interactions which are currently receiving examination.

# CHAPTER XII

# STRANGE PARTICLES

## 12.1 Introduction

In this chapter we shall discuss some of the properties of strange particles which are the members of a group of unstable elementary particles first observed in cosmic radiation. We have restricted the discussion to those properties which reveal some aspect of particle physics which has not occurred earlier in this book. In addition this chapter tries to place these particles within the context of the complete group of elementary particles.

## 12.2 Nomenclature

A most important point occurs immediately; why should a group of particles deserve the adjective "strange"? These particles were first observed in cosmic radiation and in Fig. 12.1 we reproduce a cloud chamber photograph of the production and decay of one of these particles. The general nature of such photographs indicates that the correct interpretation of the $V$ event is that a neutral particle was produced in the high-energy interaction in the metal plate and after travelling several centimetres decayed into two oppositely charged particles. The rate at which such events was observed indicated that the production cross section was of the order of $10^{-28}$ cm$^2$, which is the order of magnitude associated with strong interactions. Such interactions take place in time of about $10^{-23}$ sec, i.e., the proton radius divided by the velocity of light. At first it was presumed that such particles were produced by reactions such as

$$\pi^- + p \to \Lambda^0 + \pi^0, \tag{12.1}$$

where $\Lambda^0$ was the symbol given to the neutral particle. The distance moved by the particle before decay indicated that its half-life was of the order of $10^{-10}$ sec. One of the decay channels observed was

$$\Lambda^0 \to \pi^- + p. \tag{12.2}$$

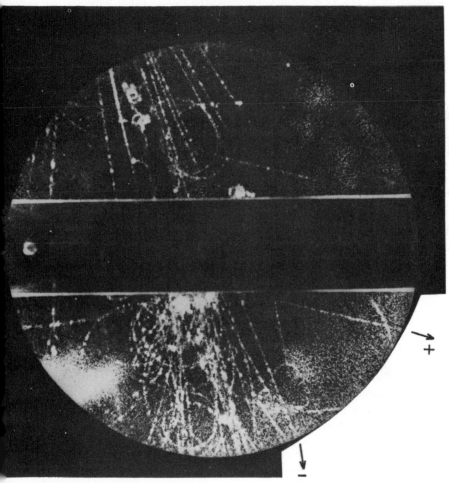

FIG. 12.1. A cloud chamber photograph of the production and decay of a neutral strange particle. It was produced in one of the nuclear interactions which have occurred in the metal plate placed across the chamber and has decayed below the plate into two charged particles. (Rochester and Butler, 1947.)

If (12.1) is the fast ($10^{-23}$ sec) production process, then the following virtual reactions are also fast,

$$\Lambda^0 \to \pi^- + p + \pi^0,$$

followed by Yukawa absorption of the $\pi^0$ by the proton

$$\pi^- + p + \pi^0 \to \pi^- + p.$$

Therefore if (12.1) is fast, then reaction (12.2) must also be fast, and the fact that the decay takes $10^{-10}$ sec instead of an expected $10^{-23}$ sec is a considerable anomaly. It is this which gave these particles the qualification "strange".

TABLE 12.1

THE STRANGE PARTICLES

| | Mass[a] $m_e$ | Half-life[a] (sec) | Spin | Strange-ness | Isotopic spin $t$ | $t_3$ |
|---|---|---|---|---|---|---|
| Mesons | | | | | | |
| $K^+$ | 967 | $1.22 \times 10^{-8}$ | | $+1$ | $\frac{1}{2}$ | $+\frac{1}{2}$ |
| $K^0$ | 973 | — | $0$ | $+1$ | $\frac{1}{2}$ | $-\frac{1}{2}$ |
| $K^-$ | 967 | $1.22 \times 10^{-8}$ | | $-1$ | $\frac{1}{2}$ | $-\frac{1}{2}$ |
| $\overline{K^0}$ | 973 | — | | $-1$ | $\frac{1}{2}$ | $+\frac{1}{2}$ |
| Hyperons | | | | | | |
| $\Lambda^0$ | 2182 | $2.77 \times 10^{-10}$ | | | $0$ | $0$ |
| $\Sigma^+$ | 2328 | $0.83 \times 10^{-10}$ | $\frac{1}{2}$ | $-1$ | $1$ | $+1$ |
| $\Sigma^0$ | 2330 | $< 10^{-11}$ | | | | $0$ |
| $\Sigma^-$ | 2342 | $1.72 \times 10^{-10}$ | | | | $-1$ |
| $\Xi^0$ | 2579 | $\sim 10^{-10}$ | ? | $-2$ | $\frac{1}{2}$ | $+\frac{1}{2}$ |
| $\Xi^-$ | 2583 | $\sim 2 \times 10^{-10}$ | ? | | | $-\frac{1}{2}$ |

[a] For more accurate data (with errors) see Appendix D.

We shall not discuss the careful experimental work which established the existence of the various strange particles. Interested readers are referred to the reviews by Rochester and Butler (1953) and by Dalitz (1957). In Table 12.1 we list these particles and their most important properties. We have omitted the antihyperons as their corresponding properties are easily derived and at the time of writing only the $\overline{\Lambda^0}$ has been observed.

At this point we define some further generic names for particle groups. Mesons are those particles intermediate in mass between electron and proton; the $K$ and $\pi$ mesons are the boson members of this group. Baryons are all those fermions which have a mass equal to or greater than that of the proton. The hyperons are the baryons which are heavier than the nucleons and are therefore strange particles. Antibaryons include the antiproton and antineutron, which have been observed, and the antihyperons.

The law of conservation of baryons has never been observed to be broken; it states that the number of baryons less the number of antibaryons is a conserved quantity; thus we attribute to every baryon a baryon number 1, and to every antibaryon a baryon number $-1$, and require the total baryon number to be conserved. We notice the close similarity to the lepton conservation law.

## 12.3 Associated Production

The prolonged decay behaviour of the strange particles suggests that some mechanism is inhibiting decay. Early in the history of these particles it was suggested that they possessed a very large intrinsic angular momentum and that the decay was retarded by the angular momentum barrier. The alternative, suggested by Pais (1952), is that strange particles possess some internal degree of freedom specified by a quantum number, which we call strangeness, and that various selection rules based upon the conservation or nonconservation of strangeness are operating in the production and decay. The retarded decay suggests that this process takes place through an interaction which does not conserve strangeness; this interaction appears to be very weak. On the other hand, the strong interaction responsible for production is supposed to conserve strangeness and it follows that the production of one strange particle is impossible and that two of opposite strangeness must be produced in the same interaction. This hypothesis of associated production is confirmed by the observation of two $V$ particles in the same cloud chamber photograph more often than the expected accidental coincidence rate.

Taking the strangeness assignments given in Table 12.1, we can give examples of reactions which conserve strangeness, baryon number, and electric charge; thus

$$\left.\begin{aligned}
\pi^- + p &\to K^+ + \Sigma^-, \\
\pi^- + p &\to K^0 + \Sigma^0 \text{ (or } \Lambda^0), \\
\gamma + p &\to K^+ + \Sigma^0 \text{ (or } \Lambda^0), \\
\gamma + p &\to K^0 + \Sigma^+.
\end{aligned}\right\} \tag{12.3}$$

These reactions have been observed. Reactions such as

$$\left.\begin{aligned}
\pi^- + p &\to K^- + \Sigma^+, \\
n + n &\to \Lambda^0 + \Lambda^0,
\end{aligned}\right\} \tag{12.4}$$

do not conserve strangeness; they have not been observed.

Let us now examine these strangeness assignments in detail. Such assignments were, of course, preceded by the observation of reactions such as (12.3) and by the concept of associated production. We proceed by considering the isotopic spin assignments to the mesons and baryons. The electric charge $Q$ in units of $e$, the electron charge, is given by

$$Q = t_3 + \tfrac{1}{2}U \qquad (12.5)$$

where $U$ is some integer number; for example, it is 0 for pi-mesons and 1 for nucleons. Now let us consider the reaction

$$\pi^- + p \to K^+ + \Sigma^-$$

which is observed. This satisfies the laws of conservation of charge and baryon number. The isotopic spin quantum numbers of the initial state are $t = \tfrac{1}{2}$ or $\tfrac{3}{2}$, $t_3 = -\tfrac{1}{2}$.‡ If we assume charge independence, then the final state must also have $t = \tfrac{1}{2}$ or $\tfrac{3}{2}$, which implies that either the $K$ or the $\Sigma$ particle belongs to a multiplet of half-odd integer isotopic spin. The $\Sigma$ hyperon has three charge states and to it we can assign $t = 1$, $U = 0$, so that $\Sigma^-$ has $t_3 = -1$; from this it follows that the $K^+$ must have $t_3 = +\tfrac{1}{2}$ and could belong to a doublet, $t = \tfrac{1}{2}$, $U = 1$. Compared to the pi-meson, this is an unusual assignment for a meson, as we might expect that the $K^+, K^0$ and $K^-$ belong to a triplet; however it appears that there are two types of neutral $K$ meson with opposite strangeness (Section 12.8), $K^0$ and $\overline{K^0}$, so that $K^+, K^0$ is one doublet and $\overline{K^0}, K^-$ is a second doublet. The first has $U = 1$; the second has $U = -1$. If the two types of neutral meson had not been observed it would still be impossible to interchange the doublet triplet assignments between $K$ and $\Sigma$. For example, suppose the $\Sigma$ was a doublet $(\Sigma^-, \Sigma^0)$. We would expect that the $\Sigma^-$ was the baryon and $\Sigma^+$ its antibaryon, in which case the conservation of baryons would forbid the reaction

$$\pi^+ + p \to K^+ + \Sigma^+.$$

This reaction is observed; in addition, the $\Sigma^-$ and $\Sigma^+$ have unequal masses which precludes their being related by charge conjugation. Thus the proposed isotopic spin assignments at least lead to a scheme consistent with observation. By analysing the observed strange particle reactions in this manner Gell-Mann and Pais (1954) and Nishijima (1954) were able to assign values of $t$, $t_3$, and $U$ to all particles such that all the observed associated production reactions satisfied the

‡ In this chapter we will use $t$, $t_3$ to represent the isotopic spin quantum number both for an assembly of particles and for an individual particle. The meaning will be clear from the context.

conservation of $Q$ and of $t_3$. All the reactions of (12.3) satisfy these conservation laws, whilst the unobserved reactions such as those of (12.4) do not; the reader can verify these facts using the data presented in Table 12.1. For example,

$$\pi^- + p \to K^- + \Sigma^+,$$

$t_3$ values:

$$(-1) + (\tfrac{1}{2}) \neq (-\tfrac{1}{2}) + (+1).$$

This reaction conserves electric charge but not $t_3$ and is therefore forbidden. This illustrates the essence of the Gell-Mann–Nishijima scheme: the conservation of $t_3$ has a significance which is different from the conservation of charge $Q$. In $\pi$-meson physics conservation of $t_3$ meant the same as the conservation of $Q$; in the physics of strange particles this is no longer the case.

We can now examine the constant $U$ of Eq. (12.5); it has the values

$$\left.\begin{aligned}
U &= 1 && \text{for} \quad K^+, K^0, n, p, \overline{\Xi^-}, \overline{\Xi^0}, \\
U &= 0 && \text{for} \quad \Sigma, \overline{\Sigma}, \Lambda, \overline{\Lambda}, \pi, \\
U &= -1 && \text{for} \quad K^-, \overline{K^0}, \bar{n}, \bar{p}, \Xi^-, \Xi^0.
\end{aligned}\right\} \tag{12.6}$$

The Gell-Mann scheme puts

$$U = N + S, \tag{12.7}$$

where $N$ is the baryon number and $S$ is the strangeness of the particle involved. From (12.6) it follows that the strangeness quantum number assignments are

$$\left.\begin{aligned}
S &= -2 && \text{for} \quad \Xi^-, \Xi^0, \\
S &= -1 && \text{for} \quad \Sigma, \Lambda, \overline{K^0}, K^-, \\
S &= 0 && \text{for} \quad n, \bar{n}, p, \bar{p}, \pi, \\
S &= +1 && \text{for} \quad \overline{\Sigma}, \overline{\Lambda}, K^0, K^+, \\
S &= +2 && \text{for} \quad \overline{\Xi^-}, \overline{\Xi^0}.
\end{aligned}\right\} \tag{12.8}$$

Equation (12.5) becomes

$$Q = t_3 + \tfrac{1}{2}(N + S) \tag{12.9}$$

and we observe that the conservation of total charge, third component of total isotopic spin, and total baryon number also implies the conservation of total strangeness. This law of conservation of strangeness is simple and direct to apply and agrees exactly with the observations of associated production and other strange-particle strong interactions. All the reactions of (12.3) conserve strangeness.

The decays of strange particles manifestly do not obey the conservation of strangeness; for example,

$$K^+ \to \pi^+ + \pi^0,$$

$$\Sigma^- \to \pi^- + n.$$

We have observed that these decays have too long a half-life for the strong interactions to be responsible. Thus it appears that these strong interactions strictly conserve strangeness and that the decays must be

TABLE 12.2

CLASSIFICATION OF ELEMENTARY PARTICLES ACCORDING TO<br>BARYON NUMBER $N$ AND HYPERCHARGE $U$

| $N$ \ $U$ | $-1$ | $0$ | $+1$ |
|---|---|---|---|
| $+1$ | $\Xi^-, \Xi^0$ | $\Sigma^+, \Sigma^0, \Sigma^-, \Lambda^0$ | $n, p$ |
| $0$ | $K^-, \overline{K^0}$ | $\pi^+, \pi^0, \pi^-$ | $K^+, K^0$ |
| $-1$ | $\bar{n}, \bar{p}$ | $\overline{\Sigma^+}, \overline{\Sigma^0}, \overline{\Sigma^-}, \overline{\Lambda^0}$ | $\overline{\Xi^-}, \overline{\Xi^0}$ |

caused by a very much weaker strangeness nonconserving interaction. We shall examine these particle decays in more detail in Section 12.10.

The assignments of Eqs. (12.6) for the values of $U$ can be displayed in a fashion which is satisfactorily symmetric. This is shown in Table 12.2. d'Espagnat and Prentki (1956) call $U$ the hypercharge and attempt to connect it with the parity, $P_t = (i)^U$, in a three-dimensional isotopic spin space. Thus the $\Sigma$ and $\pi$ are pseudovectors in this space with even parity and $U = 0$, whilst the $\Lambda$ is a scalar with even parity and $U = 0$. The remaining particles are spinors of which there can be two kinds having $P_t = +i$ and $-i$ corresponding to $U = +1$ and $U = -1$ respectively. The scheme becomes ambiguous if $P_t = -1$ (pseudoscalars or vectors in isotopic spin space) as $U$ can be $+2$ or $-2$ and there is no way of deciding which is correct. No corresponding particles have been observed, so d'Espagnat and Prentki assume that $|U| \leqslant 1$. This is a very economical scheme but leaves room for the isotopic scalar boson which has not been observed (Baldin and Kabir, 1958).

Before closing this section we will examine one of the most interesting consequences of strangeness conservation, apart from associated production. It concerns the scattering and absorption reactions of the charged $K$ mesons by hydrogen and by neutrons; there are many more reaction channels open in the $K^-$ meson reactions than are open in the $K^+$ meson reactions. The following list of reactions in hydrogen illustrates this point:

$$\left.\begin{aligned}
K^+ + p &\to K^+ + p \\
K^- + p &\to K^- + p
\end{aligned}\right\} \text{ elastic scattering,}$$

$$\to \overline{K^0} + n \qquad \text{charge exchange scattering,}$$

$$\left.\begin{aligned}
&\to \Sigma^+ + \pi^- \\
&\to \Sigma^0 + \pi^0 \\
&\to \Sigma^- + \pi^+ \\
&\to \Lambda^0 + \pi^0 \\
&\to \Lambda^0 + \pi^0 + \pi^0 \\
&\to \Lambda^0 + \pi^+ + \pi^-
\end{aligned}\right\} \text{ strangeness exchange reactions.} \qquad (12.10)$$

All these channels are open for incident $K$-meson kinetic energies greater than 7 Mev and all the strangeness exchange channels are open for $K^-$ mesons absorbed from Bohr-like orbits around protons (Alvarez et al., 1957). We have not included other reaction channels which open at higher incident energies (e.g., extra pi-meson production) or the double-exchange reactions such as

$$K^- + p \to K^0 + \Xi^0$$

(Alvarez et al., 1959). A similar list of reactions can be written for the case of a neutron target: the striking difference between $K^+$ and $K^-$ is maintained. We see that strangeness conservation allows the $K^-$ to produce hyperons by absorption in nucleons, whereas the $K^+$ cannot do this. This basic asymmetry in behaviour has the result that the mean free paths of the $K^+$ and $K^-$ meson are very different; for example, in photographic emulsions,

$K^+$: $\sim 95$ cm in the energy range $30 \to 120$ Mev (Lannutti et al., 1956),

$K^-$: $\sim 30$ cm in the energy range $16 \to 160$ Mev (Webb et al., 1958).

The mean free path for $K^-$ mesons corresponds to an interaction cross section equal to the geometrical area of the nuclei. This behaviour is in contrast to that of high-energy $\pi^+$ and $\pi^-$ mesons which both have mean free paths of approximately 30 cm.

## 12.4 The Conservation of Isotopic Spin

We have found that $t_3$ is conserved in the strong interactions involving strange particles. In addition, we expect these interactions to be charge-independent, that is, to conserve total isotopic spin. A large number of equalities and inequalities connecting strange-particle reaction cross sections have been derived, assuming charge-independence (Feldman, 1956). For example, consider the reactions:

$$(a)\ \ \pi^+ + p \rightarrow K^+ + \Sigma^+, \tag{12.11}$$

$$(b)\ \ \pi^- + p \rightarrow K^+ + \Sigma^-, \tag{12.12}$$

$$(c)\ \ \pi^- + p \rightarrow K^0 + \Sigma^0. \tag{12.13}$$

It is easy to confirm by the use of the methods used in Sections 6.5 and 7.7 that the following inequality holds if the interaction is charge-independent

$$\left(\frac{d\sigma_a}{d\Omega}\right)^{1/2} + \left(\frac{d\sigma_b}{d\Omega}\right)^{1/2} - \left(\frac{2d\sigma_c}{d\Omega}\right)^{1/2} \geqslant 0,$$

where the differential cross sections apply to the same centre of mass energy and angle. Crawford et al. (1959g) report some measurements of reactions (12.12) and (12.13) which they have combined with earlier measurements on reaction (12.11); the results satisfy the inequality.

There are simpler relations for some of the reactions which can occur when negative $K$-mesons are absorbed in helium (Lee, 1955):

$$(d)\ \ K^- + \mathrm{He}^4 \rightarrow \Sigma^- + \mathrm{He}^3,$$

$$(e)\ \ \ \ \ \ \ \ \ \ \ \ \ \ \rightarrow \Sigma^0 + \mathrm{H}^3,$$

$$(f)\ \ \ \ \ \ \ \ \ \ \ \ \ \ \rightarrow \Lambda^0 + \pi^- + \mathrm{He}^3,$$

$$(g)\ \ \ \ \ \ \ \ \ \ \ \ \ \ \rightarrow \Lambda^0 + \pi^0 + \mathrm{H}^3.$$

The cross sections are related,

$$\sigma_d = 2\sigma_e, \quad \sigma_f = 2\sigma_g.$$

At the time of writing insufficient data have been collected to test charge-independence by these helium reactions.

## 12.5 The Masses of the Elementary Particles

At the time of writing the latest tabulation of the masses and properties of the elementary particles is that of Shapiro (1956). A discussion of the methods used to measure these masses is outside the scope of this book and we shall content ourselves with discussing some of the features of the mass spectrum. We assume that particles and antiparticles have identical masses (Section 10.8).

The mass difference which exists within each isotopic multiplet can be attributed to the effect of the electromagnetic field associated with electric charge or magnetic moment. Thus the charged $\pi$-mesons are 4.5 Mev heavier than the uncharged $\pi$-meson, and this difference has a classical explanation which says that the charged meson is heavier than the uncharged by the work done in assembling the charge or, what is equivalent, by the integrated energy residing in the static electric field around the charge. Attempts have been made to calculate this mass shift using quantum electrodynamics, but it is necessary to introduce an arbitrary photon propagator cutoff in order to obtain the correct result (Feynman and Speisman, 1954). We expect that all spinless multiplets should behave in this way and it was therefore a considerable surprise when it was found that the uncharged $K$-meson is about 4 Mev heavier than the charged $K$-meson (Rosenfeld et al., 1959; Crawford et al., 1959b). This phenomenon probably reflects the greater complexity of the $K$-meson as compared with the $\pi$-meson; Matthews and Uretsky (1959) have suggested that the neutral $K$-meson has a charge distribution such as a positive cloud surrounding a negative core which is sufficient to cause the observed mass increase. In contrast the neutral $\pi$-meson is presumed to have zero charge density at all points.

The mass splitting becomes more complex in nature if the members of a multiplet have spin and anomalous magnetic moment. An anomalous moment without charge (e.g., neutron) appears to increase the mass; an anomalous moment with charge (e.g., proton) can contribute so as to decrease the mass. This could be the simple explanation of the fact that the neutron is heavier than the proton (Feynman and Speisman, 1954; Huang, 1956). However, this can only be a first-attempt explanation, for present-day theoretical techniques are inadequate to deal with a complex particle such as the nucleon with its strong meson interactions. These meson effects are probably responsible for the anomalous nucleon magnetic moments and therefore mass correction calculations should be based on a complete meson–nucleon theory.

We can at least present for examination the mass values for the hyperons (apart from the cascade hyperons):

| particle | mass (Mev) |
|----------|------------|
| $\Sigma^-$ | $1196.5 \pm 0.5$ |
| $\Sigma^0$ | $1190.5 \pm 1.0$ |
| $\Sigma^+$ | $1189.4 \pm 0.3$ |
| $\Lambda^0$ | $1115.2 \pm 0.14$ |

The mass of the $\Sigma^0$ lying between that of the $\Sigma^+$ and $\Sigma^-$ is a distinct feature of the splitting of this multiplet. There are no apparent reasons for this feature. The $\Lambda^0$ hyperon is about 75 Mev lighter than the $\Sigma^0$.

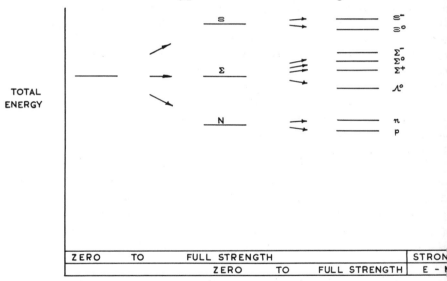

FIG. 12.2. A diagram showing how the level, representing the total energy of a simple baryon, could split as a strong interaction and the electromagnetic interaction are turned on.

The only other apparent difference between these particles lies in their total isotopic spin, 0 and 1 respectively; thus it is not clear whether this difference is electromagnetic in origin or otherwise. The masses of the cascade hyperons are not sufficiently well known to allow discussion of any mass differences which might exist.

It is evident that at present we are far from being able to calculate the mass differences within multiplets, let alone the mass spectrum.

However, attempts have been made to find empirical mass formulae (Guggenheimer, 1959; Sternglass, 1959) and there has been some discussion about the underlying symmetries which could exist and which could give the mass spectrum the broad features observed (Schwinger, 1956; Gell-Mann, 1957). Whatever the exact reasons are for mass differences within a multiplet, it is safe to assume that if the electromagnetic interaction could be turned off these multiplets would become degenerate; this degeneracy might even extend to the $\Sigma$ and $\Lambda$ hyperons since the existing difference expressed fractionally is comparable to the fractional difference within the $\pi$-meson multiplet. This degeneracy leaves three baryon states $\Xi$, $\Sigma(\Lambda)$, and $N$ (for nucleon). It is possible that these particles carry different values of some other "charge" representing the strength of an interaction; if this interaction is turned off, there would be a further degeneracy into the simple baryon. Meanwhile, the $K$- and $\pi$-mesons perhaps degenerate into a simple meson. The reverse procedure of turning on the interactions is shown in Fig. 12.2 and roughly corresponds to the splitting of atomic energy levels in a magnetic field. This is the type of discussion which has been given, and although it is of great importance it is too speculative to pursue in detail in this book.

## 12.6 Survey of Hyperon Properties

In this section we review briefly some of the properties of the hyperons; a few of these properties will be discussed under more general headings in later sections of this chapter.

### a. *Lambda Hyperon*

We have given several examples [see reactions under (12.3) and (12.10)] of reactions in which $\Lambda^0$ hyperons are produced. The $\Lambda^0$ has a half-life of $2.77 \pm 0.15 \times 10^{-10}$ sec (Gell-Mann and Rosenfeld, 1957) and the decay channels:

$$\Lambda^0 \rightarrow \pi^- + p \qquad \text{branching ratio } 0.627 \pm 0.030$$

$$\rightarrow \pi^0 + n \qquad\qquad\qquad 0.33 \ \pm 0.07$$

$$\rightarrow e^- + \bar{\nu} + p \qquad\qquad\quad < 0.003$$

$$\rightarrow \mu^- + \bar{\nu} + p \qquad\qquad\quad < 0.001.$$

The branching ratio data for the charged pi-meson channel come from an averaging of several results (Crawford *et al.*, 1959e) and for the uncharged meson from xenon bubble chamber data (Glaser, 1959). The leptonic decay modes data come from hydrogen bubble chamber data; two electron decays have been observed (Crawford *et al.*, 1958b; Nordin *et al.*, 1958) but as yet no mu-meson decays have been observed. We shall discuss these decay branching ratios as manifestation of a $\Delta t = \frac{1}{2}$ selection rule in Section 12.10.

Parity is not conserved in the decay of $\Lambda^0$; this is indicated by the existence of an up-down decay asymmetry in the charged pi-meson

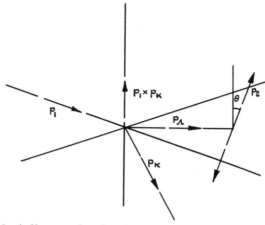

Fig. 12.3. A diagram showing the geometry of $\Lambda^0$ hyperon production and decay.

channel. The sample of $\Lambda^0$ hyperon is polarized in the production reaction

$$\pi^- + p \rightarrow K^0 + \Lambda^0,$$

with polarization vector perpendicular to the production plane defined by the normal vector $\mathbf{p}_1 \times \mathbf{p}_\Lambda$. $\mathbf{p}_1$ is the momentum vector of the incident pi-meson and $\mathbf{p}_\Lambda$ is the momentum of the produced $\Lambda^0$. We call $\mathbf{p}_2$ the momentum (in hyperon rest frame) of the pi-meson in the $\Lambda^0$ decay

$$\Lambda^0 \rightarrow \pi^- + p,$$

and put $\theta$ equal to the angle between the direction $\mathbf{p}_1 \times \mathbf{p}_\Lambda$ and $\mathbf{p}_2$ (Fig. 12.3). If $\cos\theta > 0$, we say that this is an "up" decay, whilst $\cos\theta < 0$ is a "down" decay. The angular distribution of decay mesons is given by

$$N(\cos\theta)\, d(\cos\theta) = \tfrac{1}{2}\{1 + \alpha\,|\langle\boldsymbol{\sigma}\rangle_\Lambda|\cos\theta\}\, d(\cos\theta)$$

where $|\langle\boldsymbol{\sigma}\rangle_\Lambda|$ is the average polarization magnitude for the sample of $\Lambda^0$ hyperons and $\alpha$ is the parity mixing parameter. We have discussed and derived $\alpha$ in terms of the $S$ and $P$ wave decay amplitudes in

Section 10.5 for this case of $\Lambda^0$ decay.‡ The quantity normally observed is the up-down asymmetry

$$2\frac{U-D}{U+D} = \alpha|\langle\boldsymbol{\sigma}\rangle_\Lambda|$$

where $U$ and $D$ are the number of decays up and down respectively. A value of the decay asymmetry has been measured for the charged pi-meson decay only. The $\Lambda^0$ sample was produced by 1-Gev pi-mesons and the data were analysed assuming a likely angular distribution of the polarization generated in the production reaction. The result for the up-down asymmetry was $0.73 \pm 0.14$ (Crawford *et al.*, 1958a). The polarization and mixing parameter have magnitudes which are both less than or equal to one and this asymmetry indicates that either is equal to or greater than about 0.7.

The decay protons will be longitudinally polarized, and in the laboratory the $\Lambda^0$ motion transforms this polarization so that it has transverse component which can be detected (Appendix A.6). Boldt *et al.* (1958a) have detected this component by scattering and show that the proton helicity is negative. From our analysis of Section 10.5 this indicates that $\alpha$ [Eq. (10.9)] is negative. This means that the protons are produced preferentially against the direction of the lambda spin [Eq. (10.7)] and the pi-mesons are produced preferentially along the direction of the lambda spin.§

The mixing parameter for the neutral meson decay mode must be measured in a xenon bubble chamber which can detect the photons from $\pi^0$ decay. However, such a measurement requires a knowledge of the polarization of the lambda hyperons produced in the xenon; this is obtained by measuring the up-down asymmetry for a sample of charged meson decays in the same chamber. No results are available at the time of writing.

It is evident that the $\Lambda^0$ decay asymmetry is a very powerful $\Lambda^0$ polarization analyser and as such is sure to become a very useful tool in the analysis of high-energy interactions in which the $\Lambda^0$ is produced. For example, the existence of $\Lambda^0$ polarization in the production reaction

$$\pi^- + p \rightarrow K^0 + \Lambda^0$$

‡ The sign of $\alpha$ is not defined at this point as we do not know the direction of the lambda polarization.

§ The result of Boldt and collaborators has recently been contradicted by a result due to Birge and Fowler (1960) who find the proton helicity is positive. Care must be exercised in comparing the sign of our $\alpha$ [Eq. (10.9)] with the sign of the $\alpha$ given by these authors. Our $\alpha$ is defined for an angle $\theta$ [Eq. (10.7)] which is the supplement of the angle $\theta$ used to define their $\alpha$.

indicates that at least two partial waves are effective in this reaction. A measurement of this polarization, as a function of production angle, combined with angular distribution measurements will determine the phases and amplitudes of the partial waves in the final production state without ambiguity. Again, it will become possible to measure the gyromagnetic ratio of the lambda hyperon by observing the rotation of the asymmetry as a function of the hyperon lifetime in a very strong magnetic field ($\sim 10^5$ oersteds).

It may appear that we have assumed that the $\Lambda^0$ hyperon spin is $\frac{1}{2}$. This is true in the calculation of the decay distribution in terms of $S$ and $P$ wave amplitudes, as in Section 10.5. However, without making any assumptions except conservation of angular momentum, it is possible to use the observed decay distribution to place upper limits on the spin with a considerable degree of confidence. The method was proposed by Lee and Yang (1958) and depends upon the use of a certain test function of $\cos \theta$ whose average over the distribution must satisfy certain inequalities for a given spin assumption. For example: let $N(\cos \theta) \Delta(\cos \theta)$ be the number of decays observed having the pi-meson in the interval $\Delta(\cos \theta)$ and let $\xi$ be the average value of $\cos \theta$ for the sample, i.e., $\xi = \{[\Sigma \cos \theta N(\cos \theta)]/[\Sigma N(\cos \theta)]\}$, where $\Sigma$ indicates summation over all intervals $\Delta(\cos \theta)$. Lee and Yang show that $\xi$ must satisfy the following inequalities

$$-\frac{1}{2s_\Lambda + 1} \leqslant \xi \leqslant \frac{1}{2s_\Lambda + 1}$$

where $s_\Lambda$ is the hyperon spin in units of $\hbar$. If we assume the decay distribution is linear in $\cos \theta$, that is

$$N(\cos \theta) \propto (1 + a \cos \theta),$$

the inequalities become

$$-\frac{1}{6s_\Lambda} \leqslant \xi \leqslant \frac{1}{6s_\Lambda}.$$

Crawford *et al.* (1959c) have applied this method to a sample of 614 charged meson decays of the $\Lambda^0$ hyperon. Their experimental data satisfy the spin $\frac{1}{2}$ inequality, fail the spin $\frac{3}{2}$ inequality by 3.2 standard deviations and fail the spin $\frac{5}{2}$ inequality by 4.9 standard deviations. Spin $\frac{1}{2}$ is strongly indicated.

b. *Sigma Hyperons*

These fermions are members of an isotopic spin triplet state. We have already given several examples [(12.3) and (12.10)] of reactions in which $\Sigma$ hyperons are produced. The observed decay reactions of the charged $\Sigma$ hyperons are

$$\Sigma^+ \rightarrow \pi^+ + n,$$

$$\rightarrow \pi^0 + p,$$

and

$$\Sigma^- \rightarrow \pi^- + n.$$

The experimental data on the mean life are meagre: the $\Sigma^+$ appears to have a mean life of about $0.8 \times 10^{-10}$ sec, the $\Sigma^-$ a mean life of about $1.7 \times 10^{-10}$ sec. The $\Sigma^+$ decay branching ratios are 0.54 and 0.46 for the charged and uncharged pi-meson modes respectively with errors of about 10% (Alvarez et al., 1957). The neutral $\Sigma$ decays with a mean life less than $10^{-11}$ sec, through the reaction

$$\Sigma^0 \rightarrow \Lambda^0 + \gamma$$

(Alvarez et al., 1957). Presumably pi-meson plus nucleon decay modes are allowed but cannot compete with this fast decay channel.

All these $\Sigma$ decays satisfy $|\Delta S| = 1$. We expect that decays such as

$$\Sigma^+ \rightarrow e^+ + \nu + n,$$

$$\Sigma^+ \rightarrow \mu^+ + \nu + n,$$

which also satisfy this rule, can take place. In addition the following types of decay are energetically possible

$$\Sigma^+ \rightarrow e^+ + \nu + \Lambda^0,$$

$$\Sigma^- \rightarrow e^- + \bar{\nu} + \Sigma^0 \text{ (or } \Lambda^0).$$

None of these decays has been observed. The conditions of observation place upper limits on all the branching ratios of the order of 0.005 (Leitner et al., 1959).

A search has been made for up-down $\Sigma$ decay asymmetries in order to test parity conservation in the decay interaction. The $\Sigma^+$ decay into uncharged pi-meson mode is alone in showing any significant asymmetry. The observed values of a parity mixing parameter $\alpha$, multiplied by polarization, are as follows (Cool et al., 1959).

$$\Sigma^+ \rightarrow \pi^+ + n, \quad \alpha_+ |\langle \boldsymbol{\sigma} \rangle_\Sigma| = 0.02 \pm 0.07,$$

$$\Sigma^+ \rightarrow \pi^0 + p, \quad \alpha_0 |\langle \boldsymbol{\sigma} \rangle_\Sigma| = 0.70 \pm 0.30,$$

$$\Sigma^- \rightarrow \pi^- + n, \quad \alpha_- |\langle \boldsymbol{\sigma} \rangle_\Sigma| = 0.02 \pm 0.05 \text{ and } 0.06 \pm 0.05.$$

The $\Sigma$ were produced by 1.0 or 1.1 Gev $\pi^+$ or $\pi^-$ mesons in hydrogen. The $\Sigma^+$ were all observed under the same conditions and therefore the lack of asymmetry in the charged pi-meson decay mode is not due to lack of $\Sigma^+$ polarization. We shall discuss these values in Section 12.10 in connection with a suggested decay selection rule.

The large value of $\alpha_0$ suggests that the $\Sigma$ spin is $\frac{1}{2}$; however, this cannot be confirmed until a full Lee–Yang analysis can be performed. There is an alternative method for the determination of spin which depends upon the observation of the decay of $\Sigma$ hyperons produced when $K^-$ mesons are brought to rest and absorbed in hydrogen:

$$K^- + p \rightarrow \Sigma^+ + \pi^-,$$

$$K^- + p \rightarrow \Sigma^- + \pi^+.$$

As it is almost certain that the $K$-meson spin is zero (Section 12.7), we are able to apply simple conservation of angular momentum arguments to these reactions and any subsequent $\Sigma$ decays in flight. The $K^-$ mesons are absorbed from Bohr-like orbits around the protons; it is not immediately obvious that the orbit from which absorption takes place is an $S$-state orbit as in the case of the $\pi^-$ meson, because the greater mass of the $K$-meson contracts the wave function and sharply increases the $K$-meson density at the proton, thus causing us to expect a considerable absorption probability from orbits of higher angular momentum. However, before absorption the $K^-p$ atom is under the influence of the electric fields of the atoms through which it passes; the Stark effect causes transitions from states of high orbital momentum to $S$ states and gives a high probability of absorption from $S$ states (Day et al., 1959). It follows that the total angular momentum for the absorption reaction is $j = \frac{1}{2}$. We take the axis of quantization as that of the outgoing $\Sigma$, so that $j_z = \pm\frac{1}{2}$, depending upon the spin state of the absorbing proton. Whatever the relative orbital angular momentum final state, its component $l_z$ is zero, due to our choice of axis of quantization. Thus, if $s$ is the spin of the $\Sigma$, the final state has $s_z = j_z = \pm\frac{1}{2}$; this remains unaltered on transforming to the centre of mass of the $\Sigma$. If $s = \frac{1}{2}$ the $\Sigma$ are unpolarized and even in the presence of a decay asymmetry this sample of sigma hyperons produced by $K^-$ absorption will decay isotropically. If $s = \frac{3}{2}$, this sample is aligned (Section 8.2), i.e., the states having $s_z = +\frac{1}{2}$ and $s_z = -\frac{1}{2}$ are equally populated, whilst the states having $s_z = +\frac{3}{2}$ and $-\frac{3}{2}$ are unpopulated. Such an aligned sample gives a decay product distribution $1 + 3\cos^2\theta$. This result can be shown easily by decomposing the final decay states which have $j = s = \frac{3}{2}$, $j_z = \pm\frac{1}{2}$ into the vector sum of a pi-meson-proton orbital state having $l = 1$ with the proton spin $\frac{1}{2}$. To decide between these distributions the solid angle in the centre of mass of the decaying $\Sigma$ is divided into four equal parts, two equatorial and two polar, the pole being defined by the original $z$ axis. The ratio of decays into both polar angles to decays into the equatorial angles is unity for spin $\frac{1}{2}$ and $\frac{11}{5}$ for the spin $\frac{3}{2}$. The observed ratio is close to unity and excludes spin $\frac{3}{2}$ by 5 standard deviations for the $\Sigma^+$ and 3.6 standard deviations for the $\Sigma^-$ (Glaser, 1959). These decays must be observed for $\Sigma$ hyperons in flight; this is to avoid depolarization effects for $\Sigma^+$ at rest and by necessity in the case of $\Sigma^-$ for this particle is rapidly absorbed at rest:

$$\Sigma^- + p \to \Lambda^0 + n$$

or

$$\Sigma^- + p \to \Sigma^0 + n.$$

### c. *Cascade Hyperons*

Sufficient cascade hyperons have been observed to establish the existence of this doublet $\Xi^-$, $\Xi^0$. Several $\Xi^-$ have been observed in cosmic-ray work (Cowan, 1954) and Alvarez *et al.* (1959) have observed one example of the following reaction

$$K^- + p \to K^0 + \Xi^0.$$

This observation confirms the strangeness $-2$ assignment to the $\Xi$ doublet.

The observed decays are

$$\Xi^0 \to \Lambda^0 + \pi^0,$$

$$\Xi^- \to \Lambda^0 + \pi^-.$$

These decays, followed by the normal $\Lambda^0$ decay, give the adjective "cascade" to these hyperons. The half-life appears to be about $10^{-10}$ sec and the decay interaction does not conserve strangeness; the decay process

$$\Xi^0 \to \pi^- + p$$

has not been observed so it is possible that the decay interaction satisfies the selection rule $|\Delta S| = 1$. We expect that $\beta$-decay is possible; for example,

$$\Xi^- \to e^- + \bar{\nu} + \Lambda^0$$

but to date no such decays have been observed.

There is no information available on the spin of the cascade hyperons; spin $\frac{1}{2}$ is only a reasonable guess. Presumably as more $\Xi$ hyperons are observed, any decay asymmetry can be used in a Lee–Yang analysis to put an upper limit on the spin.

## 12.7 The Charged K-Mesons

The $K^+$ mesons are readily produced associated with hyperons in reactions involving strongly interacting particles; two examples of $K^+$ producing reactions are given under Section 12.3. The $K^-$ is not so readily produced since it has the same strangeness as the hyperons and it is impossible to conserve strangeness whilst conserving baryon number in $K$-meson plus hyperon associated production. It is likely that the most abundant source is double $K$-meson production; for example,

$$\pi^- + p \to K^+ + K^- + n.$$

This reaction has a much higher threshold energy than the usual $K$-meson and hyperon production reactions with the result that high-energy proton accelerators (6–10 Bev) produce $K^-$ beams which have only about $\frac{1}{30}$ the intensity of their $K^+$ beams of the same energy. The situation may change at higher energies as more final-state channels containing $K^-$ mesons open.

The mean life of $K^+$ mesons at rest in plastic scintillator has been measured to be $1.224(\pm 0.013) \times 10^{-8}$ sec (Alvarez et al., 1956; Fitch and Motley, 1957). The lifetime of the $K^-$ meson can only be measured in flight; the observed mean life, $1.25 \pm 0.11 \times 10^{-8}$ sec (Barkas, 1957), is consistent with the two charge states having the same mean life. We shall assume that the particles are connected by the operation of charge conjugation. The observed decay modes of the $K^+$ are:

| | |
|---|---|
| $K_{\pi 2}$ (or $\theta$) $\to \pi^+ + \pi^0$, | branching ratio 0.256 $\pm 0.017$, |
| $\tau \to \pi^+ + \pi^+ + \pi^-$, | 0.0566 $\pm 0.0030$, |
| $K_{\pi 3} \to \pi^+ + \pi^0 + \pi^0$, | 0.0170 $\pm 0.0032$, |
| $K_{\mu 2} \to \mu^+ + \nu$, | 0.588 $\pm 0.020$, |
| $K_{e3} \to e^+ + \nu + \pi^0$, | 0.0419 $\pm 0.0042$, |
| $K_{\mu 3} \to \mu^+ + \nu + \pi^0$, | 0.040 $\pm 0.008$. |

No other decay modes have been definitely identified although many are energetically possible. The nomenclature in this table comes from cosmic-ray research where many of these decays were first observed. It was not certain that all these decays were due to the same particle and they were classified according to the observed decay. The $\theta$ and $\tau$ decays have been discussed earlier in this book (Section 10.5); the remainder have subscripts on the $K$ which indicate the nature of the charged decay product (letters $\pi$, $\mu$, and $e$) and the total number of decay products (number). Within the experimental errors the masses of the parent particles in all these decays were the same; investigations with charged $K$-mesons produced at accelerators have confirmed that one particle alone is responsible.

Some of these decay modes deserve comment. The $\theta$ and $\tau$ modes cannot both occur for the same spin zero particle if the decay interaction is parity conserving (Section 10.5). The $K_{\mu 2}$ decay is parity-nonconserving for it is found that the decay $\mu^+$ shows exactly the same decay asymmetry as do $\mu^+$ mesons produced in $\pi^+$-meson decays. This is strong evidence that the $K_{\mu 2}$ has spin zero. The unobserved $K_{e2}$ mode should have a branching ratio of approximately $10^{-5}$ if the universal V–A Fermi interaction is operating in these decays; at present the upper limit on this branching ratio is $2 \times 10^{-2}$. We shall discuss the nonleptonic modes and a $\Delta t = \frac{1}{2}$ selection rule in Section 12.10. The leptonic modes will be discussed in connection with a universal weak interaction in Section 12.11.

The evidence for a zero spin assignment to the charged $K$-mesons is now considerable; it is as follows. (1) There is neither decay anisotropy for the $K_{\pi 2}$ decay nor up-down $K_{\mu 2}$ decay asymmetry with respect to the $K$-meson production plane. Such anisotropy and asymmetry will be observed if the $K$-mesons are polarized at production—which is very likely if they have spin. (2) The asymmetry in the decay of the $\mu^+$ meson produced in $K_{\mu 2}$ decay is strong evidence for spin zero $K$-meson. (3) The relative angular distribution of the three $\pi$ mesons in the $\tau$ decay indicates spin 0 or 2. (4) The absence of a decay mode,

$$K^+ \to \pi^+ + \gamma, \qquad (12.14)$$

indicates that the $K$-meson has spin zero. Dalitz (1955) calculates that this mode would compete strongly with observed modes if the $K$-meson spin were nonzero; it is forbidden if the spin is zero for it would be $0 \to 0$ transition (Section 4.7).

## 12.8 The Uncharged K-Mesons

The neutral $K$-mesons are very remarkable particles; the properties they exhibit are very unusual by the standards of classical physics and can only be satisfactorily interpreted by quantum theory. Up to this point we have taken for granted the existence of two neutral $K$-mesons, just as there are two neutral nucleons—the neutron and the antineutron. Let us examine the reasons for this. The conservation of $t_3$ (or of strangeness) requires that we assign to the $K$-mesons isotopic spin $\frac{1}{2}$ and that there be two qualities of neutral $K$-meson with opposite $t_3$; thus,

$$K\text{-meson doublet}: \qquad K^+ \quad \text{has} \quad t_3 = +\tfrac{1}{2},$$
$$K^0 \quad \text{has} \quad t_3 = -\tfrac{1}{2};$$
$$\text{anti-}K\text{-meson doublet}: \quad K^- \quad \text{has} \quad t_3 = -\tfrac{1}{2},$$
$$\overline{K^0} \quad \text{has} \quad t_3 = +\tfrac{1}{2}.$$

From Eq. (12.9) we see that this implies that the $K^+ K^0$ doublet has strangeness $+1$ and that the $K^- \overline{K^0}$ doublet has strangeness $-1$. It is essential that there be two neutral $K$-mesons of opposite strangeness; otherwise some unobserved reactions would be allowed. For example, the virtual process

$$n \to K^0 + \Lambda^0 \tag{12.15}$$

is due to a strong interaction and readily occurs. It follows that the process

$$\overline{K^0} + n \to \Lambda^0 \tag{12.16}$$

also readily occurs. In rearranging (12.15) the $K$-meson ($K^0$) must be changed to an anti-$K$-meson ($\overline{K^0}$) when it is moved across the reaction sign. If the two neutral $K$-mesons are identical, that is, self-charge conjugate as is the $\pi^0$ meson, the virtual reaction (12.16) becomes

$$K^0 + n \to \Lambda^0 \tag{12.17}$$

and we can show that the real reaction

$$n + n \to \Lambda^0 + \Lambda^0 \tag{12.18}$$

will occur through the virtual process

$$n + n \to n + K^0 + \Lambda^0,$$

followed by absorption of the $K^0$ by the neutron,

$$n + K^0 + \Lambda^0 \to \Lambda^0 + \Lambda^0.$$

This reaction (12.18) is not observed and if we assume it is forbidden we can conclude that (12.17) cannot occur and that there are two distinct neutral $K$-mesons which are related by the process of charge conjugation and which have opposite strangeness. This assignment agrees with observation.

The $K^0$-mesons are produced in reactions such as

$$\pi^- + p \to K^0 + \Lambda^0,$$
$$\gamma + p \to K^0 + \Sigma^+.$$

The $\overline{K}{}^0$-meson cannot be produced in such hyperon associated reactions; however, it can, for example, be produced in double $K$-meson production or in $K^-$ charge exchange scattering:

$$\gamma \to K^0 + \overline{K}{}^0 \text{ in nuclear field,}$$

$$K^- + p \to \overline{K}{}^0 + n.$$

Gell-Mann and Pais (1955) predicted that the neutral $K$-mesons would appear to be a particle mixture and there is now substantial evidence to indicate that these mesons do have the properties predicted. To discuss these properties it is necessary to assume that the $K$-mesons have zero spin and we shall defer until later the presentation of evidence for this assumption. We now discuss the meaning and significance of this prediction.

In Section 10.7 we stated that it is necessary to describe bosons, which are distinct from their antiparticles, by complex state functions. Let us write the state function for a $K^0$-meson in its rest frame

$$\psi_K = \frac{1}{\sqrt{2}} (\psi_1 + i\psi_2), \tag{12.19}$$

where $\psi_1$ and $\psi_2$ are real functions. $K^0$ and $\overline{K}{}^0$ are connected by the operation of charge conjugation $C$. However, since these particles have important decay properties, it is more correct to connect them by charge conjugation and a parity transformation, i.e., $CP$. In the centre of mass of a spinless particle $C$ and $CP$ have the same effect. Therefore

$$CP\psi_K = \psi_{\overline{K}} = \frac{1}{\sqrt{2}} (\psi_1 - i\psi_2) \tag{12.20}$$

as required by the discussion in Section 10.7. $\psi_1$ and $\psi_2$, for which there will exist particles, are eigenstates of $CP$

$$CP\psi_1 = \psi_1, \quad CP\psi_2 = -\psi_2,$$

and will represent observable particles which we call the $K_1$ and $K_2$. When a $K^0$-meson (or a $\overline{K}{}^0$) is produced, Eqs. (12.19) and (12.20) tell us that any measurement designed to show up its $K_1$ and $K_2$ properties finds that the particle is a $K_1$ with 50% probability and $K_2$ with 50% probability. We will now show how this particle mixture is manifest in practice.

At the production of a neutral $K$-meson strangeness is conserved and it follows that when we are discussing production we must consider the neutral $K$-mesons which have a unique strangeness, that is, the

$K^0$ and $\overline{K^0}$. These $K$-mesons are unstable and eventually decay. From our knowledge of $\beta$-decay we expect that this decay interaction will conserve the eigenvalue of $CP$, whereas strangeness will not be conserved. It follows that when we are discussing the decay of neutral $K$-mesons we must consider the $K_1$ and $K_2$ nature of these particles. The $K_1$ is an even eigenstate of $CP$ and can only decay into states which are also even under $CP$, e.g., $2\pi^0$, $\pi^+ + \pi^-$, etc. The $K_2$ is odd under $CP$ and can only decay into odd states such as $3\pi^0$, $\pi^0 + \pi^+ + \pi^-$, etc. The $K_2$ and the $K_1$ can decay into $3\pi$ meson states, but the $K_1$ alone is allowed to decay into $2\pi$ meson states; the $K_1$ and $K_2$ will therefore have different mean lives. Two lifetimes associated with a neutral $K$-meson beam have been observed; the $K_1$ has a mean life of $1.00 \pm 0.04 \times 10^{-10}$ sec (Crawford *et al.*, 1959e) and the $K_2$ a mean life of $6.1(+1.6, -1.1) \times 10^{-8}$ sec (Crawford *et al.*, 1959f).

Let us follow a 500-Mev $K^0$-meson beam from its source. Initially, this beam is $50\%$ $K_1$ and $50\%$ $K_2$, but the short $K_1$ mean life implies that the $K_1$ half of the beam is rapidly lost by decay, and after about 20 cm the beam is an almost pure $K_2$ beam which slowly decays (a mean free path before decay of approximately 30 metres *in vacuo*). Bubble chambers have been used to study associated production reactions in which $K^0$-mesons are produced, e.g.,

$$\pi^- + p \to K^0 + \Lambda^0.$$

If the dimensions of the chamber are about 20 cm, most of the $K_1$ mesons will decay within the chamber whilst most of the $K_2$ mesons will decay outside. Thus of all the reactions in which a $K^0$ was produced, $\frac{1}{2}$, after correction for the finite size of the chamber, should give $K_1$ decays within the chamber. The Michigan University group has used a xenon bubble chamber in which it is possible to detect both predominant $K_1$ decay modes:

$$K_1 \to \pi^+ + \pi^-,$$

$$K_1 \to \pi^0 + \pi^0.$$

They find that $0.53 \pm 0.05$ of the $K^0$ mesons decay in this way, in excellent agreement with the expected value (Brown *et al.*, 1959).

Let us return to our neutral $K$-meson beam and discuss the properties of the pure $K_2$ beam which remains after the $K_1$ part has been lost. If this beam is passed through an absorber, strangeness conserving eactions can take place; for example,

$$\overline{K^0} + p \to \pi^0 + \Sigma^+,$$

$$\overline{K^0} + n \to \pi^0 + \Sigma^0,$$

$$K^0 + p \to K^+ + n, \text{ etc.} \tag{12.21}$$

These reactions attenuate the beam and in considering their effect on the beam it is necessary to consider its $K^0$ and $\overline{K^0}$ qualities. Solving Eqs. (12.19) and (12.20), we find that the pure $K_2$ beam can be described thus:

$$\psi_2 = \frac{1}{i\sqrt{2}} (\psi_K - \psi_{\overline{K}}). \tag{12.22}$$

This equation tells us that the pure $K_2$ beam can appear to be 50% $K^0$ and 50% $\overline{K^0}$. These fractions have different strangeness and, as in the case of $K^+$ and $K^-$ (Section 12.3), have absorption cross sections different by a factor of about 3. The result is that the $\overline{K^0}$ fraction is attenuated more rapidly than the $K^0$ fraction and the beam emerges from the absorber predominantly $K^0$. Subsequently, the beam is free to decay, but as a result of the change in $K^0$ to $\overline{K^0}$ ratio, it now contains some $K_1$ fraction, although the beam was pure $K_2$ before passing through the absorber. This $K_1$ fraction rapidly decays and leads to the reappearance of the $2\pi$ decay modes immediately after the absorber. Pais and Piccioni (1955) suggested that if neutral $K$-meson beams were observed to behave in this manner it would be strong evidence for the particle mixture hypothesis. This particular property has not been observed, but there is other evidence to suggest that the hypothesis is correct. A pure $K_0$ meson beam at its source has strangeness $+1$ and cannot produce hyperons in any low-energy nuclear interaction; however, a pure $K_2$ beam contains strangeness $+1$ and $-1$ and the latter fraction can produce hyperons by reactions such as in (12.21). Thus the observation of hyperons produced by a neutral $K$-meson beam in an absorber placed some distance from the source will be evidence for the particle mixture hypothesis. Such hyperon production has been observed by Fowler et al. (1959) and under circumstances which ensured that the neutral beam had original strangeness $+1$ (Baldo-Ceolin et al., 1958; Crawford et al., 1959d). Panofsky et al. (1958) have measured the absorption of a $K_2$ beam and find that it is consistent with results expected from a beam of mixed strangeness $+1$ and $-1$ as required in the particle mixture scheme. These observations, coupled with the observation of two lifetimes in a neutral $K^0$ beam, strongly support the Pais–Gell-Mann particle mixture scheme.

That elementary particles should behave in this manner may seem rather unusual at first sight. However, there is a classical analogy which will be more familiar to many readers. Consider a beam of plane polarized light which traverses two filters. The first absorbs only circularly (for example, right-hand) polarized light, and to describe the behaviour of the beam it is necessary to represent the plane polarization by the sum of two circular polarizations of correct amplitude and relative phase; one of these fractions (right-hand) is absorbed and the light emerges predominantly circularly polarized (left-hand). The second filter absorbs only plane polarized light and to describe the attenuation it is necessary to represent the circular polarization by the sum of two plane mutually perpendicular polarizations of correct amplitude and phase; one of these components is absorbed and the emerging beam is once more predominantly plane-polarized. These changes in the nature of the beam are analogous to those which occur in the neutral $K$-meson beam and we notice that in both cases the necessary representation depends upon the treatment which the beam undergoes; the intensities of light beams become probabilities for single neutral $K$-mesons.

All forms of the neutral $K$-meson must have the same spin and we expect that this will be the same as that of the charged $K$-mesons, namely zero. There is further evidence for this assignment.

(1) The unobserved decay mode $K^0 \to \pi^0 + \gamma$ would compete with observed modes unless the $K$-meson spin is zero.

(2) The observed decay $K^0 \to 2\pi^0$ is forbidden if the $K^0$ spin is odd. This can easily be deduced if we apply conservation of angular momentum and the symmetry requirements of the $2\pi^0$ final state. We shall take the neutral $K$-meson spin to be zero.

We can now discuss the decay modes of the neutral $K$-meson. The $K_1$ and $K_2$ mesons are eigenstates of $CP$ with opposite eigenvalues $+1$ and $-1$ respectively. If we assume that the eigenvalues of $CP$ are conserved as in $\beta$-decay, we can derive some selection rules with respect to decay into $\pi$-mesons. We showed in Section 10.7 that the $\pi^+ \pi^-$ system in a state of relative orbital motion $l$ is an eigenstate of $C$ with eigenvalue $(-1)^l$, an eigenstate of $P$ with eigenvalue $(-1)^l$ and therefore an eigenstate of $CP$ with eigenvalue $+1$. The system consisting of $2\pi^0$ mesons can only have $l$ even for reasons of symmetry, and as it is always even under $C$, it is also an eigenstate of $CP$ with eigenvalue $+1$. Therefore decay in two $\pi$-mesons is allowed for the $K_1$ and forbidden for the $K_2$ meson.

The three $\pi$-meson states have various $CP$ eigenvalues depending upon charge states and wave functions. From Section 10.5 we can see that a state of $3\pi$-mesons, two of which are identical, cannot be in a state of zero total angular momentum and even parity. If the neutral $K$-mesons have zero spin, the parity of $3\pi^0$ decay state must be odd. Such a state of three $\pi^0$ mesons is even under $C$ and hence odd under $CP$. Therefore

$$K_2 \to 3\pi^0 \text{ is allowed,}$$

$$K_1 \to 3\pi^0 \text{ is forbidden.}$$

The remaining accessible charge state is $\pi^+ + \pi^- + \pi^0$. Evidence from the decay

$$K^+ \to \pi^+ + \pi^- + \pi^+$$

suggests that the relative orbital angular momenta in these three $\pi$-meson decays are both zero (Appendix B.4) and hence the state has odd parity. This charge state is even under $C$ and hence is odd under $CP$. Thus the decay

$$K_1 \to \pi^+ + \pi^- + \pi^0$$

is forbidden into meson states of zero relative angular momenta. The decay into states of higher angular momenta will be inhibited by the angular momentum barrier by a factor of at least 100 (Gell-Mann and Rosenfeld, 1957). Coupled with the short lifetime of the $K_1$, the branching ratio for $K_1$ decay into $3\pi$-mesons is probably less than $10^{-5}$ (Pais and Treiman, 1957).

The decay rate of the $K_2$ meson into $3\pi$-mesons will probably be of the same magnitude as that of the $K^+$ meson into $3\pi$-mesons, namely $\sim 10^7$ sec$^{-1}$. This prolonged partial lifetime allows lepton decay modes to compete; these modes are open to the $K_1$ but the branching ratio is probably about $10^{-4}$ and they have not been observed. The modes are:

$$K_1 \text{ (or } K_2) \to \pi + \mu + \nu \text{ corresponding to } K_{\mu 3}{}^+,$$

$$\to \pi + e + \nu \text{ corresponding to } K_{e3}{}^+.$$

The particle or antiparticle states of decay products can be assigned according to the conservation of electric charge and lepton number.

We can now sum up these decay properties. The $K_1$ meson has a mean life of $1 \times 10^{-10}$ sec and decay modes

$$K_1 \to \pi^0 + \pi^0, \qquad \text{branching ratio} \sim \tfrac{1}{3},$$

$$\to \pi^+ + \pi^-, \qquad\qquad\qquad \sim \tfrac{2}{3},$$

$$\to \pi^+ + \pi^- + \pi^+, \qquad\qquad < 10^{-3},$$

$$\to \pi + \text{leptons.} \qquad\qquad\qquad < 10^{-4}.$$

The $K_2$ meson has a mean life of approximately $6 \times 10^{-8}$ sec and decay modes

$$K_2 \to \pi^0 + \pi^0 + \pi^0,$$

$$\to \pi^+ + \pi^- + \pi^0,$$

$$\to \pi + \text{leptons}.$$

There have been some estimates of branching ratios for $K_2$ decays (Okuba et al., 1958, 1959) but no measurements are yet available. Of all $K^0$ (or $\overline{K^0}$) mesons produced, on the average 50% decay by $K_1$ modes and 50% by $K_2$ modes.

## 12.9 Interference Effects in Neutral K-Meson Decay

The $K_1$ and $K_2$ mesons have different decay modes and this implies a difference in their interactions with other particles and a small mass difference. This leads to oscillatory terms in expressions which give the probability of finding a particular neutral $K$-meson; thus the apparent $K^0$ content of a beam which was entirely $K^0$ at source would vary between 0 and 100% if there were no depletion due to decay. Let us examine this situation in more detail. $m_1$ and $m_2$ are the masses of $K_1$ and $K_2$ mesons in units of reciprocal time $[m = \text{mass} \times (c^2/\hbar)]$; $\lambda_1$ and $\lambda_2$ are the decay constants of the $K_1$ and $K_2$ mesons. We can write down the equation which represents the time variation of a beam which was entirely $K_0$ at time $t$:

$$\psi(t) = \frac{1}{\sqrt{2}}\left\{\psi_1 \exp\left(-im_1 t - \frac{\lambda_1 t}{2}\right) + i\psi_2 \exp\left(-im_1 t - \frac{\lambda_2 t}{2}\right)\right\}. \quad (12.23)$$

At $t = 0$

$$\psi(0) = \frac{1}{\sqrt{2}}(\psi_1 + i\psi_2), \quad (12.24)$$

which agrees with Eq. (12.47) as representing a pure $K^0$ meson. At time $t$ the probability of finding a $K_0$-meson is:

$$\langle K^0 \rangle = |(\psi(0)|\psi(t))|^2,$$

$$= \left|\frac{1}{2}\left(\psi_1 + i\psi_2\middle|\psi_1 \exp\left(-im_1 t - \frac{\lambda_1 t}{2}\right) + i\psi_2 \exp\left(-im_2 t - \frac{\lambda_2 t}{2}\right)\right)\right|^2$$

$$= \frac{1}{4}\left|\exp\left(-im_1 t - \frac{\lambda_1 t}{2}\right) + \exp\left(-im_2 t - \frac{\lambda_2 t}{2}\right)\right|^2$$

$$= \frac{1}{4}\left\{\exp(-\lambda_1 t) + \exp(-\lambda_2 t) + 2\cos(m_2 - m_1)t \exp\left(\frac{-\lambda_1 t - \lambda_2 t}{2}\right)\right\}$$

$$(12.25)$$

The probability of finding a $\overline{K^0}$ meson is

$$\langle\overline{K^0}\rangle = \frac{1}{4}\left\{\exp\left(-\lambda_1 t\right) + \exp\left(-\lambda_2 t\right) - 2\cos\left(m_2 - m_1\right)t\exp\left(\frac{-\lambda_1 t - \lambda_2 t}{2}\right)\right\}.$$
(12.26)

Evidently

$$\langle K^0\rangle + \langle\overline{K^0}\rangle = \tfrac{1}{2}\{\exp\left(-\lambda_1 t\right) + \exp\left(-\lambda_2 t\right)\}.$$
(12.27)

The last equation (12.27) expresses the fact that the probability of finding any neutral $K$-meson decreases in the way expected from the fact that the $K_1$ and $K_2$ decay with different lifetimes. However, the probability of finding a $K^0$ (or $\overline{K^0}$) has an oscillatory term which has an angular velocity $\omega = (m_2 - m_1)$.

If $\omega$ is small compared with $\lambda_1$, these oscillations are very damped and a pure $K^0$-meson beam smoothly becomes a mixed $K^0$–$\overline{K^0}$ beam by the decay of the $K_1$ fraction. However, if $\omega$ is large compared with $\lambda_1$, the oscillatory term is important and the fraction of the beam which is $K^0$ oscillates rapidly until damped by the $K_1$ decay.

Let us consider a monochromatic beam which is pure $K^0$ at source. Some time later it will contain $\overline{K^0}$ which has strangeness $-1$ and can create hyperons by reactions such as

$$\overline{K^0} + p \to \Sigma^0 + \pi^+.$$

If the oscillatory term is important, then the appearance of hyperons along the beam will vary with distance in a manner related to the oscillations. If $\omega \gg \lambda_1$, the wavelength of the variation will be too small to be detected, and if $\omega \ll \lambda_1$, the oscillatory variation will be lost in the rapid $K_1$ decay. Thus there is a range of $\omega$ which it may be possible to detect and which will give a value for the corresponding mass difference. The limits of detection of this difference will probably be from about $4 \times 10^{-7}$ to $4 \times 10^{-5}$ ev ($\sim 10^{-38}$ gm).

Several schemes have been suggested for detecting these interference effects (Treiman and Sachs, 1956; Fry and Sachs, 1958; Good, 1958), but at the time of writing only one result is available (Boldt et al., 1958b) and it indicates that it is likely that the mass difference is such that $\omega \simeq \lambda_1$. The observations do not rule out a smaller mass difference but do suggest that a much larger mass difference is rather unlikely.‡

‡ The regeneration of $K_1$ mesons by the scattering of $K_2$ mesons has recently been observed and used to give a better value of the mass difference, namely $m_1 - m_2 = 0.85(+0.4, -0.25)\lambda_1$ (Muller et al., 1960). This result gives very substantial support to the particle mixture hypothesis.

In Fig. 12.4 we have plotted the relative intensities of the $K^0$ and $\overline{K}$ mesons as a function of time for a beam originally pure $K^0$, for one value of the mass difference, $\omega = \lambda_1$.

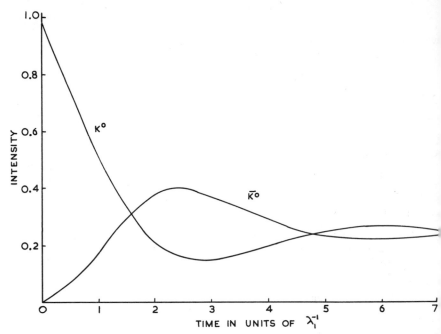

FIG. 12.4. Graph of relative intensities of $K^0$ and $\overline{K^0}$ in a beam which is pure $K^0$ at production when the mass difference corresponds to $\omega = \lambda_1$.

## 12.10 Strange Particle Decays

In this section we discuss the decay modes of strange particles which do not include leptons amongst the decay products. These decays satisfy $|\Delta t_3| = \frac{1}{2}$, which is equivalent to $|\Delta S| = 1$; this selection rule is connected with a weak decay interaction and mean lives which are very long compared with the natural times of strong interactions. The suggestion has been made that these decays are in fact governed by the more restricting selection rule $|\Delta t| = \frac{1}{2}$ and we shall discuss the consequences of this hypothesis.

As an example, let us consider the decay of the $\Lambda^0$ hyperon into mesons and nucleons:

$$\Lambda^0 \rightarrow \pi^0 + n,$$

$$\rightarrow \pi^- + p.$$

In the following discussion we shall assume that other decay modes have negligible branching ratios. The initial state has $t = 0$ and the final state can have $t = \frac{3}{2}$ or $\frac{1}{2}$. We proceed by making a general analysis which does not restrict us to a particular change in $t$. There are four decay amplitudes,

$$a_{3S}, \, a_{3P}, \, a_{1S}, \quad \text{and} \quad a_{1P},$$

corresponding to the $S$ and $P$ waves of Eq. (10.5) subdivided into states of isotopic spin $\frac{3}{2}$ and $\frac{1}{2}$. Then using Clebsch–Gordan coefficients from Table 2.1, we have

$$a_S = \sqrt{\tfrac{2}{3}} \, a_{1S} + \sqrt{\tfrac{1}{3}} \, a_{3S},$$

$$a_P = \sqrt{\tfrac{2}{3}} \, a_{1P} + \sqrt{\tfrac{1}{3}} \, a_{3P}.$$

$a_S$ and $a_P$ are the $S$ and $P$ wave amplitudes for the $\pi^- {-} p$ decay mode. The corresponding amplitudes for the $\pi^0 {-} n$ mode $b_S, b_P$ are given by

$$b_S = -\sqrt{\tfrac{1}{3}} \, a_{1S} + \sqrt{\tfrac{2}{3}} \, a_{3S},$$

$$b_P = -\sqrt{\tfrac{1}{3}} \, a_{1P} + \sqrt{\tfrac{2}{3}} \, a_{3P}.$$

Total decay rates are calculated by integrating the intensity over all directions. Interference terms disappear in the integration and we find that the total decay rate is proportional to

$$|a_{1S}|^2 + |a_{3S}|^2 + |a_{1P}|^2 + |a_{3P}|^2.$$

The branching ratio $f_-$ into the charged meson decay channel is given by

$$f_- = \frac{|\sqrt{\tfrac{2}{3}} \, a_{1S}|^2 + |\sqrt{\tfrac{1}{3}} \, a_{3S}|^2 + |\sqrt{\tfrac{2}{3}} \, a_{1P}|^2 + |\sqrt{\tfrac{1}{3}} \, a_{3P}|^2}{|a_{1S}|^2 + |a_{3S}|^2 + |a_{1P}|^2 + |a_{3P}|^2}.$$

The application of the selection rule $|\Delta t| = \frac{1}{2}$ means that there can be no isotopic spin $\frac{3}{2}$ final state and $a_{3S} = a_{3P} = 0$. It follows immediately that

$$f_- = \tfrac{2}{3}.$$

The observed value is $0.627 \pm 0.030$ (Crawford $et\ al.$, 1959e) in striking agreement with the requirement of the $|\Delta t| = \frac{1}{2}$ selection rule.

The up-down $\pi^- {-} p$ decay asymmetry is given by the parity mixing parameter $\alpha$ of Eq. (10.7):

$$\alpha = -\frac{2 \, \mathrm{Re} \, a_S^* \, a_P}{|a_S|^2 + |a_P|^2}.$$

The observed asymmetry is such that $|\alpha| \gtrsim 0.73$ (Section 12.6). This indicates that $a_S$ and $a_P$ are comparable in magnitude. The corresponding asymmetry parameter $\beta$ for the neutral mode is given by

$$\beta = -\frac{2\,\mathrm{Re}\,b_S^* b_P}{|b_S|^2 + |b_P|^2}.$$

If $|\Delta t| = \frac{1}{2}$ is a valid rule, $\alpha = \beta$. However, $\beta$ is difficult to measure and no results are available.

If the decay interaction is invariant under the $CP$ transformation and there is no interaction in the final state, the amplitudes $a_{1S}, a_{3S}, \ldots$, etc. are real quantities. The effect of final-state interactions can be taken into account by the use of the $S$-matrix method used in Section 7.12. In terms of real quantities,

$$\left.\begin{array}{ll} a_{1S} = |a_{1S}|\,e^{i\delta_1}, & a_{3S} = \pm |a_{3S}|\,e^{i\delta_3}, \\[2mm] a_{1P} = \pm |a_{1P}|\,e^{i\delta_{11}}, & a_{3P} = \pm |a_{3P}|\,e^{i\delta_{31}}, \end{array}\right\} \qquad (12.28)$$

where $\delta$ are the $\pi$-meson nucleon scattering phase shifts at the same centre-of-mass energy (Takeda, 1956). These phase shifts are known sufficiently well for a determination of the amplitudes to become significantly easier. If the decay interaction is invariant under $C$, the $P$-wave amplitudes in Eqs. (12.28) would contain an extra $i$ (cf. Section 10.8); in this case a decay asymmetry can only be due to the final-state interactions (Gatto, 1957).

The charged $\Sigma$ hyperon decays also obey the selection rule $|\Delta t_3| = \frac{1}{2}$ and we shall consider the consequences of the $|\Delta t| = \frac{1}{2}$ rule. The non-leptonic decay modes are:

$$\Sigma^+ \to \pi^+ + n,$$

$$\Sigma^+ \to \pi^0 + p,$$

$$\Sigma^- \to \pi^- + n.$$

We can apply the rule by supposing that the $\Sigma$ hyperon absorbs a "spurion" (Wentzel, 1956a) which has $t = \frac{1}{2}, t_3 = -\frac{1}{2}$, but has no charge, momentum, or energy. The $\Sigma$ plus spurion combination can then be expressed as sum of eigenfunctions of total isotopic spin:

$$\Sigma^+ + \text{spurion} = -\sqrt{\tfrac{2}{3}}\,\tau(\tfrac{1}{2}, \tfrac{1}{2}) + \sqrt{\tfrac{1}{3}}\,\tau(\tfrac{3}{2}, \tfrac{1}{2}), \qquad (12.29)$$

$$\Sigma^- + \text{spurion} = \tau(\tfrac{3}{2}, -\tfrac{3}{2}). \qquad (12.30)$$

The outgoing amplitudes for $\Sigma^+$ decay will be (assuming spin $\frac{1}{2}$) $a_{1S}^+, a_{3S}^+, a_{1P}^+, a_{3P}^+$, as in the case of the $\Lambda^0$. These are defined as the decay-state amplitudes irrespective of the actual isotopic spin mixture of the decaying state. Similar amplitudes are defined for the $\Sigma^-$ decay, but we see from Eq. (12.30) that only two are necessary, $a_{3S}^-, a_{3P}^-$. The $|\Delta t| = \frac{1}{2}$ rule connects these amplitudes in the following argument: if the matrix element connecting a $\Sigma$ plus spurion, $t = \frac{3}{2}$ state to a meson–nucleon, $t = \frac{3}{2}$ state is independent of charge, then Eqs. (12.29) and (12.30) tell us that the $t = \frac{3}{2}$ amplitude in $\Sigma^-$ decay will be $\sqrt{3}$ times that in $\Sigma^+$ decay. That is,

$$a_{3S}^- = \sqrt{3}\, a_{3S}^+, \tag{12.31}$$

$$a_{3P}^- = \sqrt{3}\, a_{3P}^+. \tag{12.32}$$

This reduces six amplitudes to four. As in the case of the $\Lambda^0$ decay, these amplitudes can be expressed as a real quantity multiplied by $e^{i\delta}$, where $\delta$ is the corresponding pi-meson–nucleon scattering phase shift. At the energy of decay these phase shifts are small and a simple analysis can be made by assuming them to be zero (Gell-Mann and Rosenfeld, 1957). The two real amplitudes belonging to each isotopic spin space are made the components of a vector; for example, $A_3$ has components $a_{3S}$ and $a_{3P}$. A convenient representation of this would be an Argand diagram where the quantity $A$ has coordinates $(a_S, a_P)$. This has no immediate physical significance and is merely a convenient shorthand. Equations (12.31) and (12.32) become

$$A_3^- = \sqrt{3}\, A_3^+$$

and we now have two vector amplitudes $A_3^+$ and $A_1^+$. We now use Table 7.6 to construct the amplitudes for various pi-meson–nucleon final states. These amplitudes are $A^+$, $A^0$, $A^-$ for $\pi^+ n$, $\pi^0 p$, and $\pi^- n$, respectively. Then we have that

$$A^+ = -\sqrt{\tfrac{2}{3}}\, A_1^+ + \sqrt{\tfrac{1}{3}}\, A_3^+,$$

$$A^0 = \sqrt{\tfrac{1}{3}}\, A_1^+ + \sqrt{\tfrac{2}{3}}\, A_3^+,$$

$$A^- = \sqrt{3}\, A_3^+,$$

from which it follows that

$$\sqrt{2}\, A^0 + A^+ = A^-. \tag{12.33}$$

The decay rate for each mode is proportional to $|A|^2$, and from the data given in Section 12.6 we find that these rates are equal within the experimental error. Therefore $|A^0| = |A^+| = |A^-|$ and the vector relation becomes the relation between the sides of a right-angled isosceles triangle. A possible arrangement of the three vectors is shown in Fig. 12.5. The vector relation (12.33) is independent of the angle $\beta$. The next step is to link this with the decay asymmetry; in any mode the asymmetry parameter $\alpha$ is given by‡

$$\alpha = \frac{2 \operatorname{Re} a_S^* a_P}{|a_S|^2 + |a_P|^2}.$$

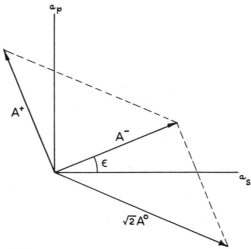

Fig. 12.5. Diagram showing the relation between the decay amplitudes for the $\Sigma$ hyperons.

All the quantities are real, so that

$$\alpha = 2 \frac{a_S}{\sqrt{(a_S^2 + a_P^2)}} \cdot \frac{a_P}{\sqrt{(a_S^2 + a_P^2)}}.$$

For the $\pi^- n$ decay of the $\Sigma^-$ this relation becomes

$$\alpha_- = 2 \sin \epsilon \cos \epsilon = \sin 2\epsilon.$$

Referring to Fig. 12.5 we see that the corresponding decay asymmetries for the remaining modes are also simply related to $\epsilon$. The expressions are:

$$\alpha_0 = \pm \cos 2\epsilon,$$

$$\alpha_+ = -\sin 2\epsilon.$$

‡ We have omitted a negative sign from the following expression [cf. Eq (10.7)] as it is not possible to find the sign of $\alpha$ from a measurement of an up-down decay asymmetry alone.

There is a sign ambiguity which can arise from the fact that the arrangement of vectors in Fig. 12.5 can be reflected about $A_-$ without failing the condition imposed by Eq. (12.33). Referring to Section 12.6, we find that

$$\alpha_0 \geqslant 0.70 \pm 0.30,$$

$$\alpha_+ \leqslant 0.03 \pm 0.11 \text{ (because } |\langle \sigma \rangle_{\Sigma^+}| \geqslant 0.70 \pm 0.30\text{)},$$

$$\alpha_- |\langle \sigma \rangle_{\Sigma^-}| = 0.09 \pm 0.13.$$

These results seem to indicate that $\epsilon$ is close to $0°$ or $90°$, which means that the $\pi^- n$ and $\pi^+ n$ decay modes are either pure $S$ wave or pure $P$ wave, as required if there is to be no decay asymmetry. If this is really the case, it follows that the $|\Delta t| = \frac{1}{2}$ selection rule requires that the decay asymmetry $\alpha_0$ be close to the maximum, unity. A more complete justification for the analysis must await more plentiful data on these decays, and, of course, the analysis may require slight modification to allow for the complex nature of the amplitudes (Kawaguchi, 1957).

### Ξ *Hyperon Decays*

Only a few examples of these particles have been observed and it is not possible to draw any conclusions about the validity of the $|\Delta t| = \frac{1}{2}$ selection rule. The observed decay modes are:

$$\Xi^- \to \pi^- + \Lambda^0,$$

$$\Xi^0 \to \pi^0 + \Lambda^0.$$

If the $|\Delta t| = \frac{1}{2}$ rule applies, the decay rate of the $\Xi^-$ will be twice that of the $\Xi^0$. This result can be derived by using the spurion technique.

### *K-meson Decays*

We can apply the $|\Delta t| = \frac{1}{2}$ rule to the decay of $K$-mesons into $\pi$-mesons. We take the $K$-mesons to have zero spin and $t = \frac{1}{2}$. The decay state consisting of two $\pi$-mesons must be in an $S$-state of relative orbital angular momentum, which is symmetric. The $\pi$-mesons are bosons. Hence the total wave function must also be symmetric and this implies that the isotopic spin wave function is also symmetric, that is, $t = 0$ or $2$; only the first of these is accessible in $K$-meson decay if $|\Delta t| = \frac{1}{2}$. Consider this applied to the $K_1$ decay modes

$$K_1 \to \pi^+ + \pi^-,$$

$$\to \pi^0 + \pi^0.$$

The final state has $t = 0$. Such a state can be expressed as eigenstates of variously charged mesons by using the Clebsch–Gordan coefficients from table $2^3$ of Condon and Shortley (1951),

$$\tau(0, 0) = \frac{1}{\sqrt{3}} (\pi^+ \pi^- - \pi^0 \pi^0 + \pi^- \pi^+).$$

It follows immediately that the decay branching ratios are predicted to be

$$R_0 = \frac{K_1 \to \pi^0 + \pi^0}{(K_1 \to \pi^0 + \pi^0) + (K_1 \to \pi^+ + \pi^-)} = \frac{1}{3},$$

$$R_1 = \frac{K_1 \to \pi^+ + \pi^-}{(K_1 \to \pi^0 + \pi^0) + (K_1 \to \pi^+ + \pi^-)} = \frac{2}{3}.$$

However, this result may be oversimplified as we can see by discussing the $K^+$-meson decay into two mesons:

$$K^+ \to \pi^+ + \pi^0.$$

The final state has $t_3 = 1$ and can only belong to a state of total isotopic spin $t = 2$ which is not accessible to the initial state if we are restricted to $|\Delta t| = \frac{1}{2}$. Thus the proposed selection rule does not allow this decay, which is in fact observed. The decay rate for $K_1 \to 2\pi$ is about 500 times that for $K^+ \to \pi^+ + \pi^0$, which suggests that although the $|\Delta t| = \frac{1}{2}$ is a good selection rule, it is not inviolate. Electromagnetic effects will cause violations but these do not seem to be sufficient to cause the observed $K^+$-meson decay rate into two pi-mesons. The alternative suggestion is that there is a small admixture of decay amplitudes involving $|\Delta t| = \frac{3}{2}$; if these amplitudes are adjusted to account for the observed $K^+$ decay there is corresponding change in $R_0$ and $R_1$ (Gell-Mann and Rosenfeld, 1957). Thus

$$0.28 \leqslant R_0 \leqslant 0.38,$$

$$0.62 \leqslant R_1 \leqslant 0.72.$$

If we believe the particle mixture theory of the neutral $K$-meson, a fraction $R_K$ should be observed to decay into the mode $\pi^+ + \pi^-$ where $R_K = \frac{1}{2}R_1$ and therefore should obey the inequalities

$$0.36 \geqslant R_K \geqslant 0.31.$$

The observed value for this ratio is $0.339 \pm 0.020$ (Crawford *et al.*, 1959e) in good agreement with the theory.

Applied to $3\pi$-meson decay modes the $|\Delta t| = \frac{1}{2}$ rule predicts the following decay rate ratios:

$$\frac{K^+ \to \pi^+ + 2\pi^0}{K^+ \to \pi^- + 2\pi^+} = \frac{1}{4}$$

(Wentzel, 1956b) and

$$\frac{K_2 \to 3\pi^0}{K_2 \to \pi^+ + \pi^- + \pi^0} = \frac{3}{2}$$

(Pais and Treiman, 1957). These predictions depend upon the assumption that the space wave function is totally symmetric. There appears to be good evidence that this is so (Appendix B.4). The observed ratio for the $K^+$ decay is $0.33 \pm 0.07$ (Gell-Mann and Rosenfeld, 1957); no observations have been made on the $K_2$ decay.

At first sight it would seem unlikely that the $|\Delta t| = \frac{1}{2}$ rule can be applied to leptonic decay modes of the $K$ meson. However, if we assign zero isotopic spin to all leptons, then it is evident that the following decays are allowed:

$$K^+ \to \mu^+ + \nu,$$

$$\overline{K^+} \to \pi^0 + \mu^+ + \nu,$$

$$K^0 \to \pi^- + \mu^+ + \nu,$$

$$\overline{K^0} \to \pi^+ + \mu^- + \bar{\nu}.$$

However, if the $|\Delta t| = \frac{1}{2}$ rule applied strictly, the following decays would be forbidden

$$K^0 \to \pi^+ + \mu^- + \bar{\nu},$$

$$\overline{K^0} \to \pi^- + \mu^+ + \nu,$$

as in these cases $|\Delta t_3| = \frac{3}{2}$. We have seen, in fact, that $|\Delta t| = \frac{3}{2}$ does occur in nonleptonic $K$-meson decays and thus we might expect these decays to occur. However, there may be reasons for $|\Delta t| = \frac{3}{2}$ to be forbidden in the leptonic modes of decay; this is discussed in the next Section, 12.11. This difference in the decay of the $K^0$ and $\overline{K^0}$ mesons could be used to detect the $K_1$–$K_2$ interference effects in the early history of an initially pure $K^0$ (or $\overline{K^0}$) meson beam. We note that, in the leptonic decays listed above, electrons can replace $\mu$ mesons; the $K_{e2}$ has not been observed but the $K_{e3}$ modes are well established.

At the time of writing it appears that the $K$-meson decay modes will be a fruitful source of information about the applicability of various selection rules and laws of conservation and symmetry. For example, if the decay interaction is invariant under $CP$, then the decay processes

$$K_1 \to \pi^+ + \mu^- + \bar{\nu},$$

$$K_2 \to \pi^- + \mu^+ + \nu$$

are connected by a $CP$ transformation so that the $\mu$-meson polarization should be equal but oppositely directed in the two decays. In addition, the polarization can only be longitudinal and any transverse component in these decays or in the decay

$$K^+ \to \pi^0 + \mu^+ + \nu$$

would indicate a breakdown in invariance under time reversal. These polarizations can be readily detected by the analysing power of the $\mu \to e$ decay.

The important evidence concerning the validity of the $|\Delta t| = \frac{1}{2}$ rule was summarized by Crawford *et al.* (1959e). Much of the data is of the kind that fits but does not necessarily require the $|\Delta t| = \frac{1}{2}$ selection rule. In the next section we shall discuss some speculations concerning the structure of the weak decay interactions; it is found to be difficult to build such a rule directly into the interaction.

## 12.11 The Universal Fermi Interaction (II)

The decay rates of the strange particles are such that the strengths of the interactions which are responsible must be comparable to the strength of the $\beta$-decay interaction; thus it is tempting to extend the concept of a universal interaction to include these decays. At first this may seem to be difficult, as no leptons are involved in many of the decays; however, we assume that there is a general four-fermion interaction which can be operative in virtual states and which will be responsible for the apparent nonconservation of parity and non-invariance under charge conjugation. In addition, we assume that it need not conserve strangeness. We can discuss two examples to show how this works; consider the lambda hyperon decay

$$\Lambda^0 \to \pi^- + p.$$

We can draw a Feynman diagram for this decay which includes a four-fermion interaction (Fig. 12.6). This type of vertex would be given by an interaction of the form

$$(\bar{\psi}_p \gamma_\rho (1 + \gamma_5) \psi_\Lambda) (\bar{\psi}_n \gamma_\rho (1 + \gamma_5) \psi_p) + \text{Hermitian conjugate.}$$

The remaining vertex at which a virtual neutron anti-proton pair annihilate to give a $\pi^-$ meson is a strong interaction, and this process occurs readily. Therefore the most important factor in determining the magnitude of the transition rate is the strength of the four-fermion vertex. Diagram a of Fig. 12.6 is not the only lowest-order contribution to this decay; the closed loop could contain any pairing of baryon and antibaryon which conserved charge and strangeness at the strong

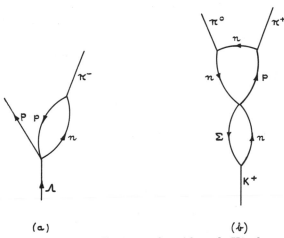

(a)                    (b)

FIG. 12.6. Feynman diagrams for $\Lambda^0$ and $K^+$ decay (a and b respectively). Each is one of many possible lowest-order diagrams.

vertex. For example, we expect to be able to replace the pair ($\bar{p}n$) with ($\overline{\Sigma^+}\Sigma^0$), ($\Sigma^-\overline{\Sigma^0}$), or ($\Xi^-\overline{\Xi^0}$), etc. to form other contributions to this lowest-order contribution. Higher-order contributions which include exchange of mesons between baryons will also be important.

Our second example is the decay

$$K^+ \rightarrow \pi^+ + \pi^0.$$

Figure 12.6b shows one contribution of lowest order. The same remarks apply here as to the baryon pairing in the closed loops. In fact, in all these decays there is a very large number of ways in which the four-fermion vertex and the strong interaction can be arranged even in the lowest order for any given decay.

We can discuss some of the recent work which has been done in an effort to find a consistent picture of a universal four-fermion interaction. At this point it is important to stress that much of this work is speculative and may be proved useless in the future development of this subject. However, the discussion will point out the difficulties which exist in the interpretation of weak interactions. Let us write down the V–A interaction which we have discussed in Chapter XI:

$\beta$-decay: $\mathscr{L}_I = (\bar{\psi}_p \gamma_\rho (C_V - C_A \gamma_5) \psi_n)(\bar{\psi}_e \gamma_\rho (1 + \gamma_5) \psi_\nu) + \text{h.c.};$

$\mu$-decay: $\mathscr{L}_I = C(\bar{\psi}_\nu \gamma_\rho (1 + \gamma_5) \psi_\mu)(\bar{\psi}_e \gamma_\rho (1 + \gamma_5) \psi_\nu) + \text{h.c.};$

$\mu$-capture: $\mathscr{L}_I = (\bar{\psi}_\nu \gamma_\rho (1 + \gamma_5) \psi_\mu)(\bar{\psi}_n \gamma_\rho (C_V - C_A \gamma_5) \psi_p) + \text{h.c.}$

We have assumed that the Fermi $(C_V)$ and Gamow-Teller $(C_A)$ coupling constants are the same in $\beta$-decay and $\mu$-capture. In Section 11.8 we found that $C$ in $\mu$-decay was closely equal to $C_V$. A universal Fermi interaction (UFI) suggests that for bare fermions (that is, without strong interactions) the magnitude of all the coupling constants is equal:

$$C = C_V = -C_A.$$

We now make a contraction in notation: covariants of the form $(\bar{\psi}_a O \psi_b)$ are written as $(\bar{a}b)$, implying an operator which destroys a particle $b$ and creates a particle $a$. The weak interactions above can therefore be written

$$\mathscr{L}_I \propto (\bar{p}n)(\bar{\nu}e)^\dagger + \text{h.c.},$$

$$\mathscr{L}_I \propto (\bar{\nu}\mu)(\bar{\nu}e)^\dagger + \text{h.c.},$$

$$\mathscr{L}_I \propto (\bar{\nu}\mu)(\bar{p}n)^\dagger + \text{h.c.}$$

We are now going to add more interaction Lagrangian densities such as

$$(\bar{p}\Lambda)(\bar{p}n)^\dagger$$

for diagram 12.6a, and

$$(\bar{p}n)(\bar{n}\Sigma^-)^\dagger$$

for diagram 12.6b, and any others which may be necessary to account for the observed strange particle decays. We can see that many covariants will appear repeatedly; for example, $(\bar{\nu}e)$, $(\bar{\nu}\mu)$, and $(\bar{p}n)$, ..., etc. At this point we recall that in quantum electrodynamics $ie(\bar{\psi}\gamma_\rho \psi)$ is the operator for the $\rho$ component of the four vector of current density; by analogy the operators $(\bar{\psi}_a \gamma_\rho (1 + \gamma_5) \psi) = (\bar{a}b)$ have come to be called "currents" or "chiral currents" (Sudarshan and Marshak, 1958). Each current is electrically charged in the sense that one particle is electrically charged and the other is not. All our currents, e.g., $(\bar{a}b)$, are such that the particle created, $a$, has charge one unit greater than the particle destroyed, $b$. The opposite changes in charge, strangeness, and third component of isotopic spin are induced by the Hermitian conjugate of a suitable covariant. We shall not make the distinction between these two and whenever we talk of a current we mean one in which the charge increases by one unit, $\Delta Q = 1$. By convention, lepton and baryon number are conserved in each current but we do not require strangeness to be conserved. The $\rho$ component of the total fermion current, $J_\rho$, is the sum of all currents, and the total interaction density is

$$\mathscr{L}_I = CJ_\rho J_\rho^\dagger + \text{Hermitian conjugate}, \tag{12.34}$$

where

$$J_\rho = J_{0\rho} + J_{1\rho} + J_{2\rho} + J_{3\rho} + J_{4\rho}.$$

The $J_0$ to $J_4$ are five categories of current which we will now define.

$J_0$ are the lepton currents $(\bar{\nu}e)$, $(\bar{\nu}\mu)$, which involve no change except that of charge.

$J_1$ are the baryon currents such as $(\bar{p}n)$, $(\overline{\Sigma^0}\Sigma^-)$ which involve no change in strangeness, $\Delta S = 0$. Taking a difference form of Eq. (12.9), we have

$$\Delta Q = \Delta t_3 + \tfrac{1}{2}\Delta S.$$

Thus $\Delta t_3 = 1$ for the currents $J_1$.

$J_2$ are the baryon currents such as $(\bar{n}\Sigma^-)$, $(\bar{p}\Sigma^0)$ which have $\Delta S = 1$. This change is taken in the same direction as the change in charge. From Eq. (12.9) we see that this current causes $|\Delta t_3| = \tfrac{1}{2}$. If our universal scheme is to include the decay of strange particles, this current is sufficient to cover all the observed decays. There are some noteworthy features of the effect of this current. It predicts that the following decays will take place:

$$\left.\begin{aligned}
K^0 &\to \pi^- + \mu^+ \ (\text{or } e^+) + \nu, \\
\overline{K^0} &\to \pi^+ + \mu^- \ (\text{or } e^-) + \bar{\nu}, \\
\Sigma^- &\to n + e^- + \bar{\nu},
\end{aligned}\right\} \tag{12.35}$$

but does not allow

$$\left.\begin{aligned}
K^0 &\to \pi^+ + \mu^- \ (\text{or } e^-) + \bar{\nu}, \\
\overline{K^0} &\to \pi^- + \mu^+ \ (\text{or } e^+) + \nu, \\
\Sigma^+ &\to n + e^+ + \nu.
\end{aligned}\right\} \tag{12.36}$$

These decays (12.35) will be caused by terms such as $J_{2\rho}J_{0\rho}^\dagger$ or $J_{2\rho}^\dagger J_{0\rho}$ from the interaction (12.34). These terms can only cause $\Delta t_3 = \pm\tfrac{1}{2}$. The reactions (12.36) all have $\Delta t_3 = \tfrac{3}{2}$. Obviously this can be generalized. If our universal interaction hypothesis is correct and only the $J_0$, $J_1$, and $J_2$ currents are operating, then all leptonic decays of strange particles have $|\Delta t_3| = \tfrac{1}{2}$. (We are assuming that no second- or higher-order transitions are effective.) The nonleptonic decay modes (no leptons among decay products) will be caused by $J_2$ currents interacting with $J_1$ currents; the latter can have $|\Delta t_3| = 1$ and the total effect is to allow $|\Delta t_3| = \frac{1}{2}$ or $\frac{3}{2}$ in the nonleptonic modes.

$J_3$ currents are baryon currents such as $(\overline{\Sigma^+}n)$ which have $\Delta S = -1$ and obviously cause $\Delta t_3 = \frac{3}{2}$. If such currents are present they will cause the decays of Eqs. (12.36) to occur. In addition, terms such as $J_{3\rho}J_{2\rho}^\dagger$ and $J_{3\rho}^\dagger J_{2\rho}$ will cause changes $\Delta S = -2$ and $+2$ respectively, thus allowing decays such as

$$\Xi^0 \to \pi^- + p,$$

$$\Xi^- \to \pi^- + n. \tag{12.37}$$

These decays have not been observed. This current will also affect the $K_1$–$K_2$ mixture in neutral $K$-meson beams. The $K_1$–$K_2$ mass difference is ascribed to the weak interactions. If these interactions are limited to $|\Delta S| \leqslant 1$, the interchange $K_1 \rightleftharpoons K_2$ is a second-order transition and as such occurs with an amplitude proportional to the square of the coupling constant $C^2$ and gives rise to a mass difference of the order $10^{-6}$ ev and $\omega \simeq 10^{10}$ sec$^{-1}$. Under these circumstances the appearance of a $\overline{K^0}$ fraction in an initially pure $K^0$ beam is associated with a time of about $10^{-10}$ sec. If $J_3$ currents are allowed, so are transitions $\Delta S = \pm 2$ and the $K_1 \rightleftharpoons K_2$ exchange occurs with amplitude proportional to $C$. The mass difference becomes about 1 ev and $\omega \simeq 10^{16}$ sec$^{-1}$. This implies that a pure $K^0$ beam rapidly oscillates between pure $K^0$ and pure $\overline{K^0}$ and is capable of $\overline{K^0}$ phenomena almost instantly after production; there is some evidence that this does not happen (Boldt et al., 1958b).

The currents $J_4$ and $J_5$ have $\Delta S = +2$ and $-2$ respectively. They can give rise to the cascade hyperon nucleonic decay modes of Eq. (12.37) and to the modes

$$\Xi^- \to n + e^- + \bar{\nu},$$

$$\Xi^0 \to p + e^- + \bar{\nu}.$$

These cascade hyperons are too rare for there to be any information of the existence of these modes. These currents can also cause the rapid mixing of the $\overline{K^0}$–$K^0$ mesons.

The evidence for currents assembled into an interaction in the proposed manner is flimsy. At present it appears necessary to include $J_0, J_1, J_2$ but no others in the suggested total fermion current. If such a current interacts with itself, then it will include self-coupling of the individual currents; for example,

$$(\bar{\nu}e)(\bar{\nu}e)^\dagger \quad \text{or} \quad (\bar{p}n)(\bar{p}n)^\dagger.$$

The first term indicates that electron–neutrino scattering will be a first-order effect with a cross section about $10^{-45}$ cm$^2$ at 1 Mev, and the second predicts that weak interactions will contribute to nuclear forces giving a parity nonconserving effect (fractionally $\sim 10^{-7}$) which could not have been detected up to the present due to the lack of sufficiently sensitive techniques. Thus the evidence for the construction of such a self-interacting current is poor and we must await further experimental data.

We must clarify the relation between this universal interaction and the $|\Delta t| = \frac{1}{2}$ selection rule discussed in Section 12.10. If we assume that only the currents $J_0, J_1, J_2$ are present, then from our statements concerning $\Delta t_3$ we see that these currents give rise to $|\Delta t| = \frac{1}{2}$ or $\frac{3}{2}$ in nonleptonic decay modes and to $|\Delta t\lceil = \frac{1}{2}$ in leptonic decay modes. This can be summarized by stating that $J_0$, $J_1$, and $J_2$ transform as scalar, spinor, and vector respectively in isotopic spin space. The universal interaction does not suppress the $|\Delta t| = \frac{3}{2}$ amplitude with respect to that for $|\Delta t| = \frac{1}{2}$ in nonleptonic modes and thus does not support the hypothesis that the latter amplitude predominates, as was suggested to explain the suppression of the $K^+ \rightarrow \pi^+ + \pi^0$ decay rate relative to that for $K^0 \rightarrow 2\pi$. Thus the postulated universal interaction does not give the selection rule in its apparently required form. The vital measurements are the decay asymmetry $\beta$ in $\Lambda^0 \rightarrow \pi^0 + n$ which will be the same as the asymmetry for the charged decay mode if $|\Delta t| = \frac{1}{2}$ is a good selection rule, and the branching ratios in $K_1$ decay which will indicate the ratio of $|\Delta t| = \frac{3}{2}$ to $|\Delta t| = \frac{1}{2}$ amplitudes.

It is assumed that the universal interaction has the common coupling constant $C$

$$\mathscr{L}_I = C(J_\rho J_\rho^\dagger + J_\rho^\dagger J_\rho)$$

where $C$ is taken to be equal to $C_V$ of $\beta$ decay, that is,

$$\sqrt{2}\, C_V \simeq 1.4 \times 10^{-49}\,\text{erg cm}^3.$$

This assumption allows the calculation of decay rates for some simpler strange particle decays

$$\Sigma^- \rightarrow n + e^- + \bar{\nu},\ 3.5 \times 10^8\ \text{sec}^{-1},$$

$$\Lambda^0 \rightarrow p + e^- + \bar{\nu},\ 5.3 \times 10^7\ \text{sec}^{-1}$$

(Feynman and Gell-Mann, 1958). These rates correspond to branching ratios of $5.6\%$ and $1.6\%$ respectively. The experimental evidence is in distinct disagreement with this prediction as it indicates that the branching ratios are certainly less than 1% (Crawford *et al.*, 1958b; Nordin *et al.*, 1958). This suggests that the $J_2$ has only about one-fifth the strength of the $J_1$ current.

It is impossible to predict other decay rates of the strange particles as the contribution of the baryon closed loops in the Feynman diagrams cannot be evaluated at present. However, it is possible to factor out the effects of such loops and to predict branching ratios for various decay modes or ratios of decay rates for similar modes of different particles. Thus Okubo *et al.* (1958) predict that the following transition rates are related as shown:

$$\omega(K_1 \to \pi^\mp + \mu^\pm \pm \nu) = \omega(K_2 \to \pi^\mp + \mu^\pm \pm \nu),$$

$$= \omega(K^0 \to \pi^- + \mu^+ + \nu),$$

$$= \omega(\overline{K^0} \to \pi^+ + \mu^- + \bar{\nu}),$$

$$= 2\omega(K^+ \to \pi^0 + \mu^+ + \nu).$$

$\omega(K_1 \to \pi^\mp + \mu^\pm \pm \nu)$ means the total transition rate into both decay states mentioned within the brackets. A similar set of relations holds for decays in which electrons are produced instead of $\mu$-mesons. Okubo *et al.* (1959) extend this analysis by using a $|\Delta t| = \frac{1}{2}$ selection rule result, namely

$$\omega(K_2 \to 3\pi) = \omega(K^+ \to 3\pi),$$

and by using the observed $K^+$ branching ratios and lifetime to predict the $K_2^0$ branching ratios and lifetime. The mean life of this particle is calculated to be $5.2 \times 10^{-8}$ sec. The observed life is approximately $6.1 \times 10^{-8}$ sec (Section 12.8). There are insufficient data available to test the branching ratio predictions. This example shows how predictions of the universal interaction can be tested; up to the present its successes have not been outstanding.

In our discussion of $\beta$-decay in Section 11.6 we found that the Fermi $(C_V)$ and Gamow-Teller $(C_A)$ coupling constants were different and this was attributed to the difference in renormalization effects due to the strong interactions of the nucleons involved. There is, however, one interesting fact: the Fermi coupling constant calculated from the decay rate of $O^{14}$ is within 1% of the coupling constant calculated from the decay rate of the $\mu$-meson (see Section 11.8). In $O^{14}$ decay, nucleons are involved and we expect that renormalization effects would alter the Fermi coupling constant from the value it has in $\mu$-decay where no nucleons are involved. These facts suggest some principle is operating which makes the renormalization of $C_V$ zero and there is a precedent for such an idea. The electromagnetic coupling, which we call electric charge, is unchanged by the presence of strong interactions and the reason for this is the fact that the four-vector electric current is conserved and has a four-dimensional divergence of zero. Thus

$$\frac{\partial j_\rho}{\partial x_\rho} = 0$$

where

$$j_\rho = ie\bar{\psi}\gamma_\rho\psi.$$

If the vector part of the baryon currents in the weak interaction $J_\rho J_\rho^\dagger + J_\rho^\dagger J_\rho$ is likewise divergenceless, the vector coupling constant is always the same, apart from small electromagnetic corrections. There appears, at present, to be no way of constructing a divergenceless axial vector current, so we expect that the Gamow-Teller coupling constant depends upon the particles involved; the surprising thing is that the GT coupling in nuclear $\beta$-decay is altered by only about 20% from the value it has in $\mu$-meson decay. In constructing the required divergenceless vector current we find, for example, that $\bar{\psi}_p\gamma_\rho\psi_n$ is not divergenceless and must be supplemented by a pi-meson current

$$J_{1\rho} = \bar{\psi}\gamma_\rho N_+\psi + \sqrt{2}\left\{\frac{\partial\phi^\dagger}{\partial x_\rho}\Pi_+\phi - \phi^\dagger\Pi_+\frac{\partial\phi}{\partial x_\rho}\right\} + \cdots$$

and other terms containing strange particle currents. This current has $\Delta Q = 1$ as required; this change is guaranteed by the isotopic spin operators $N_+$ and $\Pi_+$ which increase the charge by one unit. Such a current ensures that the vector coupling constant remains the same apart from small electromagnetic effects.

There are no immediately obvious effects of such a conserved vector current. The pi-meson current shows that the decay process

$$\pi^+ \to \pi^0 + e^+ + \nu$$

will occur directly rather than through intermediate baryon–antibaryon pairs and its decay can be calculated without uncertainty. An unconserved vector current also allows this decay but only through the baryon intermediate states, and the decay rate cannot be calculated. If the decay rate should turn out to be 0.37 sec$^{-1}$, the value expected in the conserved current theory, this will be excellent evidence for such a hypothesis for it is unlikely any other theory would predict the same rate. Unfortunately, this rate corresponds to a branching ratio of about $10^{-7}$ and is unlikely to be detected with present techniques.

## 12.12 The Parity of Strange Particles

The conservation of strangeness causes an ambiguity in the definition of the intrinsic parity of strange particles. Let us examine an associated production reaction

$$\pi^- + p \to K^0 + \Lambda^0.$$

It is evident that, if all the orbital angular momentum states are known, it is possible to determine the parity of the $K$-meson plus hyperon relative to $\pi$-meson plus proton. By convention, the charged $\pi$-meson has odd parity, so our reaction determines the parity of $K^0$, $\Lambda^0$, and proton taken together; it has become usual to assume that the $\Lambda^0$ and proton have even relative parity so the parity determined is assigned to the $K$-meson.

The most certain way of determining the $K^-$-meson parity will be by the analysis of the reactions

$$K^- + p \to \Lambda^0 + \pi^+ + \pi^-, \tag{12.38}$$

$$K^- + p \to \Lambda^0 + \pi^0 + \pi^0 \tag{12.39}$$

(Okun' and Pomeranchuk, 1958; Fonda and Russel, 1959). The first reaction is conveniently studied by absorbing $K^-$-mesons at rest in a liquid hydrogen bubble chamber. Such absorption takes place predominantly from $S$ orbital states (Section 12.6) and the initial state therefore has the parity of the $K^-$ meson and total angular momentum $j = \frac{1}{2}$. We take an axis $z$ of quantization along the direction of the emitted $\Lambda^0$. There are three final state angular momenta:

$l$, the relative angular momentum of the two $\pi$ mesons;

$l'$, the relative angular momentum of the $\Lambda^0$ and the centre of mass of the two $\pi$ mesons;

$s$, the spin of the $\Lambda^0$, taken to be $\frac{1}{2}$.

Then

$$\mathbf{J} = \mathbf{L} + \mathbf{L'} + \mathbf{S}$$

and

$$j_z = l_z + s_z.$$

Suppose $j_z = +\frac{1}{2}$. If $l_z = 0$, then $s_z = +\frac{1}{2}$, and this corresponds to no baryon spin change; there can be a baryon spin flip if $l \neq 0$, in which case $l_z = 1$, $s_z = -\frac{1}{2}$ or $l_z = -1$, $s_z = +\frac{1}{2}$, if $j_z = -\frac{1}{2}$. Whatever the $K$ parity, we expect the final states to be in the lowest accessible state of angular momentum because the kinetic energies available for penetrating angular momentum barriers are small. If the $K$ parity is even, the nearest state is $l = l' = 0$, which means that there is no correlation between momenta and no polarization of the outgoing $\Lambda^0$. If the $K$ parity is odd, the lowest accessible state has $l$ or $l' = 1$; if $l = 1$ and there is no spin flip ($l_z = 0$) or if $l' = 1$, there is a $\cos\theta$ correlation between momenta; if $l = 1$ and there is spin flip ($l_z \neq 0$) there can still be some correlation and there will be some polarization of the $\Lambda^0$ perpendicular to the plane of the three-body final state which varies with angle according to $\sin\theta\cos\theta$. The definition of $\theta$ requires that there is a distinction between the two $\pi$-mesons, i.e., of charge in reaction (12.38); if this is not the case, there is always an ambiguity in defining the plane of the final products by a normal vector. The polarization arises from the interference between spin-flipped and spin-unflipped outgoing waves and is not affected by the lack of polarization of the absorbing protons (by analogy with the recoil nucleon polarization on $\pi$-meson–proton scattering). We note that in the case of reaction (12.39) there can be no $\Lambda^0$ polarization and that $l$ can only be even. As yet there are no data available because the branching ratio for reaction (12.73) is about $10^{-4}$ and only a few examples have been observed.

There is an alternative but less definite method of determining the $K$-meson parity which has given results. Consider the reaction

$$K^- + \text{He}^4 \rightarrow {}_\Lambda\text{He}^4 + \pi^-.$$

The hypernucleus ${}_\Lambda\text{He}^4$ (Section 12.13) almost certainly has an even parity wave function and zero spin as has the $\text{He}^4$ nucleus. Thus, if absorption is from an $S$-state, the $\pi^-$ can only be emitted in an $S$-state and the reaction is forbidden unless the $K^-$ parity is the same as that of the $\pi^-$ meson. The reaction has been observed (Block *et al.*, 1959) and it follows that the $K^-$ parity is odd under the following assumptions:

(a) the absorption of the $K^-$ is from an $S$-state;

(b) the hypernucleus has zero spin;

(c) the hypernucleus has no excited states.

The mechanism that makes $S$-state $K^-$ absorption in hydrogen predominate is not operating in helium and there is no guarantee that (a) is satisfied. The remaining assumptions are based upon theoretical evidence concerning hypernuclei.

Moravscik (1959) has examined the differential cross section for $K^+$-meson photoproduction and finds some evidence that the $K^+$-meson is pseudoscalar (Section 13.5).

Many schemes have been suggested for examining the relative parities between baryons. Thus Treiman (1959) shows that the $\Lambda^0$

decay polarization analyser makes the reaction

$$\Xi^- + p \to \Lambda^0 + \Lambda^0$$

an excellent source of information about the interaction and parity involved. Similar suggestions have been made by Barshay (1959) and by Feldman and Fulton (1958). There are more subtle methods: Adair (1958) has shown that a plot of the differential cross section against energy for the reaction

$$\pi^- + p \to K^0 + \Lambda^0$$

exhibits cusps at the thresholds for the reactions

$$\pi^- + p \to K^0 + \Sigma^0$$

and

$$\pi^- + p \to K^- + \Sigma^+$$

if the hyperon parities are the same.

## 12.13 Hypernuclei

The $\Lambda^0$ hyperon can replace a neutron in many light nuclei and form a "stable" structure (that is, stable compared with nuclear frequencies $10^{23}$ sec$^{-1}$). The hyperon binding energy is comparable to that of the displaced neutron. These "hypernuclei" have mean lives of the order of $10^{-10}$ sec and less, and possess two outstanding decay branches—mesonic and nonmesonic. Mesonic decay corresponds to $\Lambda^0 \to \pi^- + p$ or $\pi^0 + n$ occurring within the nucleus and the $\pi$-meson emerging. No meson is observed to emerge from the nucleus in nonmesonic decay and presumably the decay $\pi$-meson is absorbed (internally converted) in the nucleus and its total energy converted into kinetic energy of ejected nucleons. The internal conversion branching ratio allows an estimate of the $\pi$-meson angular momentum and, by working back, provides further evidence for a spin $\frac{1}{2}$ assignment to the $\Lambda^0$ hyperon (Karplus and Ruderman, 1956). As expected, the nonmesonic branching ratio increases rapidly with the atomic number of the nucleus.

It is possible that the long life of the charged $\Sigma$ hyperons would allow their forming hypernuclei were it not for the rapidity of the exchange reactions

$$\Sigma^+ + n \to \Lambda^0 + p,$$

$$\Sigma^- + p \to \Lambda^0 + n,$$

which immediately ($10^{-23}$ sec) disrupt the hypernucleus. However, it has been suggested that the hypernuclei $\Sigma^+ p$ and $\Sigma^- n$ might exist (Snow, 1958).

For a review of hypernuclei readers are referred to an article by Fry (1958).

## 12.14 Conclusion

The reader will be aware that this chapter has two grave defects. The first concerns the subjects which have been neglected, such as $K^-$-meson absorption in hydrogen, $K$-meson scattering, etc. The reason for these omissions is our feeling that a discussion of these subjects would not add any new techniques or methods to those discussed in earlier chapters. These phenomena are analysed in the same way as the phenomena of $\pi$-meson physics: charge independence predicts the various reaction ratios and the $K$ scattering is subjected to a phase shift analysis. The second defect is the material which will be rapidly negatived or become out of date. However, we trust that, taken with the remainder of this book, this chapter will give the reader the background necessary to follow the developments in the subject of elementary particles.

# CHAPTER XIII

# RECENT TOPICS IN ELEMENTARY PARTICLE PHYSICS

## 13.1 Introduction

In this chapter we shall discuss four subjects which have, or may have in the future, considerable importance in the physics of elementary particles. Section 13.2 deals with the exploration of the electromagnetic structure of particles and is of considerable and expanding importance in the development of our knowledge of elementary particles. Section 13.3 deals with recent proposals to test the validity of quantum electrodynamics; there is no doubt about the importance of these proposals although at present there is no clue as to how this subject will develop. Section 13.4 deals with the well-established normal dispersion relations, whilst Section 13.5 concerns the controversial double-dispersion relations. This last subject has a very uncertain future at the time of writing.

## 13.2 Exploring the Structure of Elementary Particles

A very powerful technique for exploring the electromagnetic structure of nucleons has recently become available, and we shall discuss it and its implications in this section. We expect that the dimensions of any particle of mass $m$ are of the order of $\hbar/mc$, which for nucleons is about $2 \times 10^{-14}$ cm. However, nucleons are almost certainly surrounded by a "cloud of mesons" and this cloud is expected to have a dimension of approximately $\hbar/m_\pi c$, or $1.4 \times 10^{-13}$ cm. To explore structure in this range of size it is necessary to use a probe having a wavelength of this order or shorter. At the time of writing the sharpest probe has been 600-Mev electrons which have a de Broglie wavelength (divided by $2\pi$) of $3 \times 10^{-14}$ cm. By measuring the scattering of energetic electrons from nucleons it is possible to obtain information about the electromagnetic structure of the nucleon. Such scattering takes place from

he charge and magnetic moment of the nucleon and has a cross
ection which can be predicted if these qualities have a point structure.
The actual cross sections will deviate from the predicted cross section
f the charge and magnetic moment are spread out, and the deviation
s in the direction of reduced cross section, since the spread-out structure
educes the field against which the probe particles scatter. The devia-
ion becomes greater as the momentum transfer between incident
particle and target nucleon increases. This momentum transfer is best
lescribed by the invariant square of the four-momentum transfer.
We represent the momentum transfer by $\hbar q$ and in the electron
scattering

$$\hbar q = \hbar(q_1 - q_2)$$

where $\hbar q_1$ and $\hbar q_2$ are the four momenta of the incident
and scattered electron respectively. For example,
500-Mev electrons scattered at 90° in the laboratory
from protons correspond to $|q| = 3.4 \times 10^{13} \, \text{cm}^{-1}$. A
better idea of the distance probed is given by the
length $|q|^{-1}$, so our example can explore detail of
dimensions approximately $3 \times 10^{-14}$ cm.

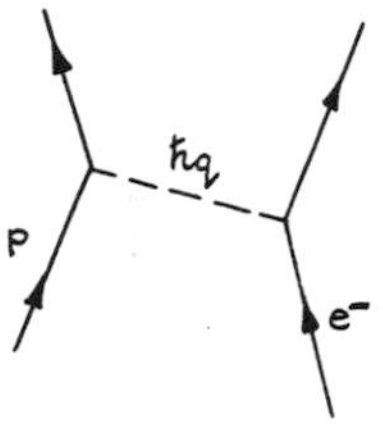

The effect of structure is formally expressed through
a form factor $F$, which is believed to be a function of
the structure and of the momentum transfer only. If
we put $\sigma_D$ as the scattering cross section if the nucleon
electric charge and magnetic moment are a point, then the actual
cross section will be given by

FIG. 13.1. The
Feynman diagram
for electron–
proton scattering.

$$\frac{d\sigma}{d\Omega} = F(q^2)\frac{d\sigma_D}{d\Omega}.$$

Similar expressions occur in all scattering situations in which the
structure of the scattering centre has an influence. For example,
X-ray scattering form factors reflect the electronic structure of the
scattering atoms.

Let us now put this formalism on a more exact foundation for the
case of electron–proton scattering. If we assume quantum electrodynamics is correct, then the electron scattering explores the electric
charge and magnetic moment structure of the proton. The Feynman
diagram for the process is given in Fig. 13.1. From our discussion in
Chapter IX we know that various parts of the diagram contribute
factors to the matrix element. If the nucleon were a pure Dirac
particle, it would contribute a factor which is the proton current with

which the electromagnetic field interacts. This current is given by

$$j_\mu = ie\bar{\psi}\gamma_\mu\psi,$$ (13.1

where $\bar{\psi}$ and $\psi$ are proton spinor field variables. This is exactly analogous to the electron–positron current in electrodynamics [Eq

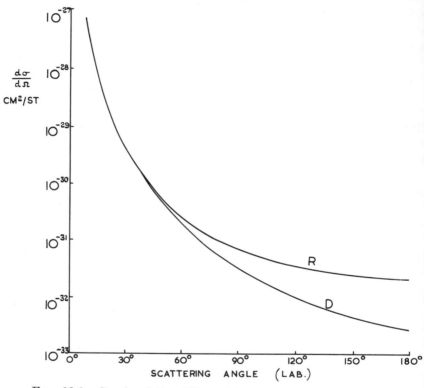

Fɪɢ. 13.2. Graph of the differential cross section for Dirac and Rosenbluth scattering of 500-Mev electrons (all quantities in the laboratory system).

(9.22a)]. It follows that a pure Dirac nucleon would scatter electrons with the following cross section:

$$\frac{d\sigma_D}{d\Omega} = \left(\frac{e^2}{2E}\right)^2 \frac{\cos^2\frac{1}{2}\theta}{\sin^4\frac{1}{2}\theta} \frac{1}{1+(2E/Mc^2)\sin^2\frac{1}{2}\theta}\left[1+\frac{\hbar^2 q^2}{4M^2 c^2}(2\tan^2\frac{1}{2}\theta)\right],$$ (13.2)

where $E$ is the incident electron energy, $M$ is the mass of the proton, and $\theta$ is the scattering angle in the laboratory. This cross section is plotted in Fig. 13.2 (curve D) for an incident electron energy of 500 Mev.

The term containing $\tan^2(\tfrac{1}{2}\theta)$ would be absent if the Dirac proton had no magnetic moment; the importance of this term at large angles indicates that the large-angle scattering is predominantly due to magnetic moment. A pure Dirac proton would have a magnetic moment of $e\hbar/2Mc$, or one nuclear magneton. However, in fact, the proton has a magnetic moment of 2.79 nuclear magnetons, an anomalous excess of 1.79 nuclear magnetons. This anomalous part adds to the effective proton current [Eq. (13.1)] a term proportional to this part and the current becomes

$$ j_\mu = ie\bar{\psi}\left(\gamma_\mu + \frac{K\hbar}{2Mc}\gamma_\mu\gamma_\nu q_\nu\right)\psi. \tag{13.3}$$

As usual, summation over repeated indices ($\nu$ in this equation) is implied. $K$ is the anomalous magnetic moment in units of nuclear magnetons. $\hbar q_\nu$ is the four-momentum transfer ($\nu = 1, 2, 3, 4$). This current leads to the differential cross section

$$ \frac{d\sigma_R}{d\Omega} = \left(\frac{e^2}{2E}\right)^2 \frac{\cos^2\tfrac{1}{2}\theta}{\sin^4\tfrac{1}{2}\theta} \frac{1}{1+(2E/Mc^2)\sin^2\tfrac{1}{2}\theta} $$
$$ \times \left\{1 + \frac{\hbar^2 q^2}{4M^2 c^2}[2(1+K)\tan^2\tfrac{1}{2}\theta + K^2]\right\}. \tag{13.4}$$

Hofstadter (1957) calls this "Rosenbluth scattering" after the author who first derived this equation (Rosenbluth, 1950). Curve R in Fig. 13.2 shows this cross section as a function of angle for 500-Mev electrons scattering from point protons with anomalous magnetic moment. We notice that the Rosenbluth scattering is considerably greater than Dirac scattering at large angles. This is a manifestation of the importance of magnetic scattering at large angles; the effect is greater in proton Rosenbluth scattering, since the magnetic moment is greater than for a pure Dirac particle.

Equations (13.2) and (13.4) apply to point protons. In fact, we are interested in structure, which has the effect of reducing the cross section. Phenomenologically this is represented by two form factors in the interaction. A convenient way of introducing these factors is to change the effective proton current to

$$ j_\mu = ie\bar{\psi}\left[\gamma_\mu F_1(q^2) + \frac{K\hbar}{2Mc}\gamma_\mu\gamma_\nu q_\nu F_2(q^2)\right]\psi. \tag{13.5}$$

$F_1$ and $F_2$ are assumed to be functions of the four-momentum transfer. $F_1$ is the form factor for the electric charge and the normal Dirac magnetic moment and as such is a way of describing the effects of any distribution these properties have. $F_2$ is the form factor for the anomalous magnetic moment and describes the effect of any distribution of this moment. Precisely the same current applies to the neutron, although it is immediately obvious that $F_{1N}(q^2 = 0) = 0$. In addition, there is the fact that $K = -1.91$ for the neutron and $1.79$ for the proton. The discussion now applies to either nucleon. The cross section predicted by this current is

$$\frac{d\sigma}{d\Omega} = \left(\frac{e^2}{2E}\right)^2 \frac{\cos^2 \frac{1}{2}\theta}{\sin^4 \frac{1}{2}\theta} \frac{1}{1 + (2E/Mc^2)\sin^2 \frac{1}{2}\theta}$$
$$\times \left\{F_1^2 + \frac{\hbar^2 q^2}{4M^2 c^2}[2(F_1 + KF_2)^2 \tan^2 \frac{1}{2}\theta + K^2 F_2^2]\right\}. \qquad (13.6)$$

We have said that $F_1$ and $F_2$ are taken to be functions of $q^2$. This is important as $q^2$ is a function of $\theta$ and consequently so are $F_1$ and $F_2$. If it is necessary to measure $F_1$ and $F_2$ at the same value of $q^2$, then two differential cross sections must be measured; the first at large angles determines the magnetic scattering ($F_2$) whilst the second at small angles determines the electric scattering ($F_1$). This second measurement must be done at a higher energy than the first in order to keep $q^2$ constant (Hofstadter, 1959).

It is not clear at present how $F_1$ and $F_2$ are connected with any structure the particle may have. Such structure means perhaps a spatial distribution of electric charge and magnetic moment over a volume of radius approximately $10^{-13}$ cm. However, it is difficult to reconcile such a spatial distribution with the relativistic concepts which must be used in treating this high-energy problem (Yennie et al., 1957). A nonrelativistic approximation would go as follows: suppose the charge distribution is of the form

$$\rho = \rho_0 e^{-r/r_0}. \qquad (13.7)$$

Then the form factor is the Fourier transform of this distribution:

$$F_1(\mathbf{q}^2) = \int \rho \, e^{i\mathbf{q} \cdot \mathbf{r}} \, d\mathbf{r} \Big/ \int \rho \, d\mathbf{r}$$

$$= \frac{1}{(1 + \mathbf{q}^2 r_0^2)^2}. \qquad (13.8)$$

This is a nonrelativistic form, for we have used the three space components of the four-momentum transfer. However, even at 600 Mev, $|\mathbf{q}|$ and $|q|$ are only different by about 10% and our approximation onsists of setting

$$F_1(q^2) = F_1(\mathbf{q}^2)$$

ith $\mathbf{q}^2$, not $q^2$, in Eq. (13.8). The rms radius, $a$, of this distribution
given by

$$a = \sqrt{12}\, r_0.$$

In the case of the proton, the experiments up to 600 Mev agree with
he following guesses about the structure: first that the magnetic
moment and charge have the same distribution so that $F_{1P} = F_{2P}$, and
hat this distribution is exponential [Eq. (13.7)], or similar, with a
ms radius of $0.80 \pm 0.1 \times 10^{-13}$ cm. The results are insensitive to choice
f distributions over a wide range but do indicate that a uniform
istribution or a distribution very peaked at the centre do not agree
with the observations. It is not immediately clear that these effects
re unequivocally attributable to proton structure and they could just
s well be explained by a breakdown in quantum electrodynamics
(including effects due to finite electron size) at these very high momentum transfers. The position is that at present we expect nucleon
tructure effects rather than a breakdown in electrodynamics. Of
ourse, the situation could be a combination of both. In the remainder
f this section we shall discuss the form factors as if they were giving
s information on nucleon structure, although it is far from obvious
s to what the information means.

We can now examine the neutron. We know that $F_{1N}(q^2 = 0) = 0$;
hat is, the neutron has no electric charge when it is measured in a
onstant electric field. However, there could be a charge distribution
which is not everywhere zero and it follows that Eq. (13.6) describes
he scattering of electrons from free neutrons. The experimental situa-
ion is not so happy because the only suitable target is the neutrons
ound into deuterium and thus the measurement of electron-neutron
cattering involves the measurement of the electrodisintegration of the
leuteron. The most obvious effect is that the scattered electron energy
listribution reflects the momentum distribution of the nucleons in the
leuteron. This spectrum must be carefully measured (Yearian and
Iofstadter, 1958) and analysed in a manner which separates effects
lue to the fact that the scattering has taken place from bound neutrons
nd which gives the cross section for scattering from free neutrons.
t is not clear whether the manner of this procedure is fully correct
nd there remain uncertainties of the order of 10% on the derived
ross section. The effects will be better understood in the future and
mprovement can be expected. At present the data are consistent with

$$F_{1N} = 0, \quad F_{2N} = F_{1P} = F_{2P}.$$

That is, the neutron is neutral throughout and has a magnetic momer distribution which is the same as the charge and magnetic momer distributions of the proton. The neutron result is confirmed by measure ments of low-energy scattering of neutrons by electrons. These sho that the electron–neutron interaction is very close to zero once th magnetic moment interaction has been subtracted from the total inte action, thus reinforcing the conclusion that $F_{1N} = 0$.

A simple meson picture of nucleons is such that we expect th proton to spend much of its time as a neutron and a $\pi^+$ meson, and neutron to spend much of its time as a proton plus a $\pi^-$ meson. Ther fore we expect that at large distances ( $> 2 \times 10^{-14}$ cm) from the nucleo core the two nucleons will have the same charge distribution but c opposite sign. The result $F_{1N} = 0$ does not satisfy this expectatio and we are left with the problem of explaining the apparent uniforr neutrality of the neutron; this problem is more puzzling in view of th fact that the neutron appears to have the same magnetic momer distribution as does the proton (Hofstadter *et al* , 1958, and references However, the conclusions reached concerning the structure of nucleon are based upon data which leave much to be desired. In the next fev years experiments will be done at even higher energies where th scattering data will reveal the structure effects more clearly.

It is evident that it would be desirable to extend these electro scattering measurements to targets of other elementary particles There are immediate difficulties but at least we can see two ways c tackling the problems involved. In the absence of a high density c free elementary particles, the first alternative is to use targets whic contain these particles in virtual states (see Section 13.5). Thus electro pi-meson scattering is measured by studying electroproduction of pi mesons at protons (or neutrons)

$$e^- + p \to \pi^+ + e^- + n.$$

This process has been detected in Hofstadter's work (Yearian an Hofstadter, 1958; see also Allton and Panofsky, 1958), but has no been analysed as a source of information on the pi-meson structure The methods of analysis will be discussed in Section 13.5. This tech nique may prove valuable and if so will be extended to all types o particles. For example, the reaction

$$e^- + p \to K^+ + e^- + \Sigma^0$$

will, in principle, measure the electron scattering from $K^+$ and $\Sigma^0$ and so on.

An alternative approach is to measure the scattering of the particles in question from stationary (atomically bound) electrons. Unfortunately, the centre-of-mass energy is only a small fraction of the incident particle's kinetic energy. For example, if we wish to measure pi-meson electron scattering at an energy equivalent to 1000-Mev electrons scattering from pi-mesons we need 273 Gev pi-mesons incident upon stationary electrons. It is evident that this method of exploring particle structure will not be available for probing to small distances for many years to come.

In this section we have not mentioned any of the other methods of observing nucleon structure, such as an examination of the energy levels of hydrogen and deuterium. These methods are insensitive as compared with the powerful method available in high-energy electron scattering. It is possible that the scattering of other types of particles will become useful methods of probing other features of nucleon structure.

## 3.3 Testing Quantum Electrodynamics

In Chapter IX we discussed quantum electrodynamics and pointed out some of its important successes. However, it has become clear that as a theory it has not been completely tested in the sense that the range of known validity is small compared with a conceivable range over which its validity will be of interest. Quantum electrodynamics is a theory which acknowledges the existence of the electromagnetic field, the electron–positron field, and other charged bodies. The interaction between electromagnetic field and charge is assumed to take place at a point (local theory) and it follows that the theory is infinite; that is to say, that there appear to be no limits to its validity. However, mesons and baryons exist and we expect that at very high energies quantum electrodynamics will suffer interference from fields of such high mass particles and that the present theory is only finite. In fact, it is probable that a unified field theory will not permit the separation of quantum electrodynamic problems. In the absence of such a theory we wish to examine the possibility of testing quantum electrodynamics at very high energies. We represent a breakdown in the theory in a phenomenological manner and from such representation search the theory for experimental conditions which might reveal such a breakdown.

For any given Feynman diagram there are three types of contribution to the matrix element and these are the photon propagator, electron (and positron) propagator, and the vertex factor. A breakdown in the theory is represented by one or more form factors which

multiply one or more of these matrix element factors and which a**
function of the invariant four-momentum transfer. These form facto**
are usually suggested in such a way as to contain a size as paramete**
in the same way as the rms radius of the proton is parameter for i**
form factor. The modification suggested to the photon propagator **
the replacement

$$\frac{1}{k^2} \to \frac{1}{k^2}\left(\frac{\Lambda_\gamma^2}{k^2 + \Lambda_\gamma^2}\right).$$

The form factor is $\Lambda_\gamma^2/(k^2 + \Lambda_\gamma^2)$. Now $\hbar k$ is a four-momentum and th**
$1/k^2$ has the dimensions (length)$^2$. Therefore $1/\Lambda_\gamma$ is the "size" **
distance which characterizes the breakdown. $\hbar\Lambda_\gamma/c$ has the dimension**
of mass and is sometimes called the regulator mass. If this mass **
that of the nucleon the size parameter is the Compton wavelengt**
divided by $2\pi$, of the nucleon, that is, $2.1 \times 10^{-14}$ cm. This suggeste**
modification to the photon propagator changes Coulomb's law from

$$V(r) \propto \frac{1}{r}$$

to

$$V(r) \propto \frac{1}{r}(1 - \exp(-\Lambda_\gamma r)).$$

A suitable modification to the electron propagator has an analogo**
form factor

$$\frac{p_\mu \gamma_\mu - imc}{p^2 + m^2} \to \frac{p_\mu \gamma_\mu - imc}{p^2 + m^2}\left(\frac{\Lambda_e^2}{p^2 + m^2 + \Lambda_e^2}\right).$$

This form factor is essentially the same as that proposed for th**
photon propagator and $\Lambda_e$ has the same qualities of related mass an**
distance as has $\Lambda_\gamma$. A suitable modification to the vertex factor wou**
be similar to that for the proton without anomalous magnetic momen**
that is,

$$j_\mu = ie\bar{\psi}\gamma_\mu \psi F(k^2).$$

For a preliminary exploration a suitable form factor would be given b**

$$F(k^2) = \frac{\Lambda_v^2}{k^2 + \Lambda_v^2}.$$

This can be compared with the proton form factor [Eq. (13.8)] whic**
is characteristic of an exponential charge distribution. This electro**

rtex form factor is characteristic of a "Yukawa" charge distribution:

$$\rho = \frac{\rho_0 \exp\left(-r\Lambda_v\right)}{r\Lambda_v}.$$

his has an rms radius of $\sqrt{6}/\Lambda_v$.

Propagators do not have a direct effect upon the behaviour of free eal) particles for which $k^2 = 0$ (photons) and $p^2 + m^2 = 0$ (electrons). follows that the form factors do not affect the behaviour of real articles. We note that, as we expect $F(k^2 = 0) = 1$, there can be no ectron form factor effects due to the absorption or emission of real hotons by electrons.

A particle which is real is said to be on the "mass shell". A virtual article $(k^2 \neq 0,\ p^2 + m^2 \neq 0)$ is said to be off the mass shell and it is irther off the shell the greater the deviation of the magnitude of the ur-momentum from its value for the real particle. It follows that sts for the existence of form factor effects mean examining processes hich involve virtual particles very far off the mass shell and such rocesses always have very low cross sections. Thus the experiments e shall discuss are far from easy to perform.

What limits have been put upon the various $\Lambda$ up to the present? e have pointed out that the deviations of electron–proton scattering oss sections from the Rosenbluth formula are usually assumed to be ue to proton structure but that they could be due to a breakdown in uantum electrodynamics and proton structure. The observed mean quare radius $\overline{r^2}$ would then be a combination of a real proton mean quare radius $a^2$ and the size of the modification to the photon propa- itor and electron vertex. The connection is

$$\overline{r^2} = a^2 + 6/\Lambda^2.$$

he scattering experiments put $\sqrt{(\overline{r^2})} = 0.8 \times 10^{-13}$ cm. Therefore the pper limit on $1/\Lambda$ is given by $a = 0$, in which case we have

$$\frac{1}{\Lambda} \leqslant 0.33 \times 10^{-13} \text{ cm.}$$

f it appears that quantum electrodynamics does break down and that he form factors have size parameters comparable with this distance, hen there is a corresponding decrease in the size of the proton. The amb–Retherford shift (Section 9.9) deviates from theory by an mount which, if not caused by proton structure, puts an upper limit f $0.5 \times 10^{-13}$ cm on $1/\Lambda$.

To test the presence of a size parameter in the photon propagato which is less than the upper limit, means measurements at very hig energies indeed. For example, if $1/\Lambda < 0.5 \times 10^{-13}$ cm, there will be r deviation due to form factors greater than 10% in the cross sectic for Møller scattering at energies of less than 100 Mev total energy

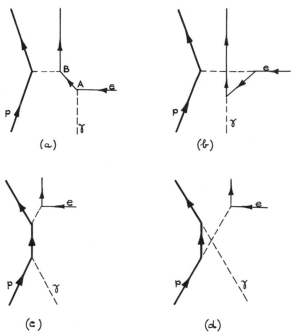

(a)    (b)

(c)    (d)

Fig. 13.3. Feynman diagrams for large angle pair production in the field of a proton.

the centre of mass. This is not possible with existing accelerator since this corresponds to 10-Gev electrons incident upon stationar electrons. However, colliding-beam experiments will soon be possibl and plans have been made to measure Møller scattering at 1000 Me in the centre of mass (O'Neill, 1959). This involves measuring th scattering from two colliding 500-Mev electron beams; in these circum stances the centre of mass is the laboratory frame and 90° scatterin corresponds to a momentum transfer of 1400 Mev/c. A comparison c scattering cross sections at 90° and at 35° with 10% accuracy wi detect the existence of a size parameter, $1/\Lambda$, which is not less tha $4 \times 10^{-15}$ cm. Of course, such an experiment does not distinguis between a photon propagator form factor or a vertex form factor.

The second modification we have mentioned is to the electron propagator. The upper limit on $1/\Lambda_e$ is about $5 \times 10^{-13}$ cm, a result which comes from a study of the Lamb–Retherford shift (Drell, 1958). However, several proposals have been made (Bjorken et al., 1958; Bjorken and Drell, 1959) for experiments which would test the electron propagator to a smaller distance. Virtual electrons sufficiently far off the mass shell occur in large angle pair production by photons. In Fig. 13.3 we show the four lowest order Feynman diagrams which apply to an experiment in which a high-energy positron is observed at a large angle with respect to the pair producing photon. The target is liquid hydrogen. In Fig. 13.3a there is a virtual electron propagating from $A$ to $B$. If the incident photon is 140 Mev and the positron is emitted at 90° with an energy of 100 Mev, then the four-momentum of this virtual electron is about 140 Mev/c. Any size parameter $1/\Lambda_e$ in the electron propagator will be apparent if it is greater than approximately $10^{-13}$ cm. Figure 13.3b also contributes to the process but unfortunately does not involve a virtual electron far off the energy shell, and it only dilutes the effect to be observed. In both diagrams, 13.3a and 13.3b, the effect of the virtual photon propagating to the proton is removed by using the experimentally observed values of the phenomenological proton form factors. This procedure in the analysis removes all effects due to that part of the diagram which corresponds to electron proton scattering (Fig. 13.1) whether they are due to proton structure or to a breakdown in quantum electrodynamics; we shall take this procedure for granted in our future discussion. In addition to Figs. 13a and 13b, Figs. 13c and 13d contribute and here the role of the proton corresponds to that of the proton in the scattering of high-energy photons at protons. This proton Compton scattering is known to have a resonance and the contribution of this diagram cannot be calculated precisely. Thus the effects of diagrams 13c and 13d will introduce further uncertainties into the interpretation of any measurements. One measurement has been made (Richter, 1958) but the results are inconclusive. A superior approach is to measure the cross section for pair production when both members of the pair are emitted at large angles ($20° \to 30°$) on opposite sides of the incident photon direction. There are still four diagrams as in Fig. 13.3, but the four-momentum transfer to the proton is small in comparison with that in the previous proposal and proton structure effects become negligible. In addition, the contribution of the "Compton" diagrams becomes very small. An experiment with 550-Mev bremsstrahlung and detecting 250-Mev electron and positron in coincidence at 30° will probe quantum electrodynamics to a distance of approximately $3 \times 10^{-14}$ cm.

Further experiments along these lines have been proposed (Bjorke and Drell, 1959). Pair production by electrons (tridents) in hydroge

$$e^- + p \rightarrow e^- + e^- + e^+ + p$$

is affected by modifications to both propagators and vertex. How ever, a comparison of pair production by photons with pair productio by electrons provides a means of testing the photon propagator an the electron vertex. Taken together, all these experiments provide way of observing and separating the three types of form factors whic could occur in quantum electrodynamics.

These suggestions have also been extended to the $\mu$-meson. Th puzzling particle behaves in all respects as a heavy electron. Th gives us no clue as to why it is so heavy and quantum electrodynami tests applied to it may give us some insight as to the meaning of th particle. The measurement of the $\mu$-meson magnetic moment indicate that it has no structure greater than approximately $2 \times 10^{-13}$ cm (Drel 1958). To reduce this limit it is necessary to do experiments analogou to those we have just discussed. Thus every experiment quoted fc electrons can be done with $\mu$-mesons; that is, pair production b photons and by electrons. A comparison of the electron and $\mu$-meso experiments at corresponding dynamic conditions will give informa tion on the $\mu$-meson form factor relative to the electron form factor.

## 13.4 Dispersion Relations

The scattered wave of a reaction can be a general term covering th amplitude of any outgoing wave of a nuclear or elementary partic] reaction. In principle, the amplitude of this wave can be calculatec given an adequate theory. However, in practice this may not b possible due to inadequate theory or to mathematical or physica complexity. This is particularly true in the theory of strongly inter acting particles. In recent years an alternative approach to the scatter ing amplitude has been developed, which aims to display the propertie of the amplitude independently of any theory. This approach give rise to dispersion relations which have been known for some time i optics and which are now proving useful in the physics of elementar particles.

The scattering amplitude is a complex quantity which is a functio of a real variable, the total energy of the system. The vital step is t assume that the amplitude is a function of a complex variable whic has the total energy as its real part. If we can show that the amplitud is analytic in the upper half-plane of its complex variable, then we ca immediately write down dispersion relations. These relations connec the real $[D(\omega)]$ and the imaginary part $[A(\omega)]$ of the scattering amplitude; for example,

$$D(\omega) = \frac{1}{\pi} P \int_{-\infty}^{+\infty} \frac{A(\omega')}{\omega - \omega'} d\omega'$$

where $\omega$ is the total energy. The symbol $P$ denotes the principal value of the integral and implies that the integral must be evaluated according to the prescription given by Cauchy. The proof of such dispersion relations rests upon proving that the scattering amplitude is analytic in the upper half-plane of its variable. We can now indicate how such a relation can be used. Consider forward scattering: the imaginary part of the amplitude is directly related to the total cross section via the optical theorem [Eq. (3.7)]. Thus the dispersion relation becomes a connection between the forward scattering amplitude and an integral of the total cross section over all energies. This is a remarkable result and has been used in many places—for example, to decide between the Fermi and the Yang sets of phase shifts, etc.

It is evident that the theory of functions of a complex variable is a basic part of dispersion relations. We refer readers to mathematical works for the theory (Whittaker and Watson, 1946; McLachlan, 1953) and to an article by Corinaldesi (1959) which gives a very clear introduction to this theory in the context of dispersion relations.

Let us now examine the relations in more detail. First let us consider the Fourier transform of real function of time $g(t)$:

$$f(x) = \int_{-\infty}^{+\infty} g(t) \, e^{ixt} \, dt.$$

If $g(t)$ has the following properties,

(1) $g(t)$ is bounded (i.e., $g(t) <$ some finite value for all $t$),

(2) $g(t)$ is square integrable $\left( \text{i.e.}, \int_{0}^{t} g^2(t) \, dt < \text{some finite value for all } t \right)$,

(3) $g(t) = 0$ for $t < 0$,

then we can define a function

$$f(z) = \int_{-\infty}^{+\infty} g(t) \, e^{izt} \, dt = \int_{0}^{\infty} g(t) \, e^{izt} \, dt$$

which is analytic in the upper half-plane of the complex variable $z = x + iy$. It follows that we can write down dispersion relations for $f(z)$. Let us suppose $f(\omega)$, the scattering amplitude, is defined in this way. The requirement $g(t) = 0$ for $t < 0$ is the same as saying that there can be no scattered wave until an incident wave arrives at the scattering centre. This, of course, is an expected result if causality applies and we can revise the argument and say if causality applies and if $f(\omega)$ can be defined by

$$f(\omega) = \int_0^\infty g(t)\, e^{i\omega t}\, dt, \tag{13.9}$$

then it follows that $f(\omega)$ is analytic on the real axis and in the upper half-plane. Therefore we can write down dispersion relations for this amplitude. We shall now assume that $f(\omega)$ can be expressed as in Eq. (13.9) and proceed to examine the steps which lead to the dispersion relations. Consider a contour integral in the complex plane. If a function $f(z')$ is analytic on and inside a contour, we have

$$\frac{1}{2\pi i}\int_C \frac{f(z')}{z'-z}\, dz' = \begin{cases} f(z) & \text{if } z \text{ is inside } C, \\ 0 & \text{if } z \text{ is outside } C. \end{cases}$$

This is the Cauchy formula. Let us form the contour $(C_1)$ so that it goes from $-\infty$ to $+\infty$ on the real axis and then back to $-\infty$ via a semicircle of infinite radius in the upper half of the complex plane. In addition, let us suppose $z$ is very close to the real axis; that is,

$$z = x \pm i\epsilon, \quad \epsilon > 0.$$

Then

$$\frac{1}{2\pi i}\int_{C_1} \frac{f(z')}{z'-z}\, dz' = \begin{cases} f(x+i\epsilon), & + \text{ sign}, \\ 0, & - \text{ sign}. \end{cases} \tag{13.10}$$

If $f(z) \to 0$ faster than $1/|z|$, as $|z| \to \infty$, we can neglect the contribution around the semicircle and our relation becomes

$$\frac{1}{2\pi i}\int_{-\infty}^{+\infty} \frac{f(x')\, dx'}{x'-(x\pm i\epsilon)} = \begin{cases} f(x+i\epsilon), & + \text{ sign}, \\ 0, & - \text{ sign}. \end{cases}$$

Therefore

$$\lim_{\epsilon \to 0} \frac{1}{2\pi i}\int_{-\infty}^{+\infty} \frac{f(x')\, dx'}{x'-(x\pm i\epsilon)} = \begin{cases} f(x), & + \text{ sign}, \\ 0, & - \text{ sign}. \end{cases} \tag{13.10a}$$

Now let us consider a contour $C_2$ which goes from $-\infty$ to $+\infty$ along the $x'$ axis but misses the point $x$ ($\epsilon = 0$) by a small semicircle above or below $x$ (Fig. 13.4). This semicircle has radius $\rho$ and we are interested in the limit of the contour integral as $\rho \to 0$. We have

$$\frac{1}{2\pi i} \int_{C_2} \frac{f(z')\,dz'}{z'-z} = \frac{1}{2\pi i} \left( \int_{-\infty}^{x-\rho} + \int_{x+\rho}^{+\infty} \right) \frac{f(x')\,dx'}{x'-x}$$

$$+ \frac{1}{2\pi i} \int_{-\pi}^{0 \text{ or } -2\pi} \frac{f(x+\rho\,e^{i\theta})\,i\rho\,e^{i\theta}\,d\theta}{\rho\,e^{i\theta}}. \qquad (13.11)$$

The upper limit on the second term is $0$ or $-2\pi$, according as to whether the contour is above or below $x$; this corresponds to the point $z$ being outside ($-$ sign) or inside ($+$ sign) the contour $C_1$ [Eq.

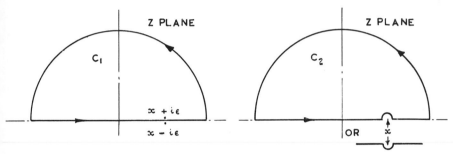

FIG. 13.4. The contours, $C_1$ and $C_2$, in the complex plane which are discussed in the text.

(13.10)]. In the limits as $\epsilon \to 0$ and as $\rho \to 0$ the contours and singularities become identical and the right-hand side of Eq. (13.10a) will become equal to the right-hand side of Eq. (13.11). The first term of this last side has a limit as $\rho \to 0$ which is called the Cauchy principal value and is denoted by a letter $P$. Thus we get

$$+ \text{ sign}: \quad f(x) = \frac{1}{2\pi i} P \int_{-\infty}^{+\infty} \frac{f(x')\,dx'}{x'-x} + \tfrac{1}{2}f(x),$$

$$- \text{ sign}: \quad 0 = \frac{1}{2\pi i} P \int_{-\infty}^{+\infty} \frac{f(x')\,dx'}{x'-x} - \tfrac{1}{2}f(x).$$

Therefore

$$\frac{1}{\pi i} P \int_{-\infty}^{+\infty} \frac{f(x')\,dx'}{x'-x} = f(x). \qquad (13.12)$$

The scattering amplitude is analytic in the real axis and in the upper half-plane and we can therefore write

$$f(\omega) = \frac{1}{\pi i} P \int_{-\infty}^{+\infty} \frac{f(\omega')\,d\omega'}{\omega'-\omega}. \qquad (13.12a)$$

We now break $f(\omega)$ into its real and imaginary parts,

$$f(\omega) = D(\omega) + iA(\omega),$$

and equating real and imaginary in Eq. (13.12a), we have that

$$D(\omega) = \frac{1}{\pi} P \int_{-\infty}^{+\infty} \frac{A(\omega')}{\omega' - \omega} \, d\omega',$$

$$A(\omega) = \frac{1}{\pi} P \int_{-\infty}^{+\infty} \frac{D(\omega')}{\omega - \omega'} \, d\omega'.$$

From Eq. (13.9) we can write

$$D(\omega) = \int_{-\infty}^{+\infty} g(t) \cos \omega t \, dt,$$

$$A(\omega) = \int_{-\infty}^{+\infty} g(t) \sin \omega t \, dt,$$

and it follows that

$$D(-\omega) = D(\omega) \quad \text{and} \quad A(-\omega) = -A(\omega).$$

Using the odd character of $A(\omega)$ we can rewrite the first dispersion relation

$$\int_{-\infty}^{+\infty} \frac{A(\omega') \, d\omega'}{\omega' - \omega} = \int_{0}^{\infty} \frac{A(\omega') \, d\omega'}{\omega' + \omega} + \int_{0}^{\infty} \frac{A(\omega') \, d\omega'}{\omega' - \omega};$$

hence

$$D(\omega) = \frac{2}{\pi} P \int_{0}^{\infty} \frac{\omega' A(\omega') \, d\omega'}{\omega'^2 - \omega^2}.$$

If this is applied to the forward scattering amplitude, we can replace $A(\omega')$ by a total cross section derived from the optical theorem [Eq. (3.7)],

$$\sigma(\omega') = \frac{4\pi}{k} A(\omega'),$$

and our dispersion relation becomes a connection between the real part of the forward scattering amplitude and the total cross section integrated over all energies. In most cases these relations contain integrals which converge too slowly at large values of $\omega'$. To avoid this, subtractions are made which lead to more rapid convergence.

Before these relations can be used it is necessary to deal with any unphysical region which may occur in the integral. We will do this by considering as an example dispersion relations applied to the scattering of pi-mesons by protons. The total energy $\omega$ is conveniently that of the pi-meson in the laboratory system and therefore the integral extends over the unphysical region where $0 < \omega' < m_\pi$ $(c = 1)$. It can be shown that $A(\omega')$ is zero in this region and there are no contributions to the integral apart from a singularity in this region. This singularity occurs when the total centre-of-mass energy is equal to the mass of the physical neutron. This occurs when $\omega$ satisfies the equation

$$(\omega + m_N)^2 - (\omega^2 - m_\pi^2) = m_N^2\,;$$

that is, when

$$\omega = \frac{m_\pi^2}{2m_N},$$

where $m_N$ is mass of the nucleon. The residue at this pole is related to the renormalized coupling constant $f^2$; the exact relation must be calculated using a specific interaction and is normally given for the pseudoscalar coupling. The final dispersion relations are (Goldberger et al., 1955)

$$D_\pm(k) = \frac{1}{2}\left(1 + \frac{\omega}{m_\pi}\right) D_\pm(0) + \frac{1}{2}\left(1 - \frac{\omega}{m_\pi}\right) D_\mp(0) + \frac{2f^2}{m_\pi^2} \frac{k^2}{\omega + (m_\pi^2/2m_p)}$$

$$+ \frac{k^2}{4\pi} P \int_{m_\pi}^\infty \frac{d\omega'}{k'} \left\{\frac{\sigma_\pm(\omega')}{\omega' - \omega} + \frac{\sigma_\mp(\omega')}{\omega' + \omega}\right\}.$$

The subscripts $+$ and $-$ refer to the quantities for positive and negative pi-mesons respectively. $k$ is the meson wave number and the relation applies in the laboratory system.

This dispersion relation has been applied by Anderson and co-workers (1955b). They find it convenient to use the $t = \frac{3}{2}$ and $t = \frac{1}{2}$ amplitudes given by

$$D_3 = D_+ \quad \text{and} \quad D_1 = \tfrac{3}{2}D_- - \tfrac{1}{2}D_+.$$

The values of the $D(k)$ can be calculated at various energies from given phase shift solutions and from their known behaviour at low energies. The values obtained are compared directly with values calculated by integration of measured total cross sections. In Figs. 13.5a and 13.5b we show the kind of curves that are obtained. The solid lines show $D_3(k)$ and $D_1(k)$ calculated from the dispersion relation [using low-energy phase shift behaviour for $D_\pm(0)$] whereas the points are the same quantities calculated from given Fermi phase shift solutions for experimental results at various energies. The authors used $f^2 = 0.08$. The good agreement justifies the use of the dispersion

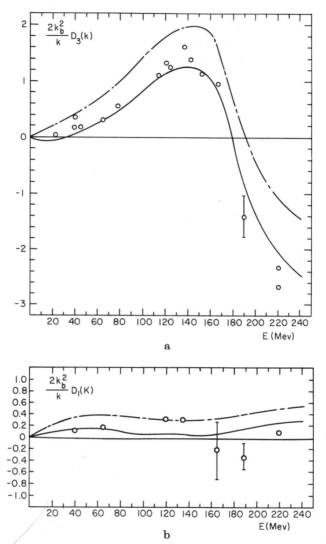

Fig. 13.5. a and b make a comparison of the quantities $(2k_b{}^2/k)\,D_3(k)$ and $(2k_b{}^2/k)\,D_1(k)$ calculated from the dispersion relations (solid and broken lines) and from the experimentally determined phase shifts (points). $k_b$ and $k$ are the meson wave number in the centre-of-mass and laboratory systems respectively. The dispersion relation calculations were made from total cross sections derived from a smooth curve drawn through the experimentally determined points; the very low energy total cross section had to be computed from $S$-wave phase shift prescriptions and the two curves correspond to two choices of prescription. (Anderson et al., 1955b.) ——$\delta_1 = 0.16\eta, \delta_3 = -0.11\eta$; —·—$\delta_1 = 0.33\eta, \delta_3 = 0.15\eta$; ○ experiment.

relations, lends support to previous values of $f^2$, and resolves the sign ambiguity which occurs in phase shift solutions (Section 7.9).

This first work does not resolve the Fermi–Yang ambiguity. A decision between the two sets can be made by a measurement of recoil proton polarization (Section 7.9) or by a dispersion relation test on the amplitudes responsible for polarization. The necessary spin-flip amplitude dispersion relation has been found and applied by Davidon and Goldberger (1956). The Fermi set satisfies the relations, whereas the Yang set does not.

Haber-Schaim (1956) has given a dispersion relation particularly suited to determining the coupling constant and obtains the result $f^2 = 0.082 \pm 0.015$. Puppi and Stanghellini (1957) used the normal dispersion relations but independently of any phase shift solutions. The best fit of the $\pi^+$ meson scattering data was obtained with $f^2 = 0.08$ but the $\pi^-$ meson scattering data required $f^2 = 0.04$. A more recent analysis by Schnitzer and Salzman (1959) finds $f^2 = 0.08 \pm 0.01$ as the best value from both $\pi^+$ and $\pi^-$ scattering data, although there remains a slight discrepancy for the $\pi^-$ data.

Dispersion relations have been used in many circumstances apart from meson–nucleon scattering. For example, they have been applied to nucleon–nucleon scattering (Cini et al., 1959; Hamilton, 1959a), to $K$-meson scattering (Matthews and Salam, 1958a, b), and to pi-meson photoproduction (Chew et al., 1957). For an extensive review, readers are referred to an article by Chew (1959).

## 13.5 Double Dispersion Relations

Let us consider the elementary particle reaction

$$1 + 2 \to 3 + 4. \tag{13.13}$$

We specify this reaction by four four-vectors of momentum and our sign convention is such that all momenta are expressed as if they applied in the initial state; that is, the conservation of momentum and energy is given by the vector equation

$$p_1 + p_2 + p_3 + p_4 = 0.$$

In reaction (13.13) the observed momenta of particles 3 and 4 are $-p_3$ and $-p_4$. We can write the scattering amplitude for reaction (13.13) as $f(p_1, p_2, p_3, p_4)$. This amplitude applies not only to reaction (13.13) but also to the reaction

$$1 + \overline{3} \to \overline{2} + 4 \tag{13.14}$$

with observed momenta $p_1, p_3, -p_2, -p_4$, and to the reaction

$$1 + \bar{4} \to \bar{2} + 3 \qquad (13.15)$$

with observed momenta $p_1, p_4, -p_2, -p_3$. The bar above the figures indicates the antiparticle.

All these reactions have dynamic conditions which can be specified by two invariants, $W$ and $\Delta$, which are given by

$$W^2 = -(p_1 + p_2)^2 = -(p_3 + p_4)^2, \qquad (13.16)$$

$$\Delta^2 = (p_1 + p_3)^2 = (p_2 + p_4)^2. \qquad (13.17)$$

We are using four-vector algebra and therefore $(p_1 + p_2)^2$ is the scalar product of the vector $p_1 + p_2$ with itself (Section 1.4). In fact, $W$ is the total centre-of-mass energy in reaction (13.13) and $\Delta$ is a momentum transfer. This last statement will be clearer if we consider an example. Suppose particles 1 and 3 are nucleons, particle 2 is a photon, and particle 4 a meson; then the momentum transferred to the nucleon in this photoproduction reaction is

$$p_1 - (-p_3) = p_1 + p_3.$$

The scattering amplitude is, in fact, a function of these two variables, that is, $f(W, \Delta)$. We observe that the normal dispersion relations which we discussed in the last section are connections between the real and imaginary parts of $f(W, \Delta)$ and include an integral of the imaginary part over the energy. We now observe that the relation is one in $W$ with $\Delta$ fixed and is normally applied to the forward scattering amplitude, for which $\Delta = 0$ in the case of elastic scattering. We are now going to examine the possibility of writing dispersion relations in $\Delta$ with $W$ fixed. To develop our argument, we return to the photoproduction example

$$N + \gamma \to N + \pi,$$

$$1 + 2 \to 3 + 4.$$

Now consider reaction (13.14), which corresponds to

$$N + \bar{N} \to \gamma + \pi \qquad (13.18)$$

or nucleon-antinucleon annihilation into a photon and pi-meson. Let us now look at the total energy $(W')$ and a momentum transfer for reaction (13.18):

$$W'^2 = -(p_1 + p_3)^2, \qquad (13.19)$$

$$\Delta'^2 = (p_1 - (-p_2))^2 = (p_1 + p_2)^2. \qquad (13.20)$$

Comparing these two Eqs. (13.19), (13.20) with Eqs. (13.16) and (13.17), we observe that $W'^2 = -\Delta^2$ and $\Delta'^2 = -W^2$. Thus the square momentum transfer in photoproduction becomes the negative of the total energy in this type of annihilation, and the square total energy becomes the annihilation square momentum transfer. In addition, a dispersion relation for photoproduction automatically is a dispersion relation for this annihilation, only it is a relation in $\Delta'$ with $W'$ fixed. Conversely, any normal dispersion relation for this annihilation reaction becomes a dispersion relation in momentum transfer for photoproduction.

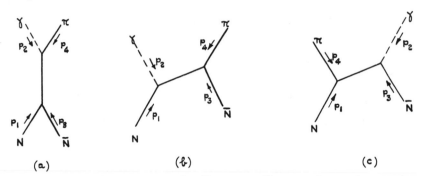

(a)        (b)        (c)

FIG. 13.6. The lowest order Feynman diagrams for nucleon and antinucleon annihilation into photon and pi-meson.

One of the most interesting features of this result is the role of the singularities which can occur in the unphysical region (we have already met one such singularity in pi-meson scattering dispersion relations). First, it is necessary to obtain a complete list of singularities which can occur. This is done by drawing all the lowest order Feynman diagrams which can contribute to the reaction to be studied. Singularities occur whenever a virtual particle in a diagram has a four-momentum which has a square equal to the negative of the square mass of one or more physical particles. These particles, which cause the singularities, can only be those which are allowed to appear if the laws of the conservation of baryon number, lepton number, strangeness, etc. are obeyed. The singularities are poles if the mass is that of a single particle and are branch points if the mass is that of two or more particles.

In Fig. 13.6 we show the three lowest order Feynman diagrams for the annihilation reaction, which contribute singularities. The lines are associated with labelled arrows which indicate the direction of the particle's four-momentum. Diagram 13.6a contributes a pole when

$$(p_1 + p_3)^2 = -m_\pi^2$$

and branch points at

$$(p_1 + p_3)^2 = -(2m_\pi)^2, -(3m_\pi)^2, ..., \text{etc.}$$

Diagram 13.6b contributes a pole when

$$(p_1 + p_2)^2 = -(m_N)^2$$

and branch points at

$$(p_1 + p_2)^2 = -(m_N + m_\pi)^2, -(m_N + 2m_\pi)^2, ..., \text{etc.}$$

Diagram 13.6c contributes a pole when

$$(p_1 + p_4)^2 = -(m_N)^2$$

and branch points at

$$(p_1 + p_4) = -(m_N + m_\pi)^2, -(m_N + 2m_\pi)^2, ..., \text{etc.}$$

A normal dispersion relation applied to the annihilation reaction will be one in $W'$ for constant $\Delta'$. The constant $\Delta'$ implies that the singularities due to diagram 13.6b do not occur in the integral of the dispersion relation and the singularities in the integral along the real axis of the complex $W'$ plane will be at the points given by the diagrams 13.6a and 13.6c singularities. The residues of these singularities will be connected with the coupling constants and relative parities of the fields which are involved.

Now let us consider photoproduction: the same singularities apply, since the Feynman diagrams are essentially the same. The normal dispersion relation for the annihilation becomes a dispersion relation in $\Delta$ at constant $W$ for photoproduction and the annihilation singularities on the real axis in $W'$ become corresponding singularities on the real axis of $\Delta$. To see where these singularities occur we will use a clearer notation. We put $k\, (= +p_2)$ as the incident photon four-momentum, $q\, (= -p_4)$ the outgoing meson momentum, $p\, (= p_1)$ the target nucleon momentum, and $p'\, (= -p_3)$ the recoil nucleon momentum. Then

$$\left. \begin{aligned} W^2 &= -(k+p)^2, \\ \Delta^2 &= (p-p')^2. \end{aligned} \right\} \tag{13.21}$$

If $W^2$ is fixed, there are poles on the real axis $\Delta$ as follows (for simplicity we consider the poles alone):

pole due to diagram 13.6a when

$$(p_1 + p_3)^2 = (p - p')^2 = -m_\pi^2 = \Delta^2; \tag{13.22}$$

pole due to diagram 13.6c when

$$(p_1 + p_4)^2 = (p - q)^2 = -m_N^2. \qquad (13.23)$$

Let us calculate the value of $\Delta^2$ at the pole due to diagram 13.6c. From Eq. (13.23) we have that

$$p^2 + q^2 - 2p \cdot q = -m_N^2$$

or

$$2p \cdot q = -m_\pi^2 \qquad (13.24)$$

which follows from the equalities

$$p^2 = -m_N^2 \quad \text{and} \quad q^2 = -m_\pi^2.$$

From the first equation under (13.21) we have

$$2p \cdot k = m_N^2 - W^2, \qquad (13.25)$$

and from the second equation under (13.21) we have

$$\Delta^2 = p^2 + p'^2 - 2p \cdot p'$$

$$= -2m_N^2 - 2p \cdot (p + k - q). \qquad (13.26)$$

Substitute Eqs. (13.24) and (13.25) into (13.26) and we find that

$$\Delta^2 = W^2 - m_\pi^2 - m_N^2,$$

at the pole due to 13.6c. For comparison, we restate that the pole due to diagram 13.6a occurs when

$$\Delta^2 = -m_\pi^2.$$

The poles occur at points which correspond to unphysical values of the photoproduction angle. For example, at the diagram 13.6a pole

$$\Delta^2 = (q - k)^2 = -m_\pi^2$$

or

$$-2q \cdot k = 0.$$

Substituting centre-of-mass quantities, we have

$$-2|\mathbf{q}||\mathbf{k}|\cos\theta + 2|\mathbf{k}|E_\pi = 0.$$

Therefore the 13.6a pole occurs when

$$\cos\theta = \frac{E_\pi}{|\mathbf{q}|} = \frac{1}{\beta_\pi},$$

where $\beta_\pi$ is the velocity of the pi-meson in the centre of mass ($c = 1$). Similarly, the 13.6c pole occurs at $\cos\theta = -1/\beta_N$ where $\beta_N$ is the recoil nucleon velocity. The branch points also correspond to unphysical angles and occur at even larger values ($+ve$ or $-ve$ wise) of $\cos\theta$.

The important point is that the residues at these poles depend upon the meson–nucleon coupling constant. Therefore, if we can extrapolate the observed photoproduction angular distribution to the values of $\cos\theta$ at the poles, the value of the extrapolated cross section will be related to the coupling constant. This procedure is analogous to that in normal dispersion relation applications where the residue of poles on the real $W$ axis are related to coupling constants.

The possibility of using extrapolated angular distributions in this manner was first discussed by Chew (1958) in connection with nucleon–nucleon scattering. The meson photoproduction case that we have discussed is due to Taylor et al. (1959). Moravscik (1959) has obtained evidence that the $K$–$\Lambda$–$N$ parity is odd by applying this method to $K$-meson photoproduction data. Chew and Low (1959) have considered similar extrapolation procedures for the analysis of reactions in which a two-particle initial state gives rise to a three-particle final state; these authors suggest that the data from a study of such reactions can determine the differential and total cross sections for the scattering of the incident particle by another particle which is normally only virtually contained in the actual target. Thus, for example, a study of the reaction

$$e^- + p \rightarrow \pi^0 + e^- + p$$

will determine the electron–neutral meson and the electron–proton scattering cross sections (Section 13.2).

The discussion of this section is an application of the double dispersion relation representation discussed by Mandelstam (1958, 1959). He has examined the conjecture that the scattering amplitude is an analytic function of two complex variables which have as real parts the total energy and a momentum transfer. The location and residues of singularities in the complex planes are also a matter of conjecture, and although there are plausibility arguments, the ideas lack formal proof at the time of writing (1959). However, this cannot obscure the possible future importance of this work and it is expected that very much attention will be applied to these concepts.

## 13.6 Conclusion

This chapter has dealt with topics that appear to the author to be of expanding importance in the physics of elementary particles. At the time of writing the double dispersion relations method is very much a newcomer to this field, and although it lacks proof, it does appear to be a subject which offers a new approach to the strong interactions. It is to be hoped that the confidence of the authors of this scheme will be justified.

# APPENDIX A

# REACTION KINEMATICS AT RELATIVISTIC ENERGIES

### A.1 Relations for a Single Particle

We start by considering a single particle of rest mass $m$, moving in an observer's frame with momentum $p$; then the total energy of the particle $\epsilon$ is given by

$$\epsilon^2 = p^2 c^2 + m^2 c^4,$$

where $c$ is the velocity of light. We can put $c = 1$ and express the quantities in suitable energy units; then

$$\epsilon^2 = p^2 + m^2. \tag{A.1}$$

In addition, we can relate the kinetic energy $t$ to the total energy, thus:

$$\epsilon = t + m.$$

If $\beta$ is the velocity of the particle in units of the velocity of light and $\gamma$ is $1/\sqrt{1-\beta^2}$, we have

$$\gamma = \frac{\epsilon}{m}, \tag{A.2}$$

$$\beta = \frac{p}{\epsilon}. \tag{A.3}$$

The rest mass of a particle is the same for all observers, that is, $m$ is an invariant. Consequently the quantity $\epsilon^2 - p^2$ is also an invariant. For a system of two or more particles the corresponding invariant is

$$\left(\sum_r \epsilon_r\right)^2 - \left|\sum_r \mathbf{p}_r\right|^2 = M^2. \tag{A.4}$$

The summation is performed over all particles. $M$ is then the rest mass of the assembly and is equal to the over-all total energy if the total momentum is zero; this is the case for the observer stationary with respect to the centre of mass of the assembly.

There is a trick that we can introduce at this point. Rearranging Eq. (A.1), we can write

$$\frac{\epsilon^2}{m^2} - \frac{p^2}{m^2} = 1.$$

Compare this with

$$\sec^2 \alpha - \tan^2 \alpha = 1. \tag{A.5}$$

Obviously, if we have $\alpha = \sec^{-1}(\epsilon/m)$, the following equations hold:

$$\gamma = \sec \alpha,$$

$$\beta = \sin \alpha,$$

$$p/m = \tan \alpha,$$

$$t/m = \sec \alpha - 1.$$

Thus if the total energy and momentum are expressed in units of the rest mass energy, we can use tables of the trigonometric functions to facilitate calculation of any one of these quantities from another. The angular intervals in secant and tangent tables become very small for large changes in $\gamma$ and $p/m$ when $\alpha$ is close to $90°$. To avoid this difficulty many authors use $\cosh^2 \alpha - \sinh^2 \alpha = 1$ instead of Eq. (A.5). However, hyperbolic tables are not so readily available as trigonometric tables.

## A.2 Lorentz Transformations between Laboratory and Centre-of-Mass Coordinates

The study of nuclear reactions involves Lorentz transformations between the laboratory coordinates and the centre-of-mass coordinates as defined in Section 1.4; we shall now consider the important relations for the incident states. Our notation is such that letters are unprimed when representing quantities observed from the laboratory coordinates and primed for the corresponding quantities observed in the centre-of-mass coordinates; no such distinction is made for invariants. In the laboratory system an incident particle of rest mass $m_1$, momentum $p_1$, and total energy $\epsilon_1$, interacts with a stationary particle of rest mass $m_2$. See Fig. A.1. The total energy of this system is given by

$$E = m_2 + \epsilon_1.$$

The rest mass $M$ is invariant and from Eq. (A.4) is given by

$$M^2 = E^2 - p_1^2.$$

In the centre of mass, the total momentum is zero and the total energy is just the rest mass; that is,

$$E' = M = \sqrt{(m_2 + \epsilon_1)^2 - p_1^2} \qquad (A.6)$$

or

$$E'^2 = m_1^2 + m_2^2 + 2m_2 \epsilon_1. \qquad (A.7)$$

We now use $\beta$ to represent the velocity of the centre of mass in the laboratory coordinates; this must not be confused with the previous $\beta$

| System | Laboratory | | Centre of mass | |
|---|---|---|---|---|
| Particle | 1 | 2 | 1 | 2 |
| | $\bullet\!\!\rightarrow$ | $\bullet$ | $\bullet\!\!\rightarrow$ | $\leftarrow\!\!\bullet$ |
| Rest mass | $m_1$ | $m_2$ | $m_1$ | $m_2$ |
| Momentum | $p_1$ | 0 | $\dfrac{p_1 m_2}{E'}$ | $\dfrac{p_1 m_2}{E'}$ |
| Total energy | $\epsilon_1$ | $m_2$ | $\dfrac{m_1^2 + m_2 \epsilon_1}{E'}$ | $\dfrac{m_2^2 + m_2 \epsilon_1}{E'}$ |
| Total energy of system | $\epsilon_1 + m_2$ | | $E' = \sqrt{m_1^2 + m_2^2 + 2m_2 \epsilon_1}$ | |

FIG. A.1. The relations between quantities in the centre-of-mass and laboratory systems for the initial state of a reaction.

used to represent the velocity of a particular particle. However, we can use Eq. (A.3) to find this velocity; hence

$$\beta = \frac{p_1}{\epsilon_1 + m_2}$$

and

$$\gamma = \frac{E}{E'}.$$

Now $\beta$ is the velocity of particle 2 in the centre-of-mass coordinates; therefore we can find $p_2'$

$$p_2' = \beta \gamma m_2 = \frac{p_1 m_2}{E'}.$$

By definition $\mathbf{p}_1' = -\mathbf{p}_2'$. By use of Eq. (A.1) applied to each particle in the centre-of-mass coordinates we find

$$\epsilon_1' = \frac{m_1^2 + m_2\,\epsilon_1}{E'},$$

$$\epsilon_2' = \frac{m_2^2 + m_2\,\epsilon_1}{E'}.$$

## A.3 Reaction Threshold Relations

We consider the collision between particles 1 and 2 causing a reaction which transforms these particles into particles 3 and 4. We assume that there is a certain minimum kinetic energy which particle 1 must have before this reaction can proceed; at this "threshold" particles 3 and 4 are produced with zero kinetic energy in the centre-of-mass coordinates, that is, $E' = m_3 + m_4$. This can obviously be extended to more than two reaction products. The $Q$ value for a two-body reaction is defined by

$$Q = m_1 + m_2 - (m_3 + m_4).$$

$Q$ is negative for reactions having a threshold. If $Q$ is positive the reaction can proceed at all energies of the incident particle.

We can calculate threshold energies for some simple reactions.

(a) $$\gamma + p \to \pi^0 + p.$$

The centre-of-mass energy $E' = \sqrt{m_1^2 + m_2^2 + 2m_2\,\epsilon_1}$. We substitute

$\epsilon_1 =$ incident photon energy,

$m_1 = 0$ (incident photon has zero rest mass),

$m_2 = m_p$, the mass of the proton.

At threshold $E' = m_\pi + m_p$, where $m_\pi$ is the rest mass of the pi-meson; then

$$m_\pi + m_p = \sqrt{m_p^2 + 2m_p\,\epsilon_1}$$

or

$$\epsilon_1 = m_\pi\left(1 + \frac{m_\pi}{2m_p}\right).$$

This equation gives the required photon energy at threshold.

(b) $$p + p \to \pi^0 + p + p.$$

We have $m_1 = m_2 = m_p$. At threshold

$$E' = m_\pi + 2m_p = \sqrt{2m_p^2 + 2m_p \epsilon_1}.$$

If we put $\epsilon_1$ equal to the rest mass of the incident proton plus its kinetic energy $t_p$, we have

$$m_\pi + 2m_p = \sqrt{4m_p^2 + 2m_p t_p},$$

then

$$t_p = 2m_\pi\left(1 + \frac{m_\pi}{4m_p}\right).$$

This equation gives the required incident proton kinetic energy at threshold.

(c) The general case of

$$1 + 2 \to 3 + 4.$$

At threshold

$$m_3 + m_4 = E' = \sqrt{m_1^2 + m_2^2 + 2m_2 \epsilon_1}.$$

Put

$$\epsilon_1 = t_1 + m_1.$$

Then

$$(m_3 + m_4)^2 - (m_1 + m_2)^2 = 2m_2 t_1$$

or

$$t_1 = -\frac{Q}{2m_2}(m_1 + m_2 + m_3 + m_4).$$

## A.4 Reactions above Threshold

If the incident energy exceeds the threshold, or if $Q$ is positive for the reaction

$$1 + 2 \to 3 + 4,$$

then the excess energy goes into kinetic energy of the particles 3 and 4. Let $\epsilon_3'$ and $\epsilon_4'$ be the total energies of particles 3 and 4 in the centre of mass

$$\epsilon_3' + \epsilon_4' = E', \tag{A.8}$$

where $E'$ is the total energy in the centre of mass [Eq. (A.6)]. These particles have equal and opposite momentum $p'$

$$p'^2 = \epsilon_3'^2 - m_3^2 = \epsilon_4'^2 - m_4^2. \tag{A.9}$$

Solving (A.8) and (A.9), we find

$$\epsilon_4' = \frac{E'^2 + m_4^2 - m_3^2}{2E'}, \tag{A.10}$$

and

$$\epsilon_3' = \frac{E'^2 + m_3^2 - m_4^2}{2E'}. \tag{A.11}$$

Equations (A.9)–(A.11) will give all required information about either particle in the centre of mass. These particles 3 and 4 will be produced at angles $\theta'$ and $180° - \theta'$ with respect to the incident direction. These centre-of-mass quantities can be transformed to laboratory coordinates by formulae given in the next section.

## A.5 Transformations for the Reaction Products

We have considered the incident particles to a reaction. The kinematics of this incident state establish the velocity and momentum of the

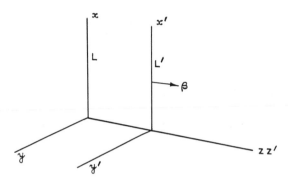

FIG. A.2. The relation between the centre-of-mass and laboratory frame.

centre of mass of the system as observed from the laboratory coordinates; these quantities are unchanged by the reaction. However, the reaction products may be moving in directions other than that of the centre of mass and we have to establish the relations between various quantities in the centre of mass and the laboratory coordinates. In addition, differential cross sections can be expressed in either coordinates and we must find the relations between such quantities.

We set up two Cartesian coordinate systems: the first, $L$, is stationary in the laboratory and oriented so that the incident particle is moving along the direction of the $z$ axis. The second system, $L'$, is essentially the centre-of-mass coordinates and is moving along the $z$ axis of $L$ with the velocity of the centre of mass $\beta$; it is oriented so that $z'$ is colinear with $z$, so that $x'$ is parallel to $x$ and $y'$ to $y$. See Fig. A.2.

Let us consider a particle moving in $xz$ plane at an angle $\theta$ to the $z$ axis with momentum of magnitude $p$ and total energy $\epsilon$, all as observed in $L$; as usual, the corresponding quantities in $L'$ are primed We use the relativistic transformation of the momentum four vector (Møller, 1952); the equations are:

$$p_x = p'_x, \quad p_y = p'_y, \quad p_z = \frac{p'_z + \beta \epsilon'}{\sqrt{1-\beta^2}}, \quad \epsilon = \frac{\epsilon' + \beta p'_z}{\sqrt{1-\beta^2}}. \quad \text{(A.12)}$$

Substituting more convenient quantities and using the rest mass invariant, we find

$$p \sin \theta = p' \sin \theta', \quad \text{(A.13)}$$

$$\gamma(p \cos \theta - \beta \epsilon) = p' \cos \theta', \quad \text{(A.14)}$$

$$\gamma(\epsilon - p\beta \cos \theta) = \epsilon', \quad \text{(A.15)}$$

where

$$\gamma = \frac{1}{\sqrt{1-\beta^2}}.$$

We must note that $\beta$ is the velocity of $L'$ in $L$. It is *not* the velocity of the particle.

We must now derive the relation between differential cross sections in the various coordinates. First we show that the quantity $d\mathbf{p}/\epsilon$ for a particle is an invariant. From Eq. (A.12) we have

$$dp_x = dp'_x, \quad dp_y = dp'_y, \quad dp_z = \gamma \, dp'_z \left(1 + \beta \frac{d\epsilon'}{dp'_z}\right).$$

Now $\epsilon d\epsilon = p_z dp_z$; then

$$d\mathbf{p} = d\mathbf{p}' \left(1 + \frac{\beta p'_z}{\epsilon'}\right) \gamma$$

or

$$\frac{d\mathbf{p}}{\epsilon} = \frac{d\mathbf{p}'}{\epsilon'}. \quad \text{(A.15a)}$$

This is the required result.

We are continuing to consider one of the particles to which Eqs. (A.9)–(A.11) apply. The probability that this particle appears from a reaction within a solid angle $d\Omega$ and in the energy range $\epsilon \to \epsilon + d\epsilon$ is proportional to the quantity

$$\left(\frac{d^2\sigma}{d\epsilon \, d\Omega}\right) d\epsilon \, d\Omega.$$

This quantity is invariant; that is,

$$\left(\frac{d^2\sigma}{d\epsilon \, d\Omega}\right)' d\Omega' \, d\epsilon' = \left(\frac{d^2\sigma}{d\epsilon \, d\Omega}\right) d\Omega \, d\epsilon, \quad \text{(A.16)}$$

here $d\Omega$ corresponds to $d\Omega'$ and the range $d\epsilon$ corresponds to $d\epsilon'$. Now we have, manipulating the invariant of Eq. (A.15a),

$$\frac{d\mathbf{p}}{\epsilon} = \frac{p^2\,dp\,d\Omega}{\epsilon} = p\,d\epsilon\,d\Omega = p'\,d\epsilon'\,d\Omega'.$$

If we substitute in Eq. (A.16) we find that

$$\left(\frac{d^2\sigma}{d\epsilon\,d\Omega}\right)'\frac{1}{p'} = \frac{1}{p}\left(\frac{d^2\sigma}{d\epsilon\,d\Omega}\right).$$

This is the first required equation.

If there are only two reaction products, each will appear with a unique energy in the centre of mass, for a given incident particle energy; therefore (A.16) becomes

$$\left(\frac{d\sigma}{d\Omega}\right)'d\Omega' = \left(\frac{d\sigma}{d\Omega}\right)d\Omega. \tag{A.17}$$

We express $d\Omega$ in the normal polar angles, that is,

$$d\Omega = d\phi\,d(\cos\theta).$$

$\phi$ and $\phi'$ are defined in the $xy$ plane and are therefore invariant and Eq. (A.17) reduces to

$$\left(\frac{d\sigma}{d\Omega}\right)' = \left(\frac{d\sigma}{d\Omega}\right)\frac{d\cos\theta}{d\cos\theta'}. \tag{A.18}$$

If we differentiate Eqs. (A.13)–(A.15) with respect to $\cos\theta$, we can find the differential $d\cos\theta'/d\cos\theta$. In doing this we recall that $d\epsilon/dp = p/\epsilon$ and, since $p'$ and $\epsilon'$ are independent of angle in the centre-of-mass coordinates, we have that $d\epsilon'/d\cos\theta$ and $dp'/d\cos\theta$ are zero. Note, however, that $d\epsilon/d\cos\theta$ and $dp/d\cos\theta$ are not zero. From (A.14) we have

$$\gamma\left(p + \cos\theta\,\frac{dp}{d\cos\theta} - \frac{\beta p}{\epsilon}\,\frac{dp}{d\cos\theta}\right) = p'\frac{d\cos\theta'}{d\cos\theta}.$$

From (A.15) we have

$$\gamma\left(\frac{p}{\epsilon}\,\frac{dp}{d\cos\theta} - \beta\cos\theta\,\frac{dp}{d\cos\theta} - p\beta\right) = 0.$$

Eliminating $dp/d\cos\theta$, we find that

$$\frac{d\cos\theta'}{d\cos\theta} = \frac{p^2}{\gamma p'(p - \beta\epsilon\cos\theta)},$$

and hence we have the second relation between differential cross sections

$$\left(\frac{d\sigma}{d\Omega}\right) = \left(\frac{d\sigma}{d\Omega}\right)' \frac{p^2}{\gamma p'(p - \beta\epsilon \cos\theta)}. \tag{A.19}$$

In the nonrelativistic limit $\gamma \to 1$ and $\beta \to 0$, and Eq. (A.19) becomes

$$\frac{1}{p}\left(\frac{d\sigma}{d\Omega}\right) = \frac{1}{p'}\left(\frac{d\sigma}{d\Omega}\right)'.$$

There is a third and trivial relation. Integrating (A.16) we find that the total cross section for production of the particle is invariant:

$$\sigma = \int\!\!\int \left(\frac{d^2\sigma}{d\Omega\, d\epsilon}\right) d\Omega\, d\epsilon = \int\!\!\int \left(\frac{d^2\sigma}{d\Omega\, d\epsilon}\right)' d\Omega'\, d\epsilon' = \sigma'.$$

This can be seen simply by remembering that total cross sections are simply areas perpendicular to the $z$ axis and therefore invariant.

## A.6 The Transformation of the Polarization Vector

In Chapter VIII we defined the polarization $\boldsymbol{\sigma}$ of a particle with non-zero rest mass by a three vector in the rest frame of the particle. We also discussed how to use and manipulate this three vector in order to have a means of describing polarization experiments. The formalism employs the three vector throughout and in such a manner that $\boldsymbol{\sigma}$ is taken to be the same in all frames related to the rest frame of the particle by a velocity transformation along the direction of motion of the particle. However, we often need to know the polarization in a frame not related to the particle's rest frame in such a simple manner and in these cases the definition of polarization is confusing. The difficulty is due to the fact that the polarization is described by a tensor which has well-defined transformation properties (Section 1.4), whereas our polarization vector is defined with respect to a rest frame and it is not clear how it transforms. We shall not discuss the tensor except to note that in certain frames it reduces to a form which can be expressed as a three vector which is our polarization vector. Therefore the transformation of our vector is accomplished by careful "book-keeping" through a series of Lorentz transformations. Let us give some examples. We can calculate [given $M_a$, Eq. (8.60)] the polarization of a neutron after it has been scattered by hydrogen. This polarization is defined with respect to the centre-of-mass frame of the scatter or any frame derived from this one by a Lorentz transformation of velocity along the direction of motion of the neutron. Suppose the neutron is now scattered at a second hydrogen target. In the centre of mass of this second scatter, or in any frame derived by a Lorentz transformation of velocity along the direction of the incident neutron,

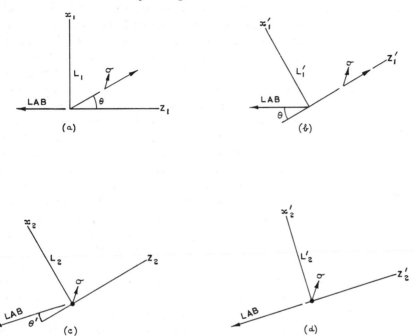

FIG. A.3. The four inertial frames used in deriving the transformation properties of the polarization vector.

the polarization is different. We are, of course, referring to the polarization which has a behaviour described by the matrix $M_a$. A second example occurs in pi-meson physics. The mu-meson generated by the decay of a pi-meson at rest is longitudinally polarized. If the pi-meson is moving with respect to the laboratory, then in this frame a decay mu-meson can have a transverse component of polarization.

Let us define some inertial frames: $L_1$ and $L_1'$ are frames with their origin at the centre of mass of the nuclear reaction which produces the particle whose polarization is of interest. $L_1'$ is related to $L_1$ by a rotation; $L_2$ is a rest frame of the particle and is related to $L_1'$ by a simple Lorentz transformation of velocity along the direction of the particle. $L_2'$ is also a rest frame of the particle and is related to $L_2$ by a simple rotation. $L_3$ is a laboratory frame and is related to $L_2'$ by a simple Lorentz transformation of velocity. We now refer to Fig. A.3.

$L_1$ is oriented so that the direction of an incident particle is along the axis $z_1$. The particle in which we are interested emerges from the reaction at a centre-of-mass angle $\theta$ with its momentum in the $x_1 z$ plane. Let its polarization be $\boldsymbol{\sigma}$, which is a vector with polar angles $\Theta$ and $\Phi$ with respect to the particle momentum (Fig. A.3a). $L_1'$ is related to $L_1$ by a rotation through an angle $\theta$ around the $y_1$ axis so that $L$ has its $z_1'$ axis lying in the direction of the particle. In $L_1'$ a suitable point of the laboratory appears to be moving at an angle $\theta$ to the $-z_1'$ axis (Fig. A.3b). $\boldsymbol{\sigma}$ has polar angles $(\Theta, \Phi)$ with respect to $z_1'$. $L_2$ is derived by a transformation from the centre of mass of the reaction to the rest frame of our particle, without a rotation. The laboratory now appears to be moving at an angle $\theta'$ with respect to the $-z_2$ axis (Fig. A.3c) where $\theta'$ is the transform of angle $\theta$. By definition the $\boldsymbol{\sigma}$ in $L_1$ is really the $\boldsymbol{\sigma}$ in $L_2$ so there is no change in $\boldsymbol{\sigma}$ during the trans formations just described. $L_2'$ is derived from $L_2$ by a rotation through an angle $\theta'$ so that the laboratory appears to be moving along the $-z_2'$ axis. Now $\boldsymbol{\sigma}$ has polar coordinates in $L_2'$ which depend upon the $\theta'$ and upon $\Theta$ and $\Phi$ (Fig. A.3d). A particularly interesting case is when the original polarization is longitudinal, i.e., $\Theta = \Phi = 0$; in $L_2'$ the polarization vector has polar coordinates $(\theta', 0)$. We can now make any Lorentz transformation along the $z_2'$ axis and in all resulting frames the polarization is by definition the same as it is in $L_2'$. One convenient frame is the laboratory frame $L_3$. Another is the centre of mass of a second scattering reaction. Thus, in general, the polarization which matters at a second scattering is the polarization that is pro duced at the first, rotated through a certain angle.

Let us consider an example in more detail. In Section 10.5 we showed that, in the decay of the lambda hyperon,

$$\Lambda^0 \to \pi^- + p,$$

we expect the proton to have a longitudinal polarization $\alpha$ [Eq. (10.9)] (that is, $\Theta = \Phi = 0$ in our discussion above). If the $\Lambda^0$ is moving in the laboratory, the decay proton will appear to have a transverse component of polarization which can be detected by a left-right scattering asymmetry at a target fixed in the laboratory. Suppose the decay proton is produced at an angle $\theta$ in the $\Lambda^0$ rest frame with respect to the direction of the $\Lambda^0$ (Fig. A.3a). In this frame the laboratory will appear to be moving with the velocity of the hyperon in the laboratory, $\beta_\Lambda$. We now transform to the rest frame of the decay proton which is moving with velocity $\beta_p$ in the rest frame of the $\Lambda^0$. In doing so, the angle $\theta$ changes to angle $\theta'$ (Figs. A.3b and A.3c) where $\theta'$ will be given by the transformation of the components of the velocity of the laboratory in the two frames. These transformations are (Møller, 1952)

$$\beta_\Lambda \sin\theta \to \beta \sin\theta' = \frac{\beta_\Lambda(1-\beta_p^2)^{1/2}\sin\theta}{1+\beta_\Lambda\beta_p\cos\theta}$$

and

$$\beta_\Lambda \cos\theta \to \beta \cos\theta' = \frac{\beta_\Lambda\cos\theta+\beta_p}{1+\beta_\Lambda\beta_p\cos\theta},$$

where $\beta$ is the velocity of the laboratory in the rest frame of the proton. Therefore

$$\tan\theta' = \frac{\beta_\Lambda(1-\beta_p^2)^{1/2}\sin\theta}{\beta_\Lambda\cos\theta+\beta_p}.$$

It follows that the original longitudinal polarization vector is rotated by the transformations through an angle $\theta'$ in the plane of the decay.

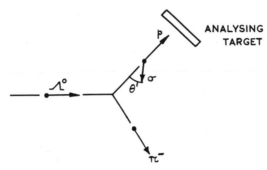

FIG. A.4. The appearance in the laboratory of the longitudinal polarization that the lambda decay proton has in the centre of mass.

This means that the decay proton will appear to have a transverse component $\alpha\sin\theta'$ in this plane which can be detected by a subsequent scattering asymmetry which will be up-down with respect to the decay plane (Fig. A.4). This transverse component has been detected and measured in a determination of the magnitude and sign of the original longitudinal polarization in the $\Lambda^0$ rest frame (Boldt et al., 1958a).

For a discussion of the effects of relativistic transformations in triple nucleon–nucleon scattering we refer readers to an article by Stapp (1956); Ascoli (1958) has given the relevant transformation for the $\tau$–$\mu$ decay.

# THE DENSITY OF STATES FACTOR

## B.I Introduction

In Section 5.3 we have discussed the transition rate formula, indicated the meaning of the density of states factor, and calculated this factor for a one-particle final state. This kind of final state never occurs in practice but the emission of one light particle by a relatively heavy particle approaches this situation.

For two or more particles the situation is more complex and must be examined in more detail. However, we first give a more general treatment for the situation in which there are $F$ final particles and the matrix element is independent of the final state, i.e., constant. An example of this situation occurs in Fermi's theory of multiple pi-meson production (Fermi, 1950; Milburn, 1958); in this theory the probability that a final state containing $F$ particles occurring is proportional to appropriate density of states factor. Due to the conservation of momentum there are only $F-1$ independent momenta in the final state. This state can be represented by a vector in a $3(F-1)$-dimensional momentum space. If the vector is further restrained by the conservation of energy, its end will trace out a surface in this momentum space. If the total energy is $E$, all the states with energy less than $E$ will have the vector representing their state ending inside the surface, those with energy $E$ will be represented by a vector ending at the surface. Let the volume in this space enclosed by the surface be $U(F, E)$. Then the total number of final states having energy less than or equal to $E$ is given by

$$N = \left[ \frac{L^3}{(2\pi\hbar)^3} \right]^{F-1} U(F, E),$$

where $L^3$ is the normalization volume and

$$U(F, E) = \prod_{r=1}^{F-1} \int d\mathbf{p}_r$$

where $\mathbf{p}_r$ is the momentum of the $r$th particle. The required density of states is $dN/dE$. The calculation of the volume $U$ is impossible for all but the simplest systems. We shall show how it is found for some of these simple cases. For more difficult cases readers are referred to an article by Block (1956).

## B.2 The Two-Particle State

Consider a final state containing two particles of total energy $E = \epsilon_1 + \epsilon_2$ and of total momentum $\mathbf{P} = \mathbf{p}_1 + \mathbf{p}_2$. Let $\theta_1$ be the angle between $\mathbf{P}$ and $\mathbf{p}_1$ and $\theta_2$ be the angle between $\mathbf{P}$ and $\mathbf{p}_2$. There is only one dynamically independent momentum if this final state is a reaction product from an initial state of total momentum $\mathbf{P}$; therefore the calculation of $U$ requires only one integration over the phase space of one particle, number 1 say,

$$U = \int_{-1}^{+1} \int_0^{p_1(\theta_1)} p_1^2 \, dp_1 \, 2\pi d(\cos\theta_1). \tag{B.1}$$

The limits of integration on $p$ are 0 and $p_1(\theta_1)$ where the latter quantity is the maximum momentum particle 1 can have in direction $\theta_1$, due to the conservation of energy, and is the momentum the particle in that direction will be observed to have when the total energy is $E$. This must be noted since it is energy conservation which determines the upper limit on these integrals over momenta. In the remainder of this appendix the upper limits are set in this way. Now

$$\frac{dN}{dE} = \frac{d}{dE} \left\{ \frac{L^3}{(2\pi\hbar)^3} \int_{-1}^{+1} \int_0^{p_1(\theta_1)} p_1^2 \, dp_1 \, 2\pi d(\cos\theta_1) \right\}.$$

Such a density of states factor would be used for a transition into all angles when the matrix element is independent of $\theta_1$. If the matrix element varies with angle, then we are essentially interested in the probability that particle 1 will be emitted into solid angle $d\Omega_1$ about $\theta_1$ where the momentum is expected to be $p_1$. In this case the appropriate $U(F, E)$ is the $U$ of Eq. (B.1) without the integration over $\theta_1$, that is,

$$U = \int_0^{p_1(\theta_1)} p_1^2 \, dp_1 \, d\Omega_1,$$

and

$$d\left(\frac{dN}{dE}\right) = \frac{d}{dE}\left\{\frac{L^3}{(2\pi\hbar)^3}\frac{p_1^3}{3}d\Omega_1\right\}.$$

(B.

In the remainder of this section we shall give $p$ the same dimension as energy (as in Appendix A). To keep our dimensions correct we wi put $\hbar c$ instead of $\hbar$ as it appears in (B.2), for example.

At this point it is worth noting that differentiation is with respe to the total energy $E$, which involves both particles, thus

$$\frac{d}{dE} = \frac{d}{dp_1}\cdot\frac{dp_1}{dE} = \frac{1}{(d\epsilon_1/dp_1)+(d\epsilon_2/dp_1)}\cdot\frac{d}{dp_1}$$

$$= \frac{1}{(d\epsilon_1/dp_1)+(d\epsilon_2/dp_2)(dp_2/dp_1)}\frac{d}{dp_1}.$$

(B.

For all particles $\epsilon^2 = p^2 + m^2$ and hence $d\epsilon/dp = p/\epsilon$. In the two-bod case $dp_1/dp_2$ can be found as follows. We have

$$P = p_1\cos\theta_1 + p_2\cos\theta_2, \quad 0 = p_1\sin\theta_1 + p_2\sin\theta_2;$$

if we differentiate, remembering that $\theta_1$ is constant and eliminatin $d\theta_2$, we find that

$$\frac{dp_2}{dp_1} = -\cos(\theta_1-\theta_2) = \frac{-\mathbf{p_1}\cdot\mathbf{p_2}}{p_1 p_2}.$$

(B.

Substituting in (B.2) and (B.3), we find

$$d\left(\frac{dN}{dE}\right) = \frac{L^3}{(2\pi\hbar c)^3}\frac{\epsilon_1\epsilon_2 p_1^3 d\Omega_1}{\epsilon_2 p_1^2 - \epsilon_1(\mathbf{p_1}\cdot\mathbf{p_2})} = \frac{L^3}{(2\pi\hbar c)^3}\frac{\epsilon_1\epsilon_2 p_1^3 d\Omega_1}{Ep_1^2 - \epsilon_1\mathbf{P}\cdot\mathbf{p_1}}.$$

(B.

Equation (B.5) can be used for calculations of transition rates an cross sections in the laboratory system. However, it is more usual t work in the centre of mass and we re-derive the equivalent of Eq. (B.5 Equation (B.2) remains the same except that we prime all quantitie to indicate that they apply to the centre of mass. In addition, we hav

$$\mathbf{P'} = 0 \quad\text{and}\quad \mathbf{p_1'} = -\mathbf{p_2'}.$$

Equation (B.4) becomes

$$\frac{dp_2'}{dp_1'} = 1$$

his refers to the magnitude of the vectors). Hence we have

$$\frac{d}{dE'} = \frac{dp'_1}{dE'}\frac{d}{dp'_1}$$

$$= \frac{\epsilon'_1 \epsilon'_2}{p'_1(\epsilon'_1 + \epsilon'_2)}\frac{d}{dp'_1}$$

nd we find that

$$d\left(\frac{dN}{dE}\right)' = \frac{L'^3}{(2\pi\hbar c)^3}\frac{\epsilon'_1 \epsilon'_2 p'_1 d\Omega'_1}{\epsilon'_1 + \epsilon'_2}. \tag{B.6}$$

f course, Eq. (B.6) can be derived directly from (B.5) by putting
$= 0.$

## .3 Three or More Particle Final States

irstly, we consider the case in which the density of states factor is
:quired for the total transition, assuming the matrix element is
constant. Let the final state have total
energy $E = \epsilon_1 + \epsilon_2 + \epsilon_3$ and total momentum $\mathbf{P} = \mathbf{p}_1 + \mathbf{p}_2 + \mathbf{p}_3$. We can
choose a particular momentum con-
figuration as in Fig. B.1. Suppose $p_1$
is fixed, leaving an energy $\epsilon'$ and momentum $p'$ to be distributed among
the particles 2 and 3. The volume in
momentum space for these two particles
is given by

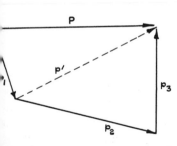

Fig. B.1. A configuration of
.omenta in the three-body final
ate.

$$U' = \int_0^{2\pi}\int_0^{\pi} d\Omega_2 \int_0^{p_2(\theta_2)} p_2^2\, dp_2. \tag{B.7}$$

The momentum integral has its upper limit set by the maximum
energy $p_2$ can have in direction defined by the solid angle $d\Omega_2$ when
₁ is fixed. In this case it is the volume enclosed by the locus of the
₂$p_3$ vertex (Fig. B.1) when $\mathbf{p}_1$ is kept fixed. The second stage of the
alculation is to include the density of states for $\mathbf{p}_1$. For every different
₁ there is a different value of $U'$; thus the final total volume is

$$U = \int_0^{2\pi}\int_0^{\pi} d\Omega_1 \int_0^{p_1(\theta_1)} p_1^2\, dp_1\, U' \tag{B.8}$$

and

$$N = \frac{L^6}{(2\pi\hbar c)^6} U$$

$$= \frac{L^6}{(2\pi\hbar c)^6} \iint d\Omega_1 \int_0^{p_1(\theta_1)} p_1^2 \, dp_1 \iint \Omega d_2 \int_0^{p_2(\theta_2)} p_2^2 \, dp_2.$$

The integration proceeds from the right.

If the density of states is required for a particular configuration of momenta in a transition then certain integrals are omitted. Strictly the problem is solved by integrating the most general differential transition rate, since the appropriate matrix element may vary and its square must be included within the integral sign. For three particles the most general differential could be

$$\frac{d^3}{d\Omega_1 \, d\Omega_2 \, dp_1} \qquad \text{(B.9)}$$

for which the density of states is

$$d^3\left(\frac{dN}{dE}\right) = \frac{d}{dE}\left\{ \frac{L^6}{(2\pi\hbar c)^6} d\Omega_1 \, d\Omega_2 \, p_1^2 \, dp_1 \int_0^{p_2(\theta_2)} p_2^2 \, dp_2 \right\}. \qquad \text{(B.10)}$$

That is, the transition rate for particle 1 into solid angle $d\Omega_1$ and momentum interval $dp_1$, and particle 2 into solid angles $d\Omega_2$, is proportional to $d^3(dN/dE)$ of Eq. (B.10).

The corresponding differential transition rate (B.9) is found by dividing through by $d\Omega_1 \, dp_1 \, d\Omega_2$. The integration in (B.10) is performed up to the limit allowed by energy conservation. The square of the matrix element cannot be put under this integral as it only has a value when the momentum $p_2$ has the value required by energy conservation. The procedure is clarified if this integral is done before we calculate the actual density of states at the upper limit.

The general case for a three-body final state is quickly completed. Suppose the upper limit on the integral in (B.10) is $p_2$, then

$$N = \frac{L^6}{(2\pi\hbar c)^6} p_1^2 \, dp_1 \, d\Omega_1 \, d\Omega_2 \frac{p_2^3}{3}.$$

Now $(dN/dE) = (dN/dp_2)(dp_2/dE)$. The intermediate differentiation is here chosen to be the independent momentum because the remaining momenta are fixed by interval restrictions: now

$$\frac{dE}{dp_2} = \frac{d\epsilon_1}{dp_2} + \frac{d\epsilon_2}{dp_2} + \frac{d\epsilon_3}{dp_2}.$$

Again $\epsilon_1$ is fixed, so we have

$$\frac{dE}{dp_2} = \frac{p_2}{\epsilon_2} + \frac{p_3}{\epsilon_3}\frac{dp_3}{dp_2}.$$

The angular relation between $\mathbf{p}_2$ and $\mathbf{p}_3$ ($p_1, \theta_1, \theta_2$ fixed) is used to find $dp_3/dp_2$; it is

$$\frac{dp_3}{dp_2} = -\frac{\mathbf{p}_2 \cdot \mathbf{p}_3}{p_2 p_3}$$

and thence

$$d^3\left(\frac{dN}{dE}\right) = \frac{L^6}{(2\pi\hbar c)^6} \frac{\epsilon_2 \epsilon_3 p_1^2 p_2^3 \, d\Omega_1 \, d\Omega_2 \, dp_1}{p_2^2(E - \epsilon_1) - \epsilon_2 \mathbf{p}_2 \cdot (\mathbf{P} - \mathbf{p}_1)}. \tag{B.11}$$

*Many-particle final states.* The steps outlined in describing the three-body case can be extended, step by step, to the required number of final particles. However, it is evident that the problem is prohibitively complex for any but a small number of particles.

## B.4 Examples

1. $\pi^-$ *Absorption by Deuterium*

Consider the reaction

$$\pi^- + d \to 2n + \gamma,$$

which occurs when $\pi^-$ mesons are absorbed from Bohr-like orbits around deuterium nuclei. If we can assume there is no final state interaction, then the matrix element is independent of the division of energy among these particles and the occurrence of a particular configuration of final particle momenta depends upon the density of states. It is therefore possible to predict the spectrum of photons emitted if the assumption is correct. We define the following quantities:

$E_0$ = energy available for neutron kinetic energy and photon energy;

$M$ = neutron mass;

$p_\gamma, p_1, p_2$ are the momenta of $\gamma$ ray, neutron 1, and neutron 2, respectively.

We have

$$\mathbf{p}_1 + \mathbf{p}_2 + \mathbf{p}_\gamma = 0$$

since there is no momentum in the initial state. The momenta triangle is shown in Fig. B.2. We can calculate the phase space volume for fixed photon as follows. The vertex of the triangle in Fig. B.2 has locus which is a sphere with radius

$$\left\{(E_0 - p_\gamma) M - \frac{p_\gamma^2}{4}\right\}^{1/2}.$$

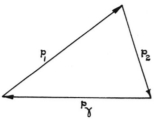

(The nucleons have been treated non relativistically.) The required volume of phase space $U'$ is the volume of this sphere hence

FIG. B.2. A configuration of momenta for $\pi^- + d \to 2n + \gamma$.

$$U' = \frac{4\pi}{3}\left\{(E_0 - p_\gamma) M - \frac{p_\gamma^2}{4}\right\}^{3/2}.$$

This is the $U'$ of Eq. (B.7). The total volume in phase space [$U$ of Eq. (B.8)] is

$$U = \int 4\pi p_\gamma^2 \, dp_\gamma \, \frac{4\pi}{3}\left\{(E_0 - p_\gamma) M - \frac{p_\gamma^2}{4}\right\}^{3/2}.$$

The required density of states is found by omitting the integration thus:

$$d\left(\frac{dN}{dE_0}\right) = \frac{L^6}{(2\pi\hbar c)^6} \frac{d}{dE_0}\left\{4\pi p_\gamma^2 \frac{4\pi}{3}\left[(E_0 - p_\gamma) M - \frac{p_\gamma^2}{4}\right]^{3/2}\right\} dp_\gamma;$$

hence the number of photons in the momentum range $p_\gamma$ to $p_\gamma + dp$ is proportional to

$$p_\gamma^2\left(E_0 - p_\gamma - \frac{p_\gamma^2}{4M}\right)^{1/2}.$$

The spectrum of $\gamma$-rays has been measured by Phillips and Crowe (1954) in an effort to detect deviations from this spectrum which would be due mainly to a neutron–neutron interaction in the final state.

## b. $\beta$-decay

We wish to calculate the density of states for $\beta$-decay; apart from Coulomb effects, there are no final state interactions and the matrix element is independent of how the energy is shared between the emitted leptons. Thus we can calculate the expected electron (or positron) spectrum. We make the usual assumption (valid for all but the smallest atomic weights) that the nucleus is very massive and does not recoil. Thus there is no correlation between the momenta of the emitted leptons. Let $E$ be the energy available which is shared between an

lectron of total energy $\epsilon_e$ and mass $m$, and a massless antineutrino.
Let the respective momenta be $p_e$ and $p_\nu$. Then

$$E = p_\nu + \epsilon_e.$$

The total volume in phase space [$U$ of
Eq. (B.8)] is

$$U = \frac{4\pi}{3} p_\nu^3 \frac{4\pi}{3} p_e^3.$$

The required density of states is found
by omitting the integral over $p_e$ which
leads to this $U$. We find that

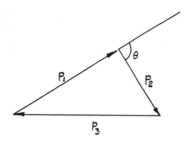

FIG. B.3. A configuration of
momenta for $K^+ \to \pi^+ + \pi^+ + \pi^-$.

$$d\left(\frac{dN}{dE}\right) = \frac{d}{dE}\left(\frac{L^6}{(2\pi\hbar c)^6}\frac{4\pi}{3}p_\nu^3\, 4\pi\, p_e^2\, dp_e\right)$$

$$= \frac{16\pi^2 L^6}{(2\pi\hbar c)^6}\frac{d}{dE}\left(\epsilon_e P_e \frac{(E-\epsilon_e)^3}{3}\right) d\epsilon_e$$

$$= \frac{L^6}{4\pi^4 \hbar^6 c^6}\epsilon_e P_e(E-\epsilon_e)^2\, d\epsilon_e. \tag{B.12}$$

Apart from differences in notation this is the density of states factor
which appears in Eq. (11.14).

### 2. The Tau-meson Decay

We wish to examine the decay of the $K^+$ meson by the charged
pi-meson mode

$$K^+ \to \pi^+ + \pi^+ + \pi^-.$$

This decay is most readily observed in nuclear photographic emulsion
and in such circumstances it is possible to measure the energy of the
decay products with considerable accuracy. As this is a three-body
decay, each decay product does not have a unique energy but can
have any energy up to a maximum allowed by energy and momentum
conservation. The probability of a certain energy division among the
products will be proportional to the density of states. This density
can be found from Eq. (B.11) by altering the intervals so that it gives
the density for one meson in the energy range $d\epsilon_1$ and another in the
range $d\epsilon_2$. In Fig. B.3 we show the momenta applicable to our
discussion. We have

$$p_3^2 = p_1^2 + p_2^2 + 2p_1 p_2 \cos\theta \tag{B.13}$$

and

$$\epsilon_1 + \epsilon_2 + \epsilon_3 = Q + 3m_\pi = E. \tag{B.14}$$

Now $\epsilon_1$ is fixed by our requirement that it lies in the range given by $dp_1$. In the centre of mass we can rewrite (B.11) thus:

$$d^3\left(\frac{dN}{dE}\right) = \frac{L^6}{(2\pi\hbar c)^6} \frac{\epsilon_1 \epsilon_2 \epsilon_3 \, d\epsilon_1 \, p_1 \, p_2^3 \, d\Omega_1 \, d\Omega_2}{p_2^2 (\epsilon_2 + \epsilon_3) + \epsilon_2 p_1 p_2 \cos\theta}. \tag{B.15}$$

We are not interested in the over-all orientation of the decay, so we put $d\Omega_1 = 4\pi$. Then we have to change $d\Omega_2$ to the corresponding interval in $p_2$ or $\epsilon_2$. From (B.13) and (B.14) we have that

$$p_3 \, dp_3 = p_2 \, dp_2 + p_1 \, dp_1 \cos\theta + p_1 p_2 \, d(\cos\theta) \tag{B.16}$$

and

$$d\epsilon_2 + d\epsilon_3 = 0.$$

Equation (B.16) can be written

$$-\epsilon_3 \, d\epsilon_2 = \epsilon_2 \, d\epsilon_2 + \frac{p_1 \epsilon_2}{p_2} \cos\theta \, d\epsilon_2 + p_1 p_2 \, d(\cos\theta);$$

hence

$$-p_1 p_2 \, d(\cos\theta) = [\, p_2(\epsilon_2 + \epsilon_3) + \epsilon_2 p_1 \cos\theta\,] \, d\epsilon_2.$$

Substituting in Eq. (B.15) and using

$$2\pi d(\cos\theta) = d\Omega_2,$$

we find that

$$d^2\left(\frac{dN}{dE}\right) = \frac{8\pi^2 L^6}{(2\pi\hbar c)^6} \epsilon_1 \epsilon_2 \epsilon_3 \, d\epsilon_1 \, d\epsilon_2. \tag{B.17}$$

The actual transition probability is proportional to the matrix element squared multiplied by the density of states. The matrix element will depend upon the energy of the particles by at least a factor $1/\sqrt{\epsilon}$ for every particle created in the final state; this comes from the Fourier expansion of the field variables [Eq. (9.9a)]. There will be a factor $1/(\epsilon_1 \epsilon_2 \epsilon_3)$ in the square of the matrix element for the transition under discussion; other factors will be constant if the final state interactions are small and if the mesons are emitted with zero orbital angular momentum. If this is the case, the probability for an energy division into the ranges $d\epsilon_1$ and $d\epsilon_2$ is just proportional to $d\epsilon_1 \, d\epsilon_2$. If we represent the kinetic energies of the decay mesons by $t$, we have

$$t_1 + t_2 + t_3 = Q$$

and the transition probability into the range $dt_1$ and $dt_2$ is proportional to $dt_1 \, dt_2$.

A convenient way of representing the decay is due to Dalitz (1953). He notes that all points within an equilateral triangle have the property

1at the sum of the perpendicular distances from the three sides is a
›nstant equal to the height of the triangle. Therefore he draws an
quilateral triangle of height $Q$ and for each observed decay marks a
›oint which has perpendicular distances from the sides equal to the

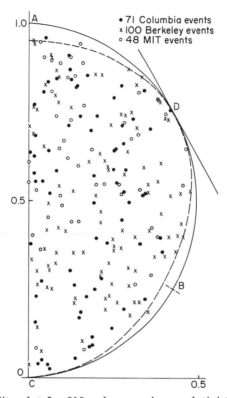

FIG. B.4. Dalitz plot for 219 $\tau$ decays. A nonrelativistic treatment
requires that, within the experimental error, all the points lie within
the semicircular boundary *ADBC*. A correct relativistic treatment
requires all the points to lie inside the broken line. The points are
experimental measured decays observed at three laboratories. (Orear
*et al.* 1956.)

netic energies of the three pi-mesons. All decays have points which
› within a region slightly smaller than the inscribed circle (Fabri,
954). The symmetry of the decay allows the plot of points to be
›stricted to one-half of this circle. In Fig. B.4 we reproduce the
alitz plot given by Orear *et al.* (1956). The interval $dt_1 dt_2$ has
1 area which is independent of its position within the circle and
 follows that the density points will be uniform if the matrix

element is independent of the energy division (apart from the variation mentioned). The points marked for the 219 events of Orear *et al*
(1956) are fairly uniform and this means that it is very likely that
three final state pi-mesons are in a state of zero orbital angular
momentum. If they were not, the angular momentum barrier would
inhibit decays in which a meson was emitted with a low kinetic energy
and the density of dots would decrease markedly near the sides of
the triangle.

# UNITS

## C.1 Natural Units

Many authors, particularly of theoretical papers, employ a system of units which is briefly defined by

$$\hbar = c = 1.$$

This system implies that the unit of length is one centimeter. Therefore we have

1 natural unit of length = 1 cm,

1 natural unit of time = $(1/c)$ sec,

1 natural unit of mass = $(\hbar/c)$ gm.

Quantities in brackets are taken to have the value which would be assigned to them in the cgs system. Hence to convert a natural time into seconds, divide by the velocity of light in cm sec$^{-1}$, etc. To find the way around this system it is convenient to use dimensions $L$, $H$, $C$ instead of $M$, $L$, and $T$. Thus electric charge has dimensions $M^{1/2}L^{3/2})/T$ or $(HC)^{1/2}$ and to convert a natural unit of electron charge to esu ($\epsilon = 1$) multiply by $(\hbar c)^{1/2}$. In any unrationalized system, the electronic charge is given by

$$\frac{e^2}{\hbar c} = \frac{1}{137}, \quad \text{(approx.)}.$$

Thus in our natural units

$$e = \sqrt{\frac{1}{137}}, \quad \text{dimension } (HC)^{1/2}.$$

In a rationalized system

$$e = \sqrt{\frac{4\pi}{137}}.$$

The Dirac magnetic moment of a particle is $e\hbar/2mc$ (unrationalized and has dimensions $(HC)^{1/2}L$. Thus to convert a natural unit of magnetic moment into emu, multiply by $(\hbar c)^{1/2}$. Conversion to Bohr or nuclear magnetons follows simply.

Another system sometimes employed puts

$$\hbar = c = m = 1$$

where $m$ is the mass of a convenient particle, often the pi-meson. In this system,

1 unit of mass $= (m)$ gm,

1 unit of length $= (\hbar/mc)$ cm,

1 unit of time $= (\hbar/mc^2)$ sec,

where, as usual, the conversion from the natural units to cgs is done by multiplying by the quantity in brackets calculated in cgs units. The convenient dimensions are $M$, $C$, $H$ rather than $M$, $L$, and $T$. Electron charge (rationalized) continues to have the value $\sqrt{4\pi/137}$ and the dimensions of charge are $(HC)^{1/2}$. Magnetic moment has dimensions $(H^3/M^2C)^{1/2}$ and therefore

1 unit of magnetic moment $= (\hbar^3/m^2c)^{1/2}$ emu.

# APPENDIX D

# USEFUL DATA

## D.I Physical Constants

In this Appendix we give the values of some of the more useful physical constants (Cohen *et al.*, 1955) and recent data on the elementary particles.

Avogadro's number $\qquad (6.02486 \pm 0.00016) \times 10^{23}$ (gm mole)$^{-1}$

Velocity of light in vacuum $\quad c = (2.997930 \pm 0.000003) \times 10^{10}$ cm sec$^{-1}$

Planck's constant $\qquad h = (6.62517 \pm 0.00023) \times 10^{-27}$ erg sec

Planck's constant reduced $\quad \hbar = (1.05443 \pm 0.00004) \times 10^{-27}$ erg sec

Mass of electron at rest $\quad m_e = (9.1083 \pm 0.0003) \times 10^{-28}$ gm

Charge on the electron $\quad e = (4.80286 \pm 0.00009) \times 10^{-10}$ esu

First Bohr radius for infinitely heavy nucleus

$$\frac{\hbar^2}{me^2} = (5.29172 \pm 0.00002) \times 10^{-9} \text{ cm}$$

Fine structure constant $\quad \dfrac{e^2}{\hbar c} = (7.29729 \pm 0.00003) \times 10^{-3}$

$$= 1/(137.0372 \pm 0.0006)$$

1 electron volt $\quad$ 1 ev $= (1.60206 \pm 0.00003) \times 10^{-12}$ erg

Classical radius of the electron

$$\frac{e^2}{m_e c^2} = (2.81785 \pm 0.00004) \times 10^{-13} \text{ cm}$$

## D.2 Elementary Particle Data

Table D.1 gives the more important properties of the known elementary particles.

## TABLE D.1
### ELEMENTARY PARTICLE DATA

| Particle | Symbol | Spin | Mass $m_e$ | Mass (Mev) | Mean life (sec) | Decay modes and branching ratios |
|---|---|---|---|---|---|---|
| Photon | $\gamma$ | 1 | 0 | 0 | $\infty$ | — |
| Leptons | | | | | | |
| Neutrino | $\nu, \bar{\nu}$ | $\frac{1}{2}$ | 0 | 0 | $\infty$ | — |
| Electron | $e^-, e^+$ | $\frac{1}{2}$ | 1 | 0.510976 | $\infty$ | — |
| Mu-meson | $\mu^-, \mu^+$ | $\frac{1}{2}$ | $206.86 \pm 0.12$ | $105.70 \pm 0.06$ | $2.22 \pm 0.02 \times 10^{-6}$ | $\rightarrow e + \nu + \bar{\nu}, \sim 100\%$ <br> $\rightarrow e + e^+ + e^- + \nu + \bar{\nu}^-,$ |
| Bose mesons | | | | | | |
| Neutral pi-meson | $\pi^0$ | 0 | $264.37 \pm 0.18$ | $135.09 \pm 0.09$ | $< 4 \times 10^{-16}$ | See Section 7.2 |
| Charged pi-meson | $\pi^+, \pi^-$ | 0 | $273.27 \pm 0.12$ | $139.63 \pm 0.06$ | $(2.56 \pm 0.05) \times 10^{-8}$ | See Section 7.2 |
| Charged K-meson | $K^+, K^-$ | 0 | $966.8 \pm 0.4$ | $494.0 \pm 0.2$ | $(1.224 \pm 0.013) \times 10^{-8}$ | See Sections 12.7, 12.10 |
| Neutral K-meson | $K_1^0$ | 0 | $972.8 \pm 1.6$ | $497.1 \pm 0.8$ | $(1.00 \pm 0.04) \times 10^{-10}$ | See Sections 12.8, 12.10 |
| Neutral K-meson | $K_2^0$ | 0 | $972.8 \pm 1.6$ | $497.1 \pm 0.8$ | $\left(6.1 {+1.6 \atop -1.1}\right) \times 10^{-8}$ | See Sections 12.8, 12.10 |
| Nucleons | | | | | | |
| Proton | $p$ | $\frac{1}{2}$ | $1836.118 \pm 0.020$ | $938.213 \pm 0.010$ | $\infty$ | — |
| Neutron | $n$ | $\frac{1}{2}$ | $1838.645 \pm 0.020$ | $939.506 \pm 0.010$ | $1013 \pm 26$ | $\rightarrow e^- + \bar{\nu} + p, 100\%$ |
| Hyperons | | | | | | |
| Lambda | $\Lambda^0$ | $\frac{1}{2}$ | $2182.5 \pm 0.3$ | $1115.2 \pm 0.14$ | $(2.77 \pm 0.15) \times 10^{-10}$ | |
| Positive sigma | $\Sigma^+$ | $\frac{1}{2}$ | $2327.7 \pm 0.5$ | $1189.4 \pm 0.25$ | $(0.83 \pm 0.05) \times 10^{-10}$ | |
| Neutral sigma | $\Sigma^0$ | $\frac{1}{2}$ | $2329.9 \pm 2$ | $1190.5 \pm 1.0$ | $< 10^{-11}$ | See Sections 12.6, 12.10 |
| Negative sigma | $\Sigma^-$ | $\frac{1}{2}$ | $2341.6 \pm 1$ | $1196.5 \pm 0.5$ | $(1.72 \pm 0.17) \times 10^{-10}$ | |
| Neutral cascade | $\Xi^0$ | ? | $2579 \pm 16$ | $1311 \ .\pm 8$ | $\sim 10^{-10}$ | |
| Negative cascade | $\Xi^-$ | ? | $2583 \pm 5.5$ | $1319.7 \pm 2.6$ | $\sim 1.8 \times 10^{-10}$ | |

# REFERENCES

Abashian, A., and Hafner, E. M. 1958. *Phys. Rev. Letters* **1**, 255 (10.6).*
Adair, R. K. 1958. *Phys. Rev.* **111**, 632 (12.12).
Alder, K., Steck, B., and Winther, A. 1957. *Phys. Rev.* **107**, 728 (11.6).
Alford, W. P., and Hamilton, D. R. 1957. *Phys. Rev.* **105**, 673 (11.5).
Allen, R. A., Burcham, W. E., Chackett, K. F., Munday, G. L., and Reasbeck, P. 1955. *Proc. Phys. Soc. (London)* **A68**, 681 (11.5).
Allton, E. A., and Panofsky, W.K.H. 1958. *Phys. Rev.* **110**, 1155 (13.2).
Alvarez, L., Crawford, F. S., Good, M., and Stevenson, M. L. 1956. *Phys. Rev.* **101**, 503 (12.7).
Alvarez, L., Bradner, H., Falk-Variant, F., Gow, J. D., Rosenfeld, A. H., Solmitz, F. T., and Tripp, R. D. 1957. *Nuovo cimento* [10] **5**, 1026 (12.3, 12.6).
Alvarez, L., Eberhard, P., Good, M., Ticho, H. K., and Wojcicki, S. G. 1959. *Phys. Rev. Letters* **2**, 215 (12.3, 12.6).
Anderson, H. L., Fermi, E., Martin, R., and Nagle, D. E. 1953. *Phys. Rev.* **91**, 155 (7.7, 7.8, 7.9).
Anderson, H. L., Davidon, W. C., Glicksman, M., and Kruse, U. E. 1955a. *Phys. Rev.* **100**, 279 (7.9).
Anderson, H. L., Davidon, W. C., and Kruse, U. E. 1955b. *Phys. Rev.* **100**, 339 (13.4).
Argo, H. V., Harrison, F. B., Kruse, H. W., and McGuire, A. D. 1959. *Phys. Rev.* **114**, 626 (11.9).
Ascoli, G. 1958. *Z. Physik* **150**, 407 (A.6).
Ashkin, J., and Vosko, S. H. 1953. *Phys. Rev.* **91**, 1248 (7.8).
Ashkin, J., Fazzini, T., Fidecaro, G., Merrison, A. W., Paul, H., and Tollestrup, A. V. 1959a. *Nuovo cimento* [10] **13**, 1240 (11.9).
Ashkin, J., Fazzini, T., Fidecaro, G., Lipman, N. H., Merrison, A. W., and Paul, H. 1959b. *Nuovo cimento* [10] **14**, 1266 (11.9).
Ashmore, A., Diddens, A. N., Huxtable, G. B., and Skarsvåg, K. 1958. *Proc. Phys. Soc. (London)* **72**, 289 (8.11).
Baldin, A. M. 1958. *Nuovo cimento* [10] **8**, 569 (7.12).
Baldin, A. M., and Kabir, P. 1958. *Doklady Akad. Nauk. S.S.S.R.* **122**, 361 (12.3).
Baldo-Ceolin, M., Huzita, H., Natali, S., Camerini, U., and Fry, W. F. 1958. *Phys. Rev.* **112**, 2118 (12.8).
Banerjee, H. 1958. *Phys. Rev.* **111**, 532 (8.15).
Bardon, M., Lande, K., Lederman, L. M., and Chinowsky, W. 1959. *Ann. phys.* **5**, 156 (11.8).
Barkas, W. H. 1957. *Proc. Ann. Rochester Conf. High Energy Nuclear Phys.* **7**, VIII, 30 (12.7).
Barshay, S. 1959. *Phys. Rev.* **113**, 349 (12.12).
Bell, J. S., and Mandl, F. 1958. *Proc. Phys. Soc. (London)* **71**, 272, 867 (8.11).
Beneventano, M., Bernardini, G., Carlson-Lee, D., and Stoppini, G. 1956. *Nuovo cimento* [10] **4**, 323 (7.12).

* Numbers enclosed in parentheses at the end of each reference indicate the section in the text of this volume in which the reference is cited.

Berman, S. M. 1958. *Phys. Rev.* **112**, 267 (11.8).
Bernardini, G. 1959. *Proc. Kiev Conf. High Energy Nuclear Phys.* (7.9, 7.12).
Beth, R. A. 1936. *Phys. Rev.* **50**, 115 (4.5).
Bethe, H. A., and de Hoffmann, F. 1955. "Mesons and Fields", Vol. II. Row, Peterson, Evanston, Illinois (7.9, 7.12, 7.13, 9.10).
Biedenharn, L. C., and Rose, M. E. 1953. *Revs. Modern Phys.* **25**, 729 (2.11).
Birge, R. W., and Fowler, W. B. 1960. *Phys. Rev. Letters* **5**, 254 (12.6).
Bjorken, J. D., and Drell, S. D. 1959. *Phys. Rev.* **114**, 1368 (13.3).
Bjorken, J. D., Drell, S. D., and Frautschi, S. C. 1958. *Phys. Rev.* **112**, 1409 (13.3).
Blatt, J. M., and Biedenharn, L. C. 1952a. *Revs. Modern Phys.* **24**, 258 (2.11, 5.7, 6.5).
Blatt, J. M., and Biedenharn, L. C. 1952b. *Phys. Rev.* **86**, 399 (6.5).
Blatt, J. M., and Weisskopf, V. 1952. "Theoretical Nuclear Physics." Wiley, New York (3.8, 4.8, 5.7, 6.5, 11.4).
Blin-Stoyle, R. J., Grace, M. A., and Halban, H. 1953. *Prog. in Nuclear Phys.* **3**, 63 (8.2).
Block, M. M. 1956. *Phys. Rev.* **101**, 796 (B.1).
Block, M. M., Brucker, E. B., Hughes, I. S., Kikuchi, T., Meltzer, C., Anderson, F., Pevsner, A., Harth, E. M., Leitner, J., and Cohn, H. O. 1959. *Phys. Rev. Letters* **3**, 291 (12.12).
Bodansky, D., Eccles, S. F., Farwell, G. W., Rickey, M. E., and Robison, P. C. 1959. *Phys. Rev. Letters* **2**, 101 (10.6).
Bogoliubov, N. N., and Shirkov, D. V. 1959. "Introduction to the Theory of Quantised Fields." Interscience, New York (9.1, 9.5, 9.6, 9.7, 9.8).
Boldt, E., Bridge, H. S., Caldwell, D. O., and Pal, Y. 1958a. *Phys. Rev. Letters* **1**, 256 (10.5, 12.6, A.6).
Boldt, E., Caldwell, D. O., and Pal, Y. 1958b. *Phys. Rev. Letters* **1**, 148 (12.9, 12.11).
Bouchial, C., and Michel, L. 1958. *Nuclear Phys.* **5**, 416 (8.14).
Brockman, K. W. 1958. *Phys. Rev.* **110**, 163 (8.9).
Brown, J., Bryant, H., Burnstein, R., Glaser, D. A., Hasting, R., Kadyk, J., Sinclair, D., Trilling, G., Van der Velde, J., and Van Pulten, J. 1959. Reported by D. A. Glaser *Kiev Conf. High Energy Nuclear Phys.* (12.8).
Brueckner, K., Serber, R., and Watson, K. 1951. *Phys. Rev.* **81**, 575 (7.4).
Burgy, M. T., Krohn, V. E., Novey, T. B., Ringo, G. R., and Telegdi, V. L. 1958. *Phys. Rev.* **110**, 1214 (11.6, 11.10).
Burhop, E. H. S. 1952. "The Auger Effect." Cambridge Univ. Press, London and New York (7.4).
Carter, R. E., Reines, F., Wagner, J. J., and Wyman, M. E. 1959. *Phys. Rev.* **113**, 280 (11.7).
Cartwright, W. F., Richman, C., Whitehead, M. N., and Wilcox, H. A. 1953. *Phys. Rev.* **91**, 677 (7.3).
Cassels, J. M., Fidecaro, G., Wetherell, A. M., and Wormald, J. R. 1957. *Proc. Phys. Soc.* (*London*) **A70**, 405 (7.4, 7.12).
Castillejo, L., Dalitz, R. H., and Dyson, F. J. 1956. *Phys. Rev.* **101**, 453 (7.9).
Cavanagh, P. E., Turner, J. F., Coleman, C. F., Gard, G. A., and Ridley, B. W. 1957. *Phil. Mag.* [8] **2**, 1105 (8.14).
Chamberlain, O., Segrè, E., Tripp, R. D., Wiegand, C., and Ypsilantis, T. 1956. *Phys. Rev.* **102**, 1659 (8.9).
Chesnut, W. G., Hafner, E. M., and Roberts, A. 1956. *Phys. Rev.* **104**, 449 (8.9).
Chew, G. F. 1958. *Phys. Rev.* **112**, 1380 (13.5).
Chew, G. F. 1959. *Ann. Rev. Nuclear Sci.* **9**, 29 (13.4).
Chew, G. F., and Low, F. E. 1956a. *Phys. Rev.* **101**, 1570 (7.9, 7.12).
Chew, G. F., and Low, F. E. 1956b. *Phys. Rev.* **101**, 1579 (7.11).
Chew, G. F., and Low, F. E. 1959. *Phys. Rev.* **113**, 1640 (13.5).

Chew, G. F., Goldberger, M. L., Low, F. E., and Nambu, Y. 1957. *Phys. Rev.* **106**, 1345 (13.4).

Cini, M., Gatto, R., Goldwasser, E. L., and Ruderman, M. 1958. *Nuovo cimento* [10] **10**, 243 (7.12).

Cini, M., Fubini, S., and Stanghellini, A. 1959. *Phys. Rev.* **114**, 1633 (13.4).

Clark, D. L., Roberts, A., and Wilson, R. 1951. *Phys. Rev.* **83**, 649 (7.3).

Clementel, E., and Villi, C. 1955. *Nuovo cimento* [10] **2**, 1165 (6.5).

Coester, F. 1957. *Phys. Rev.* **107**, 299 (10.8).

Coester, F., and Jauch, J. M. 1953. *Helv. Phys. Acta* **26**, 3 (4.7).

Cohen, E. R., Crowe, K. M., and DuMond, J. W. 1957. "The Fundamental Constants of Physics." Interscience, New York (7.2).

Cohen, E. R., DuMond, J. W., Layton, T. W., and Rollet, J. S., 1955. *Revs. Modern Phys.* **27**, 363 (D.1).

Condon, E. U., and Shortley, G. H. 1951. "The Theory of Atomic Spectra." Cambridge Univ. Press, London and New York (2.7, 4.3, 4.5, 7.11, 12.10).

Cool, R. L., Cork, B., Cronin, J. W., and Wenzel, W. A. 1959. *Phys. Rev.* **114**, 912 (12.6).

Corinaldesi, E. 1958. *Nuclear Phys.* **7**, 305 (10.7).

Corinaldesi, E. 1959. *Nuovo cimento Suppl.* [10] **14**, 369 (13.4).

Cowan, E. W. 1954. *Phys. Rev.* **94**, 161 (12.6).

Crawford, F. S., Cresti, M., Good, M. L., Gottstein, K., Lyman, E. M., Solmitz, F. T., Stevenson, M. L., and Ticho, H. K. 1958a. *Proc. Ann. Conf. High Energy Physics at C.E.R.N.* (10.5, 12.6).

Crawford, F. S., Cresti, M., Good, M. L., Kalbfleisch, G. R., Stevenson, M. L., and Ticho, H. K. 1958b. *Phys. Rev. Letters* **1**, 377 (12.6, 12.11).

Crawford, F. S., Cresti, M., Good, M. L., Solmitz, F. T., and Stevenson, M. L. 1959a. *Phys. Rev. Letters* **2**, 11 (10.5).

Crawford, F. S., Cresti, M., Good, M. L., Stevenson, M. L., and Ticho, H. K. 1959b. *Phys. Rev. Letters* **2**, 112 (12.5).

Crawford, F. S., Cresti, M., Good, M. L., Stevenson, M. L., and Ticho, H. K. 1959c. *Phys. Rev. Letters* **2**, 114 (12.6).

Crawford, F. S., Cresti, M., Good, M. L., Gottstein, K., Lyman, E. M., Solmitz, F. T., Stevenson, M. L., and Ticho, H. K. 1959d. *Phys. Rev.* **113**, 1601 (12.8).

Crawford, F. S., Cresti, M., Douglass, R. L., Good, M. L., Kalbfleisch, G. R., Stevenson, M. L., and Ticho, H. K. 1959e. *Phys. Rev. Letters* **2**, 266 (12.6, 12.8, 12.10).

Crawford, F. S., Cresti, M., Douglass, R. L., Good, M. L., Kalbfleisch, G. R., and Stevenson, M. L. 1959f. *Phys. Rev. Letters* **2**, 361 (12.8).

Crawford, F. S., Douglass, R. L., Good, M. L., Kalbfleisch, G. R., Stevenson, M. L., and Ticho, H. K. 1959g. *Phys. Rev. Letters* **3**, 394 (12.4).

Crewe, A. V., Kruse, U. E., Miller, R. H., and Pondrom, L. G. 1957. *Phys. Rev.* **108**, 1531 (7.3).

Culligan, G., Frank, S. G. F., and Holt, J. R. 1959. *Proc. Phys. Soc. (London)* **73**, 169 (11.8).

Dalitz, R. H. 1951. *Proc. Phys. Soc. (London)* **A64**, 667 (7.2).

Dalitz, R. H. 1953. *Phil. Mag.* [8] **44**, 1068 (B.4).

Dalitz, R. H. 1955. *Phys. Rev.* **99**, 915 (12.7).

Dalitz, R. H. 1957. *Repts. Progr. in Phys.* **20**, 163 (10.5, 12.2).

Davidon, W. C., and Goldberger, M. L. 1956. *Phys. Rev.* **104**, 119 (13.4).

Davis, R. 1956. *Bull. Am. Phys. Soc.* [2] **1**, 219 (11.7).

Day, T. B., Snow, G. A., and Sucher, J. 1959. *Phys. Rev. Letters* **3**, 61 (12.6).

D'Espagnat, B., and Prentki, J. 1956. *Nuclear Phys.* **1**, 33 (12.3).

Deutsch, M., Gittelman, B., Bauer, R. W., Grodzins, L., and Sunyar, A. W. 1958. *Phys. Rev.* **107**, 1733 (11.6).

Deutsch, M., and Kofoed-Hansen, O. 1959. "Experimental Nuclear Physics" (E. Segrè, ed.), Vol. 3, p. 427. Wiley (11.6).

386      REFERENCES

Devons, S., and Goldfarb, L. J. B. 1957. "Handbuch der Physik" (S. Flugge, ed.), Vol. 42, p. 362. Springer, Berlin (2.12, 4.6, 4.7).
Dickson, J. M., Rose, B., and Salter, D. C., 1955. *Proc. Phys. Soc.* (*London*) **A68**, 361 (8.9).
Dirac, P. A. M. 1947. "Quantum Mechanics", 3rd ed. Oxford Univ. Press, London and New York (1.3, 1.10, 11.7).
Drell, S. D. 1958. *Ann. Phys.* (*N.Y.*) **4**, 75 (13.3).
Dudziak, W. F., Sagane, R., and Vedder, J. 1959. *Phys. Rev.* **114**, 336 (11.8).
Durbin, R., Loar, H., and Steinberger, J. 1951. *Phys. Rev.* **84**, 581 (7.3).
Dyson, F. J. 1949. *Phys. Rev.* **75**, 486 (9.9).
Dyson, F. J. 1952. *Phys. Rev.* **85**, 631 (9.9).
Edmonds, A. R. 1957. "Angular Momentum in Quantum Mechanics." Princeton Univ. Press, Princeton, New Jersey (2.11).
Fabri, E. 1954. *Nuovo cimento* [9] **11**, 479 (B.4).
Fagg, L. W., and Hanna, S. S. 1959. *Revs. Modern Phys.* **31**, 711 (8.15).
Fano, U. 1949. *J. Opt. soc. Am.* **39**, 859 (8.15).
Fano, U. 1957. *Revs. Modern Phys.* **29**, 74 (8.6, 8.15, 8.16).
Fazzini, T., Fidecaro, G., Merrison, A. W., Paul, H., and Tollestrup, A. V. 1958. *Phys. Rev. Letters* **1**, 247 (7.2).
Feld, B. T. 1954. *Nuovo cimento* [9] **12**, 426 (8.3).
Feld, B. T. 1955. *Nuovo cimento Suppl.* [10] **2**, 139 (7.10).
Feldman, G. 1956. *Phys. Rev.* **103**, 254 (12.4).
Feldman, G., and Fulton, T. 1958. *Nuclear Phys.* **8**, 106 (12.12).
Fermi, E. 1934. *Z. Physik* **88**, 161 (11.3, 11.4).
Fermi, E. 1950. *Progr. Theoret. Phys.* (*Kyoto*) **5**, 570 (B.1).
Fermi, E. 1951. "Elementary Particles." Yale Univ. Press, New Haven Connecticut (5.2, 5.7).
Fermi, E. 1953. *Phys. Rev.* **91**, 947 (7.9, 8.3).
Fermi, E. 1955. *Nuovo cimento Suppl.* [10] **2**, 84 (8.9).
Ferrari, G., Manaresi, E., and Quareni, G. 1956. *Nuovo cimento* [10] **5**, 1651 (7.9)
Feynman, R. P. 1949a. *Phys. Rev.* **76**, 749; 1949b, *Ibid.* **76**, 769 (9.8).
Feynman, R. P., and Gell-Mann, M. 1958. *Phys. Rev.* **109**, 193 (11.7, 12.11).
Feynman, R. P., and Speisman, G. 1954. *Phys. Rev.* **94**, 500 (12.5).
Fischer, L., Leontic, B., Lundby, A., Meunier, R., and Stroot, J. P. 1959. *Phys. Rev. Letters* **3**, 349 (11.8).
Fitch, V. L., and Motley, R. M. 1957. *Phys. Rev.* **105**, 265 (12.7).
Fonda, L., and Russel, J. E. 1959. *Phys. Rev. Letters* **2**, 57 (12.12).
Ford, G. W., and Mullin, C. J. 1957. *Phys. Rev.* **108**, 476 (8.14).
Fowler, W. B., Lander, R. L., and Powell, W. M. 1959. *Phys. Rev.* **113**, 928 (12.8)
Fry, W. F. 1958. *Ann. Rev. Nuclear Sci.* **8**, 105 (12.13).
Fry, W. F., and Sachs, R. G. 1958. *Phys. Rev.* **109**, 2212 (12.9).
Gammel, J. L., and Thaler, R. M. 1958. *Phys. Rev.* **109**, 2041 (8.9).
Gamow, G., and Teller, E. 1936. *Phys. Rev.* **49**, 895 (11.4).
Gartenhaus, S. 1956. *Phys. Rev.* **100**, 900 (6.5).
Garwin, R. L., Lederman, L. M., and Weinrich, M. 1957. *Phys. Rev.* **105**, 141 (10.5, 11.8).
Gatlinburg 1959. Abstracts of papers presented at the Conference on Weak Interactions held at Gatlinburg. *Bull. Am. Phys. Soc.* [2] **4**, 76 (11.6).
Gatto, R. 1957. *Phys. Rev.* **108**, 247 (12.10).
Gell-Mann, M. 1957. *Phys. Rev.* **106**, 1296 (12.5).
Gell-Mann, M., and Pais, A. 1954. *Proc. Glasgow Conf. on Nuclear and Meson Phys.*, p. 342. Pergamon, London and New York (12.3).
Gell-Mann, M., and Pais, A. 1955. *Phys. Rev.* **97**, 1387 (12.8).
Gell-Mann, M., and Rosenfeld, A. H. 1957. *Ann. Rev. Nuclear Sci.* **7**, 407 (11.9 11.10, 12.6, 12.8, 12.10).
Gerhart, J. B. 1954. *Phys. Rev.* **95**, 288 (11.8).

Gerhart, J. B. 1958. *Phys. Rev.* **109**, 897 (11.5).

Glaser, D. A. 1959. *Proc. Kiev Conf. High Energy Nuclear Phys.* (12.6).

Goldberger, M. L., Miyazawa, H., and Oehme, R. 1955. *Phys. Rev.* **99**, 986 (13.4).

Goldhaber, M., Grodzins, L., Sunyar, A. W. 1958. *Phys. Rev.* **109**, 1015 (11.6).

Good, M. L. 1958. *Phys. Rev.* **110**, 550 (12.9).

Grodzins, L. 1959. *Progr. in Nuclear Phys.* **7**, 163 (8.14, 8.15).

Guggenheimer, K. 1959. *Nuovo cimento* [10] **11**, 287 (12.5).

Gunn, J. C. 1955. *Repts. Progr. in Phys.* **18**, 127 (9.7).

Haber-Schaim, U. 1956. *Phys. Rev.* **104**, 1113 (13.4).

Hamilton, D. R., Alford, W. P., and Gross, L. 1953. *Phys. Rev.* **92**, 1521 (11.5).

Hamilton, J. 1959a. *Phys. Rev.* **114**, 1170 (13.4).

Hamilton, J. 1959b. "The Theory of Elementary Particles", p. 358. Oxford Univ. Press, London and New York (7.11).

Heckrotte, W. 1956. *Phys. Rev.* **101**, 1406 (8.9).

Henley, E. M., and Jacobsohn, B. A. 1957. *Phys. Rev.* **108**, 502 (10.6).

Hess, W. N. 1958. *Revs. Modern Phys.* **30**, 368 (6.5, 8.12).

Hillman, P., Johansson, A., and Tibell, G. 1958. *Phys. Rev.* **110**, 1218(L) (10.6).

Hofstadter, R. 1957. *Ann. Rev. Nuclear Sci.* **7**, 231 (13.2).

Hofstadter, R. 1959. *Proc. Kiev Conf. High Energy Nuclear Phys.* (13.2).

Hofstadter, R., Bumiller, F., and Yearian, M. R. 1958. *Revs. Modern Phys.* **30**, 482 (13.2).

Holt, J. R., Edwards, D. N., and Frank, S. G. F. 1959. *Proc. Phys. Soc. (London)* **73**, 856 (8.15).

Huang, K. 1956. *Phys. Rev.* **101**, 1173 (12.5).

Impeduglia, G., Plano, R., Prodell, A., Samios, N., Schwartz, M., and Steinberger, J. 1958. *Phys. Rev. Letters* **1**, 249 (7.2).

Jackson, J. D., Treiman, S. B., Wyld, H. W. 1957. *Phys. Rev.* **106**, 517 (10.6, 11.10).

Jauch, J. M., and Rohrlich, F. 1955. "The Theory of Photons and Electrons." Addison-Wesley, Reading, Massachusetts (1.6, 9.1, 9.7, 9.9).

Jones, D. P., Murphy, P. G., and O'Neill, P. L. 1958. *Proc. Phys. Soc. (London)* **72**, 429 (10.5).

Kanellopoulos, T. V., and Brown, G. E. 1957a. *Proc. Phys. Soc. (London)* **A70**, 690; 1957b. **A70**, 703 (8.11).

Karplus, R., and Ruderman, M. A. 1956. *Phys. Rev.* **102**, 247 (12.13).

Kawaguchi, M. 1957. *Phys. Rev.* **107**, 573 (12.10).

Kemmer, N., Polkinghorne, J. C., and Pursey, D. L. 1959. *Repts. Progr. in Phys.* **22**, 368 (10.4, 10.6, 10.9).

Kinoshita, T., and Peierls, R. F. 1957. *Phys. Rev.* **108**, 161 (7.5).

Kinoshita, T., and Sirlin, A. 1957. *Phys. Rev.* **107**, 593 (11.8).

Kinoshita, T., and Sirlin, A. 1959. *Phys. Rev.* **113**, 1652 (11.8).

Koenig, S. H., Prodell, A. G., and Kusch, P. 1952. *Phys. Rev.* **88**, 191 (9.9).

Koester, L. J., and Mills, F. E. 1957. *Phys. Rev.* **105**, 1900 (7.11).

Kofoed-Hansen, O., and Winther, A. 1956. *Kgl. Danske Videnskab. Selskab, Mat-fys. Medd.* **30**, No. 20 (11.5).

Konopinski, E. J. 1954. *Phys. Rev.* **94**, 492 (11.4).

Kruger, H., and Crowe, K. M. 1958. *Phys. Rev.* **113**, 341 (11.8).

Kuehner, J. A., Merrison, A. W., and Tornabene, S. 1958. *Proc. Phys. Soc. (London)* **73**, 551 (7.4).

Kunze, J. F., Romanowski, T. A., Ashkin, J., and Burger, A. 1960. *Phys. Rev.* **117**, 859 (7.9, 8.3).

Landau, L. D. 1957. *Nuclear Phys.* **3**, 127 (11.7).

Lannutti, J. E., Chupp, W. W., Goldhaber, G., Goldhaber, S., Helmy, E., Iloff, E. L., Pevsner, A., and Ritson, D. 1956. *Phys. Rev.* **101**, 1617 (12.3).

Larsen, S., Lubkin, E., and Tausner, M. 1957. *Phys. Rev.* **107**, 856 (11.8).

Lattes, C. M. G., Occhialini, G. P. S., and Powell, C. F. 1947. *Nature* **160**, 453 486 (7.1).

Lee, T. D. 1955. *Phys. Rev.* **99**, 337 (12.4).

Lee, T. D., and Yang, C. N. 1956. *Phys. Rev.* **104**, 254 (10.5, 10.8).

Lee, T. D., and Yang, C. N. 1957. *Phys. Rev.* **105**, 1671 (11.7, 11.8).

Lee, T. D., and Yang, C. N. 1958. *Phys. Rev.* **109**, 1755 (12.6).

Lee, T. D., and Yang, C. N. 1960. *Phys. Rev. Letters* **4**, 307 (11.9).

Lee, T. D., Oehme, R., and Yang, C. N. 1956. *Phys. Rev.* **106**, 340 (10.8).

Leitner, J., Nordin, P., Rosenfeld, A. H., Solmitz, F. T., and Tripp, R. D. 1959 *Phys. Rev. Letters* **3**, 186 (12.6).

Lindenbaum, S. J. 1957. *Ann. Rev. Nuclear Sci.* **7**, 317 (7.9, 7.13).

Lindenbaum, S. J., and Yuan, L. C. L. 1958. *Phys. Rev.* **111**, 1380 (7.9).

Lipps, F. W., and Tolhoek, H. A. 1954a. *Physica* **20**, 85; 1954b. *Ibid.* **20**, 395 (8.15).

Love, W. A., Marder, S., Nadelhaft, I., Siegel, R. T., and Taylor, A. E. 1959 *Phys. Rev. Letters* **2**, 107 (11.8).

Lüders, G. 1954. *Kgl. Danske Videnskab. Selskab. Mat-fys. Medd.* **28**, No. 5 (10.8).

Lüders, G., and Zumino, B. 1957. *Phys. Rev.* **106**, 385 (10.8).

McLachlan, N. W. 1953. "Complex Variable Theory and Transform Calculus." Cambridge Univ. Press, London and New York (13.4).

McMaster, W. H. 1954. *Am. J. Phys.* **22**, 351 (8.15).

Macq, P. C., Crowe, K. M., and Haddock, R. P. 1958. *Phys. Rev.* **112**, 2061 (11.8)

McVoy, K. W. 1958. *Phys. Rev.* **111**, 1333 (8.15).

Mandelstam, S. 1958. *Phys. Rev.* **112**, 1344 (13.5).

Mandelstam, S. 1959. *Phys. Rev.* **115**, 1741, 1752 (13.5).

Margenau, H., and Murphy, G. M. 1943. "The Mathematics of Physics and Chemistry." Van Nostrand, Princeton, New Jersey (1.9, 2.9, 9.3).

Marshak, R. E. 1952. "Meson Physics." McGraw-Hill, New York (9.10).

Matthews, P. T., and Salam, A. 1951. *Revs. Modern Phys.* **23**, 311 (9.10).

Matthews, P. T., and Salam, A. 1958a. *Phys. Rev.* **110**, 565; 1958b. *Ibid.* **110**, 569 (13.4).

Matthews, P. T., and Uretsky, J. L. 1959. *Phys. Rev. Letters* **3**, 296 (12.5).

Michel, L. 1950. *Proc. Phys. Soc. (London)* **A63**, 514 (11.8).

Milburn, R. H. 1958. *Revs. Modern Phys.* **27**, 1 (B.1).

Minami, S. 1954. *Progr. Theoret. Phys. (Kyoto)* **11**, 213 (7.9).

Møller, C. 1952. "The Theory of Relativity." Oxford Univ. Press, London and New York (1.4, A.5, A.6).

Moravcsik, M. J. 1956. *Phys. Rev.* **104**, 1451 (7.11).

Moravcsik, M. J. 1957. *Phys. Rev.* **105**, 267 (7.11).

Moravcsik, M. J. 1958. *Phys. Rev.* **111**, 1657 (7.12).

Moravcsik, M. J. 1959. *Phys. Rev. Letters* **2**, 352 (12.12, 13.5).

Morita, M., and Morita, R. S. 1957. *Phys. Rev.* **107**, 139 (10.6).

Mott, N. F., and Massey, H. S. W. 1949. "The Theory of Atomic Collisions", 2nd ed. Oxford Univ. Press, London and New York (3.2, 3.5, 8.14).

Mozley, R. F., Taylor, R. E., and Tangherlini, F. R. 1958. *Bull. Am. Phys. Soc.* [2] **3**, 196 (8.3).

Mukhin, A. I., Popova, I. V., and Tentyukova, G. N. 1957. *Doklady Akad. Nauk. S.S.S.R.* **112**, 236 (7.9).

Muller, F., Birge, R. W., Fowler, W. B., Good, R. H., Hirsch, W., Matsen, R. P., Oswald, L., Powell, W. M., White, H.S., and Piccioni, O., 1960. *Phys. Rev. Letters* **4**, 418 (12.9).

Nishijima, K. 1954. *Progr. Theoret. Phys. (Kyoto)* **12**, 107 (12.3).

Nordin, P., Orear, J., Reed, L., Rosenfeld, A. H., Solmitz, F. T., Taft, H. D., and Tripp, R. D. 1958. *Phys. Rev. Letters* **1**, 380 (12.6, 12.11).

Oehme, R. 1955. *Phys. Rev.* **98**, 147 (8.10).

Okubo, S., Marshak, R. E., Sudarshan, E. C. G., Teutsch, W. B., and Weinberg, S. 1958. *Phys. Rev.* **112**, 665 (12.8, 12.11).

Okubo, S., Marshak, R. E., and Sudarshan, E. C. G. 1959. *Phys. Rev. Letters* **2**, 12 (12.8, 12.11).

Okun', L. B., and Pomeranchuk, I. Ya., 1958. *Zhur. Eksptl. i Teoret. Fiz.* **34**, 997, (*Soviet Phys. J.E.T.P.* **7**, 688) (12.12).

Olsen, H., and Maximon, L. C. 1959. *Phys. Rev.* **114**, 887 (8.15).

O'Neill, G. K. 1959. *Proc. Intern. Conf. on High Energy Accelerators and Instrumentation*, p. 125, C.E.R.N., Geneva (13.3).

Orear, J. 1954. *Phys. Rev.* **96**, 1417 (7.9).

Orear, J. 1955. *Phys. Rev.* **100**, 288 (7.9, 7.12).

Orear, J. 1956. *Nuovo cimento* [10] **4**, 856 (7.9).

Orear, J., Harris, G., and Taylor, S. 1956. *Phys. Rev.* **102**, 1676 (B.4).

Page, L. A. 1959. *Revs. Modern Phys.* **31**, 759 (8.14).

Pais, A. 1952. *Phys. Rev.* **86**, 513 (12.3).

Pais, A., and Jost, R. 1952. *Phys. Rev.* **87**, 871 (10.7).

Pais, A., and Piccioni, O., 1955. *Phys. Rev.* **100**, 1487 (12.8).

Pais, A., and Treiman, S. B. 1957. *Phys. Rev.* **106**, 1106 (12.8, 12.10).

Panofsky, W. K. H., Aamodt, R. L., and Hadley, J. 1951. *Phys. Rev.* **81**, 565 (7.4, 7.12).

Panofsky, W. K. H., Fitch, V. L., Motley, R. M., and Chesnut, W. G. 1958. *Phys. Rev.* **109**, 1353 (12.8).

Pauli, W. 1956. "Neils Bohr and the Development of Physics", p. 30. Pergamon Press, New York (10.8).

Pauli, W., and Weisskopf, V. 1934. *Helv. Phys. Acta* **7**, 769 (9.2).

Peierls, R. E. 1952. *Proc. Roy. Soc.* **A214**, 143 (9.7).

Phillips, R. H., and Crowe, K. M. 1954. *Phys. Rev.* **96**, 484 (B.4).

Plano, R. 1959. *Proc. Kiev Conf. High Energy Nuclear Phys.* (11.8).

Plano, R., Prodell, A., Samios, N., Schwartz, M., and Steinberger, J. 1959. *Phys. Rev. Letters* **3**, 525 (7.2, 7.5).

Primakoff, H., and Rosen, S. P. 1959. *Repts. Progr. in Phys.* **22**, 121 (11.7).

Puppi, G., and Stanghellini, A. 1957. *Nuovo cimento* [10] **5**, 1305 (13.4).

Reines, F., and Cowan, C. L. 1959. *Phys. Rev.* **113**, 273 (11.2, 11.7).

Richter, B. 1958. *Phys. Rev. Letters* **1**, 114 (13.3).

Rochester, G. D., and Butler, C. C. 1947. *Nature* **160**, 855 (12.2).

Rochester, G. D., and Butler, C. C. 1953. *Repts. Progr. in Phys.* **16**, 364 (12.2).

Rose, M. E. 1955. "Multipole Fields." Wiley, New York (4.7).

Rose, M. E. 1957. "The Elementary Theory of Angular Momentum". Wiley, New York (2.11).

Rose, M. E. 1958. "Handbook of Physics." 9-95, McGraw-Hill, New York (11.4).

Rosen, L., and Brolley, J. E. 1958. *Phys. Rev. Letters* **2**, 98 (10.6).

Rosenbluth, M. N. 1950. *Phys. Rev.* **79**, 615 (13.2).

Rosenfeld, A. H. 1954. *Phys. Rev.* **96**, 139 (7.3).

Rosenfeld, A. H., Solmitz, F. T., and Tripp, R. D. 1959. *Phys. Rev. Letters* **2**, 110 (12.5).

Ruderman, M. A., and Finkelstein, R. J. 1949. *Phys. Rev.* **76**, 1458 (11.9).

Sachs, R. G. 1953. "Nuclear Theory." Addison-Wesley, Reading, Massachusetts (10.6).

Salam, A. 1957. *Nuovo cimento* [10] **5**, 299 (11.7).

Schiff, L. I. 1955. "Quantum Mechanics." 2nd ed. McGraw-Hill, New York (2.9).

Schnitzer, H. J., and Salzman, G. 1959. *Phys. Rev.* **113**, 1153 (13.4).

Schweber, S. S., Bethe, H. A., and de Hoffmann, F. 1955. "Mesons and Fields", Vol. I. Row, Peterson, Evanston, Illinois (9.1, 9.8, 9.10).

Schwinger, J. 1956. *Phys. Rev.* **104**, 1164 (12.5).

Shapiro, A. M. 1956. *Revs. Modern Phys.* **28**, 164 (7.2, 12.5).

Sherr, R., and Miller, R. H. 1954. *Phys. Rev.* **93**, 1076 (11.5).
Signell, P. S., and Marshak, R. E. 1958. *Phys. Rev.* **109**, 1229 (6.5).
Skarsvåg, K. 1958. *Nuclear Phys.* **8**, 55 (8.11).
Snow, G. A. 1958. *Phys. Rev.* **110**, 1192 (12.13).
Sommerfeld, C. M. 1957. *Phys. Rev.* **107**, 328 (9.9).
Stapp, H. 1956. *Phys. Rev.* **103**, 425 (8.13, A.6).
Stehle, P. 1958. *Phys. Rev.* **110**, 1458 (8.14).
Sternglass, E. J. 1959. *Bull. Am. Phys. Soc.* [2] **4**, 228 (12.5).
Stokes, G. G. 1852. *Trans. Cambridge Phil. Soc.* **9**, 399 (8.15).
Sudarshan, E. C. G., and Marshak, R. E. 1958. *Phys. Rev.* **109**, 1860 (12.11).
Swanson, R. A., Lundy, R. A., Telegdi, V. L., and Yovanovitch, D. D. 1959. *Phys. Rev. Letters* **2**, 430 (11.8).
Taylor, J. G., Moravscik, M. J., and Uretsky, J. L. 1959. *Phys. Rev.* **113**, 689 (13.5).
Takeda, M. 1956. *Phys. Rev.* **101**, 1547 (12.10).
Thirring, W. E. 1958. "The Principles of Quantum Electrodynamics." Academic Press, New York (9.1).
Tolhoek, H. A. 1956. *Revs. Modern Phys.* **28**, 277 (8.14, 8.15).
Treiman, S. B. 1959. *Phys. Rev.* **113**, 355 (12.12).
Treiman, S. B., and Sachs, R. G. 1956. *Phys. Rev.* **103**, 1545 (12.9).
Triebwasser, S., Dayhoff, E. S., and Lamb, W. E. 1953. *Phys. Rev.* **98**, 98, 106 (9.9).
Umezawa, H. 1956. "Quantum Field Theory." North Holland Publ. Amsterdam (9.1).
Uretsky, J. L., Kenney, R. W., Knapp, E. A., and Perez-Mendez, V. 1958. *Phys. Rev. Letters* **1**, 12 (7.11).
Van Hove, L. 1952. *Phys. Rev.* **88**, 1358 (7.9).
Watson, K. M. 1952. *Phys. Rev.* **85**, 852 (7.11).
Watson, K. M., Keck, J. C., Tollestrup, A. V., and Walker, R. L. 1956. *Phys. Rev.* **101**, 1159 (7.11).
Webb, F. H., Iloff, E. L., Featherstone, F. H., Chupp, W. W., Goldhaber, G., and Goldhaber, S. 1958. *Nuovo cimento* [10] **8**, 899 (12.3).
Wentzel, G. 1956a. *Proc. Ann. Rochester Conf. High Energy Phys.* **6**, VIII–15 (12.10).
Wentzel, G. 1956b. *Phys. Rev.* **101**, 1215 (12.10).
Whittaker, E. T., and Watson, G. N. 1946. "A Course of Modern Analysis", 3rd ed. Cambridge Univ. Press, London and New York (13.4).
Wick, G. C. 1950. *Phys. Rev.* **80**, 268 (9.8).
Wick, G. C. 1958. *Ann. Rev. Nuclear Sci.* **8**, 41 (10.6, 10.7, 10.9).
Wick, G. C., Wightman, A. S., and Wigner, E. P. 1952. *Phys. Rev.* **88**, 101 (1.7).
Wightman, A. S. 1948. *Phys. Rev.* **74**, 1813 (8.15).
Wightman, A. S., and Schweber, S. S. 1955. *Phys. Rev.* **98**, 812 (1.5).
Wigner, E. P. 1932. *Nachr. Akad. Wiss. Göttingen, Math.-physik Kl. IIa No.* **32**, 35 (10.6).
Wigner, E. P. 1959. "Group Theory." Academic Press, New York (1.10).
Wilkinson, D. H. 1958. *Phys. Rev.* **109**, 1603, 1610, 1614 (10.5).
Wolfenstein, L. 1949. *Phys. Rev.* **75**, 1664; **76**, 541 (8.10).
Wolfenstein, L. 1954. *Phys. Rev.* **96**, 1654; see erratum *Ibid.* **98**, 1870 (8.10, 8.11).
Wolfenstein, L. 1956a. *Ann. Rev. Nuclear Sci.* **6**, 43 (8.11).
Wolfenstein, L. 1956b. *Phys. Rev.* **101**, 427 (8.11).
Wolfenstein, L., and Ashkin, J. 1952. *Phys. Rev.* **85**, 947 (8.11).
Woodruff, A. E. 1959. *Ann. Phys.* (N.Y.) **7**, 65 (8.11).
Wright, S. C. 1955. *Phys. Rev.* **99**, 996 (6.5, 8.11).
Wu, C. S. 1959. *Revs. Modern Phys.* **31**, 783 (11.6).
Wu, C. S., Ambler, E., Hayward, R. W., Hoppes, D. D., and Hudson, R. P. 1957. *Phys. Rev.* **105**, 1413 (10.5, 11.6).

Yang, C. N. 1948. *Phys. Rev.* **74**, 764 (3.7).

Yang, C. N. 1950. *Phys. Rev.* **77**, 242 (7.5).

Yang, C. N., and Tiomono, J. 1950. *Phys. Rev.* **79**, 495 (10.4).

Yearian, M. R., and Hofstadter, R. 1958. *Phys. Rev.* **110**, 552; **111**, 934 (13.2).

Yennie, D. R., Levy, M. M., and Ravenhall, D. G. 1957. *Revs. Modern Phys.* **29**, 144 (13.2).

Yukawa, H. 1935. *Proc. Phys.-Math. Soc. Japan* **17**, 48 (7.1).

# AUTHOR INDEX

*Numbers in italic show the page on which the complete reference is listed*

# SUBJECT INDEX

## A

Action, principle of least, 203
Adjoint function, 210
Adjoint operator, 5
Alignment, 160–161
Amplitude, 50–51
  analytic properties of, *see* Dispersion relations
  partial wave, 47–48, 50–51
  scattering, 48, 50–51, 127, 342–343, 346, 350
  spin flip, 55–56, 127
Angular distribution, 46, 47, 56–58
  of photons, 73–75
Angular momentum, 23–46
  barrier, 58
  conservation of, 28–29
  eigenfunctions of, 38–40
  eigenvalues of, 29–31
  matrix elements of, 31–33
  operators of, 24, 27
  orbital, 23–25
  and rotation, 17, 25–27, 41–46
  spin, 27, *see also* Spin
  tensor, 206, 213–214
  total, 26–28
  vector addition of, 33–38
Annihilation operator, 204–205, 207, 209, 211–212
Antibaryons, 284, *see also* Baryons, conservation of
Anticommutation properties, 211
Antileptons, 252, *see also* Conservation of leptons
Antineucleons, 251–252, 284, 287
Antineutrino, 251–252, *see also* Neutrino

Antiparticles, 211–213, 244, 251, 252, 284, 287–288
  mass and mean life of, 247–248
Antisymmetry, *see* Symmetry
Antiunitary operator, 243
Associated production, 285–290
Association, law of, 4
Axial vector, 11, 12
Axial vector interaction, 228–229, *see also under* Beta decay

## B

Baryons, 284–285
  conservation of, 207, 285
  mass of, 291–293, 382
  parity of, 327–328
Beta decay, 251–281, *see also* Universal Fermi interaction
  asymmetry, 262, 267–268, 270
  axial vector interaction in, 254, 257, 264, 275–278
  charge conjugation noninvariance in, 247, 250, 254, 255, 280
  classification of, 255–257
  correlations in, 280
  coupling constant, 252, 255, 261, 264, 267, 275, 276
  CP transformation invariance in, 280
  density of states, 258, 374–375
  double, 268–269
  electron spectrum, 258, 273
  favoured and unfavoured transitions, 260
  Fermi transitions, 254, 257
  Fierz interference, 258–259, 261–262, 263
  Gamow-Teller transitions, 257